INTRODUCTION TO GEOGRAPHY

Henry M. Kendall   SYRACUSE UNIVERSITY

Robert M. Glendinning   UNIVERSITY OF CALIFORNIA AT LOS ANGELES

MAPS AND DIAGRAMS UNDER THE DIRECTION OF
Clifford H. MacFadden   UNIVERSITY OF CALIFORNIA AT LOS ANGELES

UNDER THE EDITORSHIP OF
J. Russell Whitaker   GEORGE PEABODY COLLEGE FOR TEACHERS

Introduction to Geography

HARCOURT, BRACE AND COMPANY, NEW YORK

Title page photo: Rotkin from Standard Oil Co. (N. J.)

Cover photo: Josef Muench

End papers: U. S. Geological Survey

Contents

Part Three: Elements of the Cultural Setting

Part Four: Concluding Remarks

Foreword

....

Today, when each of us is increasingly affected by what goes on all over the world, the position of geography in college education becomes ever more important. Geography gives the student an understanding of the home-place of mankind—an essential understanding, so long as we believe that where a man lives, and what he does there, affects his character and his behavior. Geography instills understanding of, and insight into, this home-place by describing the greatly varied pattern of the earth's surface, by revealing order within the variety, and by deriving from that study a body of meaningful concepts and generalizations. This book presents these basic geographic concepts and generalizations with such skill and with so firm an understanding of student interest and capacity that both the beginner *and* the more geographically literate student can study it with pleasure and with profit. This whole work—the carefully integrated text, maps, photographs, and sketches—has this single aim.

With the growth and development of the introductory geography course in American colleges has come a full realization of the need to teach the basic world patterns as well as the concepts of geography. Too commonly the introductory course has fallen far short of developing an awareness, much less an enduring mastery, of the actual distribution of natural environments and of man and his works over the earth. The authors of this book, by means of interpretive descriptions and a wealth of maps, have clearly presented these basic world patterns. Maps and words march together. But since the symbolism of maps is less familiar to the students than the symbolism of words, the authors have used relatively few map projections. They rely chiefly on one equal-area world projection, employing portions of that map for less than world-wide coverage. A clear understanding of basic world patterns is further aided by the many world maps in full color at the front of the book.

This book focuses upon the study of the earth as the home of man. It inquires into the nature and variety of the human habitat, both natural and cultural; it presents an assessment of both physical and cultural features in terms of man living and making a living on the earth. Such an assessment provides a restriction of subject matter without which the beginning course may spread far beyond the range of an effective introduction to geography. Furthermore, such an assessment leads toward the solution of a problem that has long confronted geographers, the problem of keeping a proper balance between the physical and the cultural. Toward this end the authors have provided an unusually thorough treatment of man and his works in their world distribution. The systematic analysis of man-made features and of man himself reaches a new high, particularly in the discussion of rural and urban settlements.

In an introduction to geography it is difficult to leave together the things that belong together, the ideal emphasized by the great French geographer, Paul Vidal de la Blache. This ideal has been sought, however, and achieved with marked success here, by gradually expanding the discussion, element by element, to include the various components of the human habitat, and by the liberal use of regional studies.

In these regional studies, as elsewhere, emphasis is placed on the changing nature of the earth's surface. While the dictum "out of time, out of meaning" is not wholly true in geographic study, it does remind us that much of the meaning of what we see comes to us through a knowledge of the past and an awareness of the transitory character of the present scene. It is partly through the recognition of this dynamic quality of the earthly scene that geography joins hands with those disciplines which make special use of historical method and perspective.

The geographer's relationship to other fields of knowledge concerned with man and the earth is of critical importance. Geographic study progresses as related fields advance, and the common ground of geography and history, or biology, to name but two of many, is large. This common ground provides firm territory on which to cross from one field of intellectual endeavor to another. Thus does geography perform one of its services in general education.

The excellence of the selection and presentation of geographic concepts and patterns in this book, of general ideas and vivid details, is a testimony to the mature scholarship of the authors and to their years of thoughtful, sympathetic teaching. Their sureness of touch

appears on every page. Prompt grasp of the general structure of their thought is facilitated, moreover, by the careful organization of each chapter, as well as by the outline and other aids given at the end of each chapter.

This book goes straight to the mark. The authors have addressed themselves not to their professional colleagues, nor even to pre-professional students, but to the great majority of college students, with whose needs they are thoroughly familiar. They have steered a successful course between technical treatment on the one hand, and barren, overly simplified generalization on the other. They have adhered faithfully to their intent to provide an effective introduction to the vast, richly varied field of geography, a field of great value for orienting each citizen in the modern world.

J. RUSSELL WHITAKER

Nashville, Tennessee

Preface

....

The purpose of a textbook written primarily for college students making their first formal contact with geography is at least twofold: the book should lay an adequate foundation for a continuing study of geography's many facets, and it should serve as a thorough survey of place differences throughout the world for those who will have little or no further contact with college geography. Such a book must guard against the pretense of being encyclopaedic. Rather, it must make a discerning attack upon geographic ignorance. It must, of course, contain a clear-cut presentation of the facts with which geography works and of the manner in which geography uses these facts. But it must also demonstrate the significance both of the facts and of their manner of use. Plainly, it must show where geography fits into the everyday life of the ordinary individual; it must try to create in the individual the feeling that he better appreciates the world in which he lives because he has some knowledge of geography.

These purposes are essentially similar to those of other educational disciplines. Each discipline attempts in its own way to train minds to use facts in the whole business of living. For a few, the first contact with a particular subject is the beginning of a professional training. These few must be enabled to learn their professional alphabet, so to speak. But for a far larger number, an introductory course is simply part of a general education. In either instance, the subject matter is really a vehicle or, if one prefers, a device.

And what better device could there be than geography? In this day, when no part of the world is remote in a time sense, it behooves each one of us, if we are to be intelligent citizens, to know what this world is like, to know what are the problems of living and making a living in the different segments of the globe, to realize that there is a certain design or pattern to the differences from place to place, and, finally, to appreciate how these differences are important in conditioning human attitudes and actions. These matters are important for the professional geographer to be sure, but it is, in fact, the nonprofessional, the future business man, lawyer, salesman, doctor, and engineer, who can benefit most by discovering what geography has to offer. This great group is, in the end, a very important group among our citizenry; it is by them and through their opinions that the conduct of our life in the society of nations is determined. It is to them, therefore, that this book is primarily directed.

Viewed in this light, this text can provide not only a remedy for geographic ignorance; it can well constitute a framework for a college course designed to acquaint the student with the work of modern science, both physical and social. Astronomy, mathematics, physics, geology, chemistry, and biology are all drawn upon to explain the facts of the physical earth. Similarly, geography draws upon social sciences like cultural anthropology, economics, history, political science, and sociology to explain the cultural elements of the landscape. With a frame of reference such as this book provides, the work and interrelationships of all these disciplines can be suggested. Thus, something can be done to break down the rigid, pigeonholing attitude which still persists in our educational system. Something can be accomplished to make individuals more completely aware of the interdependence of all learning.

The plan of the book is systematic. There are four parts. Part I outlines the segment of knowledge with which geography deals, and describes the tools with which geography works. Part II examines the nature and distribution of the physical elements of man's habitat. Part III considers the nature and distribution of the cultural elements. And Part IV points out paths for continued geographic study. Appendices contain further material on maps, climate, and population, useful in discussions arising from the text itself. At the end of most chapters are questions designed to form the basis of classroom discussion, but not to elicit parrotlike repetition of text statements. There are also included at the end of most chapters short, *annotated* lists of suggested references, which are intended to be provocative rather than exhaustive. The numerous illustrations have been carefully selected not only for their appropriateness, but for their artistic strength.

The authors have designed the book on the basis of the time allotted for an introductory course extending through two semesters, terms, or quarters. The book allows ample investigation of all major points of discussion and makes possible the inclusion of further work suited to the individual instructor's choice. At the same time, the authors recognize that college programs do not always permit an introductory course to continue through so long a period. Often such a course must be confined to one term or one quarter. This contingency has been provided for; a short course can readily be devised by judicious selection. For a short course, it is suggested that Chapters 5, 6, 7, 10, and 12 be omitted in Part II and that Chapters 23, 24, 25, 26, and 27 be omitted in Part III. In addition to these excisions, it will be necessary to limit classroom discussion rather closely to the text at hand. While this is obviously less satisfactory than a longer course would be, it will nevertheless be readily workable.

What value this book may have is due primarily to the excellent teachers the authors had through their training; for its weaknesses, the authors assume all responsibility. It is impossible to list all who have contributed, either directly or indirectly, to this work. Yet, it is not inappropriate that a portion of the debt be indicated. Professor Alan G. Ogilvie of the University of Edinburgh, Professor J. Russell Whitaker of George Peabody College for Teachers, and Professor Robert B. Hall of the University of Michigan started the authors on their respective paths in geography. The then senior staff of the Department of Geography at the University of Michigan (Kenneth C. McMurry, Preston E. James, Robert B. Hall, and Stanley D. Dodge) loosed them upon the academic world. To these geographers specifically, acknowledgment is made. A large portion of what is good in this book derives immediately from Professor J. Russell Whitaker, under whose editorship it was prepared. The mechanics of preparing maps and diagrams for reproduction could never have been surmounted had it not been for the drafting skill, cooperation, and plain hard work of Mr. Milton S. Venezky.

H. M. K.
R. M. G.
C. H. M.

Shaftsbury, Vermont
Los Angeles, California
August 15, 1950

THE PLATES

Color Plates

WORLD URBAN
CENTERS OF
100,000 AND
OVER

POPULATION

· 100,000–500,000

⊙ 500,000–1,000,000

● 1,000,000 and over

Compressed Sinusoidal
equal-area projection

STATUTE MILES

0   1000   2000   3000   4000   5000

PLATE I

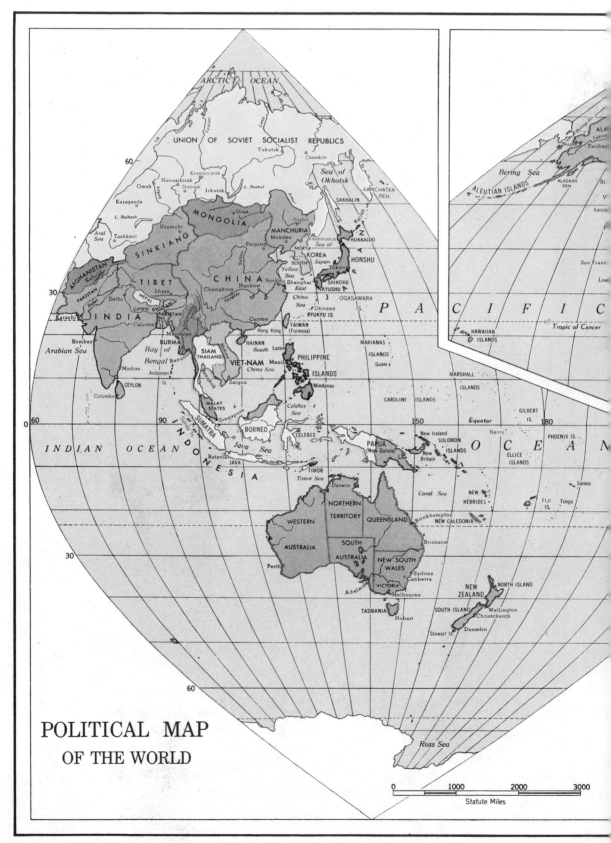

POLITICAL MAP
OF THE WORLD

PLATE II

Compressed Sinusoidal
equal-area projection

PLATE II

60

120   90   0

0

60

0   1000   2000   3000   4000   5000
STATUTE MILES

PLATE III

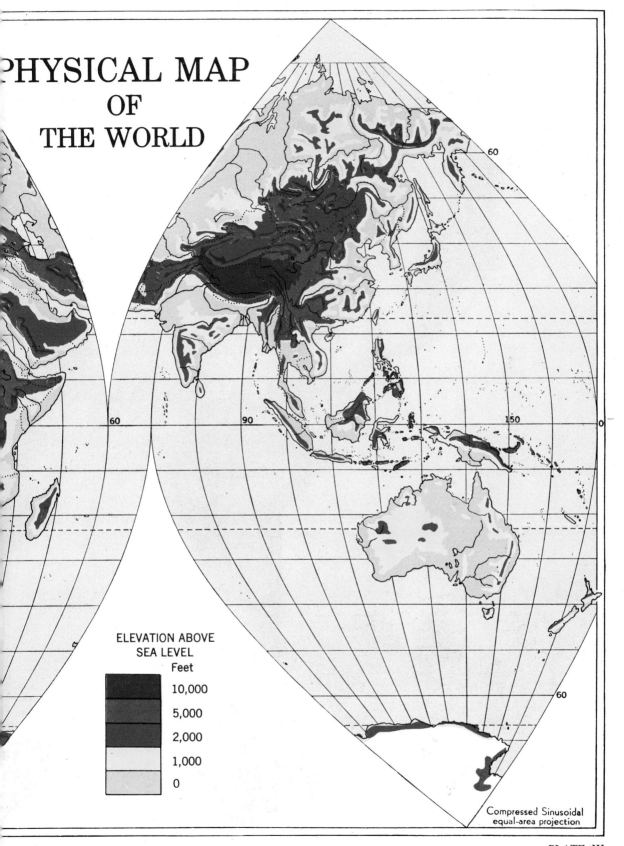

PHYSICAL MAP
OF
THE WORLD

60

60   90   150   0

ELEVATION ABOVE
SEA LEVEL
Feet

10,000

5,000

2,000

1,000

0

60

Compressed Sinusoidal
equal-area projection

PLATE III

Chiefly
Ice Plateau

1000   2000   3000   4000   5000
0
STATUTE MILES

PLATE IV

GENERAL PATTERN
OF
MAJOR
LANDFORMS

60

60

90

150

0

60

60

Chiefly
Ice Plateau

Chiefly plains (gently - moderately rolling)
Chiefly hills ("hilly country")
Chiefly plateaus ("table-lands"....including
          mountain-studded plateaus, as
          well as floors of basins within
          mountain regions)
Chiefly mountains ("mountain country")

Compressed Sinusoidal
equal-area projection

PLATE IV

STATUTE MILES

PLATE V

CLIMATIC TYPES

I TROPICAL MOIST (A)
- Tropical Rainforest (Af)
- Tropical Monsoon (Am)
- Savanna (Aw)

II DRY (B)
- Arid (Bw)
- Semiarid (BS)

III MOIST, MILD WINTER (C)
- Midlatitude Marine (Cfb-Cfc)
- Humid Subtropical (Cfa)
- Subtropical Monsoon (Cw)
- Mediterranean (Cs)

IV MOIST, SEVERE WINTER (D)
- Humid continental with hot summers (Dfa-Dwa)
- Humid continental with warm summers (Dfb-Dwb)
- Subarctic (Dfc-Dwc-Dfd-Dwd)

V POLAR (E)

MOUNTAIN (H)

Compressed Sinusoidal
equal-area projection

PLATE V

60

120   90   0   0

60

60

0   1000   2000   3000   4000   5000
STATUTE MILES

PLATE VI

WORLD MAP OF POPULATION DENSITY

Persons
per square mile

500 and over

250-500

100-250

50-100

25-50

2-25

Under 2

Compressed Sinusoidal
equal-area projection

60

60

60

60

90

150

0

PLATE VI

ICE

60

120   90

0

0

STATUTE MILES
0   1000   2000   3000   4000   5000

ICE   ICE

60

60

ICE

PLATE VII

NATURAL
VEGETATION
OF THE
WORLD

I FOREST ASSOCIATION
   A. Tropical Forests:
      Tropical rainforest
      Tropical semideciduous forest
      Tropical scrub forest
   B. Middle and High Latitude Forest
      Mediterranean scrub forest
      Broadleaf and broadleaf-conifer forest
      Coniferous forest

II GRASSLAND ASSOCIATION
   A. Tropical Grassland
      Tropical grassland
   B. Middle Latitude Grassland
      Steppe
      Prairie

III DESERT ASSOCIATION
      Desert scrub and barren desert
      Tundra

IV MOUNTAINS

V ICE | ICE |

ICE

Compressed Sinusoidal
equal-area projection

PLATE VII

PLATE VIII

WORLD MAP OF OCEAN CURRENTS AND SEA ICE

SEA ICE

Average limit of polar pack, inaccessible to free-sailing ships
Average maximum limit of ice preventing navigation by heavily built vessels
Average maximum limit of pack and land-fast ice affecting normal navigation (in southern hemisphere, the absolute maximum)
Average maximum limit of icebergs and drifting ice (Western North Atlantic)
Absolute maximum limits of icebergs
x x x   Exceptional positions of icebergs (North Atlantic)

Regions accessible to heavily built vessels:

8 to 12 months		2 to 4 months
6 to 8 months		2 months or less
4 to 6 months		with icebreaker assistance, 2 months or less

Permanent polar pack ice

Gulf Stream
North Atlantic Drift
Portugal Current
Canary Current
North Equatorial Current
Guinea Current
South Equatorial Current
Benguela Current
Agulhas
Madagascar Current
Northeast Monsoon Drift
Equatorial Counter Current
South Equatorial Current
West Australia Current
Falkland Current
West Wind Drift
West Wind Drift

Miller Cylindrical Projection

PLATE VIII

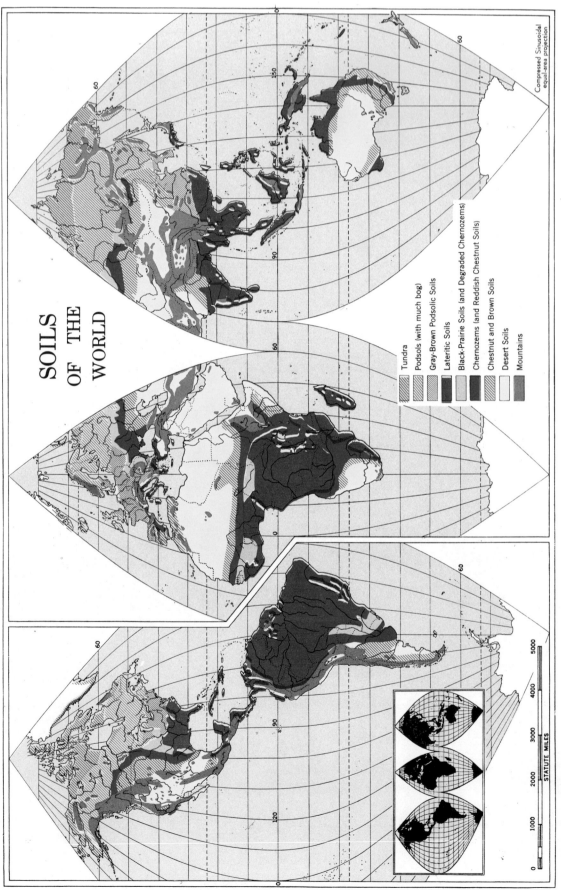

SOILS
OF THE WORLD

Tundra

Podsols (with much bog)

Gray-Brown Podsolic Soils

Lateritic Soils

Black-Prairie Soils (and Degraded Chernozems)

Chernozems (and Reddish Chestnut Soils)

Chestnut and Brown Soils

Desert Soils

Mountains

Compressed Sinusoidal
equal-area projection

STATUTE MILES

0   1000   2000   3000   4000   5000

PLATE IX

PART ONE

Introductory Survey

1 *THE EARTH is the habitat of man; geography provides the framework for
observing variety and change in that habitat. All of the elements of geography
are here pictured in simple combination.* (Newell Green)

CHAPTER 1

Some Objectives of Geographic Study

SCOPE OF GEOGRAPHY

Man's Habitat

On this planet, man lives in a kind of shell, relatively thinner than the shell of an egg. He has his permanent home on those fragments of land which stand above the great oceans and seas, but below the great thickness of atmosphere which envelops the planet. He has dug or bored into the solid crust of the earth, primarily to obtain minerals for his own use. He has ascended above the earth and now uses the atmosphere actively, to travel from one part of the solid crust to another. Yet, the deepest mine extends only a scant two miles below the surface, while the greatest height to which man has ascended is approximately fourteen miles. Only within this shell, sixteen miles in thickness, are physical conditions which make life possible known to exist. This is the space which man knows from direct contact and close observation; this is the space which he uses and alters to his own ends; and this is the space which places broad restrictions on his activities. This very thin shell and all that lies within it—animate and inanimate, including even man himself—constitutes the human *habitat*.

PHYSICAL OR NATURAL ELEMENTS. Analysis of the human habitat shows that its nature re-

sults from the coexistence and interrelation of a host of different elements. Some of these are *physical or natural elements*. They include all of those items which exist within the habitat except man and his works. The features of atmosphere, land, water, and plant and animal life are all included (Table 1).

The physical elements form the base upon which man depends for his livelihood. He has learned to control some of them. He has tamed animals to serve him and plants to provide him with food. He has discovered how to divert water for the purpose of irrigating his crops. He has learned to warm himself by burning a black mineral which he calls coal. Yet man has still to accept certain other physical elements as limitations upon his activities. For example, he uses the atmosphere for the passage of his airplanes, but, because he has not yet been able to control atmospheric conditions, his airplanes are often grounded.

CULTURAL OR HUMAN ELEMENTS. In addition to the physical elements, there is man himself and there are the features which result from his presence. These are the *cultural or human elements*. Man's numbers, kind, and distribution over the earth; his ways of using the physical equipment; marks of his fields and settlements; and lines of transportation and communication which he stretches over the earth's surface are some of the items of the cultural scene (Table 1).

Table I   GENERALIZED CHECK LIST OF ELEMENTS OF THE HUMAN HABITAT

PHYSICAL OR NATURAL ELEMENTS	CULTURAL OR HUMAN ELEMENTS
A. Atmosphere (air) *STRATOSPHERE IONISPHERE*	A. Man
1. Weather	1. Numbers
2. Climate	2. Kind
B. Lithosphere (earth)	3. Distribution over the earth
1. Earth materials	B. Works of man
a. Bedrock	1. Settlements
b. Regolith, especially soils	a. Rural
c. Minerals	b. Urban
2. Surface configuration	2. Economies or ways of life
a. Continents and islands	a. Hunting, fishing, and gathering
b. Larger landforms	b. Pastoralism
c. Smaller landforms	c. Exploitation of earth resources, i.e. lumbering, mining, etc.
C. Hydrosphere (water)	d. Agriculture
1. Oceans and seas	e. Industry
2. Water of the land	f. Commerce
a. Surface water	3. Routes of transportation and communication
b. Ground water	
3. Ice	
D. Biosphere (life)	
1. Native plants	
2. Native animals	

Both physical and cultural elements are combined and closely interrelated throughout the habitat. Yet, the combinations are in no wise constant. The proportion of the whole contributed by each element varies from place to place. In addition, the elements themselves change through time.

VARIETY AND CHANGE. Two qualities, variety and change, are ever present in the human habitat. The first of these can be easily observed by travel over the surface of the earth. Change becomes evident only with the passage of time and is hence more difficult to recognize.

Different combinations of both physical and cultural elements produce *variety* within the total habitat. No two areas are exactly alike. Much of the earth's surface is water. This portion is different from that which is land. In addition, no permanent settlement of the oceans is possible, though their temporary use as routes and as sources of food and raw material is very significant to man. Likewise, the atmosphere is unsuited to permanent habitation. In contrast, land areas do provide usable sites.

Yet there is great difference between any two areas of land. Some are wooded like the hill lands of New England (Fig. 1); others are carpeted with grasses like parts of the Great Plains (Fig. 2A); and still others are nearly devoid of vegetation like Death Valley (Fig. 2B). In some places, as in our own West, rugged mountains interrupt the

2A *THE MONOTONOUS flatness of the Great Plains. (Ewing Galloway)*

2B *ELEVEN THOUSAND feet from valley floor to highest peak! You look down into the Death Valley trench and across to the Panamint Mountains. Note the alluvial fans at the base of the Panamints. The lightest areas in the valley floor are areas of heaviest mineral salt concentration. (Robert Pease)*

smoothness of the surface and form barriers to human movement over the land.

These are a few of the easily observed differences, but there are many others, just as important to man, which are not always immediately evident. Some areas are underlain by coal or petroleum deposits. The soils of one area are fertile while those of another are infertile. Some places have climates which are moist, where ample rain falls regularly; in other regions, rain falls so infrequently and in such small amounts as to be a curiosity.

By no means are differences from place to place confined to the physical elements. Some parts of the earth are closely built up to form great cities like New York. Others are thinly peopled and empty of most signs of human activity. Intensively cultivated lands, where a tremendous amount of labor is used per unit of land, like those in Japan, contrast vividly with the extensively cultivated American wheat lands.

Time produces change within any one section of the human habitat. Volcanic eruptions like those of Mount Pelée in 1902 on the West Indian island of Martinique cause sudden and terrible change. Reforestation after lumbering operations is a slower form of change. Still slower is the wearing away of mountain surfaces by streams. This is so slow as to be almost imperceptible to man. Yet, bit by bit through ages of time, the shape of the mountain surface is continuously changing.

Change is not confined to the physical elements of the habitat. Settlements increase or decrease in size and importance. A simple fishing village becomes an important port, as did Amsterdam in the Netherlands. Great ports of one age decline through the silting up of their harbors, as did Bruges and Gent in Belgium. A net of paved highways spreads over an area previously served only by dirt roads or trails. The cutting of great water channels across land masses, like the cutting of the Panama and Suez canals, is change of magnificent and sudden proportions. It alters

the actual surface of the earth even as it modifies the direction of man's activities. Whether it involves the physical or the cultural elements, and whether the rate is fast or slow, change is continuous and is everywhere present.

Some Major Geographical Objectives

It is to provide a framework for observation of variety and change in man's habitat and man's relationship to that habitat that geography bends a large part of its efforts. Geography attempts to picture man's habitat at a specific time through the study of arrangements of natural and human elements over the earth. The effect of the past in the creation of the present is recognized; the effect of the present on the future is implied. Part of the task of geography is to answer such questions as: What kinds of physical and cultural features are encountered on this planet which man finds to be his home? Where throughout the habitat are they encountered? Why are they found thus distributed? Of what significance in human affairs are these distributions? These are among the basic questions of geography.

One geographical point of view is suggested by the growing realization, on the part of all of us, of world interdependence. In the early periods of human history, man made simple use of what he found within any small segment of the whole habitat. His world was limited to the area traversed in the constant search for the necessities of life. Many detailed features like rivers, swamps, gorges, and mountain slopes controlled his routes and offered him easily protected dwelling sites. Vegetation provided food either directly or indirectly through supporting an edible animal population; it also supplied materials for clothing and shelter. Streams offered water and supplementary food in the form of fish.

Steady and long-continued rains, snow, and ice or periods of bright sunshine made necessary some variety of clothing and shelter. Life in small groups produced only limited human contacts. Such elements, combined within a relatively small area, were man's world and he was closely tied to it. Primitive means of transportation and simplicity of manner of living effectively isolated one fragment of the habitat from another.

Through the passage of centuries, man's manner of life has increased in complexity. Correspondingly, through increased range of movement, he has expanded his known world until the whole surface of the planet is finally known. Increased speed and ease of movement have bound together fragments of the habitat shell; indeed, in the time sense, the shell has actually begun to contract. Domestication of animals provided beasts of burden and thus increased the range of man's movements. Navigation, even so primitive as the use of rafts, opened new highways. The invention and application of the steam engine materially increased the speed with which man could travel over the surface of both land and water. Oceans, at one time serious barriers, became highways. Railroads cut to a fraction the time of overland movements. In our own century, the internal-combustion engine, first a conqueror of surface space and then conqueror of the lower portion of the atmosphere, has carried the process farther. No longer can any group remain wholly isolated.

The increased complexity of present-day life is typified by the development of huge urban populations. For the individual in an urban community, emphasis is no longer on the direct production of all the goods essential to his life but rather on such specialized functions as the manufacture or distribution of one particular product. Primitive man was concerned only with satisfying his food needs and providing himself with shelter for protection and comfort. He lived or perished through his own efforts as a hunter. Human groups in those times were small and contacts between them were infrequent. Later, with the domestication of animals and plants and with the use of metals, living became less rigorous. More nearly complete use of the physical part of the habitat made possible larger groupings of men. Contacts between groups were more frequent. Surpluses of foods, clothing, shelter materials, and implements were accumulated. And commerce, the exchange of goods between human groups, came into being. Man no longer had to go after what he needed within a narrowly encompassed area; it was brought to him from ever-increasing distances. Some men could specialize in one activity like growing wheat, raising animals, weaving cloth, or making implements. Specialized workers could secure their own needs from others who carried their products to places ill-equipped for their production and returned with items which they could not produce. In this way, large groups could live without the necessity of securing the absolute essentials of life from a mere fragment of the whole habitat.

So far has the process gone under Western civilization that no areas remain self-sufficient. Long tentacles of trade spread throughout the world and along them are sucked raw materials which make possible the continuance of the urban mode of life. What once were considered luxuries, desirable yet unessential, are now classed as basic necessities. Only with a decrease in the level of living can the dependence of one area upon another be overcome. Our world is no longer a fragment of the habitat shell; it is the whole shell.

SCOPE OF THIS BOOK

Specific Objectives

The entire human habitat is our concern; hence our attention must be focused upon features of world scale. We must consider broad categories of both physical and cultural facts. We are not concerned with a complete re-cital of earth knowledge. Hence, our analysis of features which combine to differentiate por-tions of the earth must be limited to major elements. Our objectives may be summarized positively under five main headings: (1) to present an orderly treatment of the major physical elements with which man contends and co-operates; (2) to outline the principal ways man makes use of the physical setting in which he lives; (3) to present the distribu-tion over the earth of both the physical and cultural elements of the human habitat; (4) to interpret the variety which exists; and (5) to offer a standard against which change may be measured. Through these objectives, a basic outline for the understanding of the world in which we live is offered.

Outline of Approach

There are many lines of approach to the objectives which have been stated. We begin our study by examining certain phases of the earth as a planet. From this emerges a broad appreciation of the shell habitat we are about to analyze. Here is the common ground for the general beginning of many studies, but particularly of three—astronomy, geology, and geography. Because physically we human beings are so much smaller than the object of our study, we resort to a special means of reducing facts about that object to workable size: we employ a code or set of symbols— the map. Following our study of the planet as a whole, we must give some attention to maps, their construction, and their uses. By means of them, observations may be com-piled, distributions ascertained, and interrela-tionships deduced. If the pertinent data of the habitat are not reduced to map presenta-tion, the element of distribution and the na-ture of the ties between distributions cannot fully be appreciated. At all times, however,

the map must be thought of as a code or set of symbols. Otherwise, interpretation of it will be false.

Following the delimitation of the field of study and the acquisition of the major tool, we shall proceed to an orderly examination of the physical and cultural facts. Since man lives at the bottom of an "ocean" of atmos-phere and since it is that atmosphere which makes all life possible, it is reasonable to begin with the study of conditions in that gaseous envelope, climate. We proceed with the ques-tions: What kinds of climate are there? Where is each type found? Why is the ar-rangement such as it is? What is the signifi-cance of climate to man? The many forms which unite to set the stage of man's activity exist below the cover of atmosphere. Primary among these forms are the great oceans and land masses. On the land, the most conspicu-ous features are the landforms (mountains, hills, plateaus, and plains). They influence, favorably or unfavorably, many human ac-tivities. The pattern of landforms makes for variety throughout the habitat. Water forms, so intimately fused with those of the land and so directly relatable to climate, make next call upon our attention. Human, plant, and ani-mal life are all narrowly limited by availabil-ity of water. Oceans provide both highways and sources of support. In addition, the func-tion of water in inland transport and in the development of power is important.

Perhaps as significant as landforms is the cover of native vegetation. It provides a source of materials needed by man and also the life essentials for an animal population which man has, at least in part, bent to his uses. A less obvious form, soil, is fully as essential to life forms. Finally, the mineral resources, which are the basis of man's complex economy, pro-vide the element at the very bottom of the shell habitat. To extract them from the earth, man has penetrated farthest below the actual surface and has thus pushed his habitat into the solid portion of the planet. All of these forms collectively, combined in different quantities in separate areas, produce the conditions which provide the ultimate physical limits of man's activity.

From an understanding of the physical habitat, one passes to a consideration of man and his activities. The most prominent among the cultural elements is the distribution of population over the earth. Yet this is almost overshadowed by a factor which is not directly visible or instantly comprehensible. This factor is culture, the sum of the "capabilities and habits acquired by man as a member of society." While the physical setting places certain broad restrictions on man's activities, culture may, and frequently does, offer more serious obstacles. Conversely, culture may provide means of overcoming physical restrictions. Availability of water in a desert is undoubtedly a measure of restriction for a human group. If such a group does not know the technique of well drilling, it finds the desert almost useless. Another group, having a means of tapping an underground water supply, discovers a setting in which it can live satisfactorily. If the culture includes knowledge of irrigation methods, barren desert may be made to support great densities of population, like those of the Nile Valley in Egypt.

Throughout man's long history, numerous great culture groups have arisen and have produced distinctive economies, or ways of living. When progress has been maintained, the groups have increased in size and the culture they represent has spread to affect large portions of the world; other groups have barely maintained themselves and their areal influence has declined or disappeared altogether, like that of the Mayas in Middle America. In the present period, two great cultures dominate the world scene: that of Europe and the Americas (which is called Euro-American or Occidental) and that of southern and eastern Asia (which is called Oriental). Other smaller and less complex cultures still remain in considerable numbers and add materially to the mosaic pattern which man has imposed upon the physical habitat.

From a realization of the significance and variety of cultures, one passes to the observable forms—such as fields, roads, buildings, and settlements—in which they result. Distinctive economies—from the most elemental hunting, fishing, and gathering to the most intricate urban life—create notable variety in the habitat. The practice of these varied economies by individual culture groups, particularly as expressed by forms of settlement and of land use, results in variety from place to place over the whole earth. What are the settlement and land use forms? Where are they found? Why are they so distributed? What is the significance of their distribution? These are the questions toward which our attention is directed.

The world pattern of transportation routes is in reality the best summary of these studies. The routeways of the land, the sea, and the air constitute a network which holds together the parts of the pattern of population distribution. The population pattern and the transportation pattern are, accordingly, among the principal sources of information about the world. Our final aim is to understand the blending of physical and cultural elements which constitute the human habitat.

••

CHAPTER OUTLINE

Some objectives of geographic study

Scope of geography
  Man's habitat
    Physical or natural elements
    Cultural or human elements
    Variety and change
  Some major geographical objectives
Scope of this book
  Specific objectives
  Outline of approach

REVIEW QUESTIONS

1. What constitutes the human habitat?
2. Are the limits of the human habitat fixed permanently, or might they be altered? If it is possible that they might be altered, suggest how this might be accomplished.
3. What is the purpose of separating the physical from the cultural elements of the human habitat? On what basis is the division made?
4. From your own experience, give some examples of the variety to be found within the human habitat.
5. Is the quality of change constant throughout the human habitat? Explain your answer by reference to what you have observed personally.
6. What are some of the major objectives of geography?
7. What are the four basically geographic questions which must be answered about each of the physical and cultural elements if an understanding of the human habitat is to be obtained?
8. Suggest some ways in which an understanding of the human habitat can be applied to and is of great significance to everyday life.

SOME SUGGESTED REFERENCES

Bowman, Isaiah, *Geography in Relation to the Social Sciences,* Scribner, 1934. A professional statement of geography's particular contribution among the various disciplines of social science by one of America's foremost geographers of the twentieth century.

Bruhnes, Jean, *Human Geography,* Rand McNally, 1920. A translation of the French classic; one of the foundation works of present-day American study of the cultural elements of geography.

East, William Gordon, *The Geography Behind History,* Thomas Nelson & Sons, 1938. A vivid, readable demonstration of the significance of geography in the study of human actions and institutions.

Lowie, Robert Harry, *An Introduction to Cultural Anthropology,* new and enl. ed., Farrar & Rinehart, 1940. A standard work on human cultures.

MacCurdy, George Grant, *Human Origins,* Appleton, 1924, 2 vols. A scholarly account of the origin and development of man and of his prehistoric and early historic cultures; thoroughly documented.

Ritter, Carl, *Comparative Geography,* Lippincott, 1865. A series of lectures by an eminent German geographer of the nineteenth century, published posthumously; a foundation of many present concepts in geography; fully as valid now as when published.

Vidal De La Blache, Paul, *Principles of Human Geography,* Holt, 1926. An excellent translation and arrangement of unfinished book manuscript and notes of the famous French geographer, published posthumously; one of the most important attempts to suggest classification and definition of principles of human geography.

CHAPTER 2

Gross Features of the Earth

∙∙

The attention of geography is focused on the earth, particularly on the surface of the earth. Nevertheless, it is important to realize the earth's place in that broader scheme of things known as the solar system. Though the earth seems so large to us, it is only a minor member of the system; in fact, the system's center and its giant, the sun, is itself only one of the myriad of stars and is far from being the greatest of those. Yet, the sun is all-important to living things on earth. From it comes the energy which makes life possible.

THE SOLAR SYSTEM

The solar system consists of a central sun about which move nine planets with their satellites. In addition, the system includes a group of planetary fragments known as asteroids and a whole host of more chaotic wanderers known as comets and meteors. There is continuous movement within the system and the system itself is moving as a unit through interstellar space.

The details of the structure and operation of all parts of the solar system are not particularly the concern of geography. Nevertheless, understanding of the nature of the human habitat can best be obtained if one realizes the basic relationships between the earth as a planet and the sun as the major member of the solar system.

The Sun

Compared to all the other parts of the solar system, the sun is truly huge. It is a spherical, gaseous body about 1,300,000 times the size of the earth. The sun's diameter is 109 times that of the earth. If the sun were a hollow sphere and the earth were placed at its center, the surface of the sun would be 432,000 miles from the earth. Even the moon in its orbit would be only halfway from the earth to the sun's surface. The earth is literally a speck compared to such a huge body.

The sun is the only self-luminous body within the whole solar system. It is, in fact, the system's mammoth heating and lighting plant. Even on the sun's outer surface, the temperature is 6,000° centigrade. The planets and their satellites are lighted and heated by the energy emitted from this huge, tremendously hot surface.

Since energy is radiated in all directions from the sun, only a minute portion at best can be intercepted by any one planet. The particular amount intercepted depends in considerable part upon the size of the planet and upon its distance from the sun. The effectiveness of the energy received depends upon the detailed motions of the planet and upon the nature of the planet's atmosphere. Thus the earth's size and its distance from the sun, its movement in the solar system, and the nature of its atmosphere are significant from a geographical point of view.

The Planets

Nine planets travel around the sun in paths or *orbits* which are approximately circular. Each is held in its orbit by a nice balance of two opposing forces, *gravitational attraction* and *centrifugal force*.

GRAVITATIONAL ATTRACTION. The sun exerts an attractive force upon all members of the solar system. This force acts to keep the planets from "sailing out into space" as they whirl about in their orbits. The same force acts to keep the moon revolving about the earth instead of flying away in an erratic path. That the oceans, loose rock fragments, soil, buildings, and even we ourselves do not fly off the earth's surface is a result of the operation of the same force. We know this force as gravitational attraction, or gravity. The general physical law of gravity is stated as follows: *any two particles of matter attract each other with a force proportional to the product of their masses and inversely proportional to the square of the distance between them.*

Since the sun has a mass so many times greater than that of any of the planets, it exercises strong attraction upon all of them. They are thus retained within the system of which the sun is the center.

CENTRIFUGAL FORCE. If gravitational attraction acted alone, the sun would draw the planets in upon itself, eventually to destroy them in its own fiery mass. That this is not what happens is the result of what we call centrifugal force. This force tends to cause matter to fly away from any center of rotation, like mud flying off the rim of a turning wheel.

Since the planets are rotating bodies, each one develops considerable centrifugal force. The balance between the gravitational effect of the sun and the centrifugal effect of each of the planets determines the detailed paths which they follow around the sun.

RELATIVE POSITION OF THE PLANETS. The planet nearest the sun is Mercury. Its orbit has a mean distance from the sun of nearly 36,000,000 miles. Next outward from the center is Venus, at a mean distance of 67,000,000 miles. And third from the sun is the earth, at a mean distance of nearly 93,000,000 miles. Compared to that of the outermost of the planets, the earth's distance is relatively small. Pluto, farthest removed from the sun, lies at the tremendous mean distance of 3,700,000,-000 miles, about forty times as far away as the earth.

As they are stated, these figures of distance mean relatively little to the average person. It is somewhat more graphic to realize that an airliner cruising at the speed of 250 miles per hour would require 42½ years of steady flying to travel from the earth to the sun! Similarly, to fly from Pluto to the sun would require about 1,700 years of continuous flying! Even with its great speed (186,000 miles per second), light from the sun reaches the earth in slightly less than 8 minutes; it takes nearly 5½ hours to reach Pluto.

Though Mercury is the smallest of all the planets, it is so close to the sun that it receives a tremendous amount of heat. However, its motions are such that the same side of the planet is always exposed to the sun's rays. That side is always scorchingly hot while the other side is permanently very cold. On this basis alone, life is impossible on that planet. On the other hand, though Jupiter is the largest of the planets, some 1,300 times as large as the earth, it is so far away that the sun's energy received at its surface is not great enough to raise its "midsummer" temperature even as high as the lowest observed air temperature on the earth. The earth is just far enough from the source of energy, it has just the proper atmosphere, and its motions as a planet are such as to produce the very narrowly limited conditions under which life as we know it can exist.

Some of the relative features of size within the solar system are shown in Table 2.

© *Chesley Bonestell*

3 *AN ARTIST'S CONCEPT of a lunar landscape. It is illuminated by "earth-shine," the light reflected from the earth, the large white object visible above the lunar horizon. In this painting the constellation Orion appears to the right of the earth in the sky. (This view reproduces one of the illustrations in* The Conquest of Space *by Chesley Bonestell and Willi Ley. Used by arrangement with the Viking Press.)*

THE PHYSICAL EARTH

Size and Shape

The earth is essentially a sphere with a diameter of approximately 8,000 miles and a maximum circumference just short of 25,000 miles. Actually, there is a slight flattening in both polar regions: the polar diameter of the earth is 7,899.98 miles; midway between the poles, the diameter is 7,926.68 miles. The difference between the two is 26.70 miles. Though this difference may appear to be very considerable, it results in only minor departure from true sphericity. This can be illustrated by reference to a globe. It is doubtful whether a globe 18 inches in diameter is much nearer a true sphere than is the earth. The 26.70 miles difference between the earth's diameters is represented by 6/100 of an inch when reduced to the scale of an 18-inch globe.

The great heights of rugged mountains reaching far above the earth's surface provide another measure of the earth's departure from the shape of a true sphere. In the Himalaya Mountains of northern India, Mount Everest reaches over 29,000 feet above sea level. This height of nearly 5½ miles is the greatest known elevation on the earth's surface. The greatest known depth of ocean is that off the eastern side of the Philippine Islands. There, the bottom lies over 35,000 feet below the ocean's surface, a depth of over 6½ miles. The difference between the highest elevation of land and the greatest depth of ocean is approximatly 12 miles. If Mount Everest were truly represented rising above the average surface of an 18-inch globe, it would "jut out" only 12/1,000 of an inch. If the ocean's greatest depth were shown to true scale, it would indent the surface of the globe only slightly more than 14/1,000 of an inch. Both of these amounts are less than the ordinary thickness of paper covering a globe's surface.

Table 2   SOME RELATIVE FEATURES OF SIZE WITHIN THE SOLAR SYSTEM

	MEAN DISTANCE FROM SUN (*Earth equals 1.00*)	MEAN DIAMETER (*Earth equals 1.00*)	MEAN VOLUME (*Earth equals 1.00*)
Sun		109.10	1,300,000.00
Mercury	.38	.39	.06
Venus	.72	.97	.92
Earth	1.00	1.00	1.00
Mars	1.52	.53	.15
Jupiter	5.20	10.95	1,312.00
Saturn	9.54	9.02	734.00
Uranus	19.19	4.00	64.00
Neptune	30.07	3.92	60.00
Pluto	39.54(?)	.51(?)	.13(?)

Table compiled from appendix material in Henry N. Russell, Raymond S. Dugan, and John Q. Stewart, *Astronomy, Volume I, The Solar System*, rev. ed., Ginn, 1945. Reproduced by permission of the publishers.

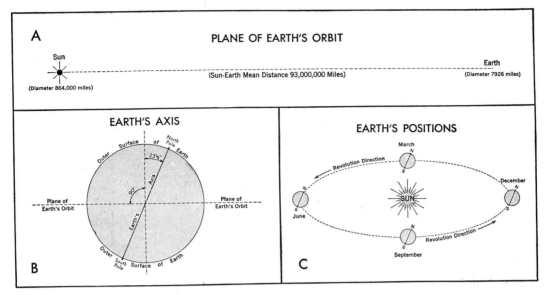

4 *SOME IMPORTANT FEATURES of the earth's relationship to the sun. (A) The plane of the earth's orbit passes through the sun (note relative sizes of sun and earth). (B) The earth's axis is inclined 23½° from the vertical with respect to the plane of its orbit. (C) The inclination of the earth's axis remains constant everywhere along the earth's orbit about the sun.*

Movements

The earth performs two basic types of movement. It turns, or *rotates*, about an imaginary axis extending through the sphere from what is called the North Pole to what is called the South Pole. At the same time, it moves, or *revolves*, in a more or less circular path around the sun.

ROTATION. The earth rotates at a uniform rate about an axis which is its shortest diameter. It makes one complete turn, always toward the east, in a period of time which we call a day. Actually, the time of rotation is 23 hours, 56 minutes, and 4.09 seconds. The speed of rotation for points along the earth's greatest circumference is approximately 1,500 feet per second, or slightly over 1,000 miles per hour. Yet, we have no conscious feeling of rapid movement at the earth's surface. This is primarily because the motion is essentially uniform.

Rotation brings about the alternation of day and night and creates the phenomena of sunrise and sunset. Likewise, it modifies movements within the atmosphere and the oceans. In later chapters of this book, some of the more significant effects of the earth's rotation will be treated in more detail.

REVOLUTION. As it spins on its axis, the earth also moves in a definite orbit around the sun. The time required for one complete journey is approximately 365¼ days. The speed of the journey averages 18½ miles per second! As with rotational speed, uniformity obliterates the feeling of rapid movement.

The earth's orbit lies in a plane which passes through the sun, but the axis about which the earth rotates is neither in that plane nor perpendicular to it. The axis is inclined from the perpendicular by 23½ degrees (Fig. 4). No matter what the position of the earth in its orbit, the inclination of the axis remains constant. Upon this relationship depend seasonal changes so noticeable on the earth's surface.

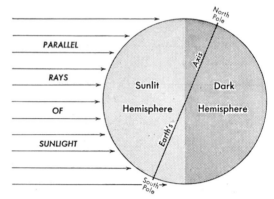

5   *THE STRIKE of the sun's rays in June and December, the times when the earth is at the extreme positions in its orbit around the sun.*

Some Effects of Earth Movements

SOLSTICES AND EQUINOXES. As it moves in its orbit, the earth approaches closest to the sun during late December and is farthest removed from it in late June. In December, the earth's axis is so inclined that the Southern Hemisphere is most completely exposed to the sun. The rays of the sun which strike the earth are essentially parallel to one another. Consequently, in the December part of the year, the half of the sphere which receives the sun's energy reaches beyond the South Pole but not quite to the North Pole (Fig. 5). Then, even though the earth turns upon its axis, the South Polar regions remain constantly in sunlight through the complete rotation. At the same time, the North Polar regions remain constantly in darkness.

In June, the earth's axis is still parallel to its position in December, but now the Northern Hemisphere is most completely exposed to the sun. Then the sunlit half of the sphere reaches beyond the North Pole, but not quite to the South Pole. As the earth rotates, the North Pole remains in the sunlit half and the South Pole in the dark half.

Between these extreme positions of late December and late June, the earth occupies two locations in which the sunlit half and the dark half stretch from pole to pole. Then, as the sphere rotates, the 24-hour path of every point on earth lies half its length across the illuminated face of the earth and half its length across the dark face. Thus, in late March and late September, the length of light and dark periods is equal over the whole globe.

In this manner, the progression of the earth through its orbit causes variation in the length of day and night for different places upon its surface (Fig. 57). The date when the South Pole is turned most directly toward the sun, December 21 or 22, is known in the Northern Hemisphere as the *winter solstice.* Then, days are longest throughout the Southern Hemisphere and nights are longest in the Northern Hemisphere. The date when the North Pole is turned most directly toward the sun, June 21 or 22, is known in the Northern Hemisphere as the *summer solstice.* Then, days are longest in the Northern Hemisphere and nights are longest in the Southern Hemisphere.

About March 21 and September 21, the earth is midway between the solstice positions. At both of these times, day and night lengths are equal over the whole globe. The former date is known as the *vernal equinox* and the latter as the *autumnal equinox*. For the Southern Hemisphere, all of these terms (winter and summer, vernal and autumnal) are reversed.

In part because of variations in the length of day and night, the heating of the earth's surface differs both from place to place and from time to time. This difference is the basic cause of the seasons. The part of the year during which heating is greatest we recognize as *summer*. That part during which heating is least is known as *winter*. The period between winter and summer is called *spring;* and that between summer and winter, *fall*. In the Northern Hemisphere summer is the June-July-August part of the year, but in the Southern Hemisphere summer is the December-January-February season.

Throughout a considerable belt centering midway between the poles, there is little difference in heating during the whole year. There, seasons cannot be based on temperature differences. Within this belt, the sun at noon appears directly overhead on two days during the year. The months just before, during, and just after these days are called the *high sun periods*. The months between are known as the *low sun periods*.

TIDES. Earth motions combined with gravitational attraction exerted by the moon and the sun are responsible for the phenomena known as *tides*. On the rigid part of the earth, the pull of the two bodies is not easily measurable, but the large water masses, being fluid, are drawn away from the solid crust of the earth. The resulting deformations or bulges and depressions are the tides which are easily observable and accurately measurable in terms of the rise and fall of water level.

The moon is the earth's lone satellite. It has a diameter a little more than one quarter as great as that of the earth. Despite its very small size, the moon exerts greater gravita-

tional attraction on the earth than the immensely larger sun does. This is because it is many times closer to the earth than is the sun. The moon revolves in an orbit at a mean distance of only 239,000 miles from the earth and it accompanies the earth throughout its circuit of the sun.

If we consider the disturbing force of the moon alone, some notion of the nature of tides in the watery portion of the earth's surface may be obtained. The moon's attraction is greatest on that portion of the water surface directly toward and, hence, nearer to it (A in Fig. 6) than on the solid mass of the earth (E in Fig. 6). There is, therefore, a tendency for the water and the earth to pull apart. The water surface on the side away from the moon (B in Fig. 6) is less strongly attracted than the solid mass of the earth. The tendency in this instance is again toward the separation of the two. The result is the creation of two bulges, one directly toward the moon and one directly away from it, and two depressions, at right angles to the bulges, in the watery portion of the earth's surface.

Both the moon and the sun create tidal disturbances. When they are both acting along the same line, deformation is greatest, for their pulls are combined; when they act at right angles to one another, distortion is much minimized, since one pulls against the other.

The moon and the sun act along roughly the same line twice during each month (Fig. 7): once at *new moon* when the moon is between the earth and the sun; and once at *full moon* when the moon is on the opposite side of the earth from the sun. At these two times the bulges in the liquid portion of the earth

6   SCHEMATIC *representation of tidal bulges created by the moon.*

are observed to be greatest; these are the *spring tides*. Between these two periods, when the moon and the sun pull along divergent lines, tides are lower. The lowest or *neap tides* occur when the two attractive forces act at right angles to one another. This happens at the *first* and *third quarters of the moon*.

As we have seen, two bulges are created in the fluid portion of the earth's surface (Fig. 6). Since the earth rotates on its axis once a day, the height of the bulge passes any given point twice during that period and the respective depressions do likewise. It is thus that there are two periods of *high* tide and two periods of *low* tide in each day. The period between successive high tides and successive low tides is somewhat longer than twelve hours, nearly twelve and one half.

Actually, tides are more complex than the foregoing statement suggests. There are four factors primarily responsible for the complexity. First, the moon's orbit is not a perfect circle. Hence, the attractive force of that body varies in strength from time to time. The force is greatest when the moon is nearest the earth; it is least when the moon is farthest away. Second, the moon's orbit is not in the same plane as that of the earth. Hence, the moon and the sun act in the same plane only at infrequent intervals. Third, the earth rotates at such a rate that the forces which produce tides in any one part of the ocean change too fast to allow the water level to adjust itself fully to them. Fourth, the irregularity of shape and depth of the ocean basins prevents even distribution of the tidal forces over the whole earth.

The Face of the Earth

The face of the planet Earth is far from uniform. The solid crust bulges outward in some places and sags inward in others. The sags or hollows contain the main water masses and the bulges rise above them as land masses. Together these features create a basic visible pattern for the earth as a whole. They are the features which sketch the broad outlines of the face of the earth.

MAJOR LAND MASSES. All land is surrounded by water. When the land area is large, the term *continent* is applied. When the land area is small, the term *island* is used. There is no precise definition for either term. Custom directs the usage.

Traditionally, we think of Europe, Asia, and Africa as three continents; actually, they are all part of one land mass, deeply indented

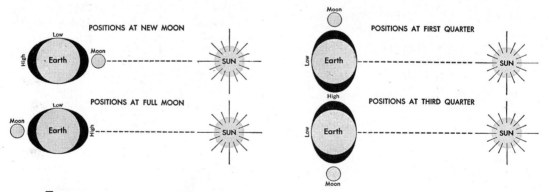

7 *RELATIVE POSITIONS of sun, moon, and earth at times of moon phases. At new and full moon, moon and sun act along essentially the same line to produce highest (spring) tides; at first and third quarters, moon and sun act at right angles to one another to produce lowest (neap) tides.*

8

ONLY the narrow water ribbon of the Suez Canal breaks the continuity of the world's largest land mass. (Screen Traveler from Gendreau)

by seas and broken by the man-made channel of the Suez Canal (Fig. 8). This land mass is the largest in the world with a total area of approximately 31,500,000 square miles, some 10½ times the size of the United States (Fig. 9A).

The second largest of the land masses is that which includes both North and South America together with the narrow strip of land, Middle America, which connects them. Here, likewise, tradition impels us to think in terms of two continents. Actually, there is only one land mass (Fig. 9B) although it is broken by a man-made channel, the Panama Canal. The Americas have an area of about 16,250,000 square miles, only slightly more than half the size of the largest land mass.

Third, in size, is Antarctica, which is mostly ice-covered but has an area of approximately 5,500,000 square miles (Fig. 9D). And last among the land masses large enough to warrant the name of continent is Australia, some 3,000,000 square miles in extent (Fig. 9C).

The four land areas large enough to be called continental have a total area of roughly 56,157,000 square miles (Table 3). Over the whole surface of the globe, there is a total of only about 1,800,000 square miles more of land, made up of islands of widely assorted sizes. Yet, with all these bits of land included, only 29 per cent of the earth's surface is land; oceans cover almost three-quarters of the whole globe.

Table 3 APPROXIMATE MAJOR LAND AND WATER AREAS (IN SQUARE MILES)

Earth's surface	197,000,000
Total area in water	139,000,000
Total area in land	58,000,000

OCEAN AREAS

Pacific	63,785,000
Atlantic	31,811,000
Indian	28,349,000
Antarctic	5,731,000
Arctic	5,439,000
Ocean total	135,115,000

CONTINENTAL AREAS

Asia (including East Indies and Philippine Islands)	17,029,000
Africa	11,596,000
N. America	9,387,000
S. America	6,863,000
Antarctic	6,000,000
Europe	3,908,000
Australia	2,975,000
Continental total	57,758,000

REPRESENTATIVE SEAS

Mediterranean	981,000
Bering	875,000
Caribbean	750,000
Japan	389,000
Red	168,000
Black	164,000
Baltic	163,000
North (with English Channel)	251,000

MAJOR WATER BODIES. There are commonly recognized only five bodies of water large enough to bear the designation of ocean. These are the Pacific, Atlantic, Indian, Antarctic, and Arctic in order of decreasing size. The Pacific, extending over an area of 64,000,000 square miles, fills the monstrous oval between the Americas and the eastern coasts of Asia and Australia (Fig. 10A). All the land surface in the world could be placed within the Pacific and there would remain an area of water more than twice the size of the United States.

The Atlantic fills the gap between the east coast of the Americas and the western coasts of Europe and Africa (Fig. 10B). It is pinched to a width of 1,800 miles between the "nose" of Brazil and the western "bulge" of Africa. Yet, its area is nearly the same as that of the largest land mass in the world, 31,500,000 square miles. The Indian Ocean, lying between Africa, Asia, and Australia, is nearly as large (Fig. 10C).

Tying together the three monster oceans at the south is the fourth in size, the Antarctic Ocean (Fig. 11). It forms the watery ring around the ice-covered Antarctic continent; it fills the openings between that continent and Australia, South America, and Africa. In the North Polar region, there is no continent similar to Antarctica. Instead, there is the Arctic Ocean separating the Euro-Asiatic and the American shores, and opening southward through narrow channels to both the Atlantic and the Pacific.

Areas of water bodies and total area of earth's surface derived from Table 5 in H. U. Sverdrup, Martin W. Johnson, and Richard H. Fleming, *The Oceans*. Copyright 1942 by Prentice-Hall, Inc. Reproduced by permission of the publisher. Areas of land derived from "Areas and Populations of the Countries of the World," *Britannica Book of the Year*, Encyclopaedia Britannica, 1950. Reproduced by permission of the publisher.

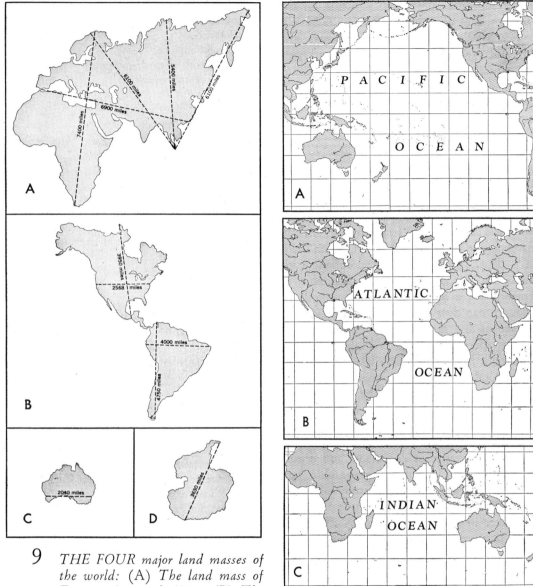

9 THE FOUR major land masses of the world: (A) The land mass of Europe, Asia, and Africa. (B) The land mass of the Americas. (C) Australia. (D) Antarctica.

10 THE THREE major oceans of the world.

The similar water surfaces formed where oceans indent continental shores or where chains of islands nearly enclose parts of ocean are known as *seas*. Along the island-fringed margins of the northern and western Pacific lie the Bering, Okhotsk, Japan, East China, and South China seas, to mention only the more prominent ones (Fig. 11). Between Australia and the islands which fringe its northern and eastern shores lie the Timor, Arafura, Coral, and Tasman seas. In the western Atlantic, the Caribbean indents and nearly separates the Americas while on the eastern side of that same ocean are the North, Baltic, Mediterranean, and Black seas. The Ross and Weddell seas extend southward from the Antarctic Ocean, indenting the continental shores. From the Arctic, the Greenland, Norwegian, Barents, White, Kara, Laptev, East Siberian, and Beaufort seas reach southward to bite into the land. Seldom are these seas clearly demarcated or sharply separated from one another, but they are all moderately closely encompassed by land.

Man has made all of these water bodies serve as routeways from one land mass to another. He has learned to secure from them raw materials and many items of food. Upon them he is dependent for many atmospheric variations which make land areas habitable in some instances and uninhabitable in others. Though man does not live permanently upon the oceans and seas, they are essential to all his activities; though he is confined for his permanent home to slightly less than a third of the total earth's surface, man cannot neglect the watery two-thirds. The arrangement, or pattern, of land and water is the pattern upon and from which variety is developed over the face of the earth. The distribution of land and water, or continents and oceans if one prefers, is a basic geographic fact upon which rests the whole study of world variety. Without this pattern as a frame of reference, interpretation of other geographic facts lacks reality and, therefore, becomes essentially meaningless.

• •

CHAPTER OUTLINE

Gross features of the earth

The solar system
  The sun
  The planets
    Gravitational attraction
    Centrifugal force
    Relative position of the planets
The physical earth

  Size and shape
  Movements
    Rotation
    Revolution
  Some effects of earth movements
    Solstices and equinoxes
    Tides
The face of the earth
  Major land masses
  Major water bodies

REVIEW QUESTIONS

1. What constitutes the solar system? Of what importance is it that the earth is part of the solar system?
2. What is the only source of energy in the solar system? How is this significant to man?
3. State the law of gravity. What is centrifugal force? Give some examples of the action of both forces from your own experience.
4. Where does the earth fit in the system of planets in terms of relative distance from the sun and relative size? Would it make any difference to man if the earth were its present size, but in the relative position of Venus? of Saturn?
5. Describe the movements of the earth within the solar system. Of what significance are these movements?
6. How can an individual distinguish between the general period of a solstice or of an equinox by simple observation? Suggest some ways in which the activities of the people of the United States, for example, are affected by the periods of solstice or equinox.
7. In what parts of the earth are the seasons most pronounced? Why?
8. What are tides? What causes tides? Why are tides of different magnitude at different times? In different places? Suggest some ways in which tides are directly important to man.
9. Distinguish between continents and islands.
10. What is the difference between a continent and a land mass?
11. List the continents in order of decreasing size.
12. What is the difference between an ocean and a sea?
13. List the oceans in order of decreasing size.
14. Locate all the place names mentioned in this chapter on an outline map of the world.

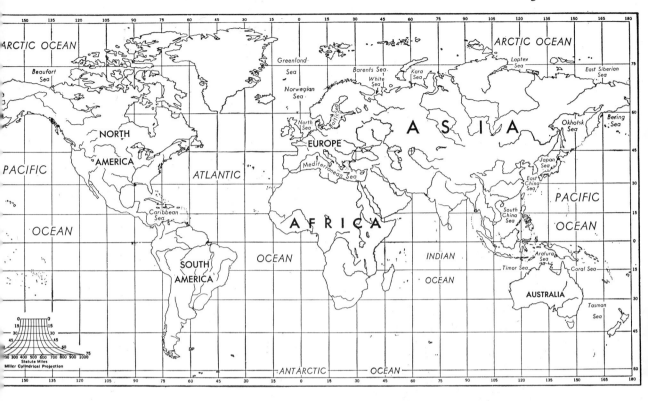

II *THE CONTINENTS, the oceans, and the major seas of the world.*

SOME SUGGESTED REFERENCES

Gamow, George, *The Birth and Death of the Sun,* Penguin Books, Inc., 1945. A readable, popular, and accurate account of present-day theory concerning the evolution of our solar system and its probable future; by a well-known physicist.

Harrison, Lucia Carolyn, *Daylight, Twilight, Darkness, and Time: Their Distribution Over the Earth and Their Relationships to Human Affairs,* Silver, Burdett & Co., 1935. An excellent account of earth-sun relations in terms of their significance to human beings; well illustrated and easily understood.

Marr, John Edward, *The Scientific Study of Scenery,* 9th ed., Methuen & Co., Ltd., 1943. A well-tried treatment of the physical elements of geography, especially landforms; for the general reader.

Mill, Hugh Robert, *The Realm of Nature,* Scribner, 1892. Despite its age, this standard late-nineteenth-century geography has many still-useful ideas; concerned largely with the broader facts of physical geography.

Renner, George Thomas, and associates, *Global Geography,* Thomas Y. Crowell Co., 1944. A text which presents a world point of view; directed toward those who have had little or no contact with what geography has to offer to the general study of human affairs.

Russell, Henry Norris; Dugan, Raymond Smith; and Stewart, John Quincy, *Astronomy. Vol. I, The Solar System,* rev. ed., Ginn, 1945. A new edition of a standard college text in astronomy; clearly written and easily understood.

12   *A GIGANTIC MODERN EXAMPLE of an ancient geographic tool, the map.
These geographers are assembling the map of Hispanic America on the scale of
1 : 1,000,000, in the court of the American Geographical Society building in
New York. (Alfred Eisenstadt from Pix, Inc.)*

CHAPTER 3

The Tools of Geography

∙∙

Each discipline or field of knowledge has certain tools and devices on which it depends to further its objectives. Those used by geography include ancient ones, as globes and maps, and modern ones, as relief models and climatic charts. As is true so often, the proven tools of one field may be of great value in other fields as well. Maps, so essential to geographical inquiry, are used to major advantage in history, economics, geology, transportation, journalism, and many other fields. Relief models serve the purposes of military tactics, civil engineering, geology, and so on, as well as those of geography. The more commonly used tools of geography have wide application.

GLOBES

The globe is man's closest approximation to the earth itself. It is a reproduction of the entire earth of such a size, or scale, that one can see it, handle it, and comprehend it, all at one time. It is, almost literally, the "world brought indoors." If carefully constructed, it will show the true shape of the earth. It will portray the shapes of the oceans and continents correctly. And it will enable one to make accurate size comparisons, as of the size of Africa compared to that of North America, or the size of Europe compared to that of Australia. The fact that globes are more common now than ever before is indicative of their utility. Many families consider a globe to be a necessary part of the equipment of the modern home.

Early Globes

The Greeks, more than 1,600 years before Columbus, felt certain that the earth was approximately spherical. It was they who first reproduced the earth in the form of a globe. The earliest globe was probably made by Crates about the year 150 B.C. (Fig. 13). Since that time, hundreds of persons have constructed globes of various sizes and types, globes carrying varying degrees of detail concerning the earth as a whole. All the early globes, especially those made prior to the Age of Discovery (roughly 1400-1700 A.D.), portrayed much guesswork. For example, the globe of Crates showed the then known world which lay along the shores of the Mediterranean Sea and extended into southern Asia. It also showed three other continents the existence of which was mere supposition; they were drawn in simply to balance the globe and provide it with a degree of symmetry. The amazing part of the supposition is that, in a sense, it predicted the existence of the Americas and Australia.

The oldest of existing globes is at the Germanic Museum in Nürnberg, Germany. Constructed by Martin Behaim, it was completed in the year 1492 A.D. (Fig. 13). It gave no hint of the Americas, but the globes which were made within the next few years showed at least the general outline of the Atlantic shores of North and South America and some sections of the Pacific shores. From then on, globes presented more and more of the earth as we know it today, although not before the mid-1700's did fancy and surmise give way entirely to the facts of land and water distribution.

Modern Globes

The globes of today are carefully constructed models of a world which is thoroughly known; at least man knows much more of the world than can be portrayed on the surface of a globe of any reasonable and readily useful size. They are made most commonly of cardboard or papier-mâché (inexpensive globes), or of glass or pressed steel (expensive globes). On spherical bases of these materials, carefully prepared strips, known as *gores,* are laid. The amount of detail which a globe shows depends on its size. Obviously one with a diameter of 18 inches can tell more of the nature of the world than can one with a diameter of 6 inches. However, for most purposes a globe must be small enough to be examined readily and, if need be, to be picked up and moved about.

Types of Globes

The globe is a tool which can be adapted to several purposes. The more common type, used chiefly to show the countries of the earth, is the *political globe.* Another type is the *physical globe,* which indicates, by means of colors, the varying depths of the oceans and the different heights of the lands. Others include those showing the distribution of climates, natural vegetation, ocean currents, etc. One type of globe is blank. It is nothing more than a spherical blackboard on which may be traced with a piece of chalk whatever earth phenomena one wishes to portray. Again, the amount of detail which may be shown depends on the globe size.

The Lines on the Globe

A glance at even the simplest of globes reveals the presence of several lines. Some of them extend from pole to pole; others form parallel curves at regular intervals north and south of the equator. More detailed globes may show additional lines, some of which are of modern significance and others of which are for purposes of decoration, or are merely carry-overs from ancient globes. It is the lines which normally appear on the most modern of globes which are of real meaning to our purposes here (Fig. 14).

MERIDIANS AND PARALLELS. The lines which extend directly from pole to pole on the surface of the earth are *meridians* (Fig. 14). It will be noted that they extend due north and south, and that, no matter how far apart any two of them may be at the equator, they meet at the polar points. The lines which cross them at right angles are *parallels* (Fig. 14). If the globe is examined, it will be seen that the parallels are not just lines, but that each one of them is a true circle (Fig. 14). Near the equator they are large circles; near the poles they are small. Careful measurements will show that they are truly parallel to one another, and that, unlike the meridians, they never intersect one another. The *equator* is the largest of the parallel circles. It is actually a *great circle* because its center, like those of all great circles on the globe, coincides with the center of the earth. While an infinite number of great circles may be drawn on the globe, the equator is the only one which is, at the same time, a parallel, i.e., is at right

GLOBE OF CRATES

ABOUT 150 B.C.

BEHAIM GLOBE

1492 A.D.

GLOBE GORES

When bent and fitted these form the "covers" for the globes at right and left.

GLOBE TIPPED

One inch globe formed from gores at right.

GLOBE "STRAIGHT"

One inch globe formed from gores at left.

GLOBE TYPES

PEDESTAL GLOBE

HANGING GLOBE

CUP-BASE GLOBE

13   *GLOBES. At the top, sketches of two early globes; center, gores and the globe made from them; bottom, three types of modern globes.*

LINES ON THE GLOBE

Meridians — Arctic Circle 66½° N — Tropic of Cancer 23½° N — Equator — Prime Meridian — Tropic of Capricorn 23½° S — Antarctic Circle 66½° S — Parallels

MERIDIANS

Any meridian is one half of a Great Circle

PARALLELS

Of the parallels, only the Equator is a Great Circle

GREAT CIRCLES

Any circle whose center coincides with the center of the globe is a Great Circle

REFERENCE LINES

North 0°–90°
South 0°–90°
Latitude
Equator
Prime Meridian
Longitude
0°–180° West   East 0°–180°

14   *THE MOST important lines on the globe are parallels and meridians, including such special meridians and parallels as the Prime Meridian, Equator, Tropics of Cancer and Capricorn, and the Arctic and Antarctic Circles. These are indicated singly and in combination above. Also shown, lower left, is the great circle. At lower right is shown the measurement of longitude east and west of the Prime Meridian and the measurement of latitude north and south of the Equator.*

angles to the meridians (Fig. 14). Meridians are used to keep track of distance or position in an east or west direction around the earth. In order to measure east or west, some starting line is necessary. By international agreement of most nations, this line is the meridian which passes through Greenwich, England (London, for all practical purposes). Because it is the first, or primary, line, it is called the *prime meridian* (Fig. 14). Distance or position measured east or west from it is known as *longitude,* and is expressed in degrees or fractions thereof. West longitude extends halfway around the earth from the Greenwich meridian; east longitude reaches halfway around the earth, in the opposite direction, from the same meridian. All the way around the earth is a circle, or 360 degrees. Halfway around is, then, 180 degrees. Thus west and east longitude alike extend from 0 to 180 degrees (Fig. 14). If a plane reported its longitude as 30 degrees west (30° W), it would be west of the prime meridian and one-twelfth of the way around the world from that meridian (Fig. 15). If the longitude of another plane were stated as 90 degrees east (90° E), its location would be somewhere on the meridian which lies one-fourth of the way around the world, to the east, from the Greenwich line (Fig. 15). Each degree of distance is broken down into minutes and seconds. A minute (′) is 1/60 of a degree and a second (″) is 1/60 of a minute.

Parallels are used to measure distance or position north and south of the equator. This distance is known as *latitude* and, like longitude, is expressed in degrees and parts of degrees. From the equator to either pole, on the earth's surface, is one-quarter of a circle, or 90 degrees. Thus, north latitude and south latitude both extend from 0 to 90 degrees (Fig. 14). If a plane were halfway between the equator and the North Pole, it would be somewhere on the parallel of 45 degrees north (45th parallel, north) and its latitude would be stated as 45° N (Fig. 15). If a plane were one-third of the way from the equator to the South Pole, its latitude would be 30° S, and it would be somewhere on the 30th parallel, or circle, or south latitude (Fig. 15).

It has been noted that meridians and parallels intersect one another at right angles

(Fig. 14). The result is a grid which enables one to determine positions, or locations, east and west of the prime meridian and north and south of the equator. However, the grid does more than that; it enables one to locate exact positions, or fixed points. If a plane were at the point where the prime meridian crosses the equator, its position would be stated as 0 degrees longitude and 0 degrees latitude; in this instance it would be located over the Gulf of Guinea, off the west coast of Africa. If a plane were where the meridian of 105° E crosses the parallel of 40° N, it would be located over interior China, a bit south of the southern border of Mongolia. Its position (Plane A) on the globe is shown in the lower portion of Fig. 15. The same portion of Fig. 15 also shows the position on the globe of planes located at 20° S, 65° E, and at 35° N, 25° W.

To appreciate most fully the utility of the simple globe lines (meridians and parallels) which have just been discussed, place a pencil mark on the surface of a tennis ball. Then, attempt to describe the location of the pencil mark on the ball's spherical surface. It cannot be done—unless there is invented some system of lines which enables one to measure "left and right" and "up and down." Sooner or later, one would be forced to establish an axis and polar points where the axis intersected the surface of the ball, and to draw meridians and parallels. Then there would be a grid by means of which the location of the pencil mark could be described. The problem of location on the tennis ball is the same as the problem of location on the spherical surface of the earth. And the solution of both problems is the same.

SPECIAL PARALLELS. A few of the parallels on the globe are shown by special symbols and, in addition, are named. These are the *Tropic of Cancer, Tropic of Capricorn, Arctic Circle,* and the *Antarctic Circle.* They, among all the parallels, are given particular recognition because they mark certain conditions and results of relationships between earth and sun.

As has previously been stated, the earth's axis is always tipped approximately 23½ degrees from the vertical, as shown in Fig. 16. Moreover, it is always tipped in the same direction in reference to outer space (Fig. 16). The energy given off from the sun reaches the earth as parallel bands of radiant energy (Fig. 16). Because the earth's surface is a curving one, only one "bundle" of sun's rays can

LONGITUDE AND LATITUDE

WEST LONGITUDE

Planes at 30° W. Long.

EAST LONGITUDE

Planes at 90° E. Long.

NORTH LATITUDE

Planes at 45° N. Lat.

SOUTH LATITUDE

Planes at 30° S. Lat.

LONGITUDE AND LATITUDE

Plane A at 40° N., 105° E.
Plane B at 20° S., 65° E.
Plane C at 35° N., 25° W.

15 *POSITIONS on the globe of airplanes at different latitudes and longitudes. On the lower globe, the tails of planes A and C mark the position described; the middle of the wing of plane B marks the described position.*

strike vertically; all others, being parallel to one another, must strike obliquely (Fig. 16). When the earth, in its revolutions about the sun, is in such a position that the Northern Hemisphere is tipped most directly toward the sun (tipped 23½ degrees), the vertical rays will strike 23½ degrees north of the equator (Fig. 16). This in itself would be of no particular consequence were it not for the fact that vertical rays provide more heat than oblique rays and the amount of heat energy which is received, latitude by latitude, is vitally significant to man and to all forms of life. To mark this farthest north reception of the sun's vertical rays, the parallel of 23½° N is given a special symbol and its own particular name, the *Tropic of Cancer* (Fig. 16). Six months later, when the Southern Hemisphere is tipped most directly toward the sun, the vertical rays are received 23½ degrees south of the equator and the position of their strike is designated the *Tropic of Capricorn* (Fig. 16). During the remainder of the year the vertical rays strike somewhere between Cancer and Capricorn.

Like Cancer and Capricorn, the lines of the Arctic and Antarctic Circles are related to the angle of the sun in reference to the earth's surface at particular times of the year. At the time when the Northern Hemisphere is tipped most directly toward the sun and the vertical ray is striking at Cancer, the most oblique rays in the Northern Hemisphere are striking across the North Pole and 23½ degrees beyond (Fig. 16). The line marking this farthest strike of the sun across the "top" of the world is the parallel known as the Arctic Circle (Fig. 16). Since it is 23½° from the North Pole, its latitude is 66½° North (23½° plus 66½° making the 90° of north latitude). Six months later, when the Southern Hemisphere is tipped most directly toward the sun, and the sun's rays are vertical at Capricorn, the most oblique rays south of the equator strike over the South Pole and 23½ degrees beyond (Fig. 16). This farthest strike across the South Pole is indicated by the

Antarctic Circle at 66½° S (Fig. 16). A study of Fig. 16 will show that the Circles also mark the positions of the most oblique rays when the given hemisphere is tipped most directly away from the sun on December 22. On that date, the most oblique rays reach *only to within* 23½ degrees of the North Pole: they reach only to the Arctic Circle.

STANDARD TIME ZONES. At first thought, standard time may seem to have no connection with globes or with lines which appear on globes. Yet, the invention of standard time came in response to man's need for keeping track of time on the rotating globe on which he lives. The time belts which he has established to determine the hours of the day are based on longitude and, hence, on the globe lines (meridians) which enable him to measure longitude.

A person who lives in one place and has no contact or business with any other parts of the world might well wonder wherein there is any problem of keeping track of the hours of the day. He looks at the sun; when it rises it is morning, when it is at the highest point in the sky it is noon, when it sets it is night. It is as simple as that—or is it?

The earth is a spheroid with only one major source of light—the sun. As the earth travels around the sun, it rotates on its axis. If it rotated in such a fashion as to present the same face, the same half, to the sun at all times as does the planet Mercury, then that half would always have day and the other would always be in darkness. However, the speed of rotation is such that the earth presents all its faces to the sun within the period which man has designated as the 24-hour day. This means, then, that there is a succession of mornings, noons, nights, and midnights. Yet, no one of them can occur all over the earth at the same time. For example, if it is noon at Chicago, it is midnight on the opposite side of the earth; when it is noon at Singapore, it is midnight at a place on the opposite side of the earth.

INCLINATION OF EARTH'S AXIS

The axis is always tipped 23½° from the vertical
as the earth makes its journey around the sun,

THE POSITION OF THE EARTH ON JUNE 21 AND DECEMBER 22

The Tropics of Cancer and Capricorn mark the Northern and Southern Limits of the Sun's Vertical Rays.
The Arctic and Antarctic Circles mark the "Across-the-Poles" Limits of the Sun's Oblique and Tangent Rays.

16 *THIS FIGURE should be read along with the text. Note (above) the positions of the earth as it travels around the sun. Note (below) the angle of strike of the sun's rays at different latitudes on June 21 (summer solstice of northern hemisphere) and on December 22 (summer solstice of southern hemisphere).*

Because the earth rotates *toward the east,* each morning approaches from the east, as does each noon, or sunset, or midnight. Thus, noon at Chicago means that it is past noon at New York City and not yet noon at such a place as Denver. Actually there are as many noons, or noon positions of the sun, as there are longitudinal positions, or meridians, on the face of the earth. Even in Chicago itself, since it is a large metropolitan region, there are several noon positions of the sun. It is noon, by the sun, in the eastern part of Chicago before it is noon in the central section, and it is noon in the central section before it is noon in the western part of the city.

One can appreciate that watches set by the noon position of the sun would show slightly different times for eastern, central, and western Chicago; also, that a watch set by the noon sun for central Chicago will show a marked difference in time compared to one set by the noon sun in the central section of New York City. The difficulties of keeping track of the time, for purposes of business, travel, etc., are apparent whether within a comparatively small region or from place to place over the earth's surface.

There used to be as many times in the United States as there were communities from coast to coast. Each settlement had its own time, determined by the noon passage of the sun across the meridian which marked the longitudinal position of the community. As long as each community lived more or less unto itself, as long as travel was slow and there were no telegraphs, telephones, or radios, it did not matter much. However, by 1883, rapid travel by rail and the quick speeding of messages by wire were common. A person sending a telegram from Chicago at noon wished to know at what time the message would be received in New York, or in San Francisco. Or, if a telegram was sent from Chicago at 8:00 A.M., would it be received in San Francisco before daylight, or before the opening of business offices? If a person living outside of Chicago wanted to catch a train in Chicago, he needed to know what time Chicago was using in comparison to the time of his own community. Something had to be done: time had to be standardized.

In 1883, the railroads agreed upon *standard time belts*. In the ensuing years, the entire United States followed suit, as did most of the remainder of the world. The United States was divided into four belts. Each belt extended from north to south and the four belts were arranged in longitudinal succession from the Atlantic to the Pacific (Fig. 17). A *central meridian* was chosen for each belt and the time within each belt was determined by the time of that central meridian (Fig. 17). The east-west width, or longitudinal extent, of each belt was determined by the rate of travel of the noon sun across the country. This rate of travel by the sun, resulting, of course from the rate of rotation of the earth on its axis, is 15 degrees in one hour ($15° \times 24$ equals $360°$, or one complete rotation, as from noon to noon). Thus, each time belt was 15 degrees of longitude in width, or, saying it in another fashion, each belt was one hour wide. All persons within each belt accepted the time of the center of the belt (central meridian), and the division lines between belts were well known so that persons crossing them would know where to change their timepieces. In this manner, time became standard and there

were four basic times in the United States, instead of a very large number.

Under such an arrangement, a person living, say, in San Francisco and wishing to hear a radio broadcast from New York City can make the proper calculations. If the program is to be on the air from New York City at 6:00 P.M. New York time, he must go to his radio at 3:00 P.M. San Francisco time. New York has Eastern Standard Time; San Francisco has Pacific Standard Time (Fig. 17). The difference in time is three hours—one hour for each belt west of the Eastern time belt. Because New York is east of San Francisco, it will have 6:00 P.M., or any other time, before San Francisco does, and it will have it three hours before. Thus, if it is 6:00 P.M. in New York City, it is only 3:00 P.M. in San Francisco (Fig. 17).

Theoretically, each time belt is bounded, to the east and west by meridians, or, each belt is set off by two meridians spaced 15° apart. If such were actually the case, the limits of the time belts would be straight north-south lines. Examination of Fig. 17 will show that the limits are not straight, but only approximately so; they merely correspond with the trend of the meridians. The reason for this is that the limits were so drawn as to avoid, as much as possible, the splitting of a given population and trade area. Thus, the limits may deviate from true meridional trends for purposes of local convenience. Fig. 18 shows the time belts of the world. It will be noted that they, like those within the United States, show deviations from true meridional positions of the time belt boundaries.

INTERNATIONAL DATE LINE. This is another line which appears on most globes. It follows, from pole to pole, the general course of the 180th meridian, although in some places it deviates from that mid-Pacific meridian (Fig. 18). It is at this line that each new calendar day is born. For example, July 1 is born at midnight at the international date line, travels west, around the earth, and dies twenty-four hours later back at the date line. Other dates (days) do the same. Thus, there is a westward procession of days, as there is a westward procession of hours of the day. Just as it is not the same time all over the earth, as discussed above, it is not the same day all over the earth. If, on June 30, one proceeds *westward* across the date line, it becomes July 1 as soon as the line is crossed. If the date is July 1 and one crosses the line in an *eastward* direction the date automatically becomes June 30. One loses a day in crossing the line going west and gains a day in crossing the line going east.

The problem of keeping track of the days is quite similar to the one of determining the hours of the day. There has to be agreement as to where each begins and ends. The choice of a "birth line" for the days in mid-ocean is a wise one, for there are few lands and few inhabitants to be affected (Fig. 18). If the date line were placed so as to intersect one or more continents and, hence, areas in which there are many persons and much human ac-

tivity, the situation would be very troublesome. Imagine the results if the date line were the meridian of Chicago. It might be daytime of December 25 in Chicago. December 25 would have been born there at midnight to begin its westward march. But to the east, as at New York City, it would not yet be December 25; December 25 would not have had time to travel around the earth to New York City. The calendar date would still be December 24 at New York; it would be Christmas in Chicago, but the day before Christmas in New York! This is only one example, but it will serve to illustrate the wisdom of the days being born (and dying) at a more convenient meridional location.

The partial deviation of the date line from the 180th meridian is a further attempt to prevent complications for man. The line deviates so as to throw certain island groups (and the easternmost finger of Siberia) entirely to one side or the other. Otherwise, the dates would be different within the same island

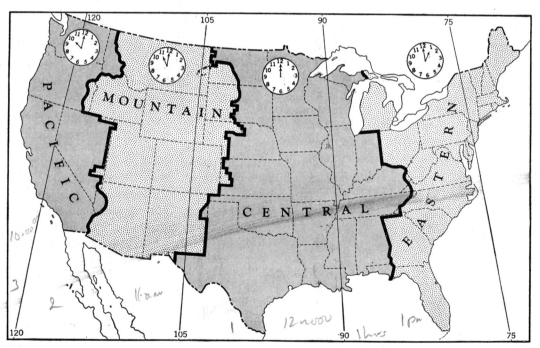

17 *THE STANDARD TIME BELTS of the United States. The meridians shown are the so-called "central" or "standard" meridians for the belts.*

cluster, or even from one side of a particular island to the other (Fig. 18). As it is, it is actually possible for a South Sea Islander to leave his abode to go fishing on, say, Monday, to fish several hours on Sunday, and yet return home on Monday. In the instance just mentioned, the fisherman lived immediately west of the date line, he crossed the line to fish east of it, and recrossed the line as he returned home on a westward course.

All of the foregoing discussions concerning globes and lines of the globe are useful in and of themselves. As the discussion proceeds to maps, it will be seen that many items noted already are basic to the understanding and use of maps as well.

MAPS

The map is the most important geographical tool. Were it not for the high cost of surveying, final drawing, and printing, a great deal of the geography of any region or district might be portrayed by maps alone. Particularly would this be true if a sufficient number of maps were prepared, if the map explanations were full and complete, and if some of the maps were combinations of several others —so as to provide understanding of geographical relationships in addition to mere factual material. As it is, geographical materials contain as many maps as is practical. Text analyses and descriptions are normally keyed closely to the maps themselves. The science of map making is known as *cartography*, a term which appears very often in geography.

Definition

Our modern term *map* is derived from the Latin word *mappa*. This word signified napkin, or cover cloth, in the sense of tablecloth. Just as a cloth may cover, or give coverage, to a table, so does a map provide coverage for the earth or any of its parts. By studying a map, one may tell what covers, or is on, the earth's surface. By definition, a *map* is a representation of all, or a portion of, the earth, drawn to scale and usually on a plane or flat surface.

Utility

That maps have been made for more than four thousand years, and are made in greater numbers today than ever before, is sufficient proof of their usefulness. Within the past few years, collections of maps, called *atlases,* also have been published in numbers far in excess of any previous time. The new emphasis on maps and atlases reflects not only the needs of modern armies, navies, and air forces, but also the desire of nearly everyone to know about the world. People have learned that maps can bring the world to them, either in whole or in part, and that many maps can provide much understanding of the earth and its inhabitants.

Small maps help to tell what the earth is like in general. Very large maps tell a detailed story of the nature of even very small sections of the earth. Maps of the latter sort may be put to many and very specific uses. One map may show the extent of a farmer's land and the detail of virtually everything which appears on the farm; another the extent of the United States Corn Belt; still another the location of the iron and steel mills of Europe. There is no apparent end to the uses of maps, whether for purposes of war, general knowledge, travel, business, or merely for a hiking trip.

Early Maps

The earliest maps were crude and inaccurate affairs. Perhaps the first map was nothing more than a rough sketch of game trails and water holes traced in the dust with

18 *THE STANDARD TIME BELTS of the world.*

the end of a sharp stick. The first map of definite record shows a portion of Mesopotamia, modern Iraq; it is in the form of a small tablet of baked clay (Fig. 19). This was made about 2,500 years before Christ was born and is now preserved in the Semitic Museum, Harvard University.

The Phoenicians, those first real traders on the sea lanes, made use of simple charts for navigating the Mediterranean. A bit later, they charted their way into the open Atlantic, from the "tin coast" of Cornwall, in England, to the far shores of western Africa. Then, as Greece rose to power and started her trade and colonization of the Mediterranean world, other simple maps were made to keep track of places, of regions, and of routes from one spot to another. The earliest of the Greek maps was probably made by Anaximander (611-547 B.C.). His map showed the then known world, consisting of southern Europe, western Asia Minor, and the northern margin of Africa. A map made by Eratosthenes about 200 B.C. showed, in addition, the broader outlines of the British Isles, a larger section of

Asia Minor, and a greatly distorted India. This map contained both meridians and parallels (Fig. 19). Ptolemy of Alexandria produced one of the most famous of early maps, some time during the second century A.D. (Fig. 19), as well as an atlas of twenty-eight maps. At about the same time, Roman cartographers were busy attempting to lay out, in map form, the world as they knew it or, in part, guessed it to be.

While all this was going on in the Mediterranean world, the Chinese were constructing their early maps (Fig. 19). They had prepared a few simple maps at least 200 years before the time of Christ. After their invention of paper, perhaps in the first century A.D., both general and detailed maps became numerous. Chinese cartography continued to make advances through the Middle Ages, the period when European cartography went into virtual eclipse. Likewise, the Arabs, with their early knowledge of astronomy and mathematics, developed their own cartography and maintained it on a high and advancing plane while Europe retrogressed.

OLDEST KNOWN MAP (2500 B.C.)

Clay Tablet from Ga-Sur.

(Preserved in Semitic Museum, Harvard University)

MAP OF ERATOSTHENES (200 B.C.)

Parallel of Thule

Parallel of Rhodes
Parallel of Alexandria
Tropic
Parallel of Meroe
S. Limit of Habit. World
Equator

PTOLEMY'S MAP (2nd Cent. A.D.)

OLD CHINESE MAP	OLDEST KNOWN CHINESE MAP (1137 A.D.)

WALDSEEMULLER'S MAP (1507 A.D.)

RIBERO'S MAP (1529 A.D.)

19

SKETCHES of old maps of different types, illustrating changing techniques and advances in man's knowledge of the world.

As Europe rose slowly from the Dark Ages, there was a marked and renewed interest in maps, particularly in improved maps of the countries of central and southern Europe. By 1500 there were world maps which showed, although in considerably distorted form, Europe, Africa, and most of Asia. The activities of explorers spurred the preparation of maps and globes although for a few years after the voyage of Columbus the known parts of the Americas continued to appear as parts of Asia. However, by 1507, there appeared a map which indicated the separate existence of the Americas and a fuller appreciation of the true size of the earth (Fig. 19). In 1529, another map showed not only parts of the Americas and Asia, but made room in between them for the vast Pacific, which Magellan's voyage had disclosed to an amazed world (Fig. 19).

Some of the more famous maps soon to follow were made by the Flemish cartographer Kremer, better known as Mercator. He constructed maps of Europe, including more accurate maps of the Mediterranean than were previously available, and, in 1569, the well-known Mercator chart of the world. From then on, what might be called modern cartography began to flourish; French map makers came to excel; English map makers, with shipping lanes and an empire to keep track of, came to rival the French; a few craftsmen emerged in Italy and Spain—the world was well on the way to knowing itself more fully and more accurately.

Map Projections

NATURE AND USE. A *map projection* is any orderly arrangement of parallels and meridians on a plane. The pattern formed by these lines is called the *grid*. Each projection

GLOBE

2 0 *THE RELATIVELY SIMPLE GRID* (left) *of one type of cylindrical projection. A sinusoidal projection* (right), *which has a relatively complicated grid. Why is a globe* (center) *the most satisfactory device for showing the relation of the earth to its parts?*

has its own peculiar grid. Some grids appear very simple, others very complicated (Fig. 20).

Map projections are necessary because the earth is not flat and, yet, man wishes to show all or part of its spherical surface on a flat sheet of paper. The ideal way to show the earth, its parts, and its many conditions is by means of the globe. But globes beyond a certain size cannot be readily handled or carried about; nor can globes be bound in atlases or other books. So man depends largely on maps which are flat, and on the projections which make the construction of maps possible.

There is no such thing as a perfect map projection. Each projection may have one major advantage, also, and several disadvantages (see separate treatment of specific projections in Appendix A of this book). Each projection should be used for its own particular purpose and the user should be aware of its limitations. Many map projections, or the maps made on them, have fallen into general disrepute because so often they have not been used for the particular purposes for which they were designed. One example is the Mercator projection (Fig. 21). It has been severely criticized, chiefly because it does not show the sizes of the parts of the earth correctly. Of course it doesn't. It was not designed to show sizes correctly; any more than a hammer was made for sawing. The Mercator was designed primarily to aid in the navigation of ships at sea.

The lack of perfection in map projections is a direct reflection of the fact that one cannot

take the spherical earth and flatten it out on a map sheet without distorting or tearing it. Nor can one lift the grid of the parallels and meridians from the globe and lay that grid out on a piece of paper without greatly spreading it, compressing it, or bending it all out of shape. One may imagine the grid of the globe as a wire framework, with some wires representing parallels and others meridians (Fig. 22). Next, he may imagine trying to

A CONFORMAL PROJECTION

2 1 *THE EARTH on the Mercator projection, one of several conformal projections. Note how Antarctica assumes a size out of all proportion to its actual size. Compare this figure with Fig. 20.*

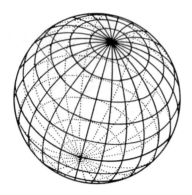

22   *A GLOBE is a "wire basket" of parallels and meridians.*

flatten that wire framework so as to form it into a flat plane *without* changing the original relationships of one wire to another. It cannot be done. Neither can any map projection show the earth correctly in all regards. However, the parallels and meridians (grid) may be arranged in such a manner as to tell the truth in at least one regard. The grid may be arranged so as to portray *area* or *shape* or *directions* or *distances* correctly, but it is impossible to show all of these at one time—if one is chosen, some of the others must be sacrificed partly or completely.

Projections which show area correctly are called *equal-area projections*. One of several such projections is the Mollweide (Fig. 23). On it the parallels and meridians are plotted

AN EQUAL-AREA PROJECTION

23   *THE EARTH on the Mollweide projection, one of several equal-area projections.*

in such a manner that any parts of the earth, as Alaska and Africa, have the same proportions to each other on the map as they have to each other on the globe—but shapes are badly distorted. Projections which portray shapes correctly, or correctly within stated limits, are known as *conformal projections*. One example is the previously mentioned Mercator (Fig. 21). Its grid is so drawn that comparatively small parts of the earth have the same shapes as they do on the globe. There is no projection which can show the shapes of large areas correctly—only the globe itself can do that. Thus one may gain a true picture of the shape of Hawaii or of Chesapeake Bay from a conformal projection, but to see the true shape of Europe or North America, he must look on the globe.

In general, the equal-area and conformal projections are encountered most commonly. However, the other two major groups of projections should at least be mentioned by name. Those which show direction correctly from a stated point on the map are called *azimuthal* or *zenithal projections*. Those portraying distances correctly from a stated point are known as *equidistant projections*. Both are given representative treatment in Appendix A. The four major groups, equal-area, conformal, azimuthal (zenithal), and equidistant, include the bulk of all map projections, although there are a few which do not fall within any one of these major categories. In other words, there are some which distort area, shape, directions, and distance all at one and the same time, although the degree of distortion may be relatively so minor as still to provide a reasonable facsimile of the earth. In any event, they are all attempts to show the spherical earth on a flat map. Moreover, they represent "controlled attempts," for the person plotting the grid knows how he is arranging the parallels and meridians and he knows what the results are in each instance.

CONSTRUCTION.   The word "projection" means throwing forward, or, in one sense, throwing onto, as onto a screen. Most map

ORTHOGRAPHIC PROJECTIONS

EQUATORIAL ASPECT   OBLIQUE ASPECT   POLAR ASPECT

24   *THREE DIFFERENT ASPECTS of the earth as shown by the orthographic projection.*

projections cannot be derived by actual projection, they must be arrived at by the careful plotting of lines and control points on the basis of mathematical formulae. However, some may be derived by true projection. It is not pertinent to discuss all of these, but one of them may be treated as an example. The consideration of it will aid in visualizing and comprehending map projections, whether they all are truly projected or not. Even many of those based solely on mathematical construction look as though they could be obtained from projections onto a screen.

The orthographic projection is one which can be derived by actual projection. The map from it looks like a photograph of the globe (Fig. 24). It can show only one hemisphere at a time, just as one can photograph only half the globe at one time. In this instance, let us suppose that the view is directly toward the equator (Fig. 24), although the view might be centered on the North Pole or at 45 degrees north, as also shown in Fig. 24, or anywhere else. This is the equatorial aspect of the orthographic projection. One may "see" it projected by mentally visualizing the following. First, a wire model of half the globe, with the poles at the top and bottom of the wire framework, as shown in Fig. 25. Next, a source of light located so far away that the light rays are parallel lines. Then, a flat plane, or screen, onto which the shadows of the wires, representing parallels and meridians, are thrown by the light. The result, indicated

in part of Fig. 25, is a map projection in which the equator and the parallels are straight lines, the central meridian extends straight from pole to pole, and the other meridians are curved lines. It will be noted that the central portion of the grid looks true, but that distortion becomes increasingly great as the margins are approached, and the meridians begin to "come together."

In the instance just discussed, the projection was onto a flat plane; therefore, it might be termed one of the flat plane projections. Another instance of projection onto a plane is shown in Fig. 26. In addition to projections

ORTHOGRAPHIC PROJECTION

PARALLEL RAYS OF LIGHT FROM INFINITY

SCREEN TURNED   SCREEN "STRAIGHT"

25   *A SIMPLE example of how cartographers obtain the equatorial aspect of the orthographic projection. The parallel rays of light pass through the half-globe and are perpendicular to the "turned" screen.*

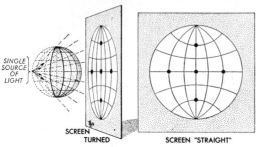

STEREOGRAPHIC PROJECTION
The diverging rays of light pass through the half-globe and are
perpendicular to the "turned" screen only at its center.

SINGLE SOURCE OF LIGHT

SCREEN TURNED

SCREEN "STRAIGHT"

26 *ANOTHER type of "projection onto a plane" (compare with Fig. 25), the equatorial aspect of the stereographic projection is shown here. Note that on this projection there is only one straight parallel and that distortions are such that the distance between meridians increases east and west and that the "parallels" actually are not parallel to each other. Such distortion of the grid means there will be similar distortion of land and water areas plotted on the grid.*

A SIMPLE CONIC PROJECTION
Source of light is at center of globe.

X   X

A   B   A   B
Y   Z   Y   Z

27 *THE SIMPLE conic projection, and example of projection onto the surface of a cone. At the left, a simple cone set over globe and touching at parallel A-B. At the right, simple cone cut on side and opened "flat."*

onto flat planes, there are those which are projected onto cones and cylinders. The general idea of conic and cylindrical projections is shown in Figs. 27 and 28. Further treatment of specific conic and cylindrical projections, as well as other projections, will be found in Appendix A.

The foregoing discussion, brief as it is, provides a basis for the understanding of what a map projection is, why map projections are necessary, the four major group names which include most projections, and some notion of how projections may be arrived at. A discussion of the projection which is used for most of the world and continental maps in this book follows directly.

THE INTERRUPTED SINUSOIDAL PROJECTION. The grid of this projection is shown in Fig. 29B. It appears here as a three-lobed, irregularly shaped figure tied together by narrow strips in the low latitude sections. The parallels are straight, evenly spaced lines and each half lobe has one meridian which crosses the parallels at right angles. The other meridians are curved in accordance with a specific mathematical formula. East-west distances and directions are true on all parallels, and north-south distances and directions are true on the *central meridian of each half lobe*. The projection as a whole is of such a nature (*equal-area*) as to allow proper size comparisons from one area to another. On it, for example, one may see the true picture of the size of Europe as compared to the size of North America or of Australia or Asia.

The interrupted sinusoidal projection had its origin in an uninterrupted form in which the entire world was shown with an oval-like shape (Fig. 29A). It was known at first as the Sanson-Flamsteed projection and later as the Mercator-Sanson-Flamsteed projection. On it the parallels are straight and evenly spaced; but there is only one central meridian for the whole grid. While it allows areas to be seen in their proper size relationships, it contains greater distortion of shapes than the more modern, interrupted, form; hence, it is seldom used for world maps of today. The newer, interrupted form, with its several, rather than one, central meridians, preserves the usefulness of the original and at the same time eliminates most of the shape distortions (compare Figs 29A and 29B). Its use in this book derives primarily from the fact that it allows correct size comparisons to be made and it provides essentially true shapes for the land masses—it is equal-area and it suggests conformality. The same qualities were re-

when the focus is on the oceans, the grid can be so constructed as to have the "splits" occur in the continents.

In order to provide as much map room as possible (on a page of given size), the interrupted sinusoidal projection has been *compressed* (Fig. 29C). Inasmuch as most of the distributions to be shown are distributions on the land (climates, natural vegetation, population, etc.), the compression has been made in water areas. No change has been made in

A CYLINDRICAL PROJECTION
The parallel rays of light pass through the globe.

PARALLEL
RAYS
OF
LIGHT

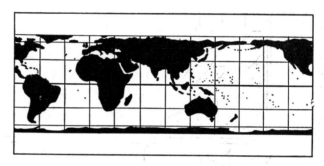

Cylindrical screen partially unrolled

Screen entirely unrolled from globe and laid "flat."

28 *TO MAKE A CYLINDRICAL PROJECTION, what is on the globe is projected onto a cylinder which touches the globe at the equator. When the cylinder is removed and unrolled, it forms the map shown at the right.*

sponsible for its selection as the major projection used in Army Service Forces Manual, M-101, an atlas issued during World War II.

The chief disadvantage of the interrupted sinusoidal projection is that it *is* interrupted. However, it must be recalled that no projection can solve all the problems incident to showing the earth on a flat piece of paper. When attention is focused on the land, the grid of this projection can be so drawn that the interruptions occur in water areas (see world maps in the front portion of this book);

the basic grid; rather a part of the ocean space between the Americas lobe and the Europe-Africa lobe is removed and the two lobes pushed closer together. This operation merely increases the amount of space available for showing distributions on the land masses. It does *not* alter the size relationships between land masses or any of their parts (compare Figs. 29B and 29C).

Maps of individual continents can easily be produced by simple enlargement of parts of the world map. In each instance, enlarge-

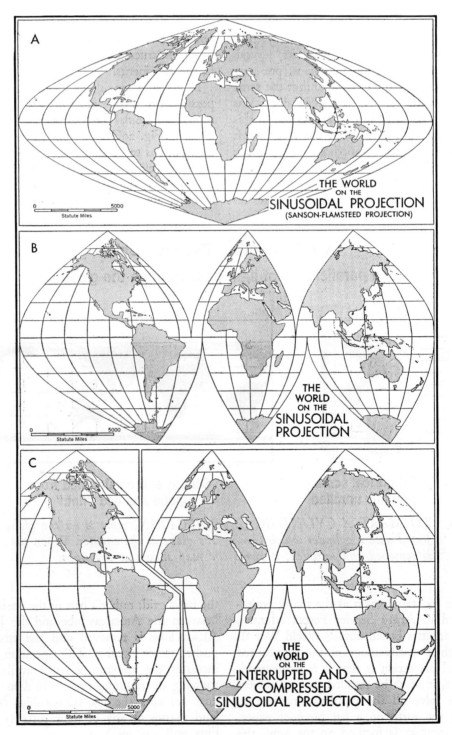

29 *THREE ASPECTS of the sinusoidal projection:* (A) *The uninterrupted and uncompressed form.* (B) *The interrupted, but uncompressed, form.* (C) *The interrupted and compressed form.*

ment should be to the *same degree*. Asia is the largest of the continents. If it were increased in size so as to fill an entire page and the other continents were enlarged to the same degree, "little" Europe would occupy only a quarter of a page, South America about three-quarters of a page, and so on. This allows constant realization of true size relationships. Fig. 30 shows the world on the interrupted sinusoidal projection; on this map are shown the actual limits of the compressed form, as well as the limits of each of the continental maps which would fit the width of this page. Throughout this book, each world map which appears in the compressed form carries a small inset map which is not compressed (see world maps in the front of this book). This has been done to prevent any misconceptions which might otherwise arise from the use of the compressed form.

Map Essentials

A map, in order to fulfill its purpose most completely, must possess certain essentials. These are *title, legend, scale, latitude and longitude,* and *direction*. Latitude and longitude may be indicated in such a fashion, as noted later, as to obviate the need for any special method of showing direction. One or more of these essentials may be omitted at times, especially where maps appear in close relation to text discussion and are thus "fastened" to a great deal of explanatory material which makes clear what the map is about and where it belongs in the world scene. Otherwise, if it is to stand by itself and be used separately from text material, a map should possess each one of the essentials mentioned.

TITLE. A map, like a book, is telling some kind of a story or explaining some problem or condition. One would not think of issuing a book without a title; no map should be prepared without its proper title. If it is a map showing the world distribution of natural vegetation, then a statement to that effect should appear somewhere on the map or the map margin. If it is a map of the average annual precipitation in the state of Ohio, then the map should say just that by means of a clearly visible title. It should not be necessary to examine a map at great length before finding out what the map is dealing with.

30   *THE WORLD as shown by the interrupted sinusoidal projection.*

Corn Field · Woods · House · Pond · Permanent Pasture · R. R. Bridge · RAILROAD · ROAD · Alfalfa Field · Creek · STATE HIGHWAY No. 66 · Telephone Line · Pasture · Woods · House · Church · Chicken Run · Barn · Silo · Pasture · Oat Field · Shed · Feed Lot · Pond

0 100 200 300
Scale in Feet

31

A DETAILED location map. This is a comparatively large map of a relatively small area. The scale is such that the features shown can be named on the map, without the need for a separate legend. Compare with Fig. 32.

LEGEND. If a very large map were prepared for a comparatively small area, the name of every place or condition shown could be printed, or written out, on the map itself (Fig. 31). However, most maps are of such a size in proportion to the areas which they represent that map symbols are necessary. For example, a given map of ordinary page size may be drawn to show the location of all the climates of the earth (see map of world climates in the front of this book). On such a map, there is not enough room to print in the names of all the climates, especially in sections where a certain climate occurs in a relatively small area. Symbols, in the form of colors or lines, have to be used. In a much more extreme instance, that of a *topographic map,* which is attempting to show a multitude of features and conditions on the same sheet, there is the need for numerous symbols of many sorts (Fig. 32). All such symbols, whether few or many, have to be shown separately and explained somewhere on the map.

Such explanation is called a *legend.* Because the symbols are often enclosed or boxed in by lines, the term *legend box* is used commonly in referring to the legend. Also, because the legend helps to unlock an understanding of the map, the term *key* may be substituted for it. An examination of the maps in this book will show several types and positions of legends and how they serve to make the maps more useful.

SCALE. A map is useless to a major degree unless it has on it some device, or statement, which will enable one to measure distance and compute area. Any such device is known as the *map scale.* The need for indication of scale may be emphasized by two examples. A map of the highways of Texas presented without scale would not allow one to ascertain the distance between towns or the mileage of a trip from one section to another. A map of the United States Cotton Belt without scale would prevent one from knowing the distance across or the size of that region.

32   *A MAP of such scale and detail that the features shown must be indicated chiefly by special symbols which are explained in a separate legend box.*

There are several methods for indicating scale. One very simple way is to print on the map that "one inch equals one mile," or, "one inch equals fifty miles," or whatever the actual scale of the map may be. This method is not completely satisfactory, for the map user has to guess at the length of an inch or he has to have a ruler handy when he studies a map. In addition, such a map may be enlarged or reduced in size after it is drawn; in either instance, the statement of scale would no longer be true.

Another manner of showing scale is by means of the *representative fraction,* or *fractional scale* (see bottom of Fig. 32). It is as the name implies, a fraction. If the fractional scale of a given map is $\frac{1}{50}$, that signifies that one unit on the map is equal to fifty *of the same units* in actuality. If an inch is chosen as a convenient unit of measurement, then one inch on the map is equal to 50 inches in reality. A fractional scale of $\frac{1}{63,360}$ means that one inch on the map equals 63,360 actual inches "in the field" (this is the scale of the map shown in Fig. 32). There are 63,360 inches in one mile, therefore this scale is often referred to as the inch-to-a-mile scale. Again, as in the instance of verbal scales, the fractional scale should not be placed on maps which are to be reproduced in either enlarged or reduced form. For example, if the original scale were $\frac{1}{50}$ and the map were enlarged twice on its linear dimensions then the representative fraction of the reproduction should be $\frac{1}{25}$ (on the original, one inch equaled 50 inches; on the copy twice enlarged, one inch equals 25 inches). Conversely, if the original were reduced by half on its linear dimensions, the new scale would be $\frac{1}{100}$, for now one unit on the map is equal to 100 of the same units in actuality.

The best and most nearly foolproof method of indicating scale is by means of a graduated line. This is called the line scale, or *linear scale.* It is merely a line with marks on it, as on a ruler. It may be of any convenient length. Fig. 32 contains several expressions of linear scale. It will be noted that they are carefully and accurately constructed and that each one states the unit of measurement involved, as feet, miles, or kilometers. Such a scale enables one to measure distances with any type of straightedge, as the edge of a sheet of paper. If two houses appear on a map and one wishes to know how far apart they actually are, he can lay the straightedge next to them and mark their positions with a pencil. Then, by laying the marked part of the straightedge along the linear scale, he can read directly the distance which separates them. Unlike the verbal and fractional scales, the linear scale will stand enlargement or reduction and still read correctly in terms of the map. This is because the linear scale will change in the same proportion as any other line, or lines, on the map: it cannot go out of scale.

LATITUDE AND LONGITUDE. A map which shows latitude and longitude can "kill two birds with one stone." First of all, indication of latitude and longitude, either by means of marginal marks or of parts of parallels and meridians which cross the map (Fig. 32), will tell the position on the globe of the area shown on the map. Secondly, a map with parallels and meridians shown and marked in degrees will provide knowledge of directions, for parallels extend east and west, and meridians north and south (Fig. 32).

DIRECTION. Some maps, whether they possess meridians and parallels or not, indicate direction by means of a *north arrow,* as shown in the lower part of Fig. 32. North arrows may be marked as *true north,* or as *magnetic north;* or there may be two arrows which join at their bases, one of them marked as true north and the other as magnetic north. An arrow marked true north is in complete alignment with a meridian and the arrow points to the North Pole. An arrow marked magnetic north is simply in alignment with the flows of magnetic force which course through the earth. The angle between true north and magnetic north is known as the *magnetic declination* (Fig. 32). If the lines of magnetic force

33 *VARIATIONS of the magnetic compass in the United States and Canada in 1940. Note the agonic line (line of no magnetic declination) and the behavior of the other isogonic lines in reference to the north magnetic pole.*

followed meridians, and if they did not fluctuate in position through time, true north would coincide with magnetic north. But the magnetic lines follow wavy paths and these paths shift with the years. Moreover, they do not flow from true pole to true pole, but between the *magnetic poles*. The north magnetic pole is located near Canada's Boothia Peninsula, appreciably removed from the true polar point (Fig. 33). A magnetic compass used at some position between these magnetic and true poles would actually point south. The south magnetic pole is located in Antarctica, a bit to the west of the Ross Sea embayment. It, too, does not coincide with the true pole. Thus, a magnetic compass, aligning itself with the wavy flows of the earth magnetism does not point true north. The only exceptions to this occur when the magnetic compass is used in such a position on the earth that, in pointing toward the north magnetic pole, it happens to point to the true North Pole.

To allow corrections of magnetic north to true north, maps are prepared which show magnetic declination. Each line on such maps is an *isogonic line* (Fig. 33); all points located on a given isogonic line have the same declination. The line along which there is no magnetic declination is called the *agonic line* (Fig. 33). Maps of magnetic declination are carefully dated and new ones are prepared at intervals, usually every five years. This is necessary because of the variation, from one year to another, in the position of the magnetic flows. Fig. 33 shows the positions of the isogonic lines in the United States in 1940. A surveyor

using a magnetic compass in southern California in 1940 would have found that his compass pointed about 16° *east* of true north (the declination was about 16° east). In central Maine, in the same year, the declination was about 20° west; that is, the magnetic compass pointed approximately 20° *west* of true north. A person using a magnetic compass there would have had to correct to the extent of 20°. He could have done this readily by facing in the direction in which his compass pointed and then have turned 20° to the right, or east; he would then have been facing true north (Fig. 34). Or, if his compass had a stationary dial, he could have rotated the compass until the north mark on the dial lay 20° to the right of the north end of the compass needle.

Relief Maps

Maps have only two dimensions. Relief features, such as hills or mountains, valleys or ridges, are not flat; they have three dimensions. The problem thus arises of how to show relief features on flat maps. Several solutions, or partial solutions, have been devised. No one of them is perfect, yet each is a useful tool to aid in giving cartographic expression to the "ups" and "downs" of the land.

HACHURE MAPS. One of the simplest types of relief maps is the *hachure map*. It uses lines (hachures) which are drawn up and down slopes. The proper arrangement of the lines gives the impression of the third dimension. If the lines are given different lengths and weights, they provide some indication of variations in the individual slopes which, in combination, comprise the major relief features. Fig. 35 (left portion) shows a typical hachure map.

SHADED MAPS. By means of "lighting effects" another type of relief map can be made. The light, in a sense, is thrown at strongly oblique angles, as though the rays were those

34   *THIS diagram illustrates the correction of magnetic north to true north at a place where the magnetic declination is 20° west.*

35   *TWO TYPES of relief maps. Left, hachure map (photographed from the Soissons sheet, revised 1912, of a French 1:50,000 series published by Dépôt de la Guerre); right, shaded map (photographed from a wall map of Switzerland, 1:200,000 published by Kummerly and Frey, Berne, 1936). Note that, in reproduction, scale of hachure map is 1:40,000 and of shaded map, 1:217,400.*

of the early morning or the late afternoon sun. In this fashion, all slopes which receive the light are highlighted and those which face away from the light are in shadow. The result is a *shaded* map, or "light and shadow map" (Fig. 35, right portion). It makes the relief features appear much as they do when viewed from an airplane.

CONTOUR MAPS. Most useful and most exact of all relief maps is the *contour map*. In the United States, this type of map is encountered most frequently in connection with the standard topographic maps issued by the United States Geological Survey, Department of the Interior. A portion of such a map appears in Fig. 32. An examination of it will show many lines which bend and curve across its surface. Each one of these is a *contour line*, and a sufficient number of them enables one to see and read the third dimension from the flat map. To the trained eye such a map does not appear flat at all, it appears much as

though it were actually a three-dimensional model of the top of the land.

A contour line is one which connects or extends through points which are the same elevation above sea level. If a given contour is marked with the number "600," it means that any and all points on that line have the same elevation and that their elevation is 600 feet (meters, if the map uses the metric system) above sea level. The datum plane (the level from which the measurement begins) is not always sea level, but usually so; if it is not, there is a statement on the map to indicate what the datum plane actually is.

To grasp the idea of contour lines and contour levels, one may imagine a somewhat irregular, cone-shaped island in the sea. The shape of such an island is shown diagrammatically in the upper portion of Fig. 36, with the view straight at the island, as from a ship nearby. Sea level is the datum plane. The intersection of this plane with the surface of

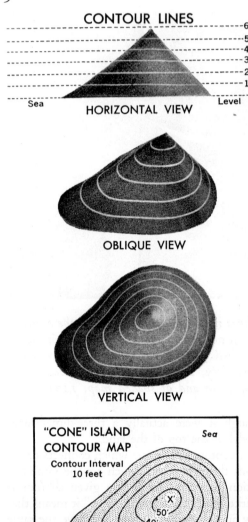

36   *CONTOUR lines as they appear on three views of a model of a roughly conical island, and as they appear on a contour map of the same island. Contours represent intersections of horizontal planes and the surface.*

the island provides the o-foot contour line; that is, the sea edge itself is the o-foot contour. Now, if another plane, parallel to the datum plane and ten feet above it, is passed

through the island, the intersection of that plane with the island's surface provides the 10-foot contour line. The next plane, parallel to the first two and ten feet above the second, intersects the island's surface to provide the 20-foot contour line. Additional and equally spaced horizontal planes provide the 30-foot, 40-foot, and 50-foot contours. The island is not quite high enough to be intersected by a horizontal plane sixty feet above sea level. Therefore, no 60-foot contour line can be traced on the surface of the island.

Next, if the conical island is tipped forward, as shown in the second portion of Fig. 36, we obtain an oblique view of the island and begin to see the contour lines at a different angle. We can now see more than their very edges and can discern a bit more of their behavior on the slightly irregular conical surface. Finally, if we look straight down on the island (third portion of Fig. 36), as from an airplane, we can see all parts of each individual contour line and how the several contour lines indicate the shape of the island. They indicate the shape in ground plan and, by their positions and numbering, the shape in a vertical sense. The fourth part of Fig. 36 is a somewhat dressed-up edition of portion three. It is a simple contour map of "Cone Island." If the island were a true, rather than irregular, cone, the contour lines would be perfect circles. Also, if the slope of the island were absolutely uniform from the sea's edge to the very top, the contour lines would be evenly spaced. The fact that the contour lines are not perfect circles and not quite uniform in spacing indicates the departure of the island's shape from that of a completely symmetrical cone.

In general summary, contour lines represent the intersection at the earth's surface of a number of horizontal contour planes—the exposed edge of each plane becomes a contour line. A sufficient number of contour lines makes possible the expression of surface form and enables one to read the third dimension from a flat map. Looking at the contour sketch map at the bottom of Fig. 36, one can see that the sea level outline of the island is somewhat rounded, that the island slopes upward rather uniformly to a single higher area, and that the vertical distance from the sea's edge to the top portion is between fifty and sixty feet. The discussion immediately following will elaborate further on contour lines and contour maps.

In using a contour map, one must know the *contour interval*. The contour interval is the *vertical* distance between contour lines or the difference in elevation between two adjacent contours. In the instance of the island discussed above, the contour interval was 10 feet. An examination of the contour map which appears in the lower part of Fig. 36 will indicate that no matter how far one travels between contour lines on that map he has gone up or down exactly 10 feet. If he should

start from one contour line, cross another, and stop at a third, he will have changed altitude exactly 20 feet—as from the 10-foot to the 30-foot contour.

The behavior of the contour lines on the map tells the story of the relief. If the lines lie close together, the slope of the land is relatively steep; if they lie farther apart, the slope is comparatively gentle. Fig. 37, a simple contour map, shows such behavior clearly. Where contour lines cross valleys they bend in an up-valley direction. This is because they, being contour lines, must indicate the same level throughout their courses. As they reach the tops of the valley sides, they must proceed upstream until they encounter parts of the valley bed which lie at the same altitude as the valley sides did farther downstream (Fig. 37). In a similar way, contour lines bend in a downstream direction as they cross the noses

A Contours bend upstream in crossing rivers.
B Contours bend in a downstream direction in crossing ridges between valleys.
△ Permanent Bench Mark (number indicates elevation above sea level).
× Temporary Bench Mark (number indicates elevation above sea level).
—50— Contour Line (number indicates elevation above sea level, i.e., above 0 contour line).
C Point located on 100 ft. contour line.
D Point located between 100 ft. and 125 ft. contours.

37 AN EXAMPLE *of a simple contour map, illustrating behavior of contours, types of bench marks, and determination of elevations.*

of ridges. Again, a study of Fig. 37 will aid in understanding such behavior.

In addition to their value for showing relief features, contour maps are useful for determining the altitude of specific points. For points which lie on contour lines, the altitude can be read directly and accurately; a point located on the 100-foot line has an altitude of 100 feet above sea level (C in Fig. 37). In some instances, the altitude of a point which is not located on a contour line is shown exactly by means of a *bench mark*. A bench mark, if it is a permanent bench mark, is shown on a contour map by means of an open triangle. Alongside the triangle are printed figures which state the exact elevation of the point in the triangle's center (Fig. 37, southwest portion of map). The triangle indicates that there is an actual marker, usually a circular bronze plate set in a small concrete base. The marker may carry no more than a reference number, but often it contains an imprinted statement of such items as exact latitude and longitude, the altitude in feet, the direction of true north and magnetic north, the date on which the marker was placed, and the name of the agency which placed it there. Contour maps show bench marks which are not permanent by means of small crosses accompanied by altitude figures (see Fig. 37, southeast portion, between the 25-foot and 50-foot contours).

For points which lie between contour lines, and for which there is provided no statement of exact altitude by permanent or temporary bench marks, altitudes cannot be accurately determined. They can be determined *only within the contour interval of the map*. If a given point is located somewhere between the 100-foot and the 125-foot contour, and the contour interval is 25 feet, all one can say is that the altitude is greater than 100 feet but less than 125 feet (D in Fig. 37). The fact that a point lies about halfway between the 100-foot and the 125-foot contours does not necessarily mean that its altitude is 112½ feet. Such would be the case if the slope were absolutely uniform between the two contour levels, but there is no way of telling, from the map, if that is true. For example, the slope may make most of its rise immediately above the 100-foot level, and then rise quite gently all the rest of the way to the next contour line. In this instance, the altitude of 112½ feet would lie very close to the 100-foot line.

LAYER MAPS. Another method of showing the lay of the land on maps is developed through the use of color. This device is used commonly for maps which show a great deal of territory on a relatively small map sheet, in other words, on small-scale maps. Each color, including black and white gradations as well as greens, yellows, browns, etc., shows the location of a given altitude zone, or layer, on

38

PHOTOGRAPH of a relief model showing about 40 miles of coastal area of southern California (land and adjacent ocean bottom). The large bay at far right is San Diego Bay. Near the middle appears a large submarine canyon. (Robert Pease)

the map and gives rise to the term *layer map*. A layer map is really another kind of contour map, because the top and bottom of each layer is a contour line. The color of each layer merely covers the parts of the land which lie between two given contour lines. Another, more technical, term is *hypsometric map*. A hypsometric map of the United States usually displays several colors because there are several altitude zones from one end of the country to the other. On a particular map, green may be used to show all parts of the United States which lie between sea level and 500 feet above sea level; a lighter green for sections which have altitudes ranging from 500-1,000 feet; yellow for 1,000-2,000 feet; and so on. Red or purplish-red is often used to indicate elevations in excess of 10,000 feet. An example of a layer or hypsometric map appears in the front portion of this book (see Plate III).

Other Relief Devices

MODELS. Relief may be indicated in other fashions than by maps. The relief model is one of these. It actually possesses the third dimension and does not have to simulate that dimension by means of hachures, colors, shadings, or contour lines. An example of a relief model cannot be reproduced here, on a flat page, but a photograph of one appears in Fig. 38. Note how readily one may see the lay of the land on a device of this sort.

PHYSIOGRAPHIC DIAGRAMS. This device has been used and perfected in the past few years. By means of so-called physiographic symbols, it creates in a drawing the impression of a relief model; the symbols, in a sense, resemble the shapes of hills, valleys, escarpments, etc., and they provide a sort of oblique airplane view of the earth's surface. Because they are created on flat surfaces, they are sometimes referred to as physiographic maps. However, they are not in correct scale in all portions and the symbols, at times, prevent expression of

39 *AN EXAMPLE of a physiographic diagram (also known as a terrain diagram and a landforms diagram). Note how physiographic symbols are used to show valleys, hills, escarpments, nearly level plain along a coast, etc.*

conditions in some of the lower lands, as in the instance of small valleys which lie behind high mountains—the symbol used for the mountains hides the valleys which lie behind the mountains. A relief device of this sort is a *physiographic diagram* or a *terrain diagram*. An example is provided by Fig. 39.

PROFILES. At times, certain conditions of relief may be shown clearly by means of surface profiles. These represent the upward profile of the land in much the same manner that an artist may show the outward profile of one's face. If the surface profile is drawn along a line which extends at right angles to the "grain" of the land, it can tell a considerable story of the relief. Fig. 40 is a generalized profile drawn along a line which extends through portions of Tennessee. It includes parts of the Cumberland Plateau, the Ridge and Valley section, and the southern Appalachian Mountains. These features possess a marked northeast-southwest trend. By drawing the profile at right angles to this trend, that is from northwest to southeast, a meaningful result is obtained. When such a profile is titled, properly labeled, and provided with both horizontal and vertical scales, one who has never

40 *A GENERALIZED SURFACE PROFILE drawn approximately northwest-southeast across the eastern part of Tennessee and into North Carolina. The vertical scale is exaggerated, as compared with the horizontal scale, in order to give the impression of surface changes much as they appear to the eye of the observer in the field.*

seen the area may receive a reasonably clear-cut impression of the variations and conditions of the relief. It is much as though he actually walked across the area, from one end of the profile line to the other. As a device, the profile will present him with a taste of reality and variety for one part of the earth's surface.

BLOCK DIAGRAMS. The block diagram, too, is a non-map device. It is one which, in a sense, combines the features of a physiographic diagram and a surface profile. It is drawn in perspective as a block of the earth's crust and is always termed a *block diagram* (Fig. 41). The upper edges of the block provide surface profiles and the top of the block provides a panoramic view. In addition, if desired, the edges of the block may carry a

partial picture of what lies below the surface and, hence, show some of the relationships which exist between relief features and the underlying rock structure. In Fig. 41, one may see readily some of the outstanding relationships between individual rock layers and specific surface features.

CHARTS

There is much geographical material which lends itself readily to expression on charts. Again, it is not the purpose to discuss here all of the kinds of charts which may be used. Instead, some samples will be taken to illustrate the nature and geographic utility of charts.

Climatic Charts

Perhaps the most commonly encountered charts in introductory geography are *climatic charts.* They may be very simple or relatively complex. In either case, it is their function to tell, in graphic form, the story of the long-time behavior of the atmosphere at a given place. Fig. 42 shows two climatic charts; the left-hand portion is a chart before the climatic data have been plotted; the right-hand portion shows a chart with the data graph-

BLOCK DIAGRAM

41 *NOTE the relationships between the geologic structure and some of the shapes of land surface.*

ically expressed upon it. The data used are given below the charts.

On the completed chart appears a curving line and several vertical columns. The curving line is the *temperature curve*. It is arrived at by noting the average monthly temperatures, as given in the data, and plotting those temperatures as points on the monthly columns of the charts. For example, the data show that the average monthly temperature for January is 53° F. By using the Fahrenheit scale at the right of the chart the position of this temperature can be ascertained and a point indicating that temperature placed in the middle of the January column. The same is done for each month of the year. Then, by connecting the points with a smooth line, the temperature curve is obtained. The vertical columns are called *precipitation columns*.

They are obtained by noting the average precipitation for each month and plotting that monthly average in the proper month column on the chart. For example, the data show that the average monthly precipitation for January is 3.5 inches. By using the precipitation scale, at the left of the chart, the position of that number of inches may be determined and indicated as a crossline in the January column. Then the column may be filled in solidly up to the level of the crossline. It is as though the January column were a container which had collected the fall of moisture from the skies; in this instance, enough fell to fill the container to a height of 3.5 inches. Plotting the other columns in the same manner provides a precipitation column for each month of the year.

The charts referred to are in black and

SANTA MONICA, CALIFORNIA

	Jan	Feb	Mar	Apr	May	June	July	Aug	Sept	Oct	Nov	Dec	Year
TEMPERATURE	53	53	55	58	60	63	66	66	65	62	58	55	59.5 F°
PRECIPITATION	3.5	3.0	2.9	0.5	0.5	0.0	0.0	0.0	0.1	0.6	1.4	2.3	14.78 In.

42 *STANDARD CLIMATIC CHARTS (blank and filled in). The chart at the right has been plotted with the data given below it. Note the temperature curve and precipitation columns on the completed chart.*

white, but very often the data are plotted in color with red dots and lines for temperature curves and a solid blue for the precipitation columns. In any event, the completed chart expresses the degree of seasonal rhythm in both temperature and precipitation, and does it more effectively than the cold figures of the unplotted climatic data. Moreover, a number of completed charts enables one to lay several graphic pictures alongside one another so that the outstanding features of the climate of many different places may be compared and contrasted, almost at a glance.

Another type of climatic chart is shown in Fig. 43. It is the type which is used in this book. It might be called the "wheel chart," for it has the shape of a wheel, as well as a hub and spokes. Each spoke is used to plot climatic data for a given month and the twelve spokes express the picture of the year. On this type of chart the year does not begin sud-

denly "out of nowhere" nor does it end suddenly at a chart margin (compare Figs. 42 and 43). The year has continuity, and December leads into January, as it does in our own experience. The temperature curve is a continuous line just as temperature conditions are continuous in actuality. The precipitation columns, although not continuous, occur in unbroken sequence; one does not have to jump from one margin of the chart to the other in order to make comparisons between the precipitation of December and that of January. The latter feature is especially important for charts of those portions of the world which receive the bulk of their precipitation during November, December, January, and February. When their precipitation is plotted on a "wheel chart," as opposed to the ordinary rectangular chart, the resultant picture is unified instead of broken and separated (compare Figs. 42 and 43).

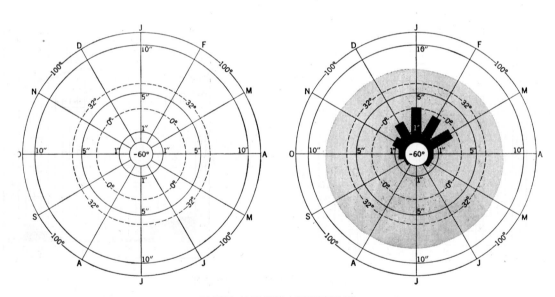

SANTA MONICA, CALIFORNIA

	Jan	Feb	Mar	Apr	May	June	July	Aug	Sept	Oct	Nov	Dec	Year
TEMPERATURE	53	53	55	58	60	63	66	66	65	62	58	55	59.5 F°
PRECIPITATION	3.5	3.0	2.9	0.5	0.5	0.0	0.0	0.0	0.1	0.6	1.4	2.3	14.78 In.

43   *BLANK AND PLOTTED climatic charts of the "wheel" type. Climatic data are the same as used in Fig. 42.*

Transect Charts

Another type of chart which may be very useful for certain geographical purposes is the *transect chart* (Fig. 45). It might be called, also, the surface profile chart, or, because it can carry so much geographical information, the geographical chart. The major basis of the transect chart is a surface profile. The profile shows the general nature of the relief features of the area which is being transected, and on top of the profile is constructed a framework to contain several categories of geographic fact. By means of vertical as well as horizontal lines, space is provided for descriptive material for each of the surface divisions shown on the profile. Below the profile, geologic information may be provided, if desired. An examination of Fig. 45 will indicate the large degree to which the geographical picture of a given area may be portrayed in this fashion.

Other Charts

In addition to those noted already, there are many other types of charts which serve as geographical tools, as well as tools for other disciplines. Such charts need little discussion. They appear in many places, in popular as well as professional publications. Fig. 44 provides a few samples of some of these other kinds of charts.

The tools of geography are many. The foregoing discussions have not pretended to be all-inclusive, nor have they pretended to provide complete treatment of the particular tools which were discussed. However, the general basic knowledge which may be obtained from the preceding pages will furnish a working foundation for the understanding and use of such fundamental tools as globes, maps, map projections, special relief devices, and charts. With that foundation, the ma-

44 *THREE types of charts. From top to bottom are examples of graph, bar, and pie charts.*

terials and ideas which follow can be more effectively interpreted.

CHAPTER OUTLINE

The tools of geography

A GENERALIZED TRANSECT chart of the Lake St. John area, Province of Quebec, Canada. A transect chart is a kind of geographic shorthand. At the base is a geologic cross-section of an area (in this case running north-south through the mid-portion of the Lake St. John area). Particulars of each of the geographic elements are noted directly above the portions of the cross-section to which they apply.

45

Column headers: SETTLEMENTS · FEW FARMS, VILLAGES · FARMS, VILLAGES, ETC. · FARMS, VILLAGES, TOWNS. · CANOE ROUTES. · LUMBER CAMPS.

COMMUNICATIONS	FEW ROADS, ONE R.R. — MANY 2ND AND 3RD CLASS ROADS. CANOE ROUTES. ONE RR. TAPS AREA. TELEPHONES AND RADIOS. UNCERTAIN PASSENGER AND FREIGHT SERVICE DURING SUMMER SEASON.
MANUFACTURING	HYDRO-ELECTRIC POWER, PULP, ETC. — HYDRO-ELECTRIC POWER AND PAPER PULP. CHEESE FACTORIES, BLUEBERRY CANNERIES.
HUNTING AND FISHING	FURS, SOME HUNTING AND FISHING FOR SPORT. — SPORT FISHING
LUMBERING	PULPWOOD, TIES, SOME LUMBER. — FIREWOOD, POSTS, FENCE RAILS. MUCH PULPWOOD, SOME LUMBER.
AGRICULTURE AND ANIMAL HUSBANDRY	HAY AND DAIRY TYPE. — CHIEF CROP IS HAY-OTHERS, OATS, WHEAT, BARLEY. CHIEF DOM. ANIMAL-THE DAIRY COW-OTHERS, HORSES, SHEEP.
MINING	SHALE, LIMEST., QUARRIES. SMALL GRANITE QUARRIES. — SAND AND GRAVEL PITS.
CLIMATE	CLIMATIC TYPE Dfb (KÖPPEN), CHARACTERIZED BY LONG, SEVERE WINTERS AND SHORT, WARM SUMMERS. AVER. ANN. TEMP. 34°F. TEMP. WARMEST MO. 63°F (JULY). COLDEST -4°F (JAN). AVER. ANN. PRECIP. 30 INCHES. PRECIP. WETTEST MO. (JULY) 3.6 INCHES. DRIEST (MAR) 1.5. ABSOLUTE MIN TEMP -49°F. MAX 97°F. AVER. 90 DAYS FROST FREE. 4 MONTHS SNOW COVER.
NATIVE ANIMAL LIFE	PLENTIFUL: MOOSE, DEER, RED FOX, RABBIT, OTTER, PORCUPINE, MUSKRAT, ETC. DUCK, BITTERN, FISH. RABBIT, FOX, SKUNK, MUSKRAT, WEASEL, ETC. WILDFOWL: ESP., DUCKS. FISH: ESP., TROUT, PIKE, PERCH. PLENTIFUL: MOOSE, DEER, RABBIT, WOLF, FOX, MINK, PORCUPINE, MUSKRAT, ETC. DUCK, BITTERN, FISH. WILDFOWL VERY PLENTIFUL. FISH: ESP., OUANANICHE, PIKE, PERCH. LAKE ST. JOHN DRAINED BY LA GRANDE AND LA PETITE DECHARGE, TO THE EAST.
DRAINAGE	YOUTHFUL DRAINAGE PATTERN, GLACIALLY DERANGED. (FLOW)
NATIVE VEGETATION	CONIFERS: CHIEFLY SPRUCE, BALSAM. SOME CEDAR, AND OTHER SWAMP VEGET. MIXED FOREST: CHIEFLY SPRUCE, BIRCH, ASPEN, JACK PINE. CONSIDERABLE AREAS OF CEDAR AND TAMARACK SWAMP. BLUEBERRY AND REINDEER MOSS UNDER-COVER COMMON. CONIFERS: CHIEFLY SPRUCE, BALSAM. SOME CEDAR AND OTHER SWAMP VEGET.
SOIL	IMMATURE SOILS, PATCHY VENEER OF SAND, GRAVEL BOULDERS, SOME SWAMP MUCK, ROCK OUTCROPS. MARINE CLAYS AND SANDS. MARINE SOILS. THICK MANTLE OF MARINE CLAYS AND SANDS, SOME SWAMP MUCKS AND RECENT RIVER ALLUVIUM. MARINE CLAYS, SANDS, ETC.
GEOLOGY AND LANDSURFACE	GLACIATED SURFACE OF LAURENTIAN SHIELD, MOSTLY SCOUR, SOME DRIFT. MARINE TERRACES, YOUTHFULLY DISSECTED. GLACIATED SURFACE OF THE LAURENTIAN SHIELD, MOSTLY SCOUR, SOME DRIFT.

GEOLOGICAL KEY:
1. QUATERNARY: SANDS, CLAYS (STRATIF.)
2. ORDOVICIAN UTICA SHALES.
3. TRENTON LIMESTONE.
4. PRE-C.: LAURENTIAN GNEISS, GRANITE.
2 AND 3 PROBABLY OVERLAIN BY DRIFT.

Elevations: 1000' · 800' · 500' · 334'

Cross-section labels: HIGHLAND · LOWLAND · ISLE DE LA TRAVERSE · LAKE ST. JOHN 334' ABOVE SEA LEVEL · R. PERIBONCA · MARINE TERRACES, YOUTHFULLY DISSECTED · GLACIALLY SCOURED BARE ROCK LICHENS · YOUTHFULLY DISSECTED

MILES: 0 · 5 · 10 · 15 · 20

After R. W. Glendinning

REVIEW QUESTIONS

1. What are the chief advantages and disadvantages of a globe as compared to a map of the world?

2. Name the lines which commonly appear on globes. Among these, name the lines which usually are indicated by a special symbol and are given special names.

3. Explain why the grid is necessary.

4. How far apart (expressed in degrees and fractions thereof) are the Tropic of Cancer and the Tropic of Capricorn? What is the distance (in degrees and fractions thereof) from the Antarctic Circle to the South Pole?

5. If you were halfway between the equator and the South Pole and one quarter of the way around the earth to the east of the prime meridian, what would your latitude and longitude be? Consult a globe or world map to see where you would be in terms of land and water areas.

6. Draw simple diagrams to show where the noon rays of the sun would strike the earth's surface vertically on June 21, on December 22, on March 21, and on September 23.

7. Explain why the noon sun is never directly overhead at Chicago.

8. Why does a place located within the tropics receive vertical noon rays from the sun twice during each year? Suggest some ways in which this condition is important to man.

9. If it is 10:00 A.M. (Standard Time) in San Francisco, what time (Standard) is it in New York City? Is this fact of any importance to the citizens of either place? How?

10. You are at a given place on the earth's surface, the date is June 21, the sun is *directly* overhead, and Greenwich Time is 3:00 P.M.; what is the latitude and longitude of your position?

11. You are aboard a ship which is crossing the international date line in a westward direction. Just before you crossed the line, the date was April 15. What is the date as soon as the line is crossed?

12. Explain why oblique sun rays provide less heat per unit of area than do vertical rays.

13. What is meant by the term "map projection" and why are map projections necessary?

14. Explain the statement, "There is no such thing as a perfect map projection."

15. To show world distribution of forests, would you choose a map based on an equal-area, a conformal, an azimuthal, or an equidistant projection? Why?

16. What are the essentials of a true and complete map?

17. If a given map has a fractional scale of $\frac{1}{24,000}$ and two points on that map are six inches apart, how far apart, in feet, are those two points actually?

18. What is the fractional scale of a map whose verbal scale is stated as "one-half inch equals one mile"?

19. Explain why a map that is to be enlarged or reduced should show only a linear scale.

20. What is the difference in meaning between "true north" and "magnetic north"?

21. The contour interval of a given map is 50 feet. Explain what is meant.

22. Distinguish between "relief model" and "relief

map"; between "relief map" and "physiographic diagram"; between "physiographic diagram" and "block diagram."

23. What is the difference between a "transect chart" and a "surface profile"?

24. Justify the plotting of climatic data on climatic charts as opposed to leaving such data in ordinary numerical form.

SOME SUGGESTED REFERENCES

Brown, Lloyd A., *The Story of Maps,* Little, Brown, 1949. A simple and yet comprehensive history of map makers, maps, and cartographic methods from the pre-Christian era to the present; 82 illustrations and extensive notes and bibliography.

Deetz, Charles H., and Adams, Oscar S., *Elements of Map Projection with Applications to Map and Chart Construction,* Special Publication 68, U. S. Coast and Geodetic Survey, Department of Commerce, 1934. A standard, comparatively technical manual on map projections and their mathematical construction.

Greenhood, David, *Down to Earth: Mapping for Everybody,* Holiday House, 1944. A simply written story of maps, map projections, map compilation, map sources, and map collecting; profusely illustrated.

Johnson, Willis E., *Mathematical Geography,* American Book Company, 1907. A simple classic; old, but not superseded in its field; deals with factors of earth form, rotation, revolution, latitude, longitude, time, tides, and map projections.

Lobeck, Armin K., *Block Diagrams and Other Graphic Methods Used in Geology and Geography,* John Wiley and Sons, Inc., 1924. The classic publication on block diagrams and how to make them; many illustrations.

Raisz, Erwin, *General Cartography,* 2nd ed., McGraw-Hill, 1948. A standard textbook dealing with the history of maps and with map scales and projections, map symbols, map drafting, and special maps and diagrams; numerous illustrations.

Ridgway, John L., *Scientific Illustration,* Stanford University Press, 1938. A simple, but relatively thorough, treatment of many different types of illustrations and illustration problems from photographs and sketches to maps and diagrams; contains 22 plates and 23 figures.

Steer, James A., *An Introduction to the Study of Map Projections,* 5th ed., University of London Press, Ltd., 1943. A basic treatment of types and problems of map projections.

Map and Aerial Photograph Reading, The Military Service Publishing Company, 1943. Based on, and presented in the style of, War Department manuals; deals with map interpretation and air photo reading; introductory and simple, rather than highly technical.

Note: Descriptive pamphlets and booklets dealing with globes and their use are available from many map-publishing and globe-making companies, such as Denoyer-Geppert, A. J. Nystrom, Rand McNally, etc.

PART TWO

Elements of the Physical Setting

....

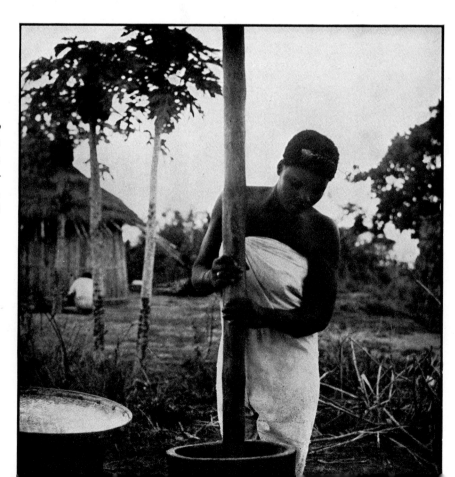

CHAPTER 4

Introduction to the Physical Setting

....

Important among the objectives of this book, as stated in Chapter 1, is an understanding of the physical world in which man lives and makes a living as well as a knowledge of the many relationships which exist between the physical setting, on the one hand, and man and his various activities, on the other. The attainment of these objectives requires, first of all, a consideration of all the *major* physical elements which comprise the many aspects of the face of the earth.

PHYSICAL ELEMENTS

Physical elements are those elements of the geographical scene which, in a sense, are "nature-made" rather than man-made (Table 1, page 4). Man may alter them to varying degrees; he may struggle to alter them and fail; or, in some instances, he may merely accept them as they are. But he cannot ignore them; they are the basic, fundamental stuff of his life on earth. Because the physical elements change their expression from one part of the earth to another, and because they occur in so many different combinations, man is confronted with a large number of physical complexes, each one a part of general earth variety.

Climate and Weather

Most completely all-pervasive in affecting life on the earth are the conditions and behavior of the atmosphere, especially the conditions of the lower portions of the atmosphere in which man and other forms of life exist. The sum total of such conditions over a long period of time constitutes *climate;* at any one moment of time, they comprise *weather*. Ensuing chapters (particularly Chaps. 5, 6, 7, 8, and 9) will emphasize the nature, consequences, and distribution of the conditions and behavior of the atmosphere.

Landforms

Underneath the atmosphere is the exposed portion of the earth's crust. It expresses itself to the eyes of man in large forms, such as continents and major islands, in medium-sized forms, such as mountains, tablelands, hills, and plains, and in smaller forms, such as valleys, ridges, deltas, or sand bars. These many shapes of the top of the earth's crust, regardless of size, are *landforms*. Both local and world-wide expressions of this sort will be examined, not only in and of themselves but, also, in terms of their significance to man and his ways of life (Chaps. 10, 11, and 12).

Water

Where the air does not cover the land it covers the surfaces of oceans, seas, lakes, rivers, and other bodies and lines of water. Man's life on earth is in a major sense an island life, for even the continents are in reality large islands surrounded by still larger oceans. But man's water world does not end there: the soils contain water, the earth materials under the soils contain water, even the very air holds much water in vapor form and drops some of it to make life possible on the land. Later discussions will emphasize the earth's waters, under such topics as *water bodies, streams,* and *underground water* (Chap. 13).

Native Vegetation and Animal Life

Many kinds of natural plants grow wherever soils are present. Seldom do they grow alone, but, rather, in groups or combinations. As a whole they comprise *native vegetation;* in specific combinations, they are *vegetation associations,* such as particular types of forests and grasslands. Living in among the natural plants are many varieties of animals ranging from flies and mosquitoes to deer and elephants. These, as opposed to man's domesticated animals, comprise *native animal life.* Because of the intimate relationships between plants and animals they are treated together, rather than separately (Chap. 14).

Soils

When solid rock is sufficiently broken up and when the residue has evolved to the point where it is capable of supporting plant life, it is known as *soil.* There are many types and varieties of soil, some highly productive and some virtually worthless, but, regardless of worth, they contribute still another part to the physical scene. Where productive, they provide one of the most fundamental of natural resources (Chap. 15).

Mineral Resources

Bedrock and loose earth materials present man with many products which he can use directly or can process and transform into useful goods. Some examples are seen in such things as iron ore, petroleum, building stone, salt, tin, and gold. All such are termed *mineral resources* (Chaps. 16, 17, and 18).

These are the physical elements of geography, from climate and weather to mineral resources. In their manifold combinations they make up the physical setting. To speak more truly, they comprise the many kinds of physical settings which occur over the earth. The elements noted need to be understood of and by themselves; just as important, they need to be understood and appreciated as they occur in natural combinations. To give emphasis to them as elements and, at the same time, to stress their significance in combination, the following "thumbnail" sketches are presented. These sketches are presented only as two examples of what is meant by "physical setting" and by "relationships between and among the natural elements." They are brief, and, because of the present stage of our inquiry, they avoid all use of technical language.

PHYSICAL SETTING

Example of a Small Area: Lake St. John Lowland

Some ninety miles nearly due north of the city of Quebec is an area known as the Lake St. John Lowland (Fig. 47). The center of the area is a relatively large body of fresh water which covers more than three hundred

47 LOCATION of Lake St. John.

48 LAKE St. John Lowland and surrounding territory.

square miles (Fig. 48). Entirely surrounding this lake is a nearly level plain rising slowly to the steep edge of a more elevated country, which is gently rolling. Within the plain are deep soils. On the encompassing higher land, soils are thin and stony or are interrupted by nearly barren hills and ridges of solid rock as well as numerous ponds and lakes. Although all of the soils of the plain are deep, they vary markedly. To the south and east of the lake, the plains soils are chiefly fine, relatively compact clays; to the north and west, they are mainly coarse sands. Flowing from the higher land and tumbling by means of numerous falls and rapids into the plain are many large and small streams. One of the larger is the Peribonca River, which is about one mile in width at its mouth. Nearly all of the streams have cut deep channels into the plain so that its surface is appreciably interrupted. In several portions, most notably just north of the lake, are large swamps.

Originally the plain and the surrounding highland were covered with forests. Where the clay soils occur there were forests comprised largely of such trees as birch and maple with a sprinkling of evergreens, such as spruce and cedar. The latter occurred chiefly where

soils were swampy. Where the sandy soils occur there were forests of tall pines. On the rocky upland there were, and still are in most sections, forests of spruce, cedar, poplar, and birch. By clearing the clay-soil areas for farming purposes, man has almost entirely removed the original forest to the south and east of the lake (Fig. 49). Because of fires, the former trees of most of the sandy lands have been replaced by a poor scrubby growth comprised largely of jack pine, mosses, blueberry bushes, and fernlike plants known as bracken. The sandy areas were not generally used for farming purposes because of the low productivity of the soil and, also, because many sections of the sandy soils are swampy. Such swampy sections are marked by dense growths of spruce and cedar.

Overlying lake and plain alike, and extending far across the encircling higher lands, is a climate which is characterized by long, cold, snowy winters and short, warm, rainy summers. It is a climate of great seasonal change. Those who live there often say, by way of exaggerating the condition, "There are two seasons here. There is winter, and there is a time when it is difficult to travel with sleighs." Actually, the summers are warm and hot

49 *AIR PHOTO of a portion of the clay-soil area of the Lake St. John Lowland, Quebec Province. (Royal Canadian Air Force)*

snowy mantle about three feet thick. Broadleaf trees such as birches and poplars become dormant during the cold period and stand completely barren of foliage. The evergreens, appearing even darker against the white snow cover, retain their needles but, of course, cannot grow in the cold weather.

With the coming of spring, the entire appearance of the countryside changes. The ice on the lake becomes wet and gray, and melts away. The river ice breaks up and moves downstream with a great deal of noise as the cakes of ice bump and grind against one another and against the banks. The mantle of snow disappears and the swamps and soils thaw out. New, green leaves appear on the broadleaf trees and the needleleaf trees become a brighter and fresher green. Songbirds and ducks, which had gone south to escape the cold, reappear. The deer, and an occasional moose, come out of their winter quarters in the spruce and cedar swamps. And swarms of mosquitoes, continuing through most of the summer, plague man and beast alike. The farmers, in the clay areas, do their spring plowing, plant their crops, and turn the domestic animals out to pasture.

Thus, in this sample area, one may see a certain type of physical setting, with its own particular conditions and patterns of arrangement of the natural elements, and with a marked seasonal rhythm incident to the behavior of the atmosphere. Moreover, there appear many relationships between and among the physical elements such as the association between the nearly level plain and deep soils, between the cold season and the migration of birds, between waterlogged soils and cedar swamps, between warm weather and open water and cold weather and snow and ice, and so on through many others. No mention was made of mineral resources. In this area they are insignificant except for some quarrying of building stone and the use of sand and gravel surfacing on roads. Also, man and his activities were mentioned only in passing because the discussion centered on natural conditions.

spells are not uncommon. However, there is no gainsaying the severe cold of the long winters. This strong seasonal behavior of the atmosphere is reflected in many other physical conditions as well as in the activities of the inhabitants. The surface of the lake is frozen with thick ice for about five months out of the year. The same is true of the rivers, except where the water at certain falls and rapids is moving too fast to freeze. Swamps and small streams are frozen completely. At the same time the soils are frozen to depths of two or three feet and are covered with a

Example of a Large Area: Amazon Basin

From the broad mouths of the Amazon to the eastern edge of the high Andes stretches a vast plain. It widens considerably in the western portion; in the east it is restricted by the presence of the Guiana Highlands to the north and the low, northern margin of the Brazilian Uplands to the south (Fig. 50).

The plain is hot and rainy the year round. There may be seasons of rain and seasons of less rain, but there is normally no season of true drought, except in the narrow, eastern portion of the basin, where a dry period occurs from approximately June to September. The hot, humid air provides a huge outdoor greenhouse for the growth of natural vegetation over the plain as a whole. With no frost to kill small plants, or to force the trees to become dormant, most of the plain is clothed in a permanently green forest mantle, broken occasionally by patches of grass. On steep slopes along river bluffs and in very wet spots in river flood plains there is a dense tangle of trees, vines, and giant ferns which is best described as a jungle (Fig. 51). Away from the rivers, on the gently rolling plain as a whole, a tall forest in which the crowns of the trees meet closely prevents much sunlight from reaching the ground (Fig. 52); without sufficient sunlight, the forest floor is relatively clear of vegetation.

Rivers support fish, eels, and turtles. Many varieties of insects, such as mosquitoes, gnats, and butterflies, and many snakes, birds, and monkeys live in the forest. Because most of them love and seek the sun, they live high in the treetops and, hence, may seldom be seen from the ground. The insects, especially mosquitoes, are very troublesome, not only because they bite, but because their bites carry diseases, such as malaria and yellow fever.

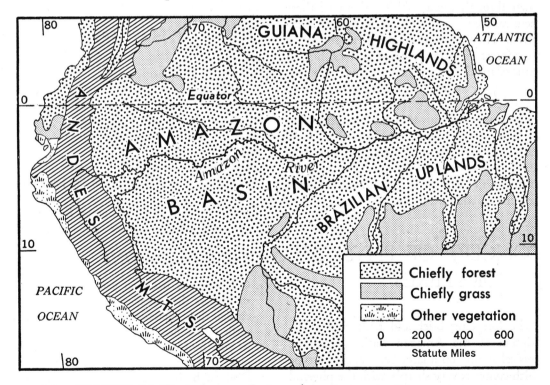

50 SKETCH MAP of Amazon Basin and contiguous territory.

Because of the abundance of rain, there are many large and small streams, and the broad Amazon is master of them all. The lines of water, fringed with jungle, mark the only major breaks in the cloak of vegetation (Fig. 53). Some of the rivers, like the lower Amazon, have cut into the plain and then widened their pathways until they have created wide valleys which are many miles across and in which occur numerous swampy jungles. Others have cut into the plain, but have not yet had a chance to carve wide valleys. Still others are barely etched into the land surface and are no more than small V-shaped valleys. Where wide valleys exist, there are broad ribbons of muddy and silty soils which have been deposited by the streams in highest flood. On the plain above the valleys, most of the soils are red and coarse. They are among the poorer soils of the world; they have been literally "washed out," but not washed away, by the abundant rain water which has seeped down through them robbing them of those chemical elements which are most easily dissolved. They are fertile enough to support a great forest of naturally adapted trees, but, in terms of man's crops which are more demanding than the natural vegetation, they are of low value.

The mineral resources of the extensive plain are little known. There are, of course, sands and clays, and recent scattered surveys indicate the presence of petroleum in the far western margin of the plain. Beyond this, there is little information available.

CONCEPT OF PHYSICAL COMPLEXES

The foregoing brief and nontechnical description of the Amazon Basin presents a physical setting on a large scale and of a type which contrasts very sharply with the physical setting of the Lake St. John Lowland. Ensu-

ing chapters will discuss in some detail the nature of the physical elements, one by one, and in terms of world distributions and patterns. As these chapters are studied it will be necessary to remember that none of the natural conditions occurs alone and unrelated to the others. One may point out, even at this early stage in our inquiry, that vegetation *is* related to climate, that soils *are* related to both vegetation and climate, that the shapes of valleys *are* related to the work of streams and to the climatic behavior which determines how much water is supplied to the streams; these are only partial and somewhat random examples, but they do make clear that physical conditions are interrelated and that knowledge of individual conditions produces no geographic completeness until it is enlarged to become a knowledge of physical complexes.

CHAPTER OUTLINE

Introduction to the physical setting

Physical elements
  Climate and weather
  Landforms
  Water
  Native vegetation and animal life
  Soils
  Mineral resources
Physical setting
  Example of a small area: Lake St. John Lowland
  Example of a large area: Amazon Basin
Concept of physical complexes

REVIEW QUESTIONS

1. Give examples based on your own experience to support the statement, "Physical elements change their expression from one part of the earth to another."
2. In your own words, what is a "physical complex" as that term is used geographically?
3. Distinguish between climate and weather. Why are they spoken of as "all-pervasive"?

51

JUNGLE growth in the rainy tropics. Workmen clear a way for a road. (Corsini, Standard Oil Co. [N. J.])

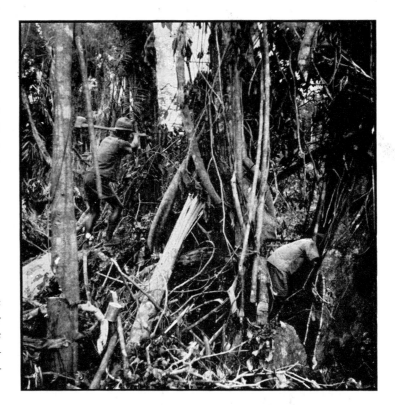

52

THE CAMERA looks out from a sunny, man-made clearing into the darkness of the tropical forest. (Belgian Government Information Center, New York)

53 *FOREST-WALLED STREAMS interrupt the dense vegetation blanket of the rainy tropics. Air photograph by Major Albert W. Stevens, U. S. Army Air Force, taken about 90 miles west of Assaby Caxoeira, Rio Uraricuera, Brazilian Guiana. (Hamilton Rice Expedition, 1924-25)*

4. What is the difference between "landforms" and "earth's surface"?

5. Native vegetation is noted briefly in this chapter. What other kind of vegetation is there?

6. What kinds or types of water comprise the "water world"?

7. Is there any difference between "resources" and "mineral resources"?

8. Describe, using your own method of description and organization, the physical setting of the Lake St. John Lowland.

9. "Of all the physical conditions present in the Lake St. John Lowland and immediately surrounding territory, conditions of climate and conditions of landforms are most important." Would you agree with this statement? Justify your answer. Suggest other areas, familiar to you, where the statement holds true.

10. Contrast the physical setting of the Amazon Basin with that of the Lake St. John Lowland. They are both plains; why, then, are they physically so different?

CHAPTER 5

Elements and Controls of Climate

···

SIGNIFICANCE OF THE ATMOSPHERE TO MAN

The existence of a blanket of atmosphere about the earth is the basic essential for all forms of life. It is the unique good fortune of earth inhabitants that the physical mixture of gases in the atmosphere is such as to support not only man, but other animals and plants as well. So far as we are aware, no other planet is blessed with just the exact gaseous mixture which can support this life; nor is there another planet known upon which the heat and moisture conditions are such as to be capable of supporting similar life forms. The individual gases which are present, the states in which they exist, and the controls to which they are subject are all vital to man's very being.

Composition of the Atmosphere

The atmosphere is a mechanical mixture of gases and of finely divided solid impurities. The dominant gases in terms of volume are nitrogen and oxygen. In dry air, nitrogen makes up about 78 per cent of the total and oxygen, by far the most important ingredient since it maintains human respiration, about 21 per cent. Both nitrogen and oxygen remain in relatively fixed proportion throughout the total mass of atmosphere. This statement may seem to contradict ordinary experience in mountain climbing or in high-altitude airplane flight; actually, it does not. True, there is a smaller amount of oxygen at high altitudes, but so is there a smaller amount of all other gases. The air becomes "thinner" with altitude. Yet, the proportion of oxygen remains essentially the same.

Of the other gases included in the mixture, water vapor, source of the world's precipitation, and carbon dioxide, necessary to the life of plants, are perhaps the most important. The proportion of these two varies markedly from place to place and from time to time, but both are concentrated in the *lower* layers of the atmosphere where they are effective agents in the maintenance of life. The solid impurities include smoke, chemical salts, microorganisms, and dust. They are likewise concentrated in the lower portion of the atmosphere. There, the finest particles, some so small as to be microscopically invisible, aid in the process which changes water vapor to water. The impurities are present in amounts which vary both from time to time and from place to place.

Climatic Elements

The atmosphere is a mobile and constantly changing body. The detailed analysis of its composition and motion are properly the field of meteorology. Nevertheless, a recognition of certain of the basic elements, of their controls, and of the nature and distribution of the combinations resulting from the action of the controls upon the elements is essential to the full appreciation of the world in which we live.

Why is one area forest-covered and another grass-covered (Figs. 1 and 2)? Why are the common trees of eastern Canada, like pine, hemlock, and spruce, lacking in the Great Plains of the United States? Why are red soils, like those of Georgia and Alabama, unknown in Iowa? Why does the housebuilder of the tropics keep his dwelling open to the winds while the northerner strives to make his dwelling as windtight as his culture allows (Fig. 54)? These are only a few of the more obvious questions whose answers depend on the average state of the atmosphere in different parts of the world.

TEMPERATURE AND PRECIPITATION. The most commonly appreciated climatic elements are heat and moisture, or *temperature* and *precipitation*. The degree of heat and the moisture content of the atmosphere affect profoundly the way man feels and acts. An oppressively sticky, steamy, summer day like one in southern Illinois, with its afternoon thunderstorm interlude bringing temporary lowering of temperature, makes one long for the sparkling days and chilly evenings of fall. The bitterly cold, blustery, snowy day of a northern New England winter makes one shudder at the thought of leaving the warm protection of a well-heated house; instead one wishes devoutly for the balmy days of summer. Yet the sullenness of the pre-shower hours of a summer day in Illinois or the frigidity of the New England winter day are typical conditions of that portion of the atmos-

pheric shell closest to the earth's surface. Without really seeing it, we are continuously affected by the atmosphere about us.

Even people of primitive cultures recognized that the major climatic elements regulated their clothing and their shelter. Prehistoric man sought shelter in caves as protection against the frigid blasts from retreating ice sheets. Later, with the disappearance of the ice, he came out from the caves to occupy rock shelters such as those that line the valley sides of the Vézère River in southwestern France. Similarly, the placing of primitive settlements near sources of water and the avoidance of waterless areas suggest recognition of the importance of moisture.

Peoples with the most advanced cultures (according to Occidental standards, at least) attempt to regulate both temperature and moisture, at least inside homes and other buildings. Air conditioning, house insulation, and centralized heating are all attempts on the part of man to control the effectiveness and the actual distribution of heat and moisture. The practice of adjusting the distribution of water, either on the surface, as in irrigation projects like those of the Nile Valley in Egypt or of the Imperial Valley of southern California, or in the air, as in the humidification of cotton-spinning mills in the Carolinas, testifies to man's recognition of atmospheric limitations.

MEASUREMENT OF TEMPERATURE. Temperature, the relative hotness or coldness of the air, is measured by instruments called *thermometers*. Our name for the instrument is derived from the Greek words *thermon,* meaning heat, and *metron,* a measure. Most commonly, these instruments are based upon the principle that bodies expand when heated and contract when cooled.

The usual thermometer consists of a spherical or capsule-shaped glass bulb to which is attached a glass tube sealed at the end away from the bulb. A very fine hole, of uniform diameter, extends the length of the glass tube. Ordinarily, the bulb is filled with either mer-

54 *THE BLANKET OF ATMOSPHERE that surrounds the earth is the basic essential for all life, whether on the tropical savanna of Venezuela* (above) *or the New England farmstead in winter* (below). (Above, *Collier from Standard Oil Co.* [N. J.] *and below, Newell Green*)

cury or normal ethyl alcohol. When heat is applied to the instrument, the liquid expands upward in the tube; cooling causes the liquid to contract back toward the bulb. The tube is marked in degrees so that one can read the temperature to which the mercury rises or sinks. Two scales of degrees of temperature are in common use, Fahrenheit and centigrade (Table 4). *Unless specifically indicated by the letter C. following the number, all temperatures used in this book are in degrees Fahrenheit.*

Table 4   SOME TEMPERATURE EQUIVALENTS IN DEGREES OF FAHRENHEIT AND CENTIGRADE

FAHRENHEIT	CENTIGRADE
100	37.8
90	32.2
80	26.7
70	21.1
60	15.6
50	10.0
40	4.4
32	0.0
30	— 1.1
20	—6.7
10	— 12.2
0	— 17.8
— 10	—23.3
— 20	—28.9

A more complicated type of temperature-measuring instrument is known as a *thermograph*. This device consists basically of two pieces of different metals welded together in a curved form. One end is fixed rigidly. As the temperature changes, the curvature of the metal strip changes, because different metals expand and contract in different amounts. A lever arm is attached to the free end of the metal strip. At the other end of the lever is a pen so placed as to record the movements of the lever arm on a cylinder which is turned by clockwork. A chart which is marked to show time (hours and days) and degrees of temperature is placed around the cylinder. The pen on the lever arm traces a line on the chart, moving in response to the expansion or contraction of the metal strip. When the chart is removed from the cylinder, there is a continuous record of temperature change.

MEASUREMENT OF PRECIPITATION. Precipitation is commonly measured by the use of an instrument called a *rain gauge*. The most common form consists of a funnel-shaped receiver to which is attached a double cylindrical container. Ordinarily, the circular lip at the top of the funnel is 8 inches in diameter. The funnel leads from this lip to the inner cylinder which is 20 inches in height and 2.53 inches in diameter. Since the *area* of the lip is just ten times that of the end of the cylinder, one inch of rain falling on the gauge will fill the cylinder to a depth of 10 inches. If more than enough falls to fill the inner cylinder, the overflow is caught in the outer one.

Measuring is done by inserting a scale, marked in inches or millimeters, into the inner cylinder. The scale is withdrawn and the depth of water read directly. This figure is divided by 10 to allow for the size of the cylinder compared with that of the funnel lip. Thus it is possible to measure amounts as small as .01 inch and 1 millimeter accurately. Table 5 gives some equivalents for inches and millimeters. *Inches are used throughout this book except where specifically noted.*

If there is water in the overflow cylinder, that remaining in the inner cylinder is measured first. Since the latter is 20 inches in height, the amount of water in it when it is full represents 2 inches of precipitation. This much must fall before any overflows. If overflow occurs, the inner cylinder remains full. When the inner cylinder has been checked, the water in it is poured out. Then that in the overflow is poured in and measured. The figure thus obtained is added to the original

2 inches. This process is continued until all of the water in the overflow receptacle has been measured.

Snow measurements are frequently made directly on the ground after the fall has taken place. Sometimes snow is gathered over a measured area, melted, and the resulting water measured. The results are, of course, far less accurate than those obtained for rain, but drifting of snow makes the use of a gauge inaccurate too.

In addition to the type described, there are several kinds of self-measuring and self-recording rain gauges. These involve rather more complicated mechanisms than do thermographs.

PRESSURE. Much less commonly appreciated as a climatic element is *atmospheric pressure*. Even air has weight, and atmospheric pressure is the force exerted against a surface by that weight. At sea level the pressure exerted by the air on the earth's surface averages 14.7 pounds per square inch.

But pressure varies from place to place and from time to time at any one place. For any given volume, warm air is light and cold air is heavy. Consequently, with high temperature, pressure is low; with low temperature, pressure is high. In addition, increase in elevation above sea level brings about decrease in pressure because the volume of air becomes less away from the earth's surface. Hence, that which remains above any specified elevation weighs less and exerts less pressure on the surface which it covers. The decrease of pressure with increased altitude proceeds slowly at low altitudes and more rapidly at higher ones. At 18,000 feet elevation, pressure averages slightly less than half that at sea level (Fig. 55).

While the slight changes of pressure common at low altitudes are seldom sensed by human beings and are thus insignificant climatic elements, the human body is not properly adjusted to the very low pressures of high altitudes. Pressure there becomes a vital element, especially in air travel. At high altitudes, the human body finds difficulty in securing enough oxygen. Since oxygen makes up about one-fifth of the whole atmosphere, it exerts about one-fifth of the total atmospheric pressure. Near sea level, the pressure and the amount of oxygen are such that the human body functions at its best. With the decrease in total pressure incident to increased altitude, there is a decrease in oxygen pressure.

Table 5 SOME EQUIVALENTS IN INCHES AND MILLIMETERS

INCHES	MILLIMETERS
.5	12.7
1.0	25.4
1.5	38.1
2.0	50.8
2.5	63.5
3.0	76.2
3.5	88.9
4.0	101.6
4.5	114.3
5.0	127.0
5.5	139.7
6.0	152.4
6.5	165.1
7.0	177.8
7.5	190.5
8.0	203.2
8.5	215.9
9.0	228.6
9.5	241.3
10.0	254.0

A deficiency of oxygen results in damage to the brain. Consequently, oxygen must be supplied artificially. The danger point is usually considered to be 15,000 feet elevation though prolonged flight above 10,000 feet requires additional oxygen supply.

WIND. For general purposes, a region or center of *high* pressure (pressure above sea-level average) may be thought of as a sort of hill in the atmosphere while a region of *low* pressure (pressure below sea-level average) may be thought of as a basin or trough. Much as water runs downhill into a valley or surface basin, so air flows from high to low pressure centers. Such a movement of air, essentially a horizontal one, is spoken of as *wind*. Obviously, the speed of flow is closely related to the rate of pressure change, or the *pressure gradient*. Wind is not a startling climatic element except where it reaches speeds capable of material destruction, as in a tropical hurricane striking Florida's east coast near a city like Miami, in a typhoon like those which lash China's southeast coast, or in the whirling fury of a Kansas tornado. Its effects, as well as those of pressure, are most significant in the control which they have over temperature and precipitation, for wind is the carrier of temperature and moisture.

MEASUREMENT OF ATMOSPHERIC PRESSURE. Pressure is measured by an instrument called a *barometer,* a word derived from the Greek *baros* meaning weight. In its simplest form, this instrument consists of a glass tube filled with some liquid and then inverted in a cup of the same liquid. If the tube is long enough, the liquid will fall away from the top, creating a vacuum. The height of the liquid in the tube is directly proportional to the atmospheric pressure exerted on the uncovered surface of the liquid in the cup.

Early barometers used water. It was found that water stood about 34 feet up the tube on the average. This meant that the atmospheric pressure was equal to that of a column of water 34 feet high. Obviously an instrument over 34 feet long was very unwieldy. Hence a heavier liquid, mercury, was substituted for water. Even with mercury, the column is about 30 inches high when measured at sea level. A mercury barometer is delicate and awkward, but very accurate measurements can be made with it. Consequently it has remained the standard for pressure measurement.

Since the column of mercury supported by the atmosphere at sea level is about 30 inches high on the average, it has become customary to say that normal sea level pressure is 30

ELEVATION IN FEET		PRESSURE	
		INCHES	MILLIBARS
80,000		.83″	28 mb
70,000	STRATOSPHERE BALLOON	1.39″	47 mb
60,000	PRESSURIZED AIRPLANE	2.17″	74 mb
50,000		3.44″	118 mb
40,000		5.54″	190 mb
30,000		8.88″	347 mb
20,000		13.75″	467 mb
10,000	MT. EVEREST	20.58″	697 mb
SEA LEVEL		29.92″	1013 mb

55

DECREASE in atmospheric pressure accompanies increase in elevation above sea level. Note relative heights of cloud (cumulo-nimbus, the type with greatest vertical development), Mt. Everest (highest known mountain peak), pressurized airplane, and stratosphere balloon.

inches. A newer unit, common in meteorological work, is the *millibar.* It is sufficient for our purposes to know the approximate relationship: 30 inches (of mercury) equals 1,016 millibars. Exact standard sea level pressure is 29.92 inches or 1,013.3 millibars. These pressures are often translated into pounds per square inch, but the use of that unit of measure has become less and less common. Some of the equivalents of pressure measurements are given in Table 6.

Because the mercury barometer is so delicate and so awkward, another type has come into more common use. Essentially, it consists of a metal box with a flexible lid. A vacuum is created in the box. For this reason, the lid responds to changes in pressure. The fluctuations of the lid's position are conveyed to a scale by means of a pointer. This type of instrument is known as an *aneroid,* meaning without fluid. Recording barometers, *barographs,* are similar to thermographs except that an aneroid replaces the curved metal strip which activates the pen on a thermograph.

MEASUREMENT OF WIND. Two measurements are common in wind observation, direction and velocity. Direction is determined by a weather vane. A rod, with a pointer at one end and a relatively wide vertical surface or plate at the other, is mounted so that it can rotate freely about a perpendicular shaft. Indicators of direction are fixed accurately on the shaft. As the wind blows, the pressure which it exerts on the vertical surface of the vane causes the pointer to swing around into the direction *from which* the wind is blowing. Thus, a *west* wind is a wind blowing *from* the west. By reference to the direction indicators, the direction of the wind can be ascertained.

Wind velocity is measured by an *anemometer,* from the Greek word *anemos,* wind. One of the most common types consists of three or four light metal cups mounted on a horizontal frame which rotates easily at the end of a vertical shaft. The difference in the effect

Table 6	SOME EQUIVALENT PRESSURE MEASUREMENTS

INCHES	MILLIBARS
27.5	931.3
28.0	948.2
28.5	965.1
29.0	982.1
29.5	999.0
30.0	1,015.9
30.5	1,032.9
31.0	1,049.8

of pressure on the inside and outside of the cups as the wind blows causes the frame to rotate. By counting the rotations, the speed of the wind can be determined in miles per hour.

A standardized scale of wind velocities has been adopted. This scale (Table 7) is called the Beaufort scale after the man who devised it.

Climatic Controls

There are many controls which act upon the climatic elements and, in so doing, produce characteristic combinations which are known as *climatic types* (Table 8). Of the many controls, those of recognized world magnitude are seven in number. They are (1) latitude, (2) land and water distribution, (3) ocean currents, (4) altitude, (5) mountain barriers, (6) pressure and winds and (7) storms. The temperature and precipitation conditions of a place are affected by each in turn. Pressure and wind, as elements, are acted upon by the other six controls. The resulting combinations are visibly observable in the forms of the land surface, the soil, the vegetation cover, and even in the features of the human scene. Numerous examples are given in later chapters. The climatic types and their distribution thus offer

Table 7   BEAUFORT SCALE OF WIND FORCE

BEAUFORT NUMBER	VELOCITY, M.P.H.	DESCRIPTION	SPECIFICATIONS
0	0-1	Calm	Smoke rises vertically.
1	1-3	Light air	Wind direction shown by smoke drift but not by waves.
2	4-7	Slight breeze	Wind felt on face; leaves rustle; ordinary wave moved by wind.
3	8-12	Gentle breeze	Leaves and twigs in constant motion; wind extends light flag.
4	13-18	Moderate breeze	Dust and loose paper, also small branches, are moved.
5	19-24	Fresh breeze	Small trees in leaf begin to sway.
6	25-31	Strong breeze	Large branches in motion; whistling in telegraph wires.
7	32-38	Moderate gale	Whole trees in motion.
8	39-46	Fresh gale	Twigs break off trees; progress generally impeded.
9	47-54	Strong gale	Slight structural damage occurs; chimney pots removed.
10	55-63	Whole gale	Trees uprooted; considerable structural damage.
11	64-75	Storm	Very rarely experienced; widespread damage.
12	Above 75	Hurricane	

Table 8   RELATION OF CLIMATIC TYPES, CONTROLS, AND ELEMENTS

		CLIMATIC CONTROLS		CLIMATIC ELEMENTS
World's climatic types	result from the action of	latitude land and water distribution ocean currents altitude mountain barriers pressure and wind storms	upon	temperature precipitation pressure and wind

clues or guides to many other distributions over the earth. Before these types can have their fullest meaning, the individual elements of which they are constituted, and the controls which those elements undergo, must be examined in their broader aspects.

ATMOSPHERIC TEMPERATURE

Source of Atmospheric Energy

The sun is the only significant source of atmospheric energy. In the form of both light and heat, that energy is essential to all life on this planet, and indirectly, to many inanimate objects as well. The sun radiates energy from its surface in all directions out into space. Most of it is lost so far as the earth is concerned. This planet is a relatively small body at a considerable distance from the sun. Hence only a very small portion, estimated at one two-billionth of the total output of solar energy, is intercepted by it. Yet that small portion is fundamental to the production of air temperatures in which living things can exist and of the light which is so essential to their growth.

Insolation

The solar radiation which is received at the surface of the earth is called *insolation*. It varies in amount from place to place over the earth's surface and from time to time at any given place. Differences in temperature and, through them, other differences in climate are thereby produced.

While the amount of insolation varies first of all with output of energy by the sun, changes resulting from this factor may be considered nonessential for our purposes in this book. The extreme variation so far observed is barely more than one per cent of the total. Similarly, variation is induced by the seasonal change in distance of the earth from the sun. The earth in January is some three million miles nearer the sun than it is in July. This causes a difference of about one per cent in the intensity of radiation, computed for the outer edge of the atmosphere, from one season to the next in any one year.

The truly significant factors are the angle of the sun's rays and the length of daylight period. The rays from the sun which reach the earth are essentially parallel to one another. Any specific group of rays (Fig. 56A) striking the earth near the equator spreads over a smaller area than another group (Fig. 56A) striking the earth near the poles. But the amount of energy is the *same* in both groups of rays. Since this energy is concentrated in the first instance and spread out in the second, the insolation *per unit of surface area* will be greater near the equator than near the poles.

Both concentration and diffusion of the sun's rays are illustrated in another way in Fig. 56B. There, A represents a group of rays striking the earth from overhead at noon and B represents the late afternoon position of the same rays. It is a common experience to look directly at the sun just prior to the time it sinks below the western horizon; it is difficult without blackened glass to look directly at the sun at noon. In the evening, no sensation of great heat is experienced even on a clear midsummer day; at noon the sensation of scorching heat accompanies the glare. The spread of the rays over a larger surface area when they come from a low angle accounts for part of the difference in effect. The thickness of atmosphere through which they penetrate is also an important factor. That thickness is about twelve times as great when the rays come from just above the horizon as it is when they come from directly overhead. Not only are the rays spread over a larger surface; they are scattered, absorbed, and reflected to a greater degree when they pass through a greater depth of atmosphere. Consequently

56 EFFECT OF ANGLE of sun's rays on insolation. Low-latitude rays (left) at A versus high-latitude rays at B. Noontime rays (right) at A versus late afternoon rays at B.

Table 9 CALCULATED VALUES OF IN-SOLATION AT THE OUTER BOUNDARY OF ATMOSPHERE AND OBSERVED VALUES AT THE EARTH'S SURFACE

(In Thousands of Calories Per Square Centimeter)

LATITUDE	OUTER BOUNDARY OF ATMOSPHERE	EARTH'S SURFACE
0	312	186
10	307	187
20	295	183
30	274	171
40	246	152
50	214	124
60	177	110
70	148	91
80	134	77
90	130	68

From a table in Helmut Landsberg, *Physical Climatology,* School of Mineral Industries, Pennsylvania State College. Copyright 1941 by Gray Printing Company, Du Bois, Pennsylvania. Reprinted by permission of Gray Printing Company.

their effectiveness when they reach the earth's surface is much diminished after a long passage through the atmosphere.

Of equal significance with the angle of the sun's rays is the length of the daylight period. Because of the movements of revolution and rotation and because of the inclination of the earth's axis, there is variation in the length of daylight period throughout the year. Along the equator, day and night are equal in length throughout the year; elsewhere over the globe, day and night are approximately equal only at the time of the equinoxes, approximately March 21 and September 21. In the Northern Hemisphere, the days are longest in late June, shortest in late December; in the Southern Hemisphere, the dates are reversed (Fig. 57).

At the period of longest day, the sun is highest in the noon sky. This means that the rays are most directly received during the same period that the sun is longest above the horizon. As a consequence, insolation during the summer months, or high-sun period, is considerably greater than during the winter, or low-sun period. The farther from the equator, the more pronounced is the seasonal rhythm insofar as it is produced by insolation.

57 *LENGTHS OF DAY and times of sunset and sunrise in the several latitudes at the two solstices.*

Distribution of Insolation

EFFECT OF LATITUDE. The net effect of all the foregoing factors of variation is an exceedingly complex distribution of insolation. In a general way, the annual total for any one latitude is constant and there is a decrease from low latitudes to high latitudes. Table

9 shows calculated values of insolation at the outer boundary of the atmosphere and observed values at the surface of the earth.

The values given in the column headed "earth's surface" are maximum values and are actually from 30 to 70 per cent less depending upon the degree of cloudiness. The greater surface insolation at 10 degrees latitude than at the equator is primarily a result of the drier air which persists there. Drier air permits a greater portion of the rays to penetrate to the surface without loss of energy on the way.

EFFECT OF DIFFERENTIAL HEATING OF LAND AND WATER. Second to latitude as a determinant of the amount of heating of the earth's surface is the nature of the surface itself. Not all materials heat at the same rate or to the same degree. The land heats very rapidly and to a high temperature since it is composed of solid materials. Common experiences on a hot summer day offer fine examples. A tar road surface which is firm and, to all appearances, quite solid in the early morning hours becomes a sticky semifluid by midday.

In contrast, the water of a lake exposed to the same sun for the same length of time is warmed only slightly. It is fluid and heats more slowly and to a lesser degree than a solid. The relief brought by an afternoon swim after a day of high temperature offers support. If the water of the lake heated to the degree that the tar pavement did, swimming would certainly be far from the pleasant pastime that it is. In part, this difference in heating results from the fact that energy received at the surface is distributed downward through a relatively thick layer of water while it is confined to a very shallow layer of the solid body. A greater volume of the water is available to absorb the energy, and, hence, there is less energy per unit of volume.

At one extreme in the scale is dry sand or bare rock; at the other, a large and deep body of water. Between these are all the variations in plant cover of the land surface and all the variations in size and depth of water bodies from the great oceans to the shallow, small-area ponds.

As a result of the differential heating and cooling of land as compared with water, the oceans of the world heat up less in summer than the land masses in the same latitudes. Likewise, in the winter, the oceans remain relatively warmer than the adjacent land

masses. Air assumes the temperature of the portion of the surface above which it lies. Consequently the regular decrease of temperature from the equator to the poles, which might be expected solely on the basis of the angle of the sun's rays and the length of the daylight period, is upset. While it is generally true that the highest temperatures occur in the low latitudes and the lowest occur in the areas nearer the poles, the pattern is not uniform.

How the Air Is Heated and Cooled

As solar energy passes through the atmosphere, only a small part of it is absorbed to warm the air. Actually, the air is heated mainly from the earth by the processes known as *radiation, conduction,* and *convection.* The same processes also operate to cause cooling of the air.

RADIATION. The energy received at the earth's surface as insolation is short-wave energy which passes readily through the atmosphere. Upon reception this energy is transformed into long-wave energy which can be absorbed readily by the atmosphere. The earth's surface becomes a radiator which heats the air. The process is called *terrestrial radiation.*

Just as the air nearest the radiator in a cool room warms most, so the air nearest the earth is heated to the greatest degree. With increased distance from the surface, the effectiveness of radiation declines. Hence, the air at low elevations is relatively warmer than that at some considerable distance above.

On the average, temperature decrease is about 3.6° F. for every 1,000 feet increase in altitude. Anyone who has been in an unheated airplane recognizes decrease of temperature with increase of altitude. While it may be very hot near the ground, it will be cold enough to require the heaviest clothing at 15,000 feet altitude. Similarly, a climb into a high mountain area in summer brings one to levels where snow remains unmelted. The hot, breathless haze hanging over Switzerland's Lake Geneva on an early August day is quickly exchanged for the clear coolness of the alpine village of Glion after a comfortable ride on the funicular railway (Fig. 58). In part, lower temperatures experienced in mountains result from the smaller amount of surface exposed to solar energy, but primarily they are a factor of distance from the main mass of the "radiator" and of the "thinner" atmosphere at high altitudes.

Regular decrease of temperature continues for approximately ten miles upward over the equator and five miles upward over the poles. At those elevations, a level, or a series of step-like levels, is reached beyond which there appears to be no appreciable drop in temperature for from twelve to fifteen miles farther upward. There is some indication that temperatures begin to increase again above this, but few direct observations are available to confirm this estimate. Most of the air, by weight, is in the lowest zone, where are also the greater part of the water vapor, the carbon dioxide, and the solid impurities.

The lowest zone is called the *troposphere* (Fig. 59). The stage at which temperatures cease to drop with increased elevation is called the *tropopause,* and the zone above is called the *stratosphere.* In the stratosphere, very low temperatures ($-112°$ F. near the equator) persist, there is little water vapor and dust, and all air movement appears to be nearly horizontal. There is no upward or downward

5 8   *TWO TYPICAL RESORT settlements—Glion at lower left and Caux at upper right—on the Alpine slopes near the eastern end of Lake Geneva, Switzerland. (Swissair)*

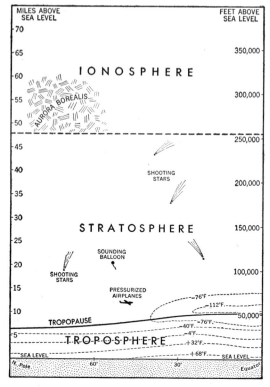

59 *GENERALIZED cross section of the lower part of the atmosphere. Note the isothermal levels in the troposphere.*

movement to cause irregularities like those common within the troposphere. Beyond the stratosphere, upward from about 50 miles above the earth, is the *ionosphere*. In this uppermost layer it is thought that temperatures may increase with distance away from the earth. Electrical phenomena like the *northern lights* occur in the ionosphere.

CONDUCTION. The second type of heat transfer from the earth to the atmosphere is *conduction*. When two bodies of different temperatures are in contact, there is a flow of heat from the warmer to the cooler until the same temperature is attained by both bodies or until the contact is broken. Again, this is a common phenomenon to most people. When a silver spoon is placed in a cup of hot coffee, the handle of the spoon becomes

too hot to hold comfortably. It is warmed by conduction from the hot coffee. When one dives into relatively cool water, the sensation of cold is in part a matter of flow of heat from the body to the water. After one has been in the water a short while, a balance is reached between skin temperature and water temperature, and the sense of cold disappears. In comparison with other heating processes, conduction plays only a small part in the heating of the atmosphere; it is significant only in that portion of the atmosphere which is in direct contact with the earth's surface.

CONVECTION. *Convection* is the third process in the heating of the atmosphere. When air is heated it expands in volume and, as a consequence, overflows aloft. This reduces the pressure which the air exerts on the heated surface and, at the same time, increases the pressure exerted by adjacent cooler air. The heavy, cooler air flows in along the surface toward the warmer, lighter column forcing the latter upward (Fig. 60). Such a circulation is called a convectional system.

On a miniature scale, convection can be observed by any smoker sitting near a lighted electric lamp. The bulb warms the air in contact with it. The air expands and overflows near the ceiling of the room increasing the weight of the air not directly in contact with the lamp or just above it. The heavier air settles in toward the lamp carrying the smoke with it. Contact with the lamp warms the air and it, in turn, moves upward only to settle back away from the column just above the lamp. The only function of the smoke is to make the air movement visible.

The boiling of water illustrates the same type of circulation. Water in a teakettle is heated by conduction from the bottom of the kettle. As it is heated, it expands and becomes lighter. The heavier water near the top sinks along the sides of the kettle and pushes the heated water upwards. Fireplaces, likewise, offer excellent examples of convectional circulation. Who has not felt the draft across the floor toward the fireplace when a fire is first lighted in a cold room?

It is by means of convectional circulation that much heat *transfer* in the atmosphere is accomplished. As a process of atmospheric heating, convection is limited to the troposphere.

Just as the processes of radiation, conduction, and convectional circulation are the major controls of air heating, so they are the main controls of air cooling. During the night when there is no receipt of solar energy at the surface, the process of earth radiation continues. The earth's surface is cooled by the continued radiation until it becomes slightly colder than the air above it. When this occurs, the air begins to lose heat to the ground as well as to outer space. Likewise, the bottom zone of air in direct contact with the cooling earth's surface becomes cooled by conduction. Where inequalities of cooling exist, convectional currents form and cool or cold air is thus imported from adjacent colder regions.

ADIABATIC HEATING AND COOLING. Inequalities in the earth's surface may cause a further type of heating or cooling in moving masses of air. When air is forced to descend, as down the slope of a mountain range, it moves from a region where atmospheric *pressure* is low to one where it is high. This movement is accompanied by compression in volume and, consequently, the air mass is heated. Similarly, when air is forced upward, it moves into regions where the pressure upon it is less. Consequently, it expands. This is accompanied by cooling. The downward movement of great masses of air is a far more commonly observed phenomenon than the upward movement.

The famous *chinook,* a wind moving with great speed down the east face of the Rocky Mountains, or the *foehn,* a down-mountain wind in the Alps, bring excessively high temperatures to the lowlands onto which they blow. Not only are they warming, but they are drying winds and they may do great dam-

60 *HEAT transfer by conduction* (left) *and by convection* (right).

age because of this feature. In many of the Swiss valleys, it is considered a criminal act to build a fire even for cooking when the foehn is blowing. In our own Great Plains, the chinook played no small part in the parching and blowing of soil in the Dust Bowl storms of the late 1930's.

ATMOSPHERIC MOISTURE

Humidity

Though the water present as a gas in the atmosphere constitutes only a small and variable percentage of the whole, yet that small amount is a very significant portion for life on this planet. Most of the gases which make up the atmosphere are present in fairly constant amounts near the earth's surface. With the exception of water vapor, the mixture of gases over the Sahara is much the same as that over the southeastern United States. The amount of water varies constantly from place to place and from time to time at any one place. Further, most of the water vapor in the total atmosphere is concentrated in the troposphere. As an invisible gas in the atmosphere, water cannot be used directly to any considerable extent by life upon the earth's surface, but when *condensation* and *precipitation* take place it does become available. Its amount, its distribution through the year, and its dependability, all combine to place definite limits upon habitability from place to place over the land surface of the earth.

SOURCE OF ATMOSPHERIC MOISTURE. By far the larger part of the moisture which is present in the atmosphere as water vapor derives from the great oceans that cover so large a portion of the earth's surface. By air movements, moisture evaporated from the oceans is carried over the land masses and there,

under certain conditions, is condensed and precipitated upon the surface. Of the water thus supplied to the land some runs off directly to the sea, some is intercepted by the vegetation, another portion sinks into the ground to become soil moisture and ground water, and part is lost by evaporation. The moisture which falls on the land supplies plants, lakes, streams, and man himself. The moisture which is evaporated from lakes and streams, and from plants may be dropped again on the land or carried by the winds to fall over the oceans and thus aid the interchange of water between the oceans and the continents (Fig. 61).

ABSOLUTE AND RELATIVE HUMIDITY. There is a certain fixed amount of water vapor which the air can contain at any given temperature.

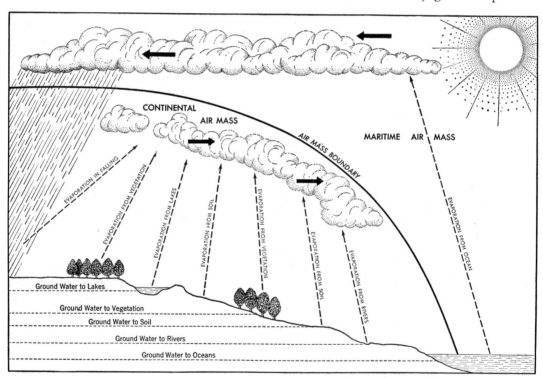

61 THE HYDROLOGIC CYCLE. *The oceans are the ultimate source of all precipitation. Moisture is evaporated from the oceans, carried inland, and precipitated. It is carried back to the oceans by evaporation, air-mass movement, and later precipitation, by running off the land as surface water, and by movement as ground water.*

This amount changes with any change of temperature as is indicated in Table 10.

Table 10   WATER VAPOR CAPACITY OF AIR AT DIFFERENT TEMPERATURES

TEMPERATURE F°	WATER VAPOR grains per cubic foot
100	19.7
90	14.7
80	10.9
70	8.0
60	5.7
50	4.1
40	2.9
30	1.9

The air is said to be *saturated* if it contains all of the water vapor possible at any given temperature. It should be noted that the capacity of the air for water vapor increases with an increase in temperature and that this capacity becomes greater at an increasing rate.

Two measurements of the moisture in the atmosphere are commonly made. There is the measurement of the actual amount or weight of water vapor per cubic foot of air; this is known as the *absolute humidity*. The other measurement is a relative one. It is the statement of the proportion of water vapor actually present to the amount which could possibly be present at a given temperature; this is known as the *relative humidity*. Relative humidity is always stated in per cent. It should be noted that *saturated* air has a relative humidity of 100 per cent.

The meaning of these various terms may be made clearer by specific examples. Suppose the temperature of a given air sample to be 70 degrees. A cubic foot of this air could hold 8 grains of water vapor (Table 10). A measurement of the actual amount in a cubic foot of the sample air shows, however, that there are only 4 grains present. Under these conditions, the *absolute* humidity is 4 grains per cubic foot; the *relative* humidity is 50 per cent—4 (the amount actually present) divided by 8 (the maximum amount the air could hold at that temperature). The air would not be saturated for it does not have in it as much water vapor as it could possibly hold at the temperature of 70 degrees.

Absolute humidity, unlike relative humidity, does not change unless some vapor is added to the air or some is taken from it. Temperature changes do not affect it *unless* there is a lowering to the point where the air becomes saturated. This point is known as the *dew point* and it is always expressed in degrees of temperature. When the dew point is reached, some of the vapor has to be removed either by deposition on some object with which the air is in contact or by condensation and precipitation.

For example, suppose the absolute humidity to be 4.1 grains per cubic foot and the temperature 80° F. If no more water is added to the air, but the temperature rises to 100° F., the absolute humidity remains 4.1 grains per cubic foot. On the other hand, suppose the temperature drops to 50° F. Then the absolute humidity is still 4.1 grains per cubic foot, all that the air can hold. Any further drop in temperature would force some of the vapor to condense and either be deposited or precipitated. Air at 50° F. with an absolute humidity of 4.1 grains per cubic foot is saturated, as a reference to Table 10 will show. The dew point of this particular sample of air is 50° F.

Generally speaking, absolute humidity is highest near the equator and over the oceans. It decreases toward the poles and toward the interiors of the large land masses. Air over the Sahara may have an absolute humidity higher than that in the British Isles, yet no surface moisture may result from it because of the high temperatures of the Sahara as opposed to the relatively low ones of the British Isles. It is likewise generally true that summer absolute humidities are higher than those of winter, for, as we have seen, air at high temperatures can hold more water vapor than can air at low temperatures.

Relative humidity varies greatly with temperature. A reference to Table 10 will show that air at 30° F. can hold only 1.9 grains of water vapor per cubic foot. If 1.9 grains are actually present in air at that temperature, the absolute humidity is 1.9 grains per cubic foot; the relative humidity is 100 per cent. Now suppose that the temperature is raised to 40° F. At that temperature, the air could hold 2.9 grains of water vapor. If no water has been added, the relative humidity at the new temperature is 65 per cent—1.9 (the amount actually present) divided by 2.9 (the amount which the air could hold). If the temperature rises to 50° F. and no more water is added, the relative humidity becomes 1.9 divided by 4.1, which is 47 per cent. On the same basis the relative humidity at 70° F. would be 24 per cent; at 80° F., 17 per cent; at 90° F., 13 per cent; and at 100° F., only 9 per cent. Thus relative humidity varies inversely with temperature; an increase of temperature brings about a decrease in relative humidity and a decrease of temperature brings about an increase of relative humidity. This relationship holds only when no additional water vapor becomes available through increased evaporation.

Condensation

PROCESS. When air is cooled, its ability to contain water vapor is reduced, or, in other words, its relative humidity is increased. Continued cooling will bring it sooner or later to a condition of 100 per cent relative humidity or saturation. If the cooling continues beyond this point, the excess of water vapor over the amount which the air can contain at the new temperature is thrown off as minute particles of water or of ice, the former if the temperature is above 32° F. and the latter if the temperature is below 32° F. This process is called *condensation* if the change is from the gas to the liquid, and *sublimation* if the change is from the gas directly to the solid form.

The amount of condensation depends upon the degree of cooling and upon the absolute humidity of the air which is being cooled. Saturated air at 90° F. contains 14.7 grains of water vapor per cubic foot. Air which is 10° F. cooler can hold only 10.9 grains per cubic foot. If the saturated air at 90° F. is cooled to 80° F., then 3.8 grains of water vapor must be condensed from each cubic foot of air. If a further cooling of 10° F. takes place, another 2.9 grains must be condensed. With still further lowering of temperature, increasingly smaller amounts are removed. It becomes obvious then that cooling of warm, moist air provides more water than that of cooler, drier air. It is for this reason that hot, summer air has greater potentialities for the production of abundant rain than does cold, winter air.

DEW AND WHITE FROST. On clear, cold nights, radiation from the earth's surface proceeds at a very rapid rate and the ground soon reaches a temperature below that of the air lying immediately in contact with it. The air in turn is chilled by radiation and conduction from it to the colder ground. When the temperature of the lower few inches of the air is brought below the dew point, condensation of moisture takes place. If the dew point is above 32° F., the condensation appears as little droplets of water and is called *dew;* if the dew point is below 32° F., moisture removed from the air appears as minute ice crystals and is known as *white frost.* Both dew and white frost collect on cold objects at the surface of the earth.

FOG. Another form of condensation is *fog.* This is no more than a mass of fine water droplets suspended in the air close to the earth's surface; in a sense, it is cloud near the ground. The water particles are condensed, but are too light to fall to the earth; rather, they float in the air and are moved about by such light winds as may occur. Condensation to form fog is brought about either by the lowering of temperature below the dew point or by the addition of water vapor so that the dew point temperature is raised. The cooling processes which cause fog are those of radiation, conduction, and mixing of warm and cold air.

CLOUDS. When the lowering of temperature to the dew point occurs mainly through movement of the air upward from the surface of the earth, the condensed particles become visible as clouds. Their forms are almost infinite and they change constantly. Yet they are good indicators of the state of the atmosphere. With increased use of the lower zones of the atmosphere by man, the study of clouds has come to be recognized as of great significance. Only a suggestion of their importance can be made in this book.

Basically, there are three major cloud forms; these are *cirroform, stratiform,* and *cumuliform.* Cirroform clouds are the filmy or feathery, wispy clouds that appear at great heights. They are usually composed entirely of ice crystals. They are fair weather clouds when scattered irregularly over the sky and, in the sunlight, they appear dazzingly white against a deep blue. When they are arranged in regular bands and appear to be heavier, they usually presage the coming of stormy weather. Stratiform clouds are sheetlike, almost without individual shapes, and usually dull gray in color. They cover the sky in a uniform layer. They are the typical winter cloud of the middle latitudes, often remaining as a leaden-gray cover over the whole sky for days at a time. They are low lying and are remarkably uniform in thickness. Neither the base nor the top of the cloud layer shows much unevenness. Cumuliform clouds are massive, rounded clouds typical of the middle latitude summer days. The base is usually quite even and of low elevation while the top appears much like a cauliflower head and may reach

elevations normal to cirrus clouds. Usually, the cumulus cloud is a fair weather form, but when, on a hot, sultry, summer afternoon, it grows to great height sending up great bulbous projections or flattening off at the top to assume the shape of an anvil, it is the indicator of sharp showers or squalls. In common parlance, it is the "thunderhead."

An international classification of clouds has been adopted by most countries and is here given for reference. The classification recognizes ten distinctive combination forms divided into four families.

Family A. High clouds—usually at elevations above 20,000 feet.
   1. Cirrus
   2. Cirro-cumulus
   3. Cirro-stratus

Family B. Middle clouds—elevations between 6,500 and 20,000 feet
   4. Alto-cumulus
   5. Alto-stratus

Family C. Low clouds—elevations from close to the surface up to 6,500 feet
   6. Strato-cumulus
   7. Stratus
   8. Nimbo-stratus

Family D. Clouds with great vertical development—bases averaging 1,600 feet and tops extending to 20,000 feet
   9. Cumulus
   10. Cumulo-nimbus

Each of these types gives definite indication of the condition of the atmosphere. For example, cirro-cumulus and cirro-stratus both occur characteristically ahead of a storm center and denote its approach. Nimbo-stratus is associated with steady rain or snow; it produces low ceilings, poor visibility, and icing conditions so that air travel is greatly handicapped. Cumulo-nimbus, the thunderhead or overgrown cumulus, is associated with violent vertical air movement, often exceeding 100 miles per hour within the cloud; it produces tremendous downpours of rain with sharp, brilliant lightning and heavy thunder, and with frequent falls of hail. The storm which accompanies it may cause great destruction and the extreme turbulence of the air within it prevents air travel or renders it extremely hazardous.

Precipitation

FORMS OF PRECIPITATION. In a meteorological sense, the term precipitation includes all forms of condensed water vapor which "fall" to the earth's surface from the atmosphere. Condensation produces six main forms of moisture in the air: dew, white frost, fog, hail, snow, and rain. Only the last three are spoken of as precipitation for they are the only ones which actually fall to the earth's surface.

Dew, white frost, and fog are of some significance as sources of usable moisture. The accumulation of water from the first two of these three forms is sufficient in many places to make notable contribution to successful agricultural land use, but by themselves these forms are very minor sources of moisture. Likewise, fog, through contact with the surface and with objects on it, does provide some moisture; far more important, however, is the handicap which fog offers to navigation, both of the oceans and of the air, and to movement overland. As producers of usable moisture, fog, dew, and white frost may have local but hardly world-wide significance.

Hail is always associated with extreme air turbulence characteristic of thunderstorms. It is rare in polar regions and in the tropics. In the former areas, thunderstorms are uncommon and hence the conditions of forma-

tion of hail are lacking. In the tropics, it is likely that such hail as may be formed in the thunderstorms melts before it reaches the ground. Hail consists of ice pellets formed in concentric layers alternately of clear hard ice and of soft white ice in which there are air bubbles. The pellets are formed in the higher parts of a cumulo-nimbus cloud. As the frozen drops fall through the cloud, they collect a coating of water. Because of the terrific updraft of air in the cloud, the water-coated pellets are tossed back upward and the water is frozen to form a concentric layer about the original nucleus. The opaque nature of the new coating results from extreme rapidity of freezing. As the heavier pellet drops back again toward the earth, it collects still more water on its surface and the freezing process is repeated. Thus the hailstone grows larger until its weight overcomes the lifting power of the upward-moving air within the cloud. Then it falls from the cloud toward the earth. Its size when it reaches the surface depends in large part upon the temperature and relative humidity of the air through which it falls; sometimes it melts entirely and at other times it may reach the surface still of sufficient size to do great damage. Hailstones of four inches diameter and with a weight of two pounds have frequently been recorded, but more commonly they are of smaller size. As a major source of moisture, hail may be overlooked, but as a destructive agent, particularly of crops, it is important. Since it is an accompaniment of thunderstorms, it is largely significant as a summer phenomenon of the middle latitudes.

It is from *rain* and *snow* that the greatest amount of moisture is supplied to the earth's surface. Rain results from the coalescence of water droplets within clouds. The individual droplets are so light that they float within the cloud, but when they are combined the weight becomes sufficient to make them drop toward the earth. Temperatures in the air through which they fall may be high enough to cause their evaporation before they reach the surface. This phenomenon is quite common in deserts where the very low relative humidity of the air gives it the power of rapid evaporation and there may be "rainstorms without rain." In humid lands, the air is more frequently near the saturation point and, consequently, the rain once formed normally falls to the surface of the earth.

Snow results from the condensation of water vapor at temperature below 32° F. Minute ice particles thus formed unite to produce snow crystals which have sufficient weight to fall from the cloud. If the air through which the flakes descend does not have a temperature near freezing, they may be melted and reach the surface as rain.

Ordinarily about twelve inches of snow provides the same amount of moisture as one inch of rain. If the snow is very fine and powdery, more will be required, whereas if it is large-flaked and moist, even partially melted as it falls, as little as four inches will provide the equivalent of one inch of rain.

MAJOR CAUSES OF PRECIPITATION. Precipitation in any form results only when air has been cooled *below* the dew point and *after* condensation has occurred. In the form of rain and snow, moisture falls to the earth's surface from clouds. Clouds result from the condensation of moisture in air which is at a considerable altitude. In other words, rain and snow can occur only as the result of cooling provided when a large volume of air rises from the surface of the earth. There are three ways in which this can happen. These are by convection, by the opposition of air masses of different temperature, and by the imposition of a barrier across which wind must blow. As has previously been stated, air moving upward in a convectional system expands. This expansion is accompanied by cooling. If the cooling is sufficient, condensation occurs and precipitation results. When two masses of air of different temperature come in contact with each other, the cooler mass tends to stick to the surface because of its greater weight and the warmer mass is forced to move up over it. Again the upward movement brings about expansion and cooling of the rising air. If these processes continue long enough, precipitation results. Finally, if air moves against a mountain range, it is forced to rise with accompanying expansion and cooling. Precipitation results if the cooling is great enough. These three types of precipitation are called respectively *convectional, cyclonic* or *frontal,* and *orographic.*

The amount of precipitation caused by these three major forms of rising air depends upon the moisture content of the air, its temperature when it begins to ascend, and the height to which it is forced to rise. Warm, moist air is buoyant. It can therefore be forced upward more easily and, when it does rise, the dew point is quickly attained. Thus, warm, moist air provides greater possibilities of heavy precipitation than does cooler, drier air.

Because of the rapidity with which air rises in a convectional system, the precipitation which results is usually more torrential than any other type. Since convectional systems are rarely very extensive, convectional precipitation is usually local and of short duration. Thunderstorm rain is frequently, though not always, of this type. The type is most common in the tropics and in the continental interiors of the middle latitudes. Both of these locations are areas of intense surface heating. In the tropics, intense heating persists throughout the year, but, in the continental interiors of the middle latitudes, it is restricted to the summer season.

Cyclonic or frontal precipitation is usually less heavy within short periods of time than is convectional. The rise of warm air over cold commonly proceeds less rapidly than that in a convectional system. At the same time, the area over which this type of rising persists is usually greater and consequently the precipitation is usually more widespread. Likewise, it persists for longer periods of time. It is this type of rain which is most common in the middle latitudes for reasons which will be amplified in a later chapter.

Orographic precipitation is local or widespread, largely depending upon the size of the barrier which is encountered and the steadiness of the winds which cross it. In the tropics where winds are dominantly from the east, this type of precipitation is most common on eastern coasts and on east-facing mountain slopes; in the middle latitudes, it is most common on west coasts and west-facing mountain slopes because the winds of these latitudes are dominantly from the west.

....

CHAPTER OUTLINE

Elements and controls of climate

Significance of the atmosphere to man
  Composition of the atmosphere
  Climatic elements
    Temperature and precipitation
    Measurement of temperature
    Measurement of precipitation
    Pressure
    Wind
    Measurement of atmospheric pressure
    Measurement of wind
  Climatic controls
Atmospheric temperature
  Source of atmospheric energy
  Insolation
  Distribution of insolation
    Effect of latitude
    Effect of differential heating of land and
      water
  How the air is heated
    Radiation
    Conduction
    Convection
    Adiabatic heating and cooling
Atmospheric moisture
  Humidity
    Source of atmospheric moisture
    Absolute and relative humidity
  Condensation
    Process
    Dew and white frost
    Fog
    Clouds
  Precipitation
    Forms of precipitation
    Major causes of precipitation

REVIEW QUESTIONS

1. Why should geography concern itself with the elements and controls of climate?
2. Give some examples from your own experience of the appreciation of climatic elements by the ordinary person.
3. Suggest some ways in which atmospheric pressure is important in everyday life.
4. What causes wind?
5. How do climatic controls differ from climatic elements?
6. Explain why insolation varies in amount from place to place over the earth's surface and from time to time at any given place.
7. In what way does the distribution of land and water affect insolation? How is this significant to the ordinary person?
8. How do the troposphere, stratosphere, and ionosphere differ from one another? Of what significance are these differences to man?
9. Discuss the whole process of heating of the earth's atmosphere.
10. How does adiabatic heating differ from other kinds of heating?
11. Explain how the chinook played an important part in the Dust Bowl storms of the 1930's.
12. What is the source of atmospheric moisture? Since the source is a single one, suggest some of the reasons why water is abundantly available in some parts of the world and not in others.
13. From the point of view of human beings, which is most noticeable, absolute or relative humidity? Why should this be so?
14. Tell how temperature change affects relative humidity. Give examples from your own experience.
15. How is the water which exists as vapor in the atmosphere made available for use by man? In this connection, what is the basic idea behind rainmaking experiments of the present day?

16. Of what conceivable use is dew? Explain.
17. What is the difference between fog and cloud?
18. Suggest some ways in which cloud forms may be good indicators for weather forecasting.
19. What matters help to determine whether precipitation will be in the form of hail, snow, or rain?
20. Can one expect hail to be more common during one season of the year than during another? If so, why? If not, why not?
21. During any period of precipitation, what might indicate whether the precipitation was convective, cyclonic, or orographic?
22. What kind of atmospheric condition is most likely to produce precipitation? In arriving at and stating your answer, consider *all* of the climatic elements.

SOME SUGGESTED REFERENCES

Berry, F. A.; Bollay, E.; and Beers, Norman R., *Handbook of Meteorology,* McGraw-Hill, 1945. A technical reference work of practical and theoretical meteorological information; fundamental theory, weather analysis, and forecasting.

Donn, William L., *Meteorology with Marine Applications,* McGraw-Hill, 1946. An exceptionally clear statement of meteorological principles; stresses application of these principles to marine matters in the last few chapters.

Landsberg, Helmut, *Physical Climatology,* School of Mineral Industries, The Pennsylvania State College, 1941. Especially useful for its discussion of the collection and use of climatic data, and for its suggestions concerning applied climatology.

Petterssen, Sverre, *Introduction to Meteorology,* McGraw-Hill, 1941. A thorough, technical study of meteorological principles.

Trewartha, Glenn T., *An Introduction to Weather and Climate,* 2nd ed., McGraw-Hill, 1943. A standard text with a distinctly geographic point of view.

62   *STORMY WINDS* roughen the surface of the North Atlantic Ocean. Of all the elements of climatic control, the sea is one of the greatest. (Corsini, Standard Oil Co. [N. J.])

CHAPTER 6

Climatic Elements over the World

··

The significance of the climatic elements to man results from their distribution or arrangement over the earth. Some places, like the lowlands of the East Indies, are hot the year round; other places, like much of the United States, are hot during part of the year and cold during the other. Similarly, some places, like the coast of British Columbia, are very wet, and other places, like Sonora in Mexico, are very dry. What the distribution of the climatic elements over the earth is, along with some consideration of the causes of those distributions, is essential to an understanding of the human habitat.

WORLD DISTRIBUTION OF TEMPERATURE

Isothermal Maps

The best means of showing the distribution of temperatures over the earth is the *isothermal* map. An isotherm is a line connecting points of equal temperature. The temperatures shown may be those for any specific time or they may be averages or means for any stated period. A commonly used period is the month. Means for January and July offer a measure of temperatures at the height of opposite seasons of the year. Hence,

they illustrate the extremes of the year from place to place over the world. In addition, they may be used to indicate the effects of some of the climatic controls.

Effects of Some of the Climatic Controls upon Temperature Distribution

MEAN MONTHLY TEMPERATURE DISTRIBUTION: JANUARY AND JULY. Fig. 63 is a world isothermal map showing actual mean temperatures for January; Fig. 64, for July. On both of these maps, the isotherms are seen to follow roughly an east-west direction. In other words, temperatures are arranged generally in belts of latitude with highest averages near the equator in Middle and South America, Africa, Arabia, India, the East Indies, and Australia. Averages become progressively lower both northward and southward from those areas. Essentially, the control of *latitude* is that of determining the amount of insolation. As we have seen, the angle of the sun's rays and the length of the daylight period combine to make insolation greatest in the low latitudes and least in the high latitudes. If there were no other variables, no other climatic controls, this would result in a regular gradation of air temperatures from the equator to the poles.

63 *WORLD DISTRIBUTION of temperatures. Actual average temperatures for January.*

The greatest departure from the regular east-to-west trend of the isotherms occurs where they pass from the land to the sea. This is primarily a reflection of the control of *land and water distribution*. The differential heating of those two kinds of surface is responsible for air temperature differences (see pages 82 ff.).

On the January map (Fig. 63) it can readily be seen that the highest temperatures occur over the land masses lying across the equator or in the Southern Hemisphere. During that month, the greater part of Australia falls within the area having temperatures over 80° F.; in the northwestern part of that continent, a small area averages over 90° F. Two areas in the interior of South America and a small area on the "nose" of that continent exhibit temperatures over 80° F. In Africa, a narrow strip along the Guinea coast and another along the central eastern coast likewise have a monthly mean over 80° F.

During the same month, extremes of low temperature are found over the Northern Hemisphere land masses. Northeast Asia exhibits the lowest mean with a considerable area where the temperature is below −40° F.! Over the Greenland icecap and over the far northern portion of North America, sub-zero temperatures are the rule.

On the July map (Fig. 64) notable changes are evidenced. The highest temperatures are no longer mainly in the Southern Hemisphere, but over the Northern Hemisphere instead. Northwestern Mexico and adjacent sections of southwestern United States stand out as a hot zone in the Americas, along with southeastern United States, the Caribbean, and the east coast of Middle America. Through most of the Sahara and on eastward through lowland Arabia, most of India, the coastal districts of southeastern Asia, and the nearby islands stretches a like zone of great heat. Regions of intense cold have all but disappeared from the Northern Hemisphere, only interior Greenland remaining as a cold center; and Antarctica has appeared as the center of the cold zone of the Southern Hemisphere, much colder than it was in January. Migration of the temperature belts with the seasons is thus demonstrated. The controls of *latitude* and of *land and water distribution* are evident.

64 *WORLD DISTRIBUTION of temperatures. Actual average temperatures for July.*

Another fact of distribution is illustrated by the courses of the isotherms. The January map shows the distinct bend of the isotherms toward the equator over the land masses of the Northern Hemisphere and the July map shows the poleward bend over the land masses of the Northern Hemisphere at that season. In the Southern Hemisphere, the directions are reversed. Also, extremes of temperature, no matter what the season, always occur over the land masses. Here again, the facts are primarily reflections of the control of *land and water distribution.*

The effect of *ocean currents* upon temperature is also demonstrated. The distinct poleward bend of the isotherms off *higher latitude west coasts,* especially off the coast of southern California during July (Fig. 64) are indicators. Off the British Isles and the Norwegian coast, the Gulf Stream, or the North Atlantic Drift as it is known in those latitudes, carries relatively warm water well northward of its usual position. Relatively high air temperatures are thus maintained. Similarly, off the California coast, the California Current brings relatively cold water southward from

the North Pacific and air temperatures are consequently lowered.

Finally, regardless of season, there is less deviation from the latitudinally arranged belts of temperature in the Southern Hemisphere than in the Northern. The Southern Hemisphere is chiefly water and this condition makes for greater uniformity. If it were all water, the deviation would be still less. Again the control of *land and water distribution* is evidenced.

SEASONAL AND HEMISPHERIC TEMPERATURE DIFFERENCES. To illustrate some of the changes from season to season and some of the differences between the hemispheres, certain isotherms should be followed in detail. The one indicating the average of 32° F. brings out the essentials. On the western side of North America, the January map shows that the mean of 32° F. for that month is encountered first of all well out along the chain of the Aleutian Islands (Fig. 63). From that position, it bends slightly northward across the Gulf of Alaska to intersect the coast just north of Sitka. The January mean temperature at Sitka is 32.4° F. A pronounced southward bend brings the isotherm well within the United States, around the southern end of the Rocky Mountains. On the eastern plains, it passes a little south of St. Louis, where the January average is 31.6° F. Toward the east coast, the isotherm turns slightly northward again to leave the continent just south of New York, where the January average is 30.6° F. Once off the land, the course of the isotherm is turned sharply northeastward over the Atlantic to cut just south of Iceland and to strike the European coast north of 60° latitude. On the land, the direction is again changed; the isotherm bends southward through coastal Norway, Denmark, Germany, and into southeastern France. There, it assumes an eastward direction through northern Italy, along the Dalmatian coast, through the Balkans, and across the northern part of the Black Sea. It passes a little south of the center of the Caspian Sea, and so on still eastward to the coast of China. It leaves this coast just south of Tsingtao where the January mean is 31.7° F. Once again the isotherm has a northeasterly trend across southern Korea and the northern end of the largest part of Japan, the island of Honshu, and on across the North Pacific to the outer Aleutians.

This isotherm sets the pattern for all winter isotherms in the Northern Hemisphere. Over the continents, it bends southward or equatorward; over the oceans, it bends northward or poleward. This characteristic is in part explained by the differential heating of land and water; the large areas of land in these latitudes of the Northern Hemisphere become very cold during the period of least insolation, while the water bodies retain heat. The very pronounced poleward bends off the west coasts, like those along the western coast of Europe of the Alaskan-British Columbian coast of North America, are in large part accounted for by the flow of warm ocean currents. These currents have a considerable warming effect upon the air which moves over them; the higher temperatures of low latitudes are thus carried well northward along the courses of the currents.

At the opposite time of year, the individual isotherms in the Northern Hemisphere show quite a different pattern. The isotherm of 60° F. for July illustrates the characteristic behavior (Fig. 64). Beginning near the west coast of North America almost at San Francisco, where the July average is 58.9° F., this isotherm follows sharply northward, paralleling the coast and only a short distance inland to reach well into northern Alberta and Saskatchewan in Canada. There it reverses its direction and extends southeastward across the rest of the continent to leave the coast in the Gaspé Peninsula. Offshore, it makes a sharp loop southward off the New England coast. It follows a nearly true east-west course across most of the width of the Atlantic along the forty-fifth parallel of latitude. Through the British Isles and onto the Scandinavian Peninsula, it reaches to higher and higher latitudes until, across most of Siberia, it follows nearly along the Arctic Circle. From this northernmost position, it turns abruptly southward to leave the Asiatic land mass just north of the mouth of the Amur River. Another abrupt southward curve brings it across Hokkaido, the northernmost island of Japan. Over most of the Pacific, the isotherm assumes an east-west trend along 40° latitude until, some distance off the California shore, it makes a final southward bulge before turning northward onto the land.

The summer isotherms of the Northern Hemisphere bend well northward or poleward over each of the land masses; over the oceans, they are relatively straight. The pattern over the land is the reverse of that of the winter period. Over the seas, where there is any departure from an east-west line, that departure is toward the equator. This is likewise the reverse of the winter tendency. The higher temperatures, latitude for latitude, over the land in this season are the result mainly of differential heating of land and water. The sharp equatorward bends of the isotherms over the oceans, like that off the New England shore (Fig. 64), result primarily from the presence of cold currents. These cold currents are found off west coasts in the latitudes between 20 and 40 degrees and off the east coasts poleward of 40 degrees.

In the Southern Hemisphere, it should be noted that the isotherms have a more nearly constant east-west trend regardless of season. Tendencies toward an equatorward bend over land in winter and a poleward bend over land in summer are best evidenced in Australia. Africa and South America show some of the same trend especially in July, their winter period. Neither of those continents imposes any considerable width to interrupt the great expanse of water in the Southern Hemisphere. There is more uniformity of heating surface in that hemisphere and hence the ordinary contrasts of differential heating of land and water are masked by other controls of temperature.

SEA-LEVEL EQUIVALENT TEMPERATURES. In order to demonstrate more clearly some of the controls of temperature distribution, it is sometimes desirable to construct isothermal maps on the basis of temperatures reduced to sea-level equivalents. This procedure does away with temperature differences which are caused by altitude changes from place to place. Effects of other controls, like latitude, land and water distribution, and ocean currents, in determining the distribution of temperature are emphasized.

An example of the use of sea-level temperatures instead of actual ones is shown in Fig. 65. On the left side, the January sea-level isotherms are shown for a portion of North America; on the right is a map of the actual January averages taken from Fig. 63. Notice that on both maps the isotherms bend generally equatorward as they cross the continent. They appear as smoothly bending lines on the map showing reduced temperatures, but, on the map of actual temperatures, they are irregular in detail. The effect of altitude is clearly shown both in the Rocky Mountain area and in the much lower Appalachian zone in the east. On the sea-level temperature map, the 20° F. isotherm never reaches as far south as the forty-fifth parallel of latitude. Actual temperatures show an average of 20° F. well

65 *COMPARISON of the pattern of actual isotherms and that of sea-level equivalent isotherms. Note the greater irregularity and the more southerly position of the isotherms showing actual temperatures, especially in the western part of the continent where altitude is greater and is, therefore, a more prominent control.*

MEAN
ANNUAL
TEMPERATURE
RANGE (Deg. F.)
(After Haurwitz and Austin, Plate III)

Sinusoidal equal-area projection

66 *GENERALIZED map of mean annual temperature range over the world.*

southward along the Rocky Mountains into New Mexico. On the sea-level map, the isotherm of 60° F. crosses through Lower California, northern Mexico, and south-central Florida, but on the map of actual temperatures, that temperature is carried southward around Lower California and around the highland area of Mexico.

Though sea-level equivalent temperatures sharpen the demonstration of temperature controls, they fail to show the real climatic state. Their use geographically is thus extremely limited.

TEMPERATURE RANGE. Isothermal maps showing actual temperatures for January and July (Figs. 63 and 64) make clear the fact that seasonal changes in temperature vary markedly over the world. The difference in degrees between the average temperatures of the warmest and coldest months of the year is called the *average annual temperature range*.

Smallest ranges between warmest and coldest months are encountered near the equator (Fig. 66) and at high altitudes. Largest ranges are encountered at low elevations in the interiors of great land masses in the higher latitudes. The greatest seasonal temperature differences occur in the Northern Hemisphere because of the great extent of land in the higher latitudes of that hemisphere. The smallest temperature differences on land occur along windward coasts near the equator and in tropical high mountains. In the latter locations, both the effect of nearly constant insolation the year round and of high altitude are operative. Over large water bodies the temperature range is relatively low and, where winds blow onshore from the oceans, the tempering effect of large water bodies is found to exist, not only along the immediate shore but also for varying distances inland.

Specifically, ranges vary from less than 5° on the equator to over 110° in interior Asia. For example, the range at Manaus, on the Amazon in Brazil, is about 3°; that at Verkhoyansk in northeastern Siberia is nearly 119°.

WORLD DISTRIBUTION OF PRESSURE AND WIND

Major Function of Wind

Wind is significant among the climatic elements primarily as an agent of transport. In any part of the United States a south wind is associated commonly with warmth; a north wind is associated with cold. This is true throughout the Northern Hemisphere. Conditions are reversed in the Southern Hemisphere; there, a south wind is relatively cold and a north wind, relatively warm. Wind, the horizontal movement of the atmosphere, is thus recognizably an agent in the movement of temperature. In a similar fashion, people in the eastern United States usually associate an east wind with rain. Thus, the function of wind as a transport agent for moisture is exemplified. But the cause of wind is difference in atmospheric pressure between adjacent regions. Hence, before any detailed understanding of wind systems can be acquired, the distribution of pressure over the earth must be sketched.

World Distribution of Pressure

ISOBARIC MAPS. As was explained previously, pressure tends to be lower than normal in areas of great heating and higher than normal in areas of little heating. While this is not the only factor in pressure determination, it is one of the most important. The distribution of pressure over the earth is best shown by maps similar to those presenting the distribution of temperature. Like isothermal maps, they may be drawn for any particular period or for any one time. The lines which appear on a pressure map connect points of equal pressure. They are called *isobars*. Since there is such a close relationship between temperature and pressure, it is desirable to consider isobaric maps for the January and July periods as was done for isothermal maps. These are Figs. 67 and 68. On both maps, sea-level equivalents of pressure are shown.

WORLD PRESSURE BELTS. On both isobaric maps, it will be noted that a zone of low pressure exists generally along the equator. This corresponds closely to the zone of greatest heating. The low pressure can be ascribed completely to the high temperatures which exist throughout the zone. Near the margins of the low latitudes, it can likewise be seen that there exists either a series of high pressure zones over the oceans or a continuous band of high pressure linking together the oceanic highs and widening materially over the continents. Closer examination will reveal that the highs exist separately over the oceans during the period which is summer in their hemisphere and are linked together across the land during the winter.

In addition to the seasonal change just suggested, it should be noted that the pressure belts shift slightly equatorward in the winter and slightly poleward during the summer. For example, the January map (Fig. 67) shows that the belt of high pressure over the North Atlantic centers about 30° North latitude whereas the July map (Fig. 68) indicates a center at nearly 40° North latitude. This seasonal shift of pressure belts corresponds moderately closely with seasonal changes in heating which result from the migration of the sun's vertical rays.

The existence of the highs over the oceans near the margins of the low latitudes cannot be accounted for solely on a basis of temperature. They are partially the result of earth rotation. But the connecting wide bands over the land areas in winter are essentially the result of continental cooling at that season and the lows which separate the oceanic highs during summer are essentially the result of continental heating in that season.

Still farther poleward, there is a second zone of low pressure. This is much more intense in the Southern Hemisphere than in the Northern, largely because in that hemisphere there is no alternation of land and water in

67 *WORLD DISTRIBUTION of mean atmospheric pressures for January. Areas of high pressure are shaded.*

these latitudes. Finally, about the poles there is presumed to be, in each instance, a polar high pressure area which expands in the winter (January in the Northern Hemisphere and July in the Southern) and contracts in the summer.

There are thus seven general belts of definitely low or high pressure: (1) an equatorial belt of low pressure, (2) a northern and (3) a southern subtropical high pressure zone, (4) a northern and (5) a southern subpolar low pressure zone, and (6) an Arctic and (7) an Antarctic high pressure zone. In a cross section or profile (Fig. 69) of any one meridian, the lows appear as troughs and the highs as ridges. The slope from any high to an adjacent low brings about a flow of air from the ridges into the troughs, and thus definite wind belts may be distinguished.

World Wind System

From the subtropical highs, both of the Northern and Southern Hemispheres, surface air moves toward the equator and toward the subpolar lows. From the polar highs, surface air flows toward the subpolar lows. There are thus created three wind belts in each hemisphere. These are the *Trades,* the *Prevailing Westerlies,* and the *Polar Winds.*

Between the Trades and the Prevailing Westerlies, in each hemisphere, there is a zone of light, variable winds and calms known as the *Horse Latitudes.* Between the Trades of the Northern Hemisphere and those of the Southern Hemisphere lies another belt of light, variable winds and calms known as the *Doldrums.*

There are in all, then, nine wind belts. These are indicated in Table 11.

CORIOLIS FORCE. If pressure differences alone controlled wind directions, those flowing from the subtropical highs toward the equator would be directly from the north in the Northern Hemisphere and directly from the south in the Southern Hemisphere. The rotation of the earth, however, exerts a deflective force on all moving bodies on its surface. That force is exerted to the *right of*

68   *WORLD DISTRIBUTION of mean atmospheric pressures for July. Areas of high pressure are shaded.*

Table 11   WIND BELTS OF THE WORLD

APPROXIMATE LATITUDE	WIND BELT
90°-60° N.	Polar Winds
60°-35° N.	Prevailing Westerlies
Centering on 30° N.	Horse Latitudes
25°-5° N.	Trades
5° N.-5° S.	Doldrums
5°-25° S.	Trades
Centering on 30° S.	Horse Latitudes
35°-60° S.	Prevailing Westerlies
60°-90° S.	Polar Winds

the direction of movement in the Northern Hemisphere and to the *left of the direction of movement* in the Southern Hemisphere. It is commonly called the *Coriolis force* after the French mathematician who first formulated a statement of it.

MAJOR WIND BELTS. As a result of the Coriolis force, winds moving toward the equator in the Northern Hemisphere are northeasterly or easterly rather than northerly. In the Southern Hemisphere, since the deflection is opposite to that in the Northern Hemisphere, that is, to the left instead of to the right, similar equatorward moving winds are dominantly southeasterly. There are two belts of equatorward moving winds, one in each hemisphere. They are known as the *Trades* or Trade Winds (Fig. 70). They are the least interrupted of any of the world wind belts and are consequently the most regular and persistent of any winds.

The winds flowing from the subtropical highs to the subpolar lows in each hemisphere are the *Prevailing Westerlies*. In the Southern Hemisphere where practically uninterrupted ocean circles the globe in the latitudes where these winds blow, they are persistent throughout the year and they blow from nearly a due west direction. Any description of "rounding the Horn" at the southern tip of South America, or Saint-Exupéry's marvelous description of air flight off the Patagonian coast in his book *Night Flight,* attest to the wildness and storminess of this wind belt. In the Northern Hemisphere where large land masses break the continuity of the subpolar low and impose frictional blocks to the clean sweep of these winds, the Westerlies are much more variable both in strength and in direction. During the winter months when the subpolar lows are best developed over the North Atlantic and the North Pacific, storminess on those bodies approaches the ferocity of the southern belt of Westerlies (Fig. 62).

The *Polar Winds* of each hemisphere are less well-known, but, since they blow toward the equator, rotational deflection makes "easterlies" of them. Their strength and blusteriness are attested by frequent references in all accounts of polar exploration and by motion picture record. The films of the Army operation "Muskox" carried out in 1946 and those of the Byrd Antarctic Expeditions indicate, in a manner that leaves no doubt, the intensity and persistence of these winds.

OCEANIC WIND CIRCULATION. But the deviations from this simple belted arrangement are so numerous as nearly to obscure the whole

69 *CONVENTIONALIZED PRESSURE profile along any meridian, indicating location of high and low pressure zones and of resulting wind belts.*

pattern. During the summer in each hemisphere, the subtropical belt of high pressure is broken; oceanic high pressure and continental low pressure centers take its place. From the highs, winds blow outward in all directions. The Coriolis force converts the outward draft into a huge whirl about the ocean basins. These whirls proceed in a clockwise direction in the Northern Hemisphere and in a counterclockwise direction in the Southern Hemisphere.

Actually, the half of the whirl toward the equator is the zone of Trades while that toward the poles is the zone of Prevailing Westerlies. Thus during the summer season there is a continuity between the two belts which is absent in the winter half of the year. On the western sides of the ocean basins, winds flow from the Trade Wind belt generally poleward, deflecting more and more until they become the Westerlies. On the eastern sides of the ocean basins, the Westerlies turn more and more equatorward until they eventually become Trades. Low pressure developed over the continents during summer has the general effect of bringing about an indraft of air toward the continent and, thus, of strengthening the continuity between Trades and Westerlies.

The actual prevailing winds over the oceans for the months of January and July are shown on Figs. 71 and 72. These figures should be compared with Fig. 70. On Figs. 71 and 72 the arrows point in the direction toward which the wind is blowing. The length of the arrows indicates the relative persistency of the wind and the thickness indicates the relative strength. It should be noted that the Trades are generally persistent in both seasons and that the Prevailing Westerlies are strongest in the winter season.

MONSOONS. Where a continental mass is sufficiently large, the tendency toward air movement inland during the summer becomes so strong as to upset the Trade Wind and Prevailing Westerly circulation completely. Asia offers the best example. On that con-

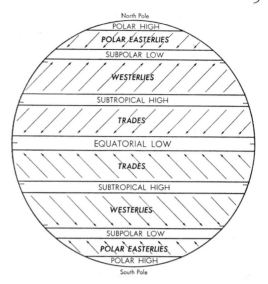

70 *CONVENTIONALIZED dia-gram of world pressure and wind belts, assuming uniformity of the earth's surface. The distribution of land and water causes notable departures from this simplified plan.*

tinent, the most intense of all continental lows develops during the April-to-September period. Opposite Asia in the Southern Hemisphere, at the same season, is an intense subtropical high. Winds coming off the Southern Hemisphere high and flowing toward the equator start as southeasterly Trades (Fig. 73). The pressure gradient toward India is sufficiently great to cause a flow of these Trades across the equator. When they move from the Southern Hemisphere into the Northern Hemisphere, the Coriolis force upon them is reversed (Fig. 73). The winds curve to blow in toward India from the *southwest* where ordinarily the *southeasterly* Trades would be expected. During the winter season, the strongest high pressure system in the world is built up over Asia; it is opposed by an intense low over northern Australia and the East Indies. The pressure gradient is southward across the equator and the outblowing northeasterly winds from India are moved into the Southern Hemisphere. Their

71 *THE ACTUAL PREVAILING wind pattern over the oceans during January. Note the well-developed counter-clockwise circulation over the* southern *hemisphere oceans. Compare with Figs. 70 and 72.*

72 *THE ACTUAL PREVAILING wind pattern over the oceans during July. Note the well-developed clockwise circulation over the* northern *hemisphere oceans. Compare with Figs. 70 and 71.*

MONSOONAL CIRCULATION
FOR JANUARY

MONSOONAL CIRCULATION
FOR JULY

Arrows fly with the wind
Length denotes measure of steadiness
The darker the arrows the greater the force

73 *MONSOONAL WIND pattern in opposite seasons. Outblowing monsoon in January is much weaker and much less constant than inblowing monsoon in July.*

deflection is reversed and they become *north-westerlies* where the belt of *southeasterly* Trades would be expected.

The seasonal indraft and outdraft of winds from a continent, like those over southern and eastern Asia, is known as a *monsoon*. Monsoons are well developed only along the southern and eastern Asiatic coast, the East Indies, northern Australia, and the westward bulge of Africa. Elsewhere, the upset to general atmospheric circulation is not sufficiently intense or sufficiently persistent to warrant recognition as a true monsoon. All continents cause a monsoonal tendency, but seldom does that tendency dominate the air movements for a whole season or for the year.

THE INTERTROPICAL FRONT. Between the belts of Trades in each hemisphere, there is a zone of very light and irregular surface winds and calms. This is known as the Doldrums. It is in this zone that air is rising from the surface, partially as a result of the high temperatures which exist near the equator, and partially as the result of slight differences between the mass of air flowing in from

the northeast and that from the southeast, the Northeast and Southeast Trades. Slight inequalities in heating, and hence in density, cause one mass to be forced upward over the other. Where active rising, or pushing upward, of air is going on, there exists what is frequently called the *Intertropical front*.

The term *front* is used to mean the surface between bodies of air of observably different quality, as for example between a body of cold, dry air containing little dust and another containing very warm, moist air with many dust particles. In a sense, a front in the atmosphere is like the surface which divides oil from water when those two liquids are poured into the same container. They do not mix, but a contact surface is formed with water on one side and oil on the other. Whether the rising of air in the zone between the Trade Wind belts is convectionally induced or whether it is brought about by action along an intertropical front, the end result is an upward movement leading to expansion, cooling, and condensation with attendant clouds and precipitation.

FRONTS AND
TEMPERATURES
TYPICAL OF
COLD WAVE CONDITIONS

▲▲▲ Cold Front

●●● Warm Front

Below 0°   0°-32°   Over 32°

0   200   400   600
Miles

74   *DURING THE WINTER season when a cold front pushes its way southward across Canada and the United States into the Gulf of Mexico, the low temperatures back of the front produce what is called a cold wave. Based on the U. S. Daily Weather Map for December 6, 1949.*

THE POLAR FRONT. Again in the middle latitudes, there are two belts of opposing winds, the Westerlies and the Polar Winds. In this instance, there is direct opposition, for the former are from a westerly direction and the latter from an easterly direction. In addition, the Westerlies are relatively warm since they come from the low latitudes, while the Polar Winds are cold. A distinct front, called the *Polar front,* is formed.

Lack of constancy of either the Westerlies or the Polar Winds causes a wavelike fluctuation in the position of the Polar front; at one time, the Polar Winds are stronger and a mass of cold air pushes well equatorward into the Westerlies; at another time, the Westerlies may be stronger, and a mass of warm air pushes well poleward. When the cold air is advancing equatorward, the front is spoken of as a *cold front;* when the warm air is advancing poleward, the front is spoken of as a *warm front.* On a weather map a cold front is always represented by a line to which are attached triangles pointing in the direction of movement. A warm front is represented by a line to which are attached semicircles rounded in the direction of movement (Fig. 74). Along both types of front, air is being forced upward with an end result of cloud formation and precipitation of moisture.

During the winter when the Polar Winds blow farther equatorward than at any other period of the year, cold front conditions carry freezing temperatures south into the Gulf of

Mexico (Fig. 74). The newspapers tell of the cold wave and thus emphasize the role of the polar portion of this zone of opposition. In summer, the similar emphasis upon the warm front conditions draws attention to a heat wave (Fig. 75). Both elements are present in both seasons, but the fluctuation seasonally of the position of the Polar front makes people in the United States more subject to the effects of one side of the front at one season and the other side at the opposite season. This shift is far more marked than that of the Intertropical front and it therefore affects a wider zone of the earth's surface.

THE HORSE LATITUDES. There remain only two sections of the world wind system to consider. These sections are those between the Trades and the Westerlies in each hemisphere.

The central part of the zone of subtropical high pressure is a region of very light, shifting, irregular winds or of calms. This zone is known as the *Horse Latitudes*. The lack of wind results primarily from the lack of appreciable pressure gradient. Generally the zone of calms is more pronounced in mid-ocean for it is there that high pressure dominates throughout the year. In the winter period, the oceanic high is extended landward over the continents on either side and with this expansion comes spreading of the belt of calms. As the high retreats to its oceanic position during summer and as lows begin to form over the continents on either side, a flow of air becomes noticeable on the continental fringes. At that time, the belt of calms is confined to the ocean centers.

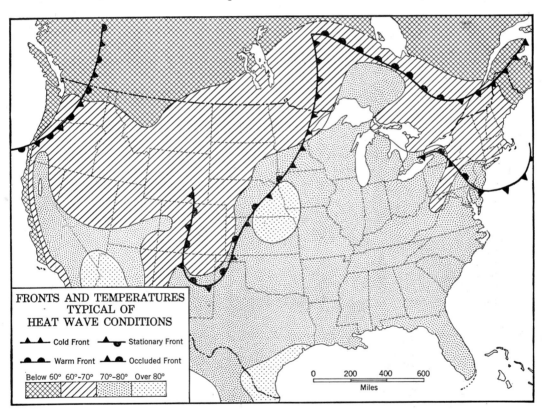

FRONTS AND TEMPERATURES
TYPICAL OF
HEAT WAVE CONDITIONS

Cold Front   Stationary Front

Warm Front   Occluded Front

Below 60° 60°-70° 70°-80° Over 80°

0   200   400   600
Miles

75 *DURING THE SUMMER season when a warm front pushes its way northward into southern Canada, the high temperatures back of the front produce what is called a heat wave. Based on the U. S. Daily Weather Map for July 26, 1949.*

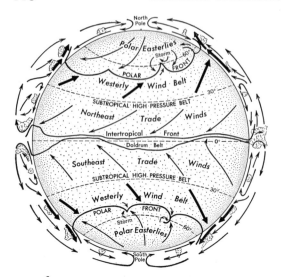

76   *SCHEMATIC diagram showing the world's major wind belts, the frontal zones, and the vertical circulation within the troposphere.*

UPPER-AIR WINDS. So far the discussion has been concerned essentially with surface winds. To complete the general picture of atmospheric circulation, it is necessary to suggest the movements above the earth, at least in that zone with which man is mainly concerned. Along the zone of greatest heating, air is rising away from the earth's surface. As has been suggested previously, there is a flow of air poleward from the top of the rising column. In the Horse Latitudes, the poleward current descends toward the earth's surface. Part of the descending air moves equatorward at the surface as the Trades and part of it moves poleward as the Prevailing Westerlies. In the higher middle latitudes, Westerlies are forced to rise over cold Polar Winds. Aloft, a portion of this rising air continues to move poleward, descending to the surface in the center of the Polar highs while the other portion moves equatorward to descend at the Horse Latitudes. There is thus created a three-celled scheme of movement which may be represented diagrammatically as in the accompanying sketch (Fig. 76).

The details of circulation are much more complex than might be concluded from this simple statement, for the assumption is that the pressure belts are continuous. This we have seen is not true. In addition, seasonal shifts of position in those that are continuous about the earth change the location of ascending and of descending currents.

SEASONAL SHIFT OF WIND BELTS. The wind belts migrate latitudinally with the passage of the seasons. The cause of the shift is, basically, seasonal change of insolation. This is reflected in the change of position of pressure belts and, consequently, of the winds.

During the Northern Hemisphere winter, the zone of maximum insolation lies south of the equator. Consequently, the equatorial belt of low pressure is somewhat south of the equator also. In response to this, the Northern Hemisphere Trades move farther toward the equator than at any other season. All of the other wind belts of the Northern Hemisphere shift equatorward also. Likewise, the Southern Hemisphere wind belts are displaced southward.

In the Northern Hemisphere summer, maximum insolation is received north of the equator. Hence, the equatorial belt of low pressure is developed somewhat north of the equator. All of the Northern Hemisphere wind belts migrate northward, which is poleward for them; the Southern Hemisphere wind belts likewise move northward, but this is equatorward for them. In other words, the wind belts of each hemisphere migrate equatorward in winter and poleward in summer.

Over the oceans, the migration is through 10 to 15 degrees of latitude; over the land masses, it may amount to as much as 35 degrees. In addition, the shift over the oceans usually lags behind the movement of the sun's vertical rays by a month or two, while over the land there is usually no lag. Both of these effects are closely related to the different heating qualities of land and water.

The areas most affected by these shifts are those that lie near the margins of the wind belts. This is well illustrated by the Mediterranean area of Europe and Africa. The Mediterranean basin lies in the general zone of the Horse Latitudes. During the summer when all wind belts move poleward, the Mediterranean comes under the partial influence of the Trades. In winter when the wind belts move equatorward, it lies just within the Westerlies. Since the Trades blow generally off the land toward the Atlantic, they bring little moisture; summer drought results. The Westerlies, blowing in off the Atlantic, carry both the moisture and the mechanism, cyclonic storms, to make the winters rainy.

WORLD DISTRIBUTION OF PRECIPITATION

Mean Annual Precipitation

As with temperature and pressure, maps are constructed to show precipitation amounts both seasonally and annually. The lines which connect points of equal precipitation are called *isohyets*. Fig. 77 indicates mean annual precipitation for the world. While annual amounts are subject to year-by-year fluctuation, nevertheless certain areas stand out as excessively moist and certain others as excessively dry. Almost without exception, equatorial areas belong among the wettest areas of the world, and polar regions among the driest. Evident as areas of dryness are the low latitude west coasts and the continental interiors. Elsewhere, precipitation is intermediate in amount.

EQUATORIAL AND TROPICAL ZONE. If the discussion of the major causes of precipitation is recalled, this broad pattern can in part be explained. It is largely a question of knowing where moist air is rising and where air, whether moist or not, is settling toward the earth. As has previously been pointed out,

air is rising in a broad zone along the equator. So long as the air contains a large amount of water vapor, precipitation results. Since air at the high temperatures common to equatorial regions is capable of holding large amounts of water vapor and since the Trades and monsoons of equatorial regions flow over large expanses of warm ocean, the moisture which they carry produces more ample precipitation than is to be found anywhere else in the world. Where onshore winds and rising air combine most effectively in this zone, tremendous amounts of rain fall to the surface. The highest mean annual rainfall in the world is recorded on the windward slopes of mountains in the Trade Wind belt. Mount Waialeale in the Hawaiian Islands has a seven year uninterrupted record showing an average of *476 inches per year;* Cherrapunji on the windward southern slope of the Himalayas in the face of the summer monsoon has recorded *241 inches in one month;* and Baguio on Luzon in the Philippine Islands has received *46 inches in one twenty-four hour period.*

LOW LATITUDE WEST COASTS. The decline in amount away from the equator and on the continental west coasts may be coupled with the existence of the subtropical belt of high pressure. Winds in these latitudes strike the east coasts; the west coast areas are regions of offshore winds. In addition, air in these latitudes is settling toward the surface, as described in the discussion of major wind belts. There is therefore no adequate source of moisture nor is there the mechanism necessary for condensation and precipitation of such moisture as may be available. While there is no absolute evidence that any one part of the earth's surface is absolutely rainless, yet there exist, for the low latitude west coast zones, several records of rain gauges which have seldom been wet from rain or snow, as at Iquique and Calama in northern Chile. In similar locations, as in the coastal desert of southern Peru, dew contributes appreciable amounts of usable moisture. Usually, the precipitation is below 10 inches per year, as

MEAN ANNUAL PRECIPITATION

(After Meinardus and Schott)

INCHES

Over 80
40-80
20-40
10-20
0-10

Sinusoidal equal-area projection

STATUTE MILES

0   1000   2000   3000   4000   5000

77   *GENERALIZED MAP of mean annual precipitation over the world.*

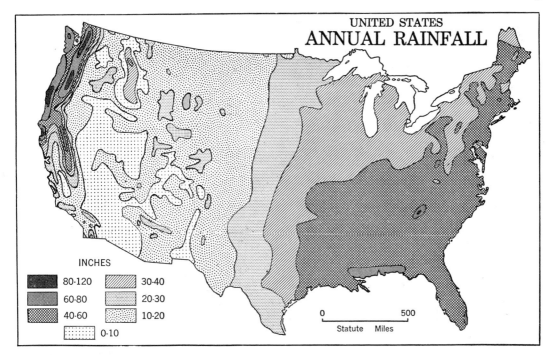

UNITED STATES
ANNUAL RAINFALL

INCHES

80-120	30-40
60-80	20-30
40-60	10-20
0-10	

0   500
Statute   Miles

78   *GENERALIZED MAP of mean annual rainfall in the United States.*

throughout the whole Sahara, and what does come occurs at irregularly spaced intervals.

MIDDLE LATITUDES. Through the middle latitudes, a moderate amount of precipitation is common, though parts of the continental interiors are characteristically dry. This is the zone in which cyclonic storms, or frontal activity, are linked to the zone of rising air between the Prevailing Westerlies and the Polar Winds. Here precipitation amount depends largely upon distance from the source of moisture, the oceans. Onshore winds carry much moisture toward the continents and orographic or cyclonic conditions bring about its precipitation. In either event, most of the moisture is removed from the air relatively near the continental margins and only a small portion of it penetrates to the interior.

Study of the map of average annual precipitation in the United States (Fig. 78) illustrates the contrast between continental margins and interiors. Large amounts of precipitation are seen to occur on the Pacific coast, especially in Oregon and Washington.

Decrease is very pronounced eastward. Here the control is in large part orographic. Along the Atlantic coast, precipitation is moderately heavy. Decrease toward the interior is again noticeable though it is more gradual than that near the Pacific coast. The Great Plains are dry largely because rain-bearing winds from the Gulf of Mexico do not regularly penetrate northwestward into the continental interior and those from the Pacific lose most of their moisture in passing over mountains before reaching that far east.

HIGH LATITUDES. In the Polar regions, air is settling toward the surface and, in addition, it contains little moisture. The ability of cold air to contain water vapor is very low and the mechanics by which that small amount might be condensed and precipitated are usually lacking. Hence the fall is light. In this instance, the amount of precipitation is of little significance, for temperatures are always low. Few measurements have been made for this reason. Upernivik, Greenland, has an average of only 9.2 inches despite its

79   *AVERAGE PRECIPITATION over the land areas of the world during January. Compare with Fig. 80.*

Rainfall in Inches

0   2   8   16-over

80   *AVERAGE PRECIPITATION over the land areas of the world during July. Compare with Fig. 79, noting especially the seasonal shift of wet and dry conditions.*

marine position and Point Barrow on Alaska's north coast has only 5.3 inches.

SEASONAL DISTRIBUTION OF PRECIPITATION. The seasonal distribution of precipitation is of equal importance with its yearly amount. This distribution is represented by the isohyetal maps for January and July (Figs. 79 and 80). On them, it can be noted that there is a shift of rainy and dry zones comparable with the shift of wind belts previously described. For example, almost all of the area in central Africa receiving over 2 inches of rain during January lies south of the equator. This is the season when the zone of greatest heating and the Intertropical front occupy their farthest south position. In the opposite period of the year, July, most of the area receiving over 2 inches during the month lies north of the equator. This, in turn, is the season when the vertical sun is well north of the equator as is also the Intertropical front.

Similar shifts may be seen in the middle and high latitudes. Almost without exception, the shift parallels that of temperature and winds which have been described previously. The specific variation in any one particular place may not correspond to the general world pattern, but the broader picture reflects the influence of the climatic controls upon precipitation as well as upon temperature.

Precipitation Variability

Mean annual or mean monthly precipitation data provide valuable measures of comparison between various parts of the world. Nevertheless, it must be remembered that the total for any one place may vary widely from the mean. Over the period from 1888 through 1938, Amherst, Massachusetts, had a mean annual precipitation of 43.70 inches. In 1938, the amount was 59.00 inches, 35 per cent above the mean; in 1908, the total was only 30.68 inches, nearly 30 per cent below the mean.

When the period is shorter than a year, even greater variability can be observed. September is usually the wettest month at Amherst with an average of 4.24 inches. September of 1938 recorded 14.55 inches, nearly three and one-half times the mean. Yet in 1914, that month had only .52 inch, less than one-eighth the mean amount.

Though variability is encountered everywhere, it is generally true that areas of little precipitation are subject to greater fluctuation than those with heavy precipitation. This can be illustrated by comparison of Figs. 77 and 81.

Middle Latitude Storms

In the zone of contact between the Prevailing Westerlies and the Polar Winds, there is a constant variation of weather. Drizzly rain of three or four days' duration gives way to dry, clear, cloudless days. The hot mugginess of summer days contrasts vividly with the biting cold of winter days. Though a certain temperature may be characteristic, sudden sharp drops in spring or sudden sharp upward swings in fall bring "unseasonable" spells of cold or of heat. The weather is constantly changing; there is no monotony to it. This is the zone of middle latitude cyclones and anticyclones.

Where the Polar front (the contact between the Prevailing Westerlies and the Polar Easterlies) exists, there is produced a stream of eastward moving eddies of air. These eddies are in reality the moving, rising-air centers, or the *cyclones,* of our mid-latitude weather. They are the main source of precipitation in the middle latitudes. Between the eddies of rising air are tongues of cold polar air flowing toward the equator. These are the *anticyclones* which are commonly associated with clear, cloudless weather in the same zone.

An eddy in the Polar front becomes more prominent as it moves along eastward. It forms, at first, a sort of crest to a wave (Fig.

82). Ahead of this crest, the relatively warm air from lower latitudes is pushing poleward actively, trying, as it were, to push colder polar air out of its way. Thus a portion of the Polar front bends poleward and assumes, more or less, a shape like that of a scythe blade (Fig. 82). Since warm air is the active force, this section is called a *warm front*. Back of the crest, cold air from higher latitudes pushes actively in behind the warm air so that this portion of the Polar front assumes a shape like that of the handle of a scythe. This section is called a *cold front* because cold air is the active force. Middle latitude cyclonic storms, then, have both warm front and cold front parts.

WARM FRONT WEATHER. Since middle latitude cyclonic storms move eastward and since the warm front is that portion ahead of the wave crest in the Polar front, it is that section of the storm which passes any given point

first. Along a warm front, warm air glides up over cold along a slope which is relatively gentle, between 1 in 100 and 1 in 300. In other words, 100 miles ahead of the line along which the front meets the *ground,* the frontal surface lies from 1,700 feet to one mile above the ground (Fig. 83). The warm air slips gently but steadily up this surface, forming cirrus-type clouds well out ahead of the front. These are followed shortly by the lower altostratus and possibly a few very low stratocumulus clouds. Gentle rain or snow begins, increasing in intensity as the front approaches the place of observation. Frequently, just before the front passes, fog or very low black clouds form with the continued light drizzly rain. As the front moves past, the clouds become higher, precipitation ceases, and temperatures rise. The wind usually shifts from easterly or northerly directions to southerly or southeasterly ones. The period of precipita-

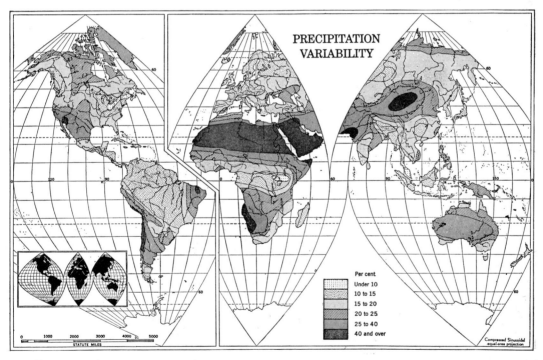

81 *HIGHLY GENERALIZED map showing average precipitation variability. Note especially that higher variability is generally more common in areas of light precipitation than in areas of heavy precipitation.*

tion is usually long-continued, it covers a wide area, but the fall is usually gentle.

COLD FRONT WEATHER. Along a cold front, warm air is forced up over cold along a slope which is relatively steep, anywhere from 1 in 25 to 1 in 100; that is, 100 miles from the line where the front meets the ground, the frontal surface may be anywhere from 1 mile to 4 miles high (Fig. 83). Cloud formation is delayed almost to the time of the passage of the cold front *on the surface*. Precipitation begins either just before or almost immediately after the passage of the front on the ground and,

82

DEVELOPMENT of cyclonic storm as a wave along the Polar front in the Northern Hemisphere: (A) *incipient,* (B) *actively developing,* (C) *well developed,* (D) *final. Note patterns of rain, clouds, pressure (figures in millibars), and winds (small straight arrows). North is at the top of each diagram.*

though heavy, is usually of short duration followed by relatively rapid clearing. Before the passage of the front, warm moist air flows in from a southerly or easterly direction, and being forced to rise rapidly, forms clouds almost above the location of the front on the ground. With the coming of cloudiness, there is a shift of wind to a westerly direction and an accompanying drop in temperature. After the passage of the rain or snow belt, there is a marked drop in relative humidity.

The evenness of progress of the storm depends upon the rate and continuity with which the front is moving. It may vary irregularly or it may remain constant. As yet, it is impossible to determine accurately the regularity with which a front moves. Consequently, any forecast of the changes is subject to many qualifications. If the front moves evenly eastward, the time of passage can be calculated and an accurate forecast of the sequence can be made. If the front becomes stagnant, the sequence may be held up at any

83 *CHARACTERISTIC SLOPES along* (A) *cold and* (B) *warm fronts. Note that warm air is actively forced steeply upward along the cold front, but glides smoothly upward along the warm front.*

point. The sequence of weather remains the same; the time element changes.

Ordinarily, cold fronts move with greater steadiness and speed than do warm fronts. Thus, the blade and handle of the scythe, the warm and cold fronts, are folded in upon one another. When a cold front finally overtakes a warm front, the condition is known as an *occlusion;* an *occluded front* is formed.

OCCLUDED FRONT WEATHER. If the air back of a cold front is of a lower temperature than that which lies ahead of the warm front, the cold front will push in under the warm front, forcing it aloft. This is known as a *cold front occlusion* (Fig. 84A) and is commonest on the eastern sides of continental areas. If the air back of the cold front is warmer than that ahead of the warm front, the cold front will be forced aloft in a *warm front occlusion* (Fig. 84B). This type of occlusion is commonest on continental west coasts.

The weather which is associated with occlusions combines the features of both types of frontal storms. Since the occlusion takes place near the center of the cyclone, bad weather is widespread, particularly at the time when occlusion begins. The length of the period of bad weather and its intensity depend again upon the rate at which air is forced upward. Eventually, if the air is forced high enough so that temperature differences are dissipated, low pressure will disappear. Air which was relatively warm and light will have been replaced by that which is colder and heavier, and the cyclone will have disappeared.

It is through the agency of cyclonic storms that most of the precipitation in the zone of Prevailing Westerlies is derived. Warm, moist air from the low latitude oceans provides water; colder, drier air from Polar regions and from the far continental interiors provides the power which forces condensation of the vapor.

84 *CROSS SECTIONS through air mass occlusions:* (A) *cold front occlusion,* (B) *warm front occlusion. In both diagrams the black line represents a cold front and the doubled line represents a warm front.*

Because there is seasonal migration of the zone of contact between warm and cold air masses, there are some areas which are always under the influence of middle latitude cyclonic storms and other areas which experience their influence during only part of the year.

THUNDERSTORMS AND TORNADOES. Within middle latitudes, especially during the summer months, two kinds of violent atmospheric disturbances of small size occur. These are *thunderstorms* and *tornadoes*. Both of them exist within the general framework which has just been described.

When, for one cause or another, masses of warm, moist air are forced to rise very rapidly and to very high levels, they are cooled excessively. Moisture in the air is condensed to form massive, vertically extensive clouds, heavy rain, and, sometimes, hail. Descending columns of cold, dry air spill downward from the tops of the clouds which often build up to an altitude of over 20,000 feet. The vertical downward movement of cold air in some parts of the storm contrasts sharply with vertical upward movement of warm air. Within these currents, velocities of over 100 miles per hour are characteristic. Electrical differences are developed, and there are electrical discharges between cloud and cloud and between clouds and the ground. The sound produced as a result of the passage of one of these charges through the atmosphere is thunder.

Thunderstorms are seldom more than a few miles in diameter though a whole series of them may follow one after another. They always occur within a warm air mass, but the force which starts the upward movement of air may be the result of a number of different factors. Sometimes, thunderstorms are convective, the result of local differences in atmospheric heating. At other times, they may be orographic, the result of movement of air up a mountain slope. And, at still other times, they may result from the passage of air mass fronts. Regardless of the starting force, the *trigger action* as it is called, the air that is

displaced upward must be warm and moist if a thunderstorm is to develop.

Another striking type of storm of small diameter which occurs in the middle latitudes especially during the summer months is the tornado. The diameter of the tornado at the ground varies between 100 and 500 yards. A funnel-shaped cloud reaches down from low, heavy cumulo-nimbus and twists erratically along the surface (Fig. 85). This cloud represents the center of very low pressure and, about it, air spirals inward and upward at rates well over 100 miles per hour. Along its path, such a storm is terrifically destructive, but it has little effect beyond its immediate locale. A tornado is in reality a "thunderstorm run crazy."

Other Storms

Cyclonic storms likewise occur in the tropics. Many of them are nonviolent, similar in many ways to the middle latitude cyclonic storms. They originate along the Intertropical front and move generally westward, carried along by the drift of the Trade Winds. As they move onto land and thus increase their distance from a source of moisture, they tend to become less intense and finally to disappear altogether.

Quite frequently in their westward path, tropical cyclones veer toward the margins of the middle latitudes. When their path is over water, as for example over the Caribbean Sea, they sometimes become violent. Such violent tropical storms are spoken of as *hurricanes* when they occur off the east coast of North America, or as *typhoons* when they occur in the same latitudes on the east coast of Asia. They are inward and upward spirals of air about a low pressure center. Their diameters are usually between 100 and 400 miles. At the center, there is a relatively calm, cloudless, and rainless zone, known commonly as the *eye*. Around the edge of the eye, wind velocities may exceed 120 miles

85 *A TORNADO in eastern Colorado. Note the heavy, turbulent clouds with the characteristic funnel reaching to the ground. (Soil Conservation Service, U. S. Department of Agriculture)*

per hour. The passage of a hurricane or typhoon brings a deluge of rain. Since these storms originate over the ocean, they cause serious damage to shipping as well as great destruction in coastal districts onto which they move.

The havoc wrought by small area storms like thunderstorms, tornadoes, hurricanes, and typhoons far surpasses that resulting from the larger, less violent middle latitude or tropical cyclonic storms. But the smaller types are all limited in their occurrence both as to area and as to time. Their very infrequency makes them subject to specific study and comment; as origins of precipitation or as agents of temperature change, they are not significant from a world point of view. They are important in their limited distribution, but they are far less significant in the world as a whole than the more extensive cyclones which develop along either the Polar or the Intertropical fronts.

CONCLUSION

What has been said in this chapter gives only a suggestion of the almost infinite variety of combinations of climatic elements which occur at or near the earth's surface—in the zone where man's activity goes on. Understanding of the major elements, temperature, precipitation, and pressure and wind, and of the controls which are active upon them provides a basis for understanding the variety of the physical setting in which man lives (Table

8, page 78). From this point, it is necessary to proceed to a systematic study of the major combinations of climatic elements and to the distribution of these combinations over the face of the earth.

∙∙

CHAPTER OUTLINE

Climatic elements over the world

World distribution of temperature
  Isothermal maps
  Effects of some climatic controls upon temperature distribution
    Mean monthly temperature distribution
    Seasonal and hemispheric temperature differences
    Sea-level equivalent temperatures
    Temperature range
World distribution of pressure and wind
  Major function of wind
  World distribution of pressure
    Isobaric maps
    World pressure belts
  World wind system
    Coriolis force
    Major wind belts
    Oceanic wind circulation
    Monsoons
    The Intertropical front
    The Polar front
    The Horse Latitudes
    Upper-air winds
    Seasonal shift of wind belts
World distribution of precipitation
  Mean annual precipitation
    Equatorial and tropical zone
    Low latitude west coasts
    Middle latitudes
    High latitudes
    Seasonal distribution of precipitation
  Precipitation variability
  Middle latitude storms
    Warm front weather
    Cold front weather
    Occluded front weather
    Thunderstorms and tornadoes
  Other storms
Conclusion

REVIEW QUESTIONS

1. Present a logical argument, supported by specific illustrations, why the distribution of climatic elements over the earth is significant to man.
2. How is an isothermal map constructed? Of what specific use is an isothermal map?
3. In what specific ways do isothermal maps show the effects of the climatic controls upon temperature distribution?
4. Why are January and July isothermal maps better for general study of temperature distribution over the earth than those for March and September?
5. Explain why the lowest temperatures on the earth are experienced in northeastern Asia.
6. Why is it that sea-level equivalent temperatures are often used instead of actual temperatures in constructing world isothermal maps? Why are maps made by using actual temperatures more significant geographically?
7. Suggest ways in which average annual temperature range is important to human beings.
8. Distinguish between wind and air currents. In what ways may wind be considered essential to man?
9. For what purposes might it be more satisfactory to use actual observed atmospheric pressures rather than sea-level equivalent pressures in constructing an isobaric map?
10. Give some reasons why a knowledge of the world pressure belts contributes to an understanding of the world climatic pattern.
11. Why is it that the Trade Winds in the Northern Hemisphere are generally northeasterly winds?
12. Is there any difference in the persistence and direction between winds, like the Trades and Prevailing Westerlies, over oceans and the same winds over land areas? Explain.
13. Explain the conditions under which a monsoon develops. How does a monsoon affect the general world wind belts?
14. In what way is the Intertropical front important climatically?
15. How does the Intertropical front differ from the Polar front? Are the differences significant to man? If so, tell how.
16. Explain the reasons for and the major results of the seasonal shift of the world wind belts.

17. What are the major reasons for differences in the seasonal distribution of precipitation from place to place over the earth?

18. Give some of the reasons for differences in amount of precipitation from place to place over the earth.

19. What are warm fronts and cold fronts? How can one tell when a warm front or a cold front passes? If possible, give examples from your own experience.

20. Why should Florida be more subject to "cold waves" than is southern California?

21. Why should Chicago be more subject to "heat waves" than is San Francisco?

22. Explain the higher frequency of thunderstorms in Mississippi, for example, than in coastal California.

23. In what parts of the world do hurricanes or typhoons occur? What is their significance to man?

24. Are cyclonic storms encountered in the low latitudes? If they are, how do they differ from those in the middle latitudes; if they are not, why are they absent?

SOME SUGGESTED REFERENCES

Brooks, C. E. P., *Climate, a Handbook for Businessmen, Students and Travellers,* Scribner, 1930. A practical discussion, by a leading British climatologist, of the essentials of climate for the nonprofessional person.

Kendrew, W. G., *Climatology,* Clarendon Press, 1949. Really the third edition of this author's *Climate;* emphasizes distributional aspects of climatic elements and effects of climatic controls.

Kimble, George, and Bush, Raymond, *The Weather,* Pelican Books, Inc., 1946. A delightfully written, accurate discussion of the weather elements; primarily for the general reader.

Stewart, George R., *Storm,* Modern Library, 1947. A portrayal in novel form of the life of a cyclonic storm; accurately and dramatically told; excellent general reading.

Tannehill, I. R., *Weather Around the World,* Princeton University Press, 1943. Exceptionally usable descriptions of weather phenomena in many parts of the world; includes statistical tables.

86A *ANGULAR LANDFORMS characterize regions of arid climate like those of southwestern United States. (Josef Muench)*

86B *ROUNDED LANDFORMS in a moist climatic area, the Green Mountains of Vermont. (Newell Green)*

CHAPTER 7

Climatic Types: the Tropical Moist and the Dry Climates

....

CLASSIFICATION OF CLIMATIC TYPES

Early Recognition of Climatic Types

From earliest times, students of man's habitat have attempted to classify climatic elements so as to provide a means of comparison between one land and another. The early Greeks established one such classification based largely upon the single element of temperature. They knew the climate of the area in which they lived, with its hot, dry summers and mild, rainy winters, with its clear summer skies occasionally blurred by the fine particles of dust blown northward from the great desert of Africa, and with its cloud-filled skies of winter. They realized fully the vital importance of securing additional water for agriculture during the summer, but beyond this, the climate of the area in which they lived posed few problems of sustenance and fewer still of shelter and clothing. To them, it was the ideal climate—the Temperate Climate.

Their knowledge of the burning desert to the south led them to believe that even hotter lands lay beyond, lands where the sun was so hot as to burn a man's skin to a blackish color, hot enough to be uninhabitable by civilized peoples. This was their concept of the Torrid Climate. In a similar manner, they deduced the opposite extreme. The occasional cold, north winds of the Aegean Sea in winter, the skin clothing of the few northern peoples who penetrated the Grecian world, and the stories of the hardships of travelers to the north combined to lead to the concept of an area too cold for human habitation, at least by civilized peoples like themselves. This was their Frigid Climate.

Almost on the basis of temperature alone, they erected this three-fold climatic classification which, even to this day, remains in the frequent reference to Torrid, Temperate, and Frigid zones. But this classification is not adequate. It recognizes fully only one of the climatic elements. While there is an approach to truth in such a system, it does not really reflect the actual combinations of climatic elements known to exist over the face of the earth.

Purposes of Classification

SYSTEMATIC COMPARISON. When we hear the radio comedian's overworked remarks about the "heavy dews" of the California winter, we are hearing a reference, in a loose way, to winter rains. It has been observed that winter rain is a recurrent feature in that part of the world. But such a statement is hardly adequate to allow comparisons between California and other parts of the world where characteristic winter rains have also been observed. The problem is to define precisely what is meant by winter rains.

Equally common is the expression, "Hot for this time of year, isn't it?" Such a remark points to an everyday recognition of the factor of temperature and to the recurrence of certain temperatures at certain times of the year. We cannot use such everyday remarks as the basis for definite comparison. Precisely how hot is it during a particular season and at a particular place?

While there is great variety in the possible combinations of climatic elements, certain broadly similar ones have been observed to recur frequently throughout the world. Such combinations are the basic climatic types. Each type can be given exact quantitative, rather than mere qualitative, definition. On the basis of these definitions, a system or classification can be erected. Such a scheme not only defines each of the types, but indicates, in terms of observable and measurable amounts, the relationships between them. Through the use of such a classification, descriptive statement is made exact. No matter who may use the classification, or to what part of the world it may be applied, the meanings are standard. It is possible to state whether or not one area exists under essentially the same combination of climatic elements as another. Thus, one means of systematic comparison in the study of man's habitat is made possible.

DETERMINATION OF A BASIC WORLD PATTERN. A climatic classification is a tool which makes possible the determination of the pattern of climate over the world. For any chosen area, observed records of as many places as possible can be classified. The location of each place, with the climatic type represented by its record, can be plotted on a map. Then lines can be added in such a way as to separate the places with one type of climate from those with another. The result is a climatic map of the area. The lines on such a map are primarily indicators of direction of change. That change is greatest at right angles to the lines and least along them or in a direction parallel to them. If the same process is followed for the whole earth, one of the basic world patterns is obtained (Plate V).

The distribution of climatic types, or the climatic pattern, is basic because of the close relationship between climate and the many other elements of the human habitat. Visible forms of the physical setting, like landforms, vegetation, and soil, are all greatly modified by the climate under which they exist. A hot, rainy climate produces certain characteristic forms of the actual surface, of the cover of plants on that surface, and of the soil in which the plants grow. These forms are quite unlike those produced under a cold, dry climate.

To be sure, there are many influences other than that of climate involved in the shaping of the earth's surface. The more prominent of these will be discussed in later chapters of this book. However, climate does impose general differences from place to place. Sharp, angular landforms are common through the arid southwestern United States. More subdued, rounded landforms characterize the rainier eastern part of the country (Fig. 86).

Variable supplies of water available for plant life cause vegetation differences from place to place locally, but in the main, the vegetation existing under one climate is notably different from that found under another. For example, the sparse, drought-resistant vegetation of much of Arizona contrasts vividly with the forests of the Pacific Northwest (Fig. 239).

Similarly, local soil types may reflect certain differences in rock material from which they are formed. Yet, given the same basic materials, the soil developed under one climate is vastly different from that formed under another. The reddish and yellowish soils of Georgia are a far cry from the deep black and dark brown ones of Iowa.

Even the forms of human utilization of the physical setting are affected by climate. The type of building admirably suited for human use in the constantly hot, wet climate of an equatorial forest is hardly adequate protection against the severe winters of northeastern Siberia. That cotton should dominate the agriculture of the southeastern United States and be absent from that of the New England states is primarily a reflection of climatic difference. The contrast between the intensive use of the lowlands of Japan and the near emptiness of the lowlands that face upon the Arctic Ocean is, in part, the result of the respective climates of these two areas. To much that man does in the land in which he lives, climate is a limiting force either directly or indirectly. Consequently, the distribution of climatic types over the world, the climatic pattern in other words, is the key to the arrangement of many other features of man's habitat. From this point of view, climate classification is a tool; it is not a desired end in itself.

Plan of Classification

To serve the purposes just stated, the climates of the world are grouped into categories based upon the two elements which are most significant to man as he attempts to live and make a living on the face of the earth. These two elements are temperature and precipitation. Long-time records of each are available for numerous and widely scattered places on the earth. When these records are analyzed, it is found that certain outstanding combinations regularly occur. For example, some places show a combination of "hot and moist," others are "hot and dry," still others are "cold and moist," and so on through many temperature and moisture combinations.

There are five major categories of climate. These are as follows: (1) Tropical Moist (or A) climates; (2) Dry (or B) climates; (3) Moist, Mild Winter (or C) climates; (4) Moist, Severe Winter (or D) climates; and (5) Polar (or E) climates. Each of these broad categories is subdivided to indicate further significant climatic differences from place to place within any wide zone. For example, within the Moist, Mild Winter climates, there are some places that have summer drought, like the San Joaquin Lowland of California; other places in the same broad class have characteristic winter drought, like parts of southern China; and still other places are moist the year round, like Washington, D. C.

Still further subdivision is possible and, for some types of climate, essential. In the Moist, Severe Winter climates, for example, there is a great difference between the climate of Chicago with its hot summers and that of, say, Quebec, where the summers are shorter and warm rather than hot.

This classification is essentially the one known as the Köppen system. The Köppen system uses letter symbols rather than descriptive names to represent the various climatic types, and each letter has a specific definition. Thus, a Moist, Mild Winter climate in which the summers are characteristically droughty is know as a Cs climate. If such a climate had hot summers, it would be known as a Csa climate; if the summers were warm rather than hot, it would be known as a Csb climate. And each of these terms, like hot or warm or droughty or mild winter, are defined in exact temperatures or amounts of precipitation.

In what follows, the descriptive names will be used and the Köppen equivalent letter symbols will be added in parentheses. *For general purposes,* it is unnecessary to follow the great detail of the Köppen system in its entirety. That detail is stated in Appendix B.

THE TROPICAL MOIST (A) CLIMATES

Characteristics

TEMPERATURE. The common characteristic of all Tropical Moist (A) climates is constant high temperature. In the definition of these types, an average temperature for the *coolest* month is specified as a limit. Such a temperature is an indication of whether or not a season exists in which truly tropical vegetation cannot flourish—a period of plant rest from growth induced by relatively low temperatures. The average of 64° F. for the *coolest* month is taken as the limit of the A climates. This temperature corresponds closely with a notable change in vegetation type. Trees like the palm begin to drop out of the forests and their place is taken by types like the oak. Likewise, with cool month averages below 64° F., other features of the physical setting are markedly affected, as will be exemplified in later chapters.

On some tropical uplands, as in southeastern Africa and southeastern Brazil, elevations are great enough to reduce temperatures somewhat below 64° F. Except for this one item, however, the climate of these uplands is very like that of Tropical Moist (A) lowlands. Tropical uplands may therefore be considered to have a climate which is a phase rather than a distinctive type, for general purposes.

In the heart of the zones having Tropical Moist (A) climates, monthly averages are in the 70's and 80's, and the ranges between the average for the coolest month and that for the warmest month are very small. The graph of the statistics for Singapore in southeastern Asia (Fig. 87A) indicate these two conditions. Here the coolest month average is 78° F. while the average for the warmest month is 81° F.—a difference of 3°. This is typical of the most pronounced of the Tropical

	J	F	M	A	M	J	J	A	S	O	N	D	Year
Temp.	78	79	79	80	81	80	80	80	80	80	79	78	79
Prec.	9.7	7.1	7.3	7.8	6.5	7.0	6.7	7.8	6.9	7.9	10.1	10.4	94.2

87 CLIMATIC charts and statistics for

Moist (A) climates. Often the differences between day and night are far greater than those between the coolest and warmest months. A daily range as high as 15° is not unusual. At Singapore, the average daily range varies between 12° in July and 15° in March. Monotony is the keyword for such a temperature condition and monotony prevails throughout the heart of all Tropical Moist (A) climatic regions.

As one proceeds toward the margins of the Tropical Moist (A) climatic regions, greater range between coolest and warmest month averages is encountered. This tends to make the daily range less significant and to emphasize the seasonal quality of the climate. The graph of the statistics for Corumbá in Brazil (Fig. 87B) illustrates this condition. There, the coolest month average is 70° F. while the warmest month average is 80° F.—a difference of 10°. The average daily range is approximately 20°. Other factors, particularly moisture differences between these two places, tend to emphasize the differences shown in temperature. But the monotony so pronounced

	J	F	M	A	M	J	J	A	S	O	N	D	Year
Temp.	80	80	80	79	74	70	71	73	77	79	80	80	77
Prec.	6.4	6.7	4.8	5.0	3.3	1.9	0.3	1.3	2.3	3.9	6.0	7.4	49.3

	J	F	M	A	M	J	J	A	S	O	N	D	Year
Temp.	70	73	79	83	84	82	81	81	82	82	78	72	79
Prec.	0.1	0.2	0.5	2.0	13.7	49.4	53.7	42.5	24.6	11.6	5.0	0.6	203.9

Singapore, Corumbá, and Akyab.

at Singapore is greatly modified at Corumbá.

PRECIPITATION. It is in the amount of precipitation and in its distribution through the year that the greatest contrasts between the various phases of the Tropical Moist (A) climates are to be noted. All phases are sufficiently moist to be included in the wet climates; in many places, there is excessive wetness. But there the common quality ends. Some of the Tropical Moist (A) climates have rainfall distributed evenly throughout the year or if they do show any period of appreciable dryness, that period is relatively short. Frequently, the precipitation during the greater part of the year is very high; yet, never is there a true season of drought. When there is no drought, the climate is of the *Tropical Rainforest (Af)* type.

In other areas of Tropical Moist (A) climate, intense drought during one season alternates with heavy rain during another. Where such a condition prevails, the climate is of the *Savanna (Aw)* type. It is obvious that the transition from one extreme to the other is gradual and, consequently, that the

definition of any divide between Tropical Rainforest (Af) and Savanna (Aw) types is arbitrary.

Intermediate between these extremes is the rainfall type encountered along parts of the southern and southeastern coast of Asia, where excess of precipitation at one time of the year compensates for lack of it at another. There, where monsoons are most typically developed, a characteristic distribution of rainfall through the year occurs. This distribution is shown on the graph of the climatic statistics for Akyab in Burma (Fig. 87C). It is similar to that in areas of Savanna (Aw) climate; there is a rainy season and a dry season. But the rainy season is generally longer and the dry season shorter than those in Savanna (Aw) zones. In addition, the amount of rain which falls during the rainy season is tremendous. While this rain cannot be as effective, coming during a relatively short period, as it would be if spread through the year, it is still effective enough to prevent a complete cessation of growth processes and hence to produce a setting more nearly like that encountered under a Tropical Rainforest (Af) climate than that of a Savanna (Aw) climate. This type is the *Tropical Monsoon (Am)* type.

The relationship between the total precipitation for the year and the amount which falls during the driest month determines which of the three varieties—Tropical Rainforest, Tropical Monsoon, and Savanna (Af, Am, and Aw)—is represented by any one set of precipitation statistics. This relationship is mirrored in the native vegetation. Tropical Rainforest (Af) climate, in which there is no season of rest for plant growth, supports a heavy forest. Savanna (Aw) climate, in its drier phases, supports a mixed cover of sparse grass and thorny bushes which, though lush and green during the rainy season, is dull, brown, and lifeless during the height of the dry season. Again, in the intermediate position, Tropical Monsoon (Am) climate supports a light forest with heavy undergrowth rather than the heavy forest of Tropical Rainforest (Af) climate or the grass and bush cover of the drier Savanna (Aw) climates. In Tropical Monsoon (Am) forests, relative dryness rather than absolute drought is characteristic. It must be noted, however, that one type of vegetation merges gradually with another; there is no sharp line between one type and another.

Subdivisions of the Tropical Moist (A) Climates

TROPICAL RAINFOREST (Af) CLIMATE. For direct comparison of the extremes to be found within the Tropical Moist (A) climates, we may refer again to the graphs for Singapore, Corumbá, and Akyab (Fig. 87). Singapore has a yearly precipitation of 93 inches. The driest month is February in which 6 inches falls; the wettest month is December in which 11 inches falls. In no conceivable way can it be said that Singapore has a dry sea-

son. Accompanying this constantly high rainfall in an area of high temperatures, there is naturally continued high relative humidity, frequently in excess of 90 per cent. Even though the temperature may drop slightly from the high 70's, there is little or no relief from the steamy, sticky feel of the air. Seldom if ever does the thermometer register 100° F., a figure common enough in the central United States, but seldom is the heat dry. A shopworn, but still useful, expression tells the story—"It isn't the heat; it's the humidity." That is man's greatest problem in the areas of extreme Tropical Rainforest (Af) climate.

SAVANNA (AW) CLIMATE. At Corumbá, the total yearly precipitation is 49 inches. The driest month is July with an average of .3 inch; the wettest month is December with an average of over 7 inches. The graph (Fig. 87B) shows the pronounced nature of the dry season. When this is coupled with the temperature curve, it can be noted that the period of greatest dryness comes when the temperatures are lowest. The doubled effect of seasonal difference is thus made the more noticeable. Relative humidity is less than at Singapore and shows considerable fluctuation through the year. The average for December, the rainiest month, is 84 per cent and that for August, one of the drier months, is 68 per cent. The wet season approximates the characteristics of the Tropical Rainforest (Af) climate; the dry season approximates the climate found along the margins of the moisture-deficient or Dry (B) climates farther away from the equator.

TROPICAL MONSOON (Am) CLIMATE. The graph for Akyab (Fig. 87C) shows a temperature curve similar to that of the other Tropical Moist (A) climates with the slight exception that the highest temperatures come in the months just preceding the maximum rainfall. The precipitation distribution through the year suggests the characteristics of the Savanna (Aw) climate. The amount of rain which comes during the rainy season, however, is much greater than that at Corumbá. The total for the year at Akyab is 204 inches; of this, over one-quarter, about 54 inches actually, comes during the single month of July. This amount is sufficient, along with the amounts during the other months of the rainy season, to prevent long-continued drought fully comparable in terms of intensity with that of the Savanna (Aw) climate. This is true despite the fact that each of four months, December through March, receives less than one inch of rain. As is true in the Savanna (Aw) climate, seasonal change is quite pronounced. Temperatures throughout most of the dry season are appreciably lower than those during the rainy season. Just at the end of the dry season, high temperatures do occur. Relative humidity averages about 70 per cent through most of the dry season; it averages in excess of 90 per cent from May through September. In terms of human reactions, there are really three seasons in such a climate: the cool (relatively), dry season; the hot, dry season; and the rainy season. It represents a kind of merging between the extremes of the Tropical Rainforest (Af) and of the Savanna (Aw) climates, partaking as it does of certain of the features of both.

Distribution

Fig. 88 shows the actual distribution of the Tropical Moist (A) climates for the whole world, distinction being made among the three subdivisions; Tropical Rainforest (Af), Tropical Monsoon (Am), and Savanna (Aw). It should be noted especially that the Tropical Monsoon (Am) type forms a transition between the Tropical Rainforest (Af) and the Savanna (Aw) types throughout most of the zone of the Tropical Moist (A) climates. It is probable that more complete information in the form of a closer net of observations over the whole tropical region would show this transition between all areas of Tropical Rainforest (Af) and Savanna

(Aw) types. Such information is lacking, however, and, consequently, there are some places such as the northern edge of the Congo Basin in Africa and the inner part of the Amazon Basin in South America where Tropical Rainforest (Af) and Savanna (Aw) types are shown abutting directly upon one another.

Dominant Controls

TEMPERATURE. The constant high temperatures experienced in areas of Tropical Moist (A) climate are primarily the result of location near the equator. It is in equatorial regions that insolation is greatest and most nearly constant throughout the year. The angle of the sun's rays and the length of the daylight period are primarily responsible for this condition. While the general effects of these two factors were discussed in Chapter 5, it is well to restate the essentials here.

Along the equator, the noon sun is vertically overhead twice during the year, about March 21 and September 21. Hence, the receipt of heat at the earth's surface is most intense at these two times. In consequence, the atmosphere above the equatorial surface is heated to its highest degree at these two times also. Along each of the Tropics, the noon sun is vertically overhead on only one day of the year, about June 21 at the Tropic of Cancer and about December 21 at the Tropic of Capricorn. There is only one period of greatest surface heating in each instance and, hence, only one period of maximum atmospheric heating.

At all places between the Tropics, the noon sun is overhead twice during the year; as the Tropics are approached, these periods come closer together until they finally merge. At *no* time during the year within this same zone is the noon sun far from the overhead position. Because of this, there is no period when heating is greatly reduced. In terms of air temperatures, this means that the range be-

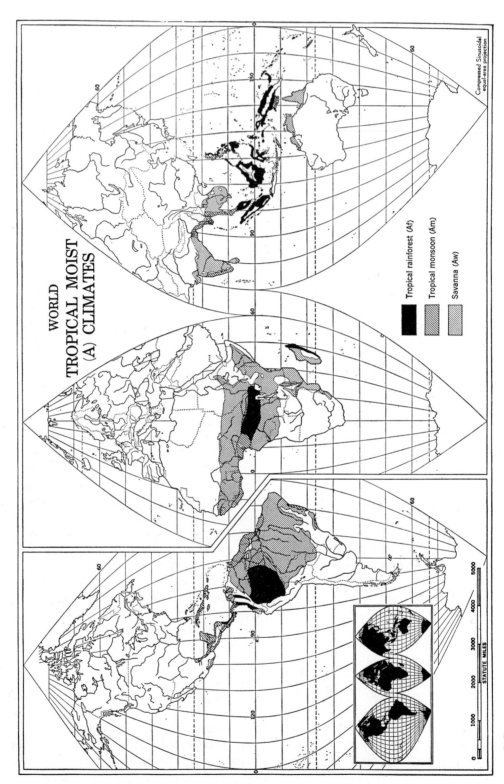

WORLD
TROPICAL MOIST
(A) CLIMATES

Tropical rainforest (Af)

Tropical monsoon (Am)

Savanna (Aw)

Compressed Sinusoidal
equal-area projection

STATUTE MILES

0   1000   2000   3000   4000   5000

88 *WORLD DISTRIBUTION of Tropical Moist (A) climates.*

tween one part of the year and another is never very great. It is least along the equator; it increases in both directions away from the equator.

Equally important in the control of temperature is length of the daylight period. Along the equator, the daylight period is of equal length throughout the year (Fig. 57). In both directions away from the equator this length increases during one season and decreases during the other. At the Tropics, the longest daylight period is about 13⅓ hours out of the 24 and the shortest, about 10⅔ hours. Likewise, at the Tropics, the period of longest day corresponds with the period of highest sun and the period of shortest day with that of lowest sun. Hence, heating is essentially constant throughout the year along the equator, but it varies appreciably at the Tropics.

Between the equator and the Tropics, the period of longest day comes between the two high-sun periods that are closest together. For example, at 12° North latitude, roughly halfway from the equator to the Tropic of Cancer, the noon sun is vertically overhead one day during the first part of May and on another day in early August; the longest day is roughly June 21. At either of the Tropics, the period of longest daylight is also the time of highest sun. Thus, at the Tropics, both controls of insolation, angle of sun's rays and length of daylight period, operate to produce greatest heating at one season and least at the opposite season. At the equator, the angle of the sun's rays varies less than at either Tropic and the length of daylight period is constant. Hence, the variation in amount of insolation through the year in the low latitudes (latitudes between the Tropics) is greatest at the Tropics and least at the equator. This means that mean annual temperature range decreases from the Tropics to the equator.

Despite this condition, the annual temperature range at the Tropics is relatively small. There is no season when insolation is so reduced as to produce low air temperatures and there is, hence, no "winter" season.

In addition, position near a coast onto which winds are blowing (a windward coast) tends to reduce the range during the year. Conversely, position in a continental interior tends to exaggerate the range. These effects are the result of different rates of heating and cooling of land and water masses.

Since ranges are notably small within all Tropical Moist (A) climates, increased elevation above sea level produces monotonously uniform temperatures in tropical mountains. The extreme of this condition is illustrated by Quito in Ecuador (Fig. 89). Quito lies within one degree of the equator and is at an altitude of 9,350 feet. This elevation, of course, lowers all temperatures so much that the climate is *not* of the Tropical Moist (A) type, but it is the range in tropical mountains which is here the point in question. The warmest month at Quito is September, with an average of 54.9° F. The lowest average, shown alike by February, March, April, July, and November, is 54.5° F. The average annual range is thus only .4°.

Though Tropical Moist (A) climates are never found at elevations like that of Quito, the control which altitude exercises over the average annual temperature range is of great significance to human activity in tropical plateau and mountain country throughout the world. Latitudinal position insures relatively even heat reception throughout the year, and altitudinal position insures coolness. At latitudes and altitudes comparable to those of Quito, the result is a climate often described as "perpetual spring." At still higher altitudes, but approximately the same latitudes, the result is a climate of "perpetual winter." Thus, even on the equator, it can be "winter all the time" and snow fields, small mountain glaciers, and barren rock surfaces are present.

PRECIPITATION. The precipitation in all regions of Tropical Moist (A) climate is associated with a relatively small number of atmospheric conditions. These are: (1) the zone of rising air between the belts of Trade Winds; (2) onshore winds where land masses intercept the flow of the Trade Winds; (3) local convectional storms; and (4) monsoons.

Within the Doldrums, there is a zone of rising air, either thermally induced or resulting from the presence of the Intertropical front (see pp. 103 ff.). Cooling accompanies the general updraft and brings about condensation of moisture with resultant heavy precipitation. Migration of the Trade Wind belts with the seasons is accompanied by a similar shift of the zone of rising air. As a consequence, the precipitation caused by it is effective from about 10° North latitude to about 10° South latitude during the course of the year. At no one time, however, is this cause effective over the whole twenty-degree belt.

Since the Trades blow from an easterly direction, any east-facing coast within the regions where these winds blow provides a means of forcing air to rise and, hence, of producing rain. The seasonal migration of the Trades brings onshore winds, for part of the year at least, nearly to the margins of the low latitudes. The influence of these winds decreases away from the equator and inland from the east coasts.

In regions of such heat as those of the Tropical Moist (A) climates, local convectional storms form frequently during the warmer part of the day and produce torrential downpours accompanied by brilliant displays of lightning and heavy, almost continuous, rolls of thunder. Several of these storms usually succeed one another from shortly before noon through to evening. Each storm is more severe than the one which preceded it until, finally, with the early evening shower, the convectional circulation is destroyed. The presence of the zone of rising air between the Trades contributes to the frequency of these storms.

The Tropical Rainforest (Af) climate occurs characteristically where the three forces so far mentioned are most strongly developed. The farther one is from the zone of convergence of the Trades, the farther one is from an east coast, and the farther one is from the zone of greatest heating in which local convection is at a maximum, the smaller is the amount of rain and the more seasonal is its distribution. Hence, one passes from the Tropical Rainforest (Af) to the Savanna (Aw) climate.

Monsoons upset the simplicity of this pattern. Only where a tremendous land mass, through intense summer heating or winter cooling, forms the center of a huge indraft of moist air or a great outdraft of dry air is a monsoon typically developed. Even with the existence of monsoon circulation, the rising of air and the resultant precipitation are accomplished primarily by movement onshore at an angle to the direction of the coastline or by the presence of a considerably displaced Intertropical front. Monsoons are best developed on low-latitude coasts where the Trade Wind circulation is interrupted. Such a condition exists in southern and southeastern Asia. There the presence of a huge land mass north of the equator and an open ocean opposite it in the Southern Hemisphere allows the existence of a well-developed Trade Wind belt in the Southern Hemisphere, but not in the Northern. The intense heating of Asia in the period from May through September makes possible an indraft of air from over the Indian Ocean, with resultant heavy rains. During the period from November through March, the accumulation of intensely cold air over the continent not only prevents any indraft, but causes a strong movement outward, with consequent lack of rain. A similar summer indraft occurs on the Guinea coast of Africa, but the winter outdraft is far less pronounced.

There is uncertainty and irregularity of precipitation throughout all areas of Tropical Moist (A) climate, largely because of variation in intensity of the forces which cause rain. In any one year, the strength of the Trade Wind circulation may be increased or weakened beyond the average. The Intertropical front may be more or less well-devel-

89A STREET SCENE in Quito, Ecuador, where the low latitude and high altitude combine to produce a climate of "perpetual spring." (Grace Line)

oped than usual. The frequency of convectional storms may change. Monsoon winds may blow with varied strength. In regions where several of these forces act together to produce the total precipitation, the failure of any one may be accompanied by the strengthening of another. And thus there is less uncertainty and less irregularity of precipitation in such places than there is where only one force alone is the control. Hence it is within the marginal areas of Savanna (Aw) climate, farthest removed from the equator, from an east coast, or from a monsoon coast, that uncertainty and irregularity of precipitation are most pronounced.

	J	F	M	A	M	J	J	A	S	O	N	D	Year
Temp.	55	55	55	55	55	55	55	55	55	55	55	55	55
Prec.	4.2	4.3	5.2	7.4	5.0	1.5	0.9	1.5	3.0	3.7	3.8	3.8	44.3

89B CLIMATIC chart and statistics for Quito.

THE DRY (B) CLIMATES

Characteristics

PRECIPITATION. The outstanding features of all Dry (B) climates are the meagerness and uncertainty of precipitation. The amount of rain is nowhere equal to the potential evaporation. And even the normally small average is subject to great variation from year to year. Under such conditions, the moisture available for plant life is incapable of supporting a heavy forest vegetation. No permanent streams can rise within such areas though large ones may cross them. Channels of intermittent streams, full flowing for short periods after the infrequent and irregularly spaced rains, and salt lakes or mud flats resulting from the accumulation and evaporation of moisture in shallow undrained depressions, are more characteristic. Consequently, the few usable sources of water assume importance to man far beyond that of other features of the physical setting.

The general moisture deficiency of the Dry (B) climates cannot be expressed in terms of one specific amount of precipitation. Yearly and seasonal temperature averages affect the evaporation rate profoundly. Under some conditions of temperature, 25 inches of rain is sufficient to exceed the amount of evaporation and, thus, to produce a moist climate and its accompanying heavy vegetation. With higher temperatures, the same amount produces a dry climate with sparse vegetation. The divide between the Dry (B) climates on the one hand and all of the moist climates on the other can therefore be expressed only in terms of relationship between temperature and precipitation, not in terms of either element singly. A temperature-precipitation relationship which attempts to define the condition of dryness which brings about a change in the natural vegetation from forest to grassland is taken as the limit between the Dry climates and those that are moist. Actually, the limit

thus defined lies *within* the grasslands, rather than at the dry edge of the forest, in most parts of the world. It is really close to the median line between the moist and the dry limits of the grassland zones of the world.

The primary division of the Dry (B) climates is into the Semiarid (BS) and the Arid (BW) types. Both types are deficient in moisture, but the Semiarid (BS) climate is wetter than the Arid (BW) type. As a consequence of this, the vegetative and soil features of the areas of Semiarid (BS) climate differ markedly from those with Arid (BW) climate. There is enough soil moisture in the semiarid areas to support a continuous cover of grasses, tall on the moist margins and short on the dry margins. Within the arid areas, complete sod cover is lacking, though the land is by no means necessarily bare of all vegetation. A sparse cover of drought-resistant grasses, bushes, and thorny plants takes the place of the continuous cover of the Semiarid (BS) areas. No parts of the world are known to be absolutely rainless though some approach that state closely. Hence, except for areas of moving sand dunes and stretches of bare rock with no cover of soil material, areas of Arid (BW) climate do have some vegetation.

Rain within areas of Arid (BW) climate comes at infrequent and irregularly spaced intervals. As a rule, there is no definite season of general rains nor is widespread rain a common occurrence. Storms are local and the effects of any single storm are not felt over any considerable area. Several months or even years may pass between successive rains. But when they do occur, they may be violent cloudbursts during which a large amount of water falls in a very short time. This form of precipitation often does extensive damage. The few stream channels fill rapidly and overflow, bringing destruction to villages and oasis gardens lying near them. And yet, it is these storms which replenish the meager underground supplies of water and thus make life possible in these regions. The more gentle showers which occasionally fall barely wet the surface, and the moisture from them is soon returned to the air by evaporation. Often clouds form and rain is seen to fall from them; yet no moisture reaches the ground. High temperatures and dry air cause the evaporation of the rain during its descent. Under such conditions, the figure of average yearly rainfall fails to present a complete and true statement. It suggests meagerness only. To that must be added the concept of uncertainty and irregularity.

Precipitation in areas of Semiarid (BS) climate is not only of greater amount than in Arid (BW) areas; it is more certain, it occurs at more frequent intervals, and it is more widespread in its effects. Local convectional storms are less commonly the source of rain, and they are less violent when they occur. Ordinarily, rains come from the same sources and at the same times as those within adjacent moister regions. For example, where the Semiarid (BS) climate adjoins a moist region with winter rains, as where the Sahara grades into the lands along the southern shore of the Mediterranean Sea, the precipitation within the Semiarid (BS) climate shows pronounced winter concentration. Where, on the other hand, the Semiarid (BS) climate lies close to a moist region with summer rains, its precipitation also is mainly concentrated in the summer season. The amount of rain is, of course, smaller. Because of this close causal tie, rain is more certain and affects a wider area within the Semiarid (BS) climate than within the Arid (BW) climate.

TEMPERATURE. Temperatures in Dry (B) climates represent the whole range found from the low latitudes to the equatorward margins of the high latitudes. The common feature of dryness implies no specific set of temperature values. Yet, the temperatures of the Dry (B) climates have in common the element of exceptionally great range, both annual and daily, for the latitudes in which they occur.

In the middle latitudes, the range between the coolest and warmest months is usually between 40° and 50°. Summers are notably hot and winters pronouncedly cold. This condition is illustrated by the statistics and graph for Denver, Colorado [1] (Fig. 90A). There, January has an average temperature of 30° F. and July, an average of 72° F. The average annual range is 42°. There is a definite summer season and a definite winter season.

In the low latitudes, the annual range is still very large compared to those in the Tropical Moist (A) climates or in the climates of tropical uplands or mountains. The range is usually between 15° and 30°. At Kayes in French West Africa (Fig. 90B), the coolest month average, shown alike by December and January, is 77° F. May is the warmest month with an average of 96° F. The average annual range is 19° F. Even though one season is markedly cooler than the other, no true winter can be said to exist.

It is largely on the basis of the presence or absence of a winter season that further differences within both the Semiarid (BS) and Arid (BW) climates is made. The lack of a cold winter season is a characteristic of Dry (B) climates within the low latitudes or on their margins. Kayes in French West Africa (Fig. 90B) offers a good example. Within the middle latitudes, the Dry (B) climates have true winter and summer seasons, as at Denver, Colorado (Fig. 90A).

Dry (B) climates with relatively low temperatures do, however, occur in two kinds of places in the low latitudes. Along low latitude west coasts, roughly between latitudes 20° and 30° in both hemispheres, oceanic influences reduce the warm season temperatures and raise those of the cold season. Not only are annual ranges thereby made smaller, but yearly averages are reduced below the figures commonly expected in low latitude locations. High elevation produces similar lowering of low latitude temperatures.

[1] Where possible, examples of the several climatic types will be drawn from the United States even though they may not be the best possible world examples.

Low latitude Dry (B) climates have furnished the highest temperatures to be recorded on the face of the earth. Azizia, just southwest of Tripoli on the northern coast of Africa, has registered 136° F. in the shade. L. M. Nesbitt, in a semipopular account of travel across the Danakil Lowland of northeastern Ethiopia, suggests readings even higher. Maximum temperatures of over 100° F. have been recorded in every month except January at Wadi Halfa, in Egypt, and, in that month, 99° F. has been attained. In the north central Australian desert, temperature is known to have exceeded 100° F. for over sixty consecutive days.

Despite such excessively high temperatures during the day, night readings are often painfully low, frequently below freezing. The average daily range in areas of Arid (BW) climate in the low latitudes is usually between 25° and 30°. Extreme daily ranges are often as great as 70°; at Azizia, which holds the record, daily range has attained exactly 100°, from 126° F. to 26° F., within the same 24-hour period. Ordinarily, the daily ranges are greater in the warmer part of the year than in the cooler part. But, at all times and in all Dry (B) climates, the contrast between day and night is startling.

OTHER FEATURES. Two other features are outstanding in areas of Dry (B) climate. They are sunshine and wind. Both are at a maximum in low latitude Dry (B) climate, but they are significant elements in the other Dry (B) climates as well. Throughout the hotter and drier sections, skies are seldom obscured by clouds (Fig. 91). Over 80 per cent of the possible sunlight is received at the earth's surface. Cloudiness increases to about 50 per cent in the cooler and more moist sections, such as those that border the ocean or that adjoin moist climates in the middle latitudes. High winds are likewise common, especially during the daytime. As a result, the air is frequently laden with dust particles. Dust storms are often sufficiently heavy to blot out the sky. Their force is great enough, though they

A   DENVER

	J	F	M	A	M	J	J	A	S	O	N	D	Year
Temp.	30	32	39	47	57	67	72	71	62	51	39	32	50
Prec.	0.4	0.5	1.0	2.1	2.4	1.4	1.8	1.4	1.0	1.0	0.6	0.7	14.3

B   KAYES

	J	F	M	A	M	J	J	A	S	O	N	D	Year
Temp.	77	81	89	94	96	91	84	82	82	85	83	77	85
Prec.	0	0	0	0	0.6	3.9	8.3	8.3	5.6	1.9	0.3	0.2	29.1

90   *CLIMATIC charts and statistics for Denver and Kayes.*

Daily temperature range is considerable in all Dry (B) climates. It is more pronounced in areas of Arid (BW) climate in the low latitudes than elsewhere within the Dry (B) climates.

91 *MEAN ANNUAL amount of cloud, expressed in terms of percentage of the sky covered by clouds. Note that most areas of Dry (B) climate, shown in Fig. 93, are likewise areas of low cloudiness.*

seldom last for long periods, to make them among the most destructive, hazardous, and uncomfortable phenomena of the Dry (B) climatic regions of the world.

Subdivisions of the Dry (B) Climates

ARID (BW) CLIMATES. The general characteristics of the Arid (BW) type, as it occurs near the margins of the low latitudes, are illustrated by Yuma, Arizona (Fig. 92A). Precipitation is insignificant in amount and what there is, is unevenly distributed through the year. Though a yearly average of 3.3 inches is shown, the rain is uncertain and variable in amount; one year Yuma received less than one inch while in another it had over eleven inches. January is the coolest month with an average temperature of 55° F. and July is the hottest with an average of 91° F. Thus the yearly range is 36°. A maximum of 120° F. has been recorded while the minimum is 22° F. There is, on the average, bright sunshine 90 per cent of the possible time. The terrifically high temperatures caused by continued blazing sun in July and August are made bearable by the dryness of the air. Relative humidity is low, averaging 55 per cent in the early morning and only 27 per cent in the late afternoon. Human utilization of an area with this type of climate is strictly limited to those parts which can be supplied with additional water beyond that which is received as rain.

The climate of Albuquerque, New Mexico (Fig. 92B) is more truly representative of middle latitude Arid (BW) climate than Yuma. In contrast to Yuma, the hot season is less intense and there is a pronounced winter. The highest monthly average temperature, that for July, is 77° F., nearly 14° less than at Yuma; the coldest month average, that for January, is 24° F., over 20° lower than at Yuma. The maximum in summer

reaches 104° F., but the winter minimum drops to −10° F. Killing frosts may be experienced at any time from the end of October to the middle of April. Snow is not unknown as a form of winter precipitation. Bright sunshine occurs nearly as much of the time as at Yuma and the air has the same characteristic dryness. Water limits human utilization of the land as it does in all Arid (BW) climates.

SEMIARID (BS) CLIMATE. Kayes (Fig. 90B) has a representative low latitude Semiarid (BS) climate. A true winter season is lacking, as in the Tropical Moist (A) climates, but the range of 19° between the warmest and coolest months exceeds that which is found in the Tropical Moist (A) types. Precipitation is small in amount, yet it is much larger than that in Arid (BW) climates. Rain is distributed through the year in a manner similar to that in the Savanna (Aw) climate (Fig. 87B) in which drought occurs during the period of lowest temperatures. Kayes is in a region adjacent to an area of Savanna (Aw) climate and its rain is produced by the same forces. The precipitation at Kayes is, however, too small in amount to equal the potential evaporation at the temperatures there experienced. The dependence upon additional sources of moisture is less than in areas of Arid (BW) climate. Yet, any continued intensive cultivation of the soil demands irrigation.

Semiarid (BS) climate in the middle latitudes is characteristically represented at Denver (Fig. 90A). There is a marked winter season during which most of the precipitation is in the form of snow. The average annual temperature range is high, 43°. High summer temperatures are common, with 105° F. as the maximum recorded; low winter temperatures are indicated by the minimum of record, −29° F. As in the low latitudes, total precipitation is greater in amount and much more dependable than in Arid (BW) areas. While relative humidity is still low as compared with that of the moist climates, the average is much higher than that in the Arid (BW) climates. Consequently, the temperatures, especially those of winter, appear to be even more extreme than they actually are. Intensive agricultural use of land with this type of climate demands irrigation, though pastoral use and certain phases of extensive cultivation are possible without it.

Distribution

The distribution of the Dry (B) climates throughout the world is shown on Fig. 93. The Dry (B) climates extend inland from the low latitude west coasts, swinging poleward as they penetrate into the hearts of the land masses. The areas of Arid (BW) climate are flanked by zones of Semiarid (BS) climate. On the equatorward side of the areas of Arid (BW) climate, the Semiarid (BS) zone provides the transition from Arid (BW) to Savanna (Aw); on the poleward side, the Semiarid (BS) zone indicates the transition from Arid (BW) climate to Moist, Mild Winter (C) or to Moist, Severe Winter (D) types.

Dominant Controls

PRECIPITATION. Distance from sources of moisture, orographic barriers, or the lack of winds moving in the right direction to transport moisture are responsible for meager rainfall in all Dry (B) climates. The total rainfall in Semiarid (BS) areas is greater than that in Arid (BW) areas because the former are nearer moisture sources or are so located that rain-bearing winds are experienced more frequently. Such precipitation as there is in areas of Arid (BW) climate results usually from local convectional storms, whereas that in areas of Semiarid (BS) climate is usually produced by causes effective in adjacent moist climatic regions. Within the low latitudes, the controls are those of the Tropical Moist (A) climates; in the middle latitudes, cy-

	J	F	M	A	M	J	J	A	S	O	N	D	Year
Temp.	55	59	65	70	77	85	91	90	84	72	61	56	72
Prec.	0.5	0.4	0.3	0.1	0	0	0.2	0.6	0.3	0.2	0.3	0.4	3.3

	J	F	M	A	M	J	J	A	S	O	N	D	Year
Temp.	34	39	47	56	65	73	77	75	68	57	43	34	56
Prec.	0.4	0.2	0.2	0.5	0.4	0.8	1.2	1.3	0.9	0.7	0.5	0.4	7.5

92 *CLIMATIC charts and statistics for Yuma and Albuquerque.*

clonic storms cause the greater part of the precipitation.

TEMPERATURE. The great annual and daily ranges of temperature experienced within areas of Dry (B) climate are directly related

WORLD
DRY
(B) CLIMATES

Arid (BW)

Semiarid (BS)

Compressed Sinusoidal
equal-area projection

STATUTE MILES

0   1000   2000   3000   4000   5000

93   *WORLD DISTRIBUTION of Dry (B) climates.*

to the dryness of the air and to the sparsity of the vegetation cover. Dry air permits a high proportion of solar energy to reach the surface during the daylight period. Clear, cloudless skies, resulting from the relatively low moisture content of the air, allow heating to continue uninterruptedly over long hours. Little of the energy is absorbed by the sparse plant cover or is used in the evaporation of water. Thus, the surface is heated to temperatures often so high as to be painful to human touch. Rapid radiation from the surface produces very high air temperatures. The receipt of solar energy stops with the setting of the sun, but the dry air and cloudless skies allow rapid radiation to continue. Consequently, air temperatures drop with startling rapidity, so that the nights often seem very chilly after the glaring heat of the day. As a rule, sundown is a signal for persons to don heavier clothing.

Maximum daytime heating occurs when the noon sun is most nearly overhead. There are two periods during the year in the low latitudes when the noon sun is directly overhead. In the areas of Dry (B) climate, these are close together. Hence only one hot season results, but that season is relatively long. Day after day, burning high sun produces the highest recorded air temperatures on the earth's surface. Though the noon sun is never at a very low angle in these latitudes, the difference in heating between the high- and low-sun seasons is more marked than in moist areas in the same latitudes. A change in surface heating is reflected quickly and almost completely because little absorption of heat by plants or little use of it in the evaporation of water takes place.

In the middle latitudes, there is no period in the year when the noon sun is directly overhead. But, in the season when the sun is highest, the length of daylight period is much longer than in the low latitudes (Fig. 57). Hence, total insolation in summer is relatively large in amount; that season is relatively hot. In winter, the sun is at a much lower angle than it ever is in the low latitudes and the daylight period is much shorter. The receipt of solar energy is thus greatly reduced. But the process of radiation is as little interrupted in the middle latitude areas of Dry (B) climate as it is in those of the low latitudes. Consequently, the low-sun season is notably cold. The range between the seasons in the middle latitudes is thus even greater than in the low latitude areas of Dry (B) climate.

Reduced temperatures and ranges are encountered in arid and semiarid areas along continental west coasts. For example, the average annual range at Lima, Peru, is only 12°, from 73° F. in February and March to 61° F. in July, August, and September. At Port Nolloth in southwest Africa, the average annual range is only 6°, from 59° F. in the warmest month to 53° F. in the coolest; and, at Cape Juby in northwest Africa, it is only 8°, from 69° F. in the warmest month to 61° F. in the coolest. In such locations, cool currents exist offshore. Air above them is cool and moisture-laden. As this cool air moves toward the warmer land, carrying fog and cloud with it, it is warmed. The fog and cloud are soon evaporated. Nevertheless, for a short distance inland, they form a moisture blanket which greatly reduces both the receipt of solar energy at the earth's surface and the rate of radiation of heat from the surface to the atmosphere. As a result, both the daily and seasonal extreme temperatures characteristic of the Dry (B) climates as a whole are rarely experienced and the ranges are thus made smaller.

CHAPTER OUTLINE

Climatic types: the Tropical Moist and the Dry climates

REVIEW QUESTIONS

1. Discuss the purpose of climatic classification.
2. Why is the ancient Greek classification of climate inadequate?
3. What does a map of climatic types actually show? How is such a map made?
4. A boundary between one kind of climate and another is represented on a climatic map by a line. Exactly what does such a line imply? If you were traveling from Chicago to New Orleans, could you tell exactly where you crossed the boundary between one type of climate and another? Discuss.
5. Why is the classification of climate based upon temperature and precipitation?
6. The Tropical Moist (A) climates are defined as having an average temperature of at least 64° F. for the coolest month of the year. Is there any specific reason for choosing this figure rather than some other?
7. Explain the lack of any considerable annual temperature range in the Tropical Moist (A) climates.
8. In what major way do the Tropical Moist (A) climates of one part of the world differ from those of another? Or, are all Tropical Moist (A) climates exactly alike?
9. A climatic graph is actually a conventionalized picture of a climatic type. Tell how one may distinguish between a Tropical Rainforest (Af) and a Savanna (Aw) climate from climatic graphs alone.
10. What position does a Tropical Monsoon (Am) climate occupy with respect to a Tropical Rainforest (Af) and a Savanna (Aw) climate?
11. Explain why Tropical Moist (A) climates have constant high temperatures.
12. Why are temperatures in tropical highland areas even more monotonously uniform than those in tropical lowlands?
13. What are the major controls of precipitation in Tropical Moist (A) climates? What is their effect on the distribution of the different phases of the Tropical Moist (A) climates?
14. How does the climate of the northern Congo Basin, for example, differ from that of southwestern India? Explain some of the causes of the differences.
15. How are the outstanding features of all Dry (B) climates reflected in man's attitude toward and uses of areas with Dry (B) climates?
16. Floods are especially disastrous hazards in many areas of Dry (B) climate. Explain this apparent paradox.
17. From the description of the Dry (B) climates, it is obvious that temperatures vary considerably from place to place within areas having these climates. Why is this a matter of secondary importance whereas in Tropical Moist (A) climates temperature is a matter of primary importance?
18. Explain the fact that there is a greater range of temperature, both diurnally and seasonally,

in the Dry (B) climates generally than in the Tropical Moist (A) climates.

19. Account for the generally meager rainfall in all areas of Dry (B) climate in terms of the dominant controls of precipitation.

20. Why are temperature ranges along Arid (BW) and Semiarid (BS) continental west coasts less than in other areas with these two types of climate?

SOME SUGGESTED REFERENCES

Haurwitz, Bernhard, and Austin, James M., *Climatology,* McGraw-Hill, 1944. A treatment of both physical and regional climatology which implies considerable familiarity with meteorological principles; useful for descriptions of climatic classifications and of climatic types.

James, Preston E. (with the collaboration of Hibberd V. B. Kline, Jr.), *A Geography of Man,* Ginn, 1949. An excellent study of major world regions; stresses cultural elements of geography, but includes clear, readable descriptions of climatic types.

Kendrew, W. G., *The Climates of the Continents,* 3rd ed., Clarendon Press, 1937. A standard work on regional climatology; organized on a continent basis.

Trewartha, Glenn T., *An Introduction to Weather and Climate,* 2nd ed., McGraw-Hill, 1937. A basic and thoroughly workmanlike text; deals with both physical and regional climatology primarily from a geographical point of view.

94 *AUTUMN SCENE in an area of Severe Winter (D) climate. (Newell Green)*

CHAPTER 8

Climatic Types: the Mild Winter, the Severe Winter, and the Polar Climates

From the Tropics to the equatorward margins of the high latitudes, it has been seen that the interiors of the world's land masses are occupied by great expanses of Semiarid (BS) and Arid (BW) climate. The dry continental interiors are flanked oceanward and poleward by regions of moist climates, all of which are characterized by the presence of marked temperature changes from one part of the year to another. Seasons defined by temperature change constitute the distinguishing characteristic. It should be recalled that seasons are defined largely in terms of precipitation and that temperature change is of only minor importance in areas of Tropical Moist (A) climates. In the moist areas of the middle latitudes, temperature change is the outstanding climatic feature; precipitation provides only the secondary variations. Two major climatic categories can be distinguished: the Moist, Mild Winter (C) and the Moist, Severe Winter (D) climates.

In the high latitudes, where the receipt of heat from the sun is small in amount during one part of the year and nonexistent during the other, low temperatures at all times characterize the climate. There, the last of the major climatic categories, the Polar (E) climate, is encountered.

THE MOIST, MILD WINTER (C) CLIMATES

Characteristics

TEMPERATURE. One common feature of a large group of climatic types is the presence of a definite, though mild, winter season. Temperatures during one part of the year drop below those in the Tropical Moist (A) climates previously described. The lower temperatures induce a period of rest from growth activity in the plant life. Not only does this bring about a change in the individual plant species from those characteristic of the moist tropics; it introduces a definite seasonal rhythm in the cycle of plant life which becomes more pronounced with increased severity of the winter season.

Along the contact with the Tropical Moist (A) climates or the low latitude Dry (B) climates, the seasonal rhythm is poorly developed; many of the forest trees remain leaf-covered and green throughout the year. Near the poleward margins of the Moist, Mild Winter (C) climates, the seasonal change is marked with budding, flowering, and leafing in spring and the loss of leaves in fall. The presence of a winter is reflected in many other features of the physical setting. The crops which are grown, the systems of cultivation

which are followed, the types of buildings in which man lives, all likewise point toward a recognition of the seasonal rhythm.

On the tropical margins, the winter temperatures average in the high 50's, as at Hong Kong in China (Fig. 95A). There, the average for the coolest month, February, is 59° F. Somewhat farther poleward, the low average is in the 40's, as at Sacramento, California (Fig. 95B), where the average for January is 46° F. In the continental interiors and likewise near the poleward margins of the Moist, Mild Winter (C) climates, low monthly averages are in the 30's. Nashville, Tennessee (Fig. 95C), records an average of 39° F. for January. The winter is considered to become truly severe approximately where the average temperature for the coldest month is 27° F. It is this figure which is taken as the cold limit of the Moist, Mild Winter (C) climates.

The nature of the summer is fully as significant, from the point of view of human activity, as that of the winter. Near the Tropics and in the continental interiors, the summers are long and hot, frequently with averages in the high 70's or low 80's. Hong

95 *CLIMATIC CHARTS and statistics for Hong Kong, Sacramento, and Nashville.*

	J	F	M	A	M	J	J	A	S	O	N	D	Year
Temp.	60	59	63	70	77	81	82	82	81	76	69	63	72
Prec.	1.3	1.6	2.7	5.4	11.7	15.9	13.8	14.1	9.8	4.9	1.9	1.4	84.5

	J	F	M	A	M	J	J	A	S	O	N	D	Year
Temp.	46	50	54	58	63	69	73	72	69	62	53	46	60
Prec.	3.8	2.9	3.0	1.6	0.8	0.1	0	0	0.2	0.9	2.1	4.0	19.4

	J	F	M	A	M	J	J	A	S	O	N	D	Year
Temp.	39	41	50	59	68	76	79	78	72	61	49	41	59
Prec.	4.7	4.2	5.1	4.4	3.8	4.2	4.1	3.5	3.5	2.4	3.5	3.9	47.3

A   SAN FRANCISCO

	J	F	M	A	M	J	J	A	S	O	N	D	Year
Temp.	49	51	53	54	56	57	57	58	60	59	56	51	55
Prec.	4.8	3.6	3.1	1.6	0.7	0.1	0	0	0.3	1.0	2.4	4.6	22.2

B   GREENWICH

	J	F	M	A	M	J	J	A	S	O	N	D	Year
Temp.	39	40	42	47	53	59	63	62	57	50	44	40	50
Prec.	1.9	1.5	1.6	1.6	1.9	2.0	2.4	2.3	2.1	2.7	2.2	2.0	24.2

Kong has a July average of 82° F. and Nashville has one of 79° F. In coastal locations and where marine influences penetrate well into the land, the summers are warm rather than hot and are somewhat shorter. San Francisco's warmest month (Fig. 96A) averages only 60° F. and Greenwich in England (Fig. 96B) records only 63° F. Some parts of west coasts in the higher middle latitudes have a very short and a very cool summer. At Lerwick in the Shetland Islands (Fig. 96C) off the northern coast of Scotland, the warmest month is August with an average of only 52° F. and only three months have averages over 50° F.

Average annual ranges of temperature increase generally away from the Tropics and inland from windward coastal positions. At Hong Kong, the range is 23°; it is 40° at Nashville. The range at San Francisco is only 11°, but at Sacramento, only 90 miles away, it is 27°. A characteristic small range is encountered in all continental west coast areas even though they may be in relatively high latitudes. Lerwick is in latitude 60° North; the average annual range there is only 14°. This condition reflects strong marine controls.

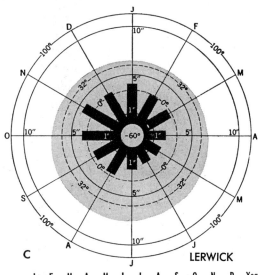

C   LERWICK

	J	F	M	A	M	J	J	A	S	O	N	D	Year
Temp.	39	38	39	41	45	49	52	52	50	46	43	40	45
Prec.	4.2	3.4	3.1	2.3	2.0	1.8	2.2	3.0	3.0	3.9	4.3	4.7	37.9

96   *CLIMATIC CHARTS and statistics for San Francisco, Greenwich, England, and Lerwick, Scotland.*

PRECIPITATION. None of the Moist, Mild Winter (C) climates is deficient in moisture for the year as a whole; yet many of them show seasonal deficiencies. There are three possibilities so far as rainfall distribution through the year is concerned; the rain may be rather evenly distributed through the year, as at Nashville (Fig. 95C); or it may be concentrated in the winter period, as at Sacramento (Fig. 95B); or it may be concentrated in the summer season, as at Hong Kong (Fig. 95A).

In some respects, an area with summer rains is like one in which the rain is spread evenly through the whole year. In both, there is usually rain in plentiful amount during the warmer part of the year when growth activity is greatest. The advantage of evenly distributed and summer rains for man's crops and, hence, his food supply, is obvious. That the winter should be dry in one instance serves only to emphasize the period of plant rest induced by lower temperatures.

The condition represented by winter rain is quite different. The rain of winter is followed by summer drought fully as intense as the dryness of the Dry (B) climates. Plant growth is greatly restricted and intensive cultivation is dependent on irrigation during the growing season. Fortunately, the winters in areas where rainfall is concentrated in winter are usually mild, or even warm, so that cessation of plant growth is not characteristic, as, for example, in southern California or along the Mediterranean shores of Europe and Africa.

Precipitation varies widely in amount and in form of occurrence throughout the Moist, Mild Winter (C) climates. On windward coasts, especially if they are hilly or mountainous like that of northwestern Scotland, and on the tropical margins as along the coast of Mississippi, Alabama, and western Florida, the amount is often excessive; 80 to 100 inches a year are not uncommon. The total is markedly less in continental interiors as in eastern Kansas and Oklahoma, or in the lee of highlands as in southeastern Scotland. Adjacent to areas of Semiarid (BS) climate, the rainfall in Moist, Mild Winter (C) climates may

be as little as 15 inches, as at Los Angeles. But *all* Moist, Mild Winter (C) climates have average annual rainfall which exceeds average annual evaporation.

Rains in Moist, Mild Winter (C) climates are of both the general and the local types. The controls of precipitation vary widely but, regardless of what they are specifically, areas within this climatic zone are subject both to the kind of rain which continues gently over relatively long periods of time and to that which falls torrentially for a short period. Where the summer is rainy, thunderstorms are frequent. On the tropical margins, they are nearly as frequent as in areas of Tropical Rainforest (Af) climate. The summer precipitation generally is of the short shower type while that of winter more commonly is lighter, but lasts through many hours or even days.

Along western coasts in the higher middle latitudes, even the summer precipitation is gentle. Local convectional storms are almost unknown. Here occur some of the cloudiest and rainiest places in the world, in terms of the number of rainy days per year. Yet the amount of rain is often remarkably small. Lerwick, though recording an average yearly rainfall of only 38 inches, has an average of 260 rainy days per year; on the average, between seven- and eight-tenths of the skies are covered by clouds each month. Precipitation occurring under these conditions is aptly described by the expression "Scotch mist." Never is the rain really heavy enough to prevent outdoor activity, but seldom can one pass a whole day in the open without encountering some very fine rain at least.

General rains are common in Moist, Mild Winter (C) areas, where precipitation is concentrated in the winter. They may be heavy or light, and may vary in duration from a few hours to three, four, or five days. Local convectional storms are infrequent and the rain which they cause is negligible in amount.

Subdivisions of the Moist, Mild Winter (C) Climates

As has been suggested, all of the Moist, Mild Winter (C) climates have in common the facts (1) that they have more precipitation than the Dry (B) climates, and (2) that they all have definite cool and warm seasons. However, differences in the occurrence of precipitation through the year and in the relative warmth of the summer are sufficient to create four distinctive types within the major category.

These four distinctive types are: (1) Humid Subtropical (Cfa) climate; (2) Mid-latitude Marine (Cfb and Cfc) climate; (3) Subtropical Monsoon (Cw) climate; and (4) Mediterranean (Cs) climate.

HUMID SUBTROPICAL (Cfa) CLIMATE. The climatic statistics and graph for Nashville (Fig. 95C) illustrate this type of climate. The long, hot summer, four months with average temperature over 70° F., contrasts sharply with the winter when the lowest monthly average is 39° F. Daily temperatures in midsummer are high, usually in the 80's or 90's, and they occasionally exceed 100° F. This heat is normally accompanied by high relative humidities so that the temperature one "feels" (*sensible temperature*) is much higher than the thermometer temperature would lead one to expect. The sensible temperature is often even more oppressive, for a short time, than that produced by the steaminess of a Tropical Rainforest (Af) climate. Relief in the form of lower temperatures and drier air may be expected at irregular intervals, however. During the winter, relative humidity is considerably reduced and temperatures often drop below freezing from November through March. However, the periods of cold are seldom long continued. Precipitation shows a maximum in spring and a minimum in late summer or fall. Yet, in contrast to areas of well-defined seasonal concentration, the rainfall is rather evenly spread through the whole year. Though the average figures show adequate moisture the year round, droughts of short duration are a common occurrence. These droughts result from the high temperatures of summer coupled with the receipt of less rain than the average figures indicate. Snow is common in winter, but it seldom remains on the ground for more than a few days at a time. The ground likewise rarely freezes deeply and never remains frozen continuously through the season.

MID-LATITUDE MARINE (Cfb AND Cfc) CLIMATES. Though there are areas with these types of climate on the west coast of North America, better examples are to be found in northwestern Europe. Consequently, Greenwich in England (Fig. 96B) is chosen to represent the Mid-latitude Marine (Cfb) type. In contrast to those of the Humid Subtropical (Cfa) climate, the summers are warm rather than hot and the winters are milder. Nashville and Greenwich have the same low average temperature of 39° F. for January, yet Greenwich is 15° of latitude farther poleward than Nashville. The warmest month at Greenwich is 16° cooler than that at Nashville. The Mid-latitude Marine (Cfb) summers are cooler and the winters warmer than in the Humid Subtropical (Cfa) climate; relative humidity is higher over the year period; and there is greater cloudiness. In the Mid-latitude Marine (Cfb) climate, precipitation is distributed through the year in a manner similar to that in the Humid Subtropical (Cfa) climate, but rarely is it of the local convectional type.

There is an extreme phase of the Mid-latitude Marine (Cfc) type, the essential features of which are illustrated in the statistics and graph for Lerwick, Scotland (Fig. 96C). The summers are so cool that agricultural use of the land is almost impossible, yet the winters are only slightly more severe than in the Humid Subtropical (Cfa) climate. Lerwick is nearly 25° of latitude farther north than

WORLD
MILD WINTER
(C) CLIMATES

Humid subtropical (Cfa)

Midlatitude marine (Cfb-Cfc)

Subtropical monsoon (Cw)

Mediterranean (Cs)

Compressed Sinusoidal
equal-area projection

STATUTE MILES
0 1000 2000 3000 4000 5000

97 WORLD DISTRIBUTION of Mild Winter (C) climates.

Nashville, yet its coolest winter month averages only a fraction of a degree lower. On the other hand, freezing temperatures have been recorded at Lerwick in every month except July and August. Even though the total precipitation is only 38 inches, that amount is excessive for, at the prevailing temperatures, evaporation is low. The land is sodden, and only at infrequent intervals does the sun break through the cloud cover to create even the impression of a dry period.

SUBTROPICAL MONSOON (Cw) CLIMATE. This type of climate is represented by Hong Kong (Fig. 95A), where a very hot and humid summer contrasts with a cooler and drier season. Except for the low temperatures at one season, weather conditions are similar to those in the Tropical Monsoon (Am) climate, as at Akyab (Fig. 87C). The winter, or cool season, dry period is seldom completely without rain, and usually enough rain falls during the summer to maintain soil moisture through the year. Since the winter is not cool enough to experience more than rare frosts, it is possible to carry on agriculture throughout the year. The average annual range, 23°, is about that which occurs on the cooler margins of the Tropical Moist (A) climates.

MEDITERRANEAN (Cs) CLIMATES. The remaining type of climate in the Moist, Mild Winter (C) category is known as the Mediterranean (Cs) climate. Among all the world's climates, it is unique in that precipitation is concentrated in winter and summers are droughty. Despite this unique feature, there are two distinct phases of Mediterranean (Cs) climate; one has long, hot summers and the other has short, warm summers.

On a continental coast fully exposed to oceanic influences, summer temperatures are reduced and winter ones increased. Relative humidity is high throughout the year. Cloudiness is characteristic and fog is a common phenomenon. Summer high temperatures seldom attain 100° F. and freezing days are likely to occur only during a very brief period in midwinter and then chiefly on the poleward margins of these areas. This type is represented by San Francisco (Fig. 96A).

Inland, away from marine influences, summer temperatures are higher; winter ones are lower; relative humidity is lower, especially in summer; and cloud and fog are greatly reduced. This type is represented by Sacramento (Fig. 95B). Burningly dry, sunny days succeed one another almost without interruption through the summer. Temperatures at that season frequently approach those of the low latitude Semiarid (BS) and Arid (BW) climates, with daily maxima between 85° and 95° F. Absolute maxima are usually well over 100° F.; Sacramento, for example, has recorded 114° F. Freezing temperatures are more common than in the Mediterranean (Cs) climatic areas along coasts and may occur over a two-month period in winter. Sacramento has recorded as many as seven nights in one year during which temperatures below 32° F. were experienced.

Distribution

Poleward from the tropics, the Dry (B) climates lie inland from both continental coasts, as we have seen. Between the coasts and the dry interiors, Moist, Mild Winter (C) climates are found (Fig. 97). West of the dry interiors, Mediterranean (Cs) types occur between, roughly, 30 and 40 degrees of latitude in both hemispheres. They are succeeded poleward by Mid-latitude Marine (Cfb and Cfc) types which continue to approximately 60° latitude in both hemispheres. Small areas of Humid Subtropical (Cfa) climate are found in the interior adjacent to the dry margin, particularly in parts of southeastern Europe. East of the dry interiors, Humid Subtropical (Cfa) or Subtropical Monsoon (Cw) types extend poleward to about 40° latitude from areas of Tropical Rainforest (Af) and Savanna (Aw) climates.

Dominant Controls

TEMPERATURE. The presence of a winter season, with temperatures too low for Tropical Moist (A) climates, is a direct reflection of distance from the equator. In addition, distance from the equator produces increased average annual temperature range. Average annual range is controlled basically by seasonal change of insolation (see Chap. 5). Since seasonal change of insolation becomes greater as one travels away from the tropics, average annual ranges increase in that direction. Marine influences counteract this tendency and continental influences amplify it. Since the middle latitudes, where the Moist, Mild Winter (C) climates occur, are the zone of Prevailing Westerlies, it is along the continental west coasts that marine influences are best developed. In these latitudes, marine influences are less effective along east coasts and least effective in continental interiors.

PRECIPITATION. Numerous controls of precipitation are operative in the different types of Moist, Mild Winter (C) climates. The Prevailing Westerlies are rain-bearing, onshore winds throughout the year in Mid-latitude Marine (Cfb and Cfc) areas. Cyclonic storms, following the general path of the Westerlies, add materially to the total precipitation. Areas of Mediterranean (Cs) climate likewise receive most of their rain from Westerlies and cyclonic storms, but these two controls are effective only during the winter in the latitudes where the Mediterranean (Cs) climate occurs. This is primarily a reflection of the seasonal shift of wind belts. In areas of Humid Subtropical (Cfa) climate, cyclonic storms are the major source of rain in all seasons, but to their contribution must be added that derived from local convectional storms in summer. Within areas of Subtropical Monsoon (Cw) climate, major controls are the same as those in Savanna (Aw) and Tropical Monsoon (Am) climates. These are convection, movements of the Inter-

tropical front, onshore winds in the belt of Trades, and monsoons. The slight rains of winter in Subtropical Monsoon (Cw) areas are associated with the passage of weakly developed cyclonic storms.

THE MOIST, SEVERE WINTER (D) CLIMATES

Characteristics

TEMPERATURE. Colder, longer, and more continuous winters and greater range from season to season distinguish the Moist, Severe Winter (D) from the Moist, Mild Winter (C) climates. On the equatorward margins of the Moist, Severe Winter (D) climates, the coldest month average is 27° F. Poleward from that and toward the continental interiors, winters become more and more severe. The extreme is reached in northeastern Siberia where continental influences are strongest and marine influences are totally lacking. The coldest winters in the world occur there. Verkhoyansk (Fig. 98A) has an average of −59° F. for January; Sredne Kolymsk (Fig. 98B), of −41° F. On winter nights, temperatures well below those figures are regularly experienced. An absolute minimum for the world has been reported at Oimekon in that same general area, −108° F.!

Extreme continental position in high latitudes is necessary to the production of such low temperatures. In the Southern Hemisphere, there are no large land masses in these latitudes; consequently, the Moist, Severe Winter (D) climates occur only in the Northern Hemisphere.

Not only are the winters cold; the season of low temperatures is long and continuous. Frosts are not uncommon features of the more continental of the Moist, Mild Winter (C) climates, but in the Moist, Severe Winter

(D) climates they are never lacking. The ground freezes to great depth and remains effectively frozen for several months. In the most extreme areas, the subsoil is always frozen; only the topsoil ever thaws completely. The winter thus places a marked restriction on plant growth and the period during which agriculture is possible is sharply defined. The length and continuity of the winters are made more pronounced by the suddenness of the transition to and from summer. The expression "spring comes with a bang" is literally true. True, also, is the corollary expression "winter comes overnight." Both spring and fall are short. Further emphasis is provided by the long daylight hours of summer and the correspondingly long hours of darkness in winter (Fig. 57).

Just as in the Moist, Mild Winter (C) climates, there is great variation in the character of the summers. Long, hot summers characterize the southern margin in the continental interiors. Averages in the 70's are usual and not infrequently during the summer 100° F. is exceeded for a short period. More frequent

daytime fluctuations, regularly lower night temperatures, and lower relative humidity make these high summer temperatures less oppressive than in the Moist, Mild Winter (C) climates. Summers become cooler rapidly in a northward direction (Table 12A) and toward coasts (Table 12B). One passes from the areas with long, hot summers to those with short, warm summers and, finally, in the northern part of the Moist, Severe Winter (D) climates, to those with very short, cool summers. The coolness and shortness of the summer in the higher latitudes are partially compensated by the longer daylight hours during that season. Close to the Arctic Circle and within it, midsummer is a time of no real darkness and the growing season is fully as long in hours as in regions much farther south (Fig. 57).

The average annual ranges within the Moist, Severe Winter (D) climates are the greatest in the world. Verkhoyansk, previously mentioned, has a warm month average of 60° F. and a cold month average of −59° F. Its range is thus 119°! This is, of course, the

98 *CLIMATIC CHARTS and statistics for Verkhoyansk and Sredne Kolymsk.*

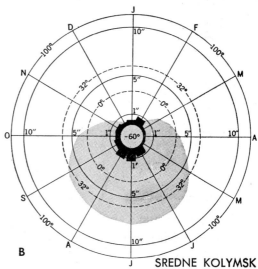

	J	F	M	A	M	J	J	A	S	O	N	D	Year
Temp.	−59	−47	−24	7	35	55	60	50	36	5	−34	−53	3
Prec.	0.2	0.1	0	0.1	0.2	0.5	1.2	0.9	0.2	0.2	0.2	0.2	4.0

VERKHOYANSK

	J	F	M	A	M	J	J	A	S	O	N	D	Year
Temp.	−41	−32	−17	7	31	53	57	48	37	12	−20	−35	8
Prec.	0.4	0.4	0.2	0.2	0.2	0.9	1.3	1.1	0.7	0.5	0.5	0.4	6.8

SREDNE KOLYMSK

extreme. In coastal locations and along the southern margins, the range is between 40° and 50°. It increases northward and toward continental interiors. For example, the average annual range at Keokuk, Iowa, is 54°; at Winnipeg, it is 70°; that at Portland, Maine, is 44° while that at La Crosse, Wisconsin, is 57°. The ranges, greater than those of the Moist, Mild Winter (C) climates, result largely from increased severity of the winters and not from increased summer heat.

PRECIPITATION. Precipitation varies greatly in amount and in distribution through the year in the Moist, Severe Winter (D) climates, as it does in the Moist, Mild Winter (C) climates. The amount is largest in coastal areas as at Portland, Maine (Fig. 99A), where as much as 40 to 50 inches may be expected. It decreases toward the continental interiors where, along the southern margins, the amount is commonly between 25 and 35 inches, as at Chicago, Illinois (Fig. 101A). The amount likewise decreases northward to an extreme of less than 5 inches, as at Verkhoyansk. Such a small amount recalls the precipitation of the Dry (B) climates, where the rain is uncertain in occurrence and irregular in amount. In the Moist, Severe Winter (D) climates, there is little variation from year to year either in period or amount. That so small an amount should suffice to create a moist climate is a measure of the effectiveness of moisture at low temperatures.

Throughout most of the Moist, Severe Winter (D) climates, the snows of winter and the rains of summer are rather evenly distributed. However, in northeastern Asia, snowfall is meager and most of the pre-

---

Table 12   EFFECT OF LATITUDE AND LOCATION WITH RESPECT TO COAST ON AVERAGE SUMMER TEMPERATURES

A. DECREASE OF AVERAGE TEMPERATURES NORTHWARD IN D CLIMATIC REGIONS

PLACE	APPROXIMATE LATITUDE N	AVERAGE TEMPERATURE JULY
Keokuk, Iowa	40°	76.1°
Cedar Rapids, Iowa	42°	75.6°
Charles City, Iowa	44°	73.2°
St. Paul, Minnesota	45°	72.2°
Bemidji, Minnesota	48°	68.9°
Winnipeg, Manitoba	50°	66°

B. DECREASE OF AVERAGE SUMMER TEMPERATURES FROM INTERIOR TOWARD COAST IN D CLIMATIC REGIONS

PLACE	APPROXIMATE LATITUDE N	APPROXIMATE DISTANCE FROM OCEAN IN MILES	AVERAGE TEMPERATURE JULY
La Crosse, Wisconsin	43-44°	1,050	72.8°
Mt. Pleasant, Michigan	43-44°	730	71.0°
Rutland, Vermont	43-44°	130	69.0°
Plymouth, New Hampshire	43-44°	100	68.1°
Portland, Maine	43-44°	0	67.8°

	J	F	M	A	M	J	J	A	S	O	N	D	Year
Temp.	22	24	32	43	54	63	68	66	60	49	38	27	46
Prec.	3.8	3.4	3.9	3.2	3.6	3.3	3.5	3.5	3.3	3.7	3.7	3.8	42.7

	J	F	M	A	M	J	J	A	S	O	N	D	Year
Temp.	5	12	26	39	49	57	66	69	61	49	30	14	40
Prec.	0.1	0.2	0.3	1.2	1.3	1.5	2.2	3.5	2.4	1.6	0.5	0.2	15.0

A — PORTLAND, MAINE

B — VLADIVOSTOK

99   *CLIMATIC CHARTS and statistics for Portland, Maine, and Vladivostok.*

cipitation is received as summer rain. In terms of effectiveness for man's use, the presence of adequate moisture during the season of greatest heat is of major importance. Hence, whether the precipitation is evenly distributed through the year or concentrated in summer, the end results are very similar. There are regions in which the precipitation is concentrated in winter, but these are so small and so scattered that they may be neglected in a general study of world patterns.

Winter precipitation is almost entirely in the form of snow. On all except the southern margins of the Moist, Severe Winter (D) climates, snow accumulates to form a lasting blanket through the winter; even on those margins, it may remain for several weeks at a time. The thickness of the blanket decreases away from the coasts and toward the poleward margins, not only because of the decrease in amount of precipitation, but also because of the nature of the snow crystals. Very fine, dry, tightly packed snow results from the extreme low temperatures and the relatively dry air of the continental interiors; heavy, moist, loosely packed flakes characterize snowfall in coastal regions.

Subdivisions of the Moist, Severe Winter (D) Climates

From the point of view of significance to man, there are three subdivisions of the Moist, Severe Winter (D) climates. Distinction is made primarily on the basis of the relative warmth of the summer season. The three types are: (1) Humid Continental climate with hot summers (Dfa and Dwa); (2) Humid Continental climate with warm summers (Dfb and Dwb); and (3) Subarctic (Dfc, Dwc, Dfd, and Dwd) climate.

HUMID CONTINENTAL CLIMATE WITH HOT SUMMERS (Dfa AND Dwa). Within areas of this type of climate, there is variation in the distribution of precipitation through the year. In some places, no part of the year is dry; in others, there is drought during the winter season. However, the summer, or growing season, is moist in both.

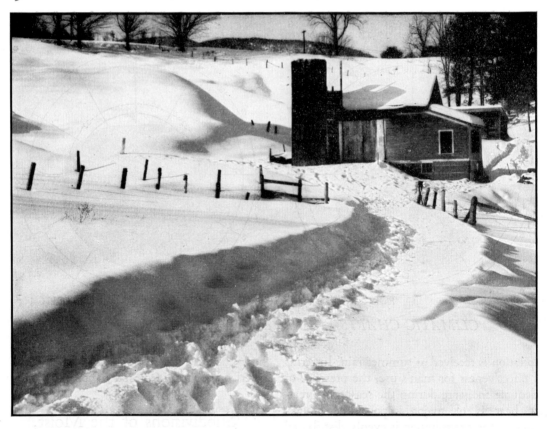

100 *THE TYPICAL WINTER snow cover in an area of Humid Continental (D) climate. (Newell Green)*

Chicago (Fig. 101A) and Mukden in Manchuria (Fig. 101B) represent these phases. The essential difference between them is in the distribution of precipitation through the year. At Chicago, no season is markedly drier than another though there is somewhat more precipitation in the summer months than there is in winter. At Mukden, there is notable contrast between the seasons. The three mid-winter months receive a total of less than one inch while the three summer months receive 14.5 inches, 58 per cent of the total for the year. In addition, the contrast between the seasons at Mukden is marked by high relative humidity in summer and low relative humidity in winter. There is little change in relative humidity between the seasons in Chicago. Clear, cold winter days succeed one another with few interruptions at Mukden, while spells of biting, damp cold, often windy and snowy, alternate with spells of relatively mild, drizzling rains in Chicago winters. The summers are much more nearly alike. Both places are subject to prolonged periods of sticky heat with frequent, sudden downpours of rain alternating with cool, dry periods of clear weather. In both places, likewise, the summers are long as well as hot.

HUMID CONTINENTAL CLIMATE WITH WARM SUMMERS (Dfb AND Dwb). Here, as in the Humid Continental climate with hot summers (Dfa and Dwa) just described, two phases may be recognized, one in which precipitation is spread evenly through the year and one in which there is winter drought. But this distinction is one of detail; the character of the summer is the significant feature.

Portland, Maine (Fig. 99A), and Vladivostok on the Sea of Japan coast of Siberia (Fig. 99B) illustrate the temperature and precipitation features of this type of climate. Compared to the hot summer type of climate just described, the summers in this type are only warm and are generally short. Where two months average over 70° F. at Chicago, no months average as high as 70° F. in Portland, Maine; at Mukden, three months average over 70° F., but none averages as high as 70° F. at Vladivostok. Along with less hot and shorter summers, the winters are somewhat more severe and longer at Portland and Vladivostok than at Chicago and Mukden.

The remarkably even distribution of precipitation through the year and its large amount at Portland are indicators of coastal position. The less intense summer concentration at Vladivostok, in comparison with Mukden, is likewise a measure of coastal position. At both Portland and Vladivostok, the day-to-day fluctuation of weather is less pronounced than at Chicago and Mukden.

SUBARCTIC (Dfc, Dfd, Dwc, Dwd) CLIMATE. Longer and more severe winters, shorter and cooler summers, practical elimination of spring and fall, and decreased amount of precipitation: these are the features which set the Subarctic climate off from the Humid Continental types. Dawson in Canada (Fig. 103A) and Okhotsk in eastern Siberia (Fig. 103B) are respectively good representatives of the different phases of Subarctic climate. At both places, average temperatures are below freezing for over half the year. Yet, summer temperatures often reach 80° F. Frosts may occur in nearly every month. Thus, the growing season is short and uncertain. Only the long sunlight hours of the short summer offer any inducement to the pursuit of agriculture.

Where continentality is extreme, as in northeastern Siberia, a phase of the Subarctic climate develops the most severe winters (Dfd and Dwd) on the earth. Sredne Kolymsk (Fig. 98B) and Verkhoyansk (Fig. 98A) illustrate this phase. Summers are essentially the same as those in other regions of Subarctic (Dfc and Dwc) climate. Maximum daily temperatures through the long days of that

101   *CLIMATIC CHARTS and statistics for Chicago and Mukden.*

	J	F	M	A	M	J	J	A	S	O	N	D	Year
Temp.	26	27	37	47	58	68	74	73	66	55	42	30	50
Prec.	2.1	2.1	2.6	2.9	3.6	3.3	3.4	3.0	3.1	2.6	2.4	2.1	33.2

	J	F	M	A	M	J	J	A	S	O	N	D	Year
Temp.	8	14	30	47	60	71	77	75	61	48	29	14	45
Prec.	0.2	0.3	0.7	1.2	2.2	3.4	5.8	5.3	3.3	1.5	0.9	0.2	25.0

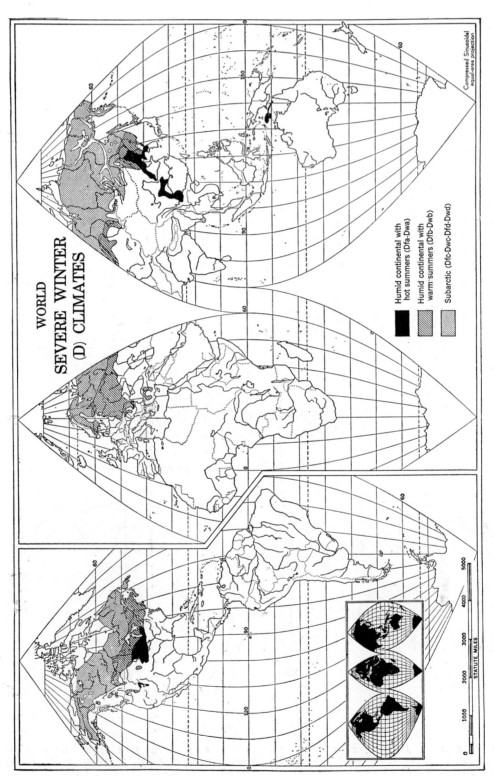

WORLD
SEVERE WINTER
(D) CLIMATES

Humid continental with
hot summers (Dfa-Dwa)

Humid continental with
warm summers (Dfb-Dwb)

Subarctic (Dfc-Dwc-Dfd-Dwd)

Compressed Sinusoidal
equal-area projection

STATUTE MILES
0   1000   2000   3000   4000   5000

102   *WORLD DISTRIBUTION of Severe Winter* (D) *climates.*

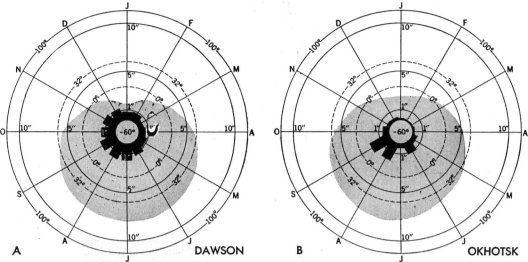

	J	F	M	A	M	J	J	A	S	O	N	D	Year
Temp.	-23	-11	4	29	46	57	59	54	42	25	1	-13	23
Prec.	0.8	0.8	0.5	0.7	0.9	1.3	1.6	1.6	1.7	1.3	1.3	1.1	13.6

	J	F	M	A	M	J	J	A	S	O	N	D	Year
Temp.	-11	-7	7	21	35	45	55	55	46	27	6	-8	23
Prec.	0.1	0.1	0.1	0.2	0.5	1.1	0.5	1.8	2.1	0.7	0.2	0.2	7.6

103 *CLIMATIC CHARTS and statistics for Dawson, in the Yukon Territory, Canada, and Okhotsk, in eastern Siberia.*

season often reach 80° F., but the possibility of frost is never absent. Winter air is very dry and clear through the long hours of darkness at that season. This dryness, accompanied by very little, if any, wind helps to make the low temperatures less severe in their effects on man and wild animal life than would otherwise be the case. Rarely during the winter does the maximum daily temperature rise even to 0° F.

Distribution

Poleward of the Dry (B) and the Moist, Mild Winter (C) climates in the Northern Hemisphere and spreading from west to east coasts, the Moist, Severe Winter (D) climates are more extensive than other types (Fig. 102). They are entirely lacking in the Southern Hemisphere for reasons previously explained. The two great areas are in North America and Eurasia. On the southern edge, both west and east of the dry interior, are the areas of Humid Continental climate with hot summers (Dfa and Dwa). These give way

northward to Humid Continental climate with warm summers (Dfb and Dwb), and to the Subarctic (Dfc, Dwc, Dfd, and Dwd) type.

Dominant Controls

TEMPERATURE. The great difference between summer and winter temperatures is primarily the result of location in high latitudes. The summer sun, though never vertically overhead, is above the horizon for many hours of the day. Surface heating is small per unit of time as compared with areas farther equatorward, but it continues over a longer time in a single day. Total heating is therefore considerable. In addition, there is only a short time during each summer day when radiation from the earth continues without the receipt of some solar energy. At the opposite time of year, the sun is at a lower angle than during the summer. It is above the horizon for only a few hours a day through most of the Moist, Severe Winter (D) climatic zone (Fig. 57) and actually below the horizon for many days in those areas within the Arctic Circle. Hence, receipt of solar energy is very small at that season, but earth radiation continues uninterruptedly. Thus, air temperatures become very low. The absence of any considerable amount of water vapor in the air, especially in the continental interiors, intensifies both the summer warmth and the winter cold. Marine and continental influences likewise cause variation in the degree of heat and cold.

PRECIPITATION. Precipitation in summer results both from the passage of cyclonic storms and from local convectional storms, while precipitation in winter is almost exclusively from cyclonic storms. The characteristic small amount is mainly the result of great distance from moisture sources.

The pronounced dryness of winter in northeastern Asia results from the intense cooling of that continent in winter. A tremendous mass of cold, dry air forms over the continent and prevents the movement of cyclonic storms across it. In summer, the mass of cold air does not exist; in fact, it is replaced by relatively warm air. A wind movement inland from off the cooler fringing oceans results. This is the means by which moisture is moved onto the continent, there to become the source of precipitation either from cyclonic storms or from local convectional systems. Along the coasts and for some distance inland, the rain at this season is remarkably like that in areas of Subtropical Monsoon (Cw) climate.

THE POLAR (E) CLIMATES

Subdivisions of the Polar (E) Climates

The Polar (E) climates are at the opposite extreme from the Tropical Moist (A) climates; the latter have no winters and the former have no summers. An average temperature for the *coolest* month is specified as the limit of the Tropical Moist (A) climates; an average for the *warmest* month is set for the Polar (E) climates. This average is 50° F. Where no month has an average temperature of 50° F. or over, the climate is of the Polar (E) type.

There is a twofold subdivision of the Polar (E) climates. Where the average for the warmest month rises above freezing, but does not exceed 50° F., the climate is of the Tundra (ET) type; it is of the Icecap (EF) type where even the warmest month averages below 32° F.

TUNDRA (ET) CLIMATE. Poleward from the areas of Moist, Severe Winter (D) climate in the Northern Hemisphere and from areas of Moist, Mild Winter (C) climate in the Southern Hemisphere, there is a zone in which there is no true summer, but in which temperatures do rise above freezing during part of the year at least. Severe frosts occur even during this warmer period and temperatures are too low to permit agriculture. A cushion of mosses, lichens, flowering herbs, and coarse grasses, hard frozen through most of the year, but waterlogged and spongy during a few short months, covers the surface. Trees are lacking or exist as stunted caricatures of the same species in warmer climates. This is the tundra. Toward the poles, the plant cover becomes discontinous and spotty; in the opposite direction, it gives way first to thickets of bushes and stunted trees and then to the forests of the Moist, Severe Winter (D) climates. The warmer season is hardly a summer. Yet, it is warm enough to allow some plant activity. Temperatures rise into the high 60's. Then, since the boggy ground supplies excessive moisture for evaporation, the air becomes sticky and oppressive. Myriads of insects, bred in the waterlogged vegetation mat, add to the discomfort of man and beast alike. Animals like the reindeer and caribou pasture on the vegetation made available to them during this warm season. Upon these animals a scant human population, like that along the Arctic fringe of Eurasia, is based.

Point Barrow in Alaska (Fig. 104A) indicates the temperature and precipitation features of the Tundra (ET) type of climate.

ICECAP (EF) CLIMATE. In areas of Icecap (EF) climate, monthly average temperatures never rise above freezing. Snow and ice cover the surface throughout the year. Even though the sun remains above the horizon continuously for four to six months of the year, it circles about the horizon so low in the sky that little heating results. A steep slope facing the sun for a few hours may warm sufficiently to cause slight melting of snow and ice. In exceptional instances, the temperature may rise into the 70's for a few minutes, only to drop back again below freezing as the sun swings round and leaves the slope in shadow. An equally long period at the opposite season during which the sun is below the horizon brings continued hours of darkness and unrelieved cold. Records of temperature over long periods are not available, but those taken by polar exploring expeditions suggest the general conditions. Little America, the Antarctic base of the Byrd expeditions, offers an example (Fig. 104B). Only tempera-

ture observations are available. Precipitation is entirely in the form of snow. Blowing and drifting of snow have been insurmountable handicaps to accurate measurement. Observations made have been even more spotty than temperature observations. They indicate only that the amount is small, possibly equivalent to as much as 10 or 15 inches of water.

MOUNTAIN (H) CLIMATES

Within any mountain area, climate is largely determined by altitude and exposure. Increased altitude lowers temperature and exposure to winds determines the raininess or dryness of any specific slope. Consequently, frequent changes of climatic type are the rule. In other words, the distribution of climatic types is spotty. No single type is characteristic of any extensive mountain area. There is no distinctive Mountain (H) type as there is a Tropical Rainforest (Af), and Arid

	J	F	M	A	M	J	J	A	S	O	N	D	Year
Temp.	-20	-13	-13	-2	22	35	41	39	32	16	0	-15	10
Prec.	0.1	0.4	0.2	0.3	0.3	0.8	0.3	0.9	0.5	0.7	0.3	0.4	5.2

	J	F	M	A	M	J	J	A	S	O	N	D	Year
Temp.	19	7	-9	-21	-25	-18	-39	-38	-38	-15	1	19	-13

104 CLIMATIC CHARTS and statistics for Point Barrow, Alaska, and Little America.

(BW), a Subarctic (Dfc, Dfd, Dwc, Dwd), or any of the other types already discussed.

Generally, increase of altitude lowers temperatures just as does increase of distance from the equator. There is this difference, however. Decreased average annual range accompanies increased altitude. Consequently, seasons are less marked in mountains than they are in adjacent lowlands. Temperatures are monotonously uniform at high altitudes, especially if the highland rises from a region of very slight average annual range. This is indicated by the graph and statistics for Quito (Fig. 89), previously referred to in the discussion of the Tropical Moist (A) climates.

Temperature zones can be distinguished in all mountain areas. The greatest number occur in tropical mountains. These highlands rise from the hot, steamy lowlands of Tropical Moist (A) climate and are often high enough to extend into zones where temperatures are always below freezing. Farther from the equator, say on a mountain rising from a lowland with Moist, Severe Winter (D) climate, continuously low temperatures are encountered at a much lower elevation.

One important difference between tropical highlands and those in other parts of the world, from the point of view of human use, should be stated. In the tropics, the highlands stand above areas of excessive heat. Consequently, their middle elevations provide temperatures more desirable for human habitation than the lowlands. Outside the tropics, the lowlands have a cool or cold season which places limits on human activity. Any increase of altitude increases the intensity and length of the cool season and hence imposes even further limitations.

Up to certain levels, which vary with the local controls, mountains tend to increase total precipitation. Above those levels, the total decreases. The zone of maximum rains is usually between 4,000 and 8,000 feet above sea level. There is thus created a zoning of mountain climates where mountains lie across the path of rain-bearing winds. But this zoning is not always the dominant feature. Within any highland, the slopes facing into the wind are moist while those in the lee are dry. Very sharp changes from moist to dry climates may hence be expected.

Coupling together the elements of vertical zoning of temperature, vertical zoning of precipitation, and precipitation spottiness resulting from varied exposure, it becomes evident that no one particular climatic type dominates in all highlands or even in a very large area of one highland. Highland climate is intricately detailed. The term "Mountain (H) climate" does not imply uniformity; it implies variety and spottiness of distribution too detailed for generalization on a world scale.

CONCLUSION

Excluding the mountain areas of the world, there are fourteen climatic types arranged in five categories. These main categories with the types which each includes are as follows:

A. Tropical Moist climates
 1. Tropical Rainforest (Af) climate
 2. Tropical Monsoon (Am) climate
 3. Savanna (Aw) climate
B. Dry Climates
 1. Arid (BW) climate
 2. Semiarid (BS) climate
C. Moist, Mild Winter climates
 1. Humid Subtropical (Cfa) climate
 2. Mid-latitude Marine (Cfb and Cfc) climate
 3. Subtropical Monsoon (Cw) climate
 4. Mediterranean (Cs) climate
D. Moist, Severe Winter climates
 1. Humid Continental climate with hot summers (Dfa and Dwa)
 2. Humid Continental climate with warm summers (Dfb and Dwb)
 3. Subarctic climate (Dfc, Dfd, Dwc, Dwd)
E. Polar climates
 1. Tundra (ET) climate
 2. Icecap (EF) climate

CHAPTER OUTLINE

Climatic types: the Mild Winter, the Severe Winter, and the Polar climates

REVIEW QUESTIONS

1. What characteristic most easily distinguishes the Moist, Mild Winter (C) and the Moist, Severe Winter (D) climates from the Tropical Moist (A) climates? Account for the existence of this characteristic.

2. Suggest some of the ways in which the presence of a winter season is significant from a human point of view.

3. Account for the seasonal deficiency of moisture in certain of the Moist, Mild Winter (C) climates.

4. Enumerate some of the principal differences between the climate of Los Angeles and that of New Orleans. Give a reasoned explanation of the causes of the differences.

5. What part of North America has a climate basically similar to that of the British Isles? to that of Barcelona, Spain? to that of Tokyo, Japan?

6. Why is there no Subtropical Monsoon (Cw) climate in southeastern United States while there is an area with that type of climate in southeastern Asia?

7. Explain the absence of Moist, Severe Winter (D) climates from the Southern Hemisphere.

8. In the Moist, Severe Winter (D) climates, spring and fall are very short seasons. Why is this so?

9. Give a reasonable explanation of the fact that summer temperatures in areas of Moist, Severe Winter (D) climates often exceed 100° F. whereas in areas of Tropical Moist (A) climates that temperature is seldom attained.

10. From the point of view of significance to man, what are the three subdivisions of the Moist, Severe Winter (D) climates? Exactly what is it that gives significance to each subdivision?

11. Is there any part of South America in which the climate is similar to that in Chicago? If so, where, specifically? If not, why not?

12. Why is it that temperatures in northern Canada in winter have never been recorded that are as low as those that have been recorded in northeastern Siberia?

13. Where in North America is the climate similar to that in Vladivostok? in Leningrad? in Hokkaido? Suggest the main reasons for the similarities.

14. The yearly amount of precipitation in Verkhoyansk is very small. Why is the climate there *not* classified as the Dry (B) type?

15. Why is precipitation a relatively insignificant factor in Polar (E) climates?

16. What is the meaning of "spotty distribution" as that phrase is used to describe Mountain (H) climates? Explain the expression "vertical zoning" as applied to Mountain (H) climates.

105 *CLIMATE SHOWS INFINITE VARIETY from place to place over the world. At top, a winter view of Mt. Ascutney, Vermont, in an area of Humid Continental (Dfb) climate. At bottom, a dry season view of Santa Marta, Colombia, in an area of Savanna (Aw) climate. (Top, Newell Green, bottom, Collier from Standard Oil Co. [N. J.])*

CHAPTER 9

The World Pattern of Climatic Types

An understanding of world climates provides a basis on which to build systematic knowledge about many of the differences from place to place over the earth's surface. In Chapters 7 and 8, specific climatic types have been described and their distribution over the world has been noted. Our next problem is to see more clearly how these types fit collectively into a definite world plan. A map (Plate V) showing where the various types of climate occur is actually a part of the design or pattern of world differences. Also, such a map shows the distribution of one of the physical elements with which man has to deal. Within broad limits, it indicates some of the major restrictions which are placed upon all life forms, human and otherwise.

DISTRIBUTION OF CLIMATIC TYPES

Since climatic types represent quantitative measurements of temperature and precipitation, it is easy to erect a simplified plan, indicating diagrammatically the place of occurrence of the major types. One such plan is shown in Fig. 106. Each of the corners of the rectangle represents extreme combinations of the two elements, temperature and precipitation. The upper left-hand corner indicates the extreme of cold and dry; the lower left-hand corner, hot and dry; the upper right-hand corner, cold and wet; and the lower right-hand corner, hot and wet.

The hottest of the wet climates are those of the Tropical Moist (A) category. Somewhat less hot, but still definitely humid, are the Moist, Mild Winter (C) climates. Still cooler, and yet still wet, are the Moist, Severe Winter (D) climates. And the coldest of those that are moist are the Polar (E) climates. This arrangement is shown along the right-hand side of the diagram. On the driest side are the Dry (B) climates. It will be remembered that some of the Dry (B) climates are hot and some of them are cool; hence there are no subdivisions across the diagram as there are on its wet side. Where temperatures are sufficiently low, dryness and wetness are not significant; the Polar (E) climates prevail regardless of the amount of precipitation.

THE GENERALIZED CONTINENT DIAGRAM

The very simple pattern shown on Fig. 106 takes into account only the factor of quantity for both of the basic climatic elements. To get at the pattern for the world, there must be included some indication of the distribution of land and water, which is so powerful a control of distribution for both temperature and precipitation.

It has been pointed out that there are two great "world islands," the Americas on the one hand and the Europe-Asia-Africa land mass on the other. These "world islands" are roughly triangular in broad outline. Their widest extent occurs at about 60° North latitude and they taper into the Southern hemisphere where both of them pinch out in the middle latitudes. After a short break, land appears again in the circumpolar continent of Antarctica. In the Northern Hemisphere, the continents fray out poleward toward the Arctic Ocean and do not extend to the Pole.

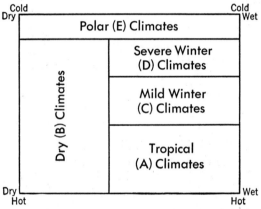

106 SCHEMATIC diagram showing the relationship of temperature and precipitation to major classifications of climate.

This very generalized distribution of land in each hemisphere is represented diagrammatically in Fig. 107A. The outline circle represents the outer edge of a hemisphere. The top-shaped figure upon it represents the outline of land. The continent thus delineated indicates simply land as opposed to water. No attempt is made to show generalized differences of elevation, nor is any attempt made to show detailed position of any actual coastline. The smaller triangular figure is a generalization of the Antarctic continent. The whole

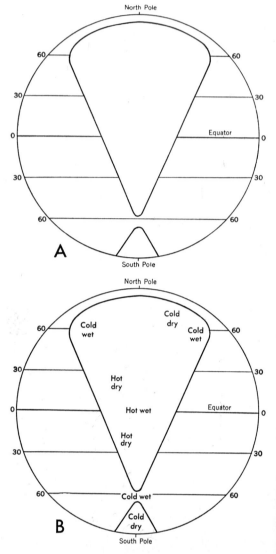

107 GENERALIZED Continent diagram. (A) Distribution of land and water, (B) distribution of de-

figure is called the generalized continent diagram.

Distribution of Major Climatic Categories

The discussion in preceding chapters pointed out several broad principles of climatic distribution. It was noted that the zone of great-

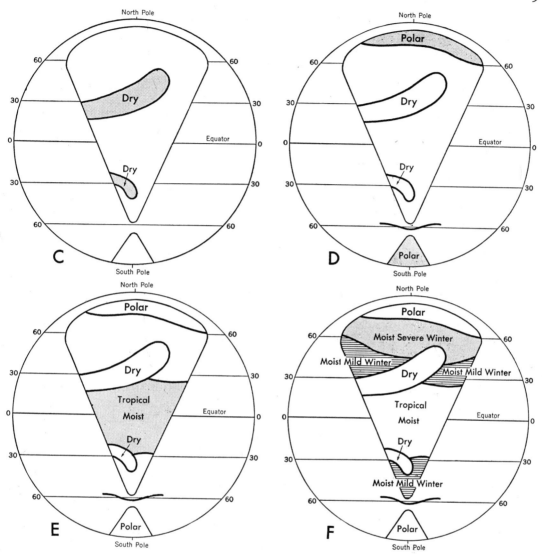

scriptive climatic terms, (C) *Dry* (B) *climates,* (D) *Polar* (E) *and Dry* (B) *climates,* (E) *Tropical Moist* (A), *Polar* (E), *and Dry* (B) *climates,* (F) *five major climatic types.*

est heating and of highest precipitation occurs along the equator, and that the greatest cold, whether dry or wet, occurs in the higher latitudes near, but not at, the Poles. In the higher latitudes, coastal positions are wet and continental positions are comparatively dry. The remaining combination, hot and dry, is found within the tropics extending inland from the continental west coasts. These facts can be

placed upon the generalized continent diagram as in Fig. 107B.

Now, instead of the pattern which appeared on the rectangular diagram (Fig. 106), a new pattern can be drawn. A line must appear between the hot-wet and the hot-dry focal points. Likewise, lines must be drawn between the hot-dry and the two cold-wet locations. Finally, there must be indicated the limit, in the continental interior, where dryness becomes less significant than coldness. There are thus formed, on the generalized continent diagram, curving loops which extend from the west coasts between about 20° and 30° latitude both North and South into the continental interiors of the higher middle latitudes (Fig. 107C). The areas within the loops are distinguished by their dryness; everything outside, by wetness. The loops, then, outline the areas of Dry (B) climate. Outside them lie the Tropical Moist (A); the Moist, Mild Winter (C); the Moist, Severe Winter (D); and the Polar (E) climates.

Across the Polar reaches in both hemispheres, perennial cold is so dominant that relative wetness and dryness are not significant. Lines may be drawn (Fig. 107D) in both hemispheres to indicate the equatorward limit of the Polar (E) climates. The portion of the generalized continent not yet subdivided includes now only Tropical Moist (A); Moist, Mild Winter (C); and Moist, Severe Winter (D) types.

Temperatures characteristic of the Tropical Moist (A) climates occur only within the low latitudes. On the generalized continent, the only portion of these latitudes remaining unspecified is that between and east of the two areas of Dry (B) climate. A line in each hemisphere from the east coast to the dry interior approximately at the edges of the low latitudes provides the remaining boundaries for the Tropical Moist (A) climates (Fig. 107E).

There remain only the Moist, Mild Winter (C) and Moist, Severe Winter (D) climates to delimit. In previous discussion, it has been pointed out that there is not sufficient continentality in the Southern Hemisphere to allow the development of the Moist, Severe Winter (D) type. Hence, it is only necessary to indicate the separation between the two in the Northern Hemisphere. To the east, the west, and the north of the Dry (B) zone, climate is characterized as humid or wet. As one proceeds away from the equator, coldness increases. Therefore, the boundary between the Moist, Mild Winter (C) and the Moist, Severe Winter (D) climates must cross the diagram from east to west. Latitude for latitude, west coast temperatures in the middle latitudes are higher for winter than are those of the east coast. Hence, the limit between the Moist, Mild Winter (C) and the Moist, Severe Winter (D) climates begins on the west coast at approximately 60° North latitude, curves equatorward across the continent, and leaves the east coast at about 40° North. In the section where it crosses the Dry (B) climate, its significance is lost for the climates are dry on either side of it. In that section, the line is omitted from the diagram. The *generalized* distribution of the five major categories of climate as they occur over the land thus appears in Fig. 107F.

VARIATIONS FROM THE BASIC PATTERN. It must be thoroughly understood that Fig. 107F is not a detailed map of climatic distribution over the world. It is simply a key to the *relative* position assumed by each major category on any one land mass. Variations from this pattern are induced first by irregularities of land surface and secondly by the detailed position of the coastline.

The effects of irregularities of surface can be seen in many places on the map showing the world distribution of all climatic types (Plate V). For example, consider the African portion of that map. The Tropical Moist (A) climates do not extend to the east coast of that continent north of the equator. On the generalized continent diagram, (Fig. 107F), the Tropical Moist (A) climates extend the whole breadth of the tropics along the east coast. A glance at the surface map of the world (Plate IV), will show that eastern Africa is a plateau region with hills and mountain masses upon it. The surface character is not the whole reason for the absence of Tropical Moist (A) climates along the east coast, but it is a strong contributory factor. Another instance occurs in South America.

On the generalized diagram (Fig. 107F), the Tropical Moist (A) climates extend along the equator unbroken from east coast to west coast. In South America, a break occurs near the west coast (Plate V). Reference to the surface map (Plate IV) shows that the break is located where the towering Andes stretch north-south across the equator. Their high elevations produce temperatures

eralized continent omits the large indentation of the Gulf of Mexico. If that shape is superimposed upon the generalized diagram, as in Fig. 108, it can be seen that there is no real discrepancy.

Again, part of the reason for the lack of Tropical Moist (A) climate on the African east coast north of the equator is the actual position of the coastline, this time in relation

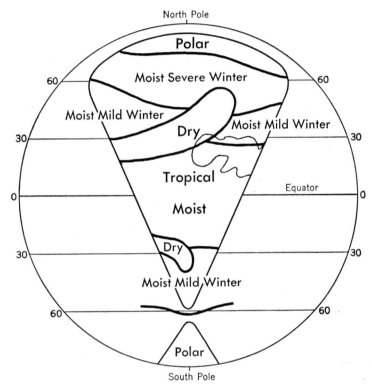

108   *RELATIVE position of Caribbean coastline on generalized continent diagram.*

lower than those which characterize the Tropical Moist (A) climates.

The effect of irregularities of coastline are well illustrated in the Caribbean region of the Americas. The climatic map (Plate V) shows that the Dry (B) climate comes to the east coast near the boundary between Mexico and the United States. On the generalized continent diagram (Fig. 107F), the Dry (B) climates are seen to be well inland from the east coast. The apparent contradiction results from the fact that the coastline on the gen-

to wind directions. Figs. 71 and 72 show that the prevailing winds are parallel to this coast no matter what the season. Consequently, little moisture is carried onshore from the Indian Ocean. The precipitation necessary to the Tropical Moist (A) climates is therefore lacking from that source. When this is coupled with the control induced by the surface, which was stated above, the greater part of the dryness of the African east coast is explained and the absence of Tropical Moist (A) climate is reasonably well understood.

Distribution of Climatic Types

The use of the generalized continent diagram may be further enhanced by the addition to it of the facts of seasonal distribution of

109   *GENERALIZED continent diagram showing distribution of precipitation types:* (A) *areas of winter rain,* (B) *areas of summer rain,* (C) *areas of year-round rainfall.*

precipitation. On continental west coasts between approximately 25° and 40° of latitude both North and South, there is a zone in which such precipitation as falls is concentrated in the winter half of the year. This zone extends inland to form rough half ovals, as in Fig. 109A. Within the shaded areas, precipitation occurs mainly during the winter and the summer is droughty.

The opposite condition, summer rain and winter drought, is characteristic of truly continental locations. As has been explained previously, there is a tendency toward an indraft of air into continents in summer and an outdraft in winter. This means that more moisture is available for precipitation in summer than in winter. The indraft is pronounced only when there is a very considerable land mass, but the characteristic tendency toward summer precipitation concentration is everywhere prominent away from coastline locations. Generalization of the regions in which this condition prevails is indicated on Fig. 109B.

The only other possibility is that precipitation be relatively evenly spread through the year. When the zone of winter concentration (Fig. 109A) and the zone of summer concentration (Fig. 109B) are plotted, that which is left is the area of year-round precipitation.

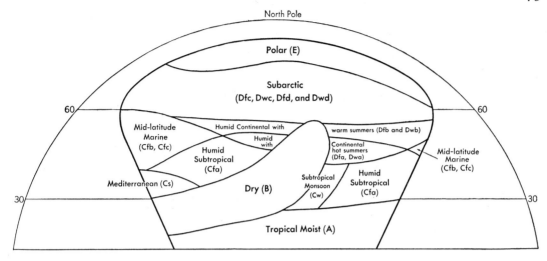

110 *NORTHERN HEMISPHERE portion of generalized continent diagram showing in greater detail the distribution pattern of the subdivisions of Moist, Mild Winter (C) and Moist, Severe Winter (D) climates.*

Fig. 109C shows the characteristic location of each of the three possible rainfall regimes.

We now have one diagram (Fig. 107F) showing the generalized pattern of the five major categories of climate: Tropical Moist (A), Dry (B), Moist, Mild Winter (C), Moist, Severe Winter (D), and Polar (E); and one diagram (Fig. 109C) showing the generalized pattern of precipitation types. By superposition (Fig. 111A), we secure the key to the expected location of the Tropical Rainforest (Af), Savanna (Aw), Dry (B), Humid Subtropical and Mid-latitude Marine (Cf), Subtropical Monsoon (Cw), Mediterranean (Cs), Humid Continental and Subarctic (Df and Dw), and Polar (E) climates on the generalized continent. As has been stated previously, departures from this design result primarily from the controls emphasized by irregularities of surface and by detail of coastline position.

As has been stated in Chapter 8, further subdivision of the Moist, Mild Winter (C) and Moist, Severe Winter (D) climates is made on the basis of the character of the summers. Without discussing this breakdown in detail, the generalized pattern is shown in Fig. 110. In this diagram, part of the Northern Hemisphere portion of the generalized continent has been enlarged so as to show the relationship of the types more clearly.

CLIMATE OF THE OCEANS

Largely because human beings live permanently on the land masses, climate over the oceans is generally neglected. Nevertheless, the same major types are found there as on land. Simply to indicate the general position of these types, the pattern shown on Fig. 111A is extended to include the whole hemisphere in Fig. 111B.

Two specific features should be noted. First, the area of Dry (B) climate is greatly reduced over the ocean. This is to be expected, for the existence of Dry (B) climate is based primarily on two conditions: (1) the absence of large amounts of water vapor in the air and (2) the absence of some means of forcing the condensation of such vapor as is present. Over the oceans both of these deficiencies are generally restricted to sections close to the continental west coasts. Second, the area of Moist, Severe Winter (D) climate is likewise very

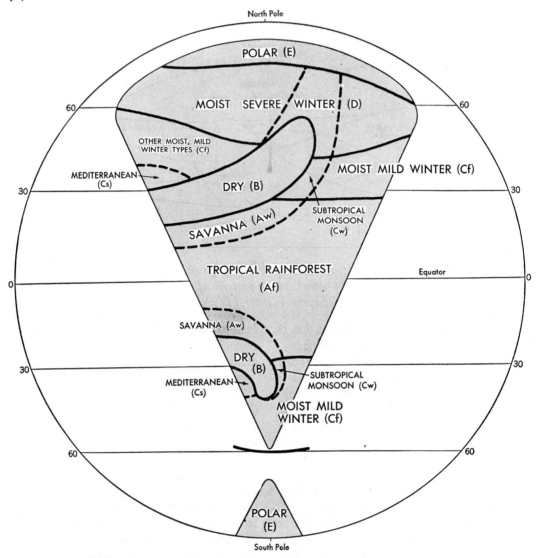

111A *DISTRIBUTION PATTERN of principal climatic types on the generalized continent.*

small in proportion to that over the continents. By definition, the Moist, Severe Winter (D) climates have very large temperature ranges. In other words, they are continental. As we have seen, the presence of large water bodies tends to reduce temperature range. The result of this tendency is to produce insufficient range over the oceans to satisfy the definition of the Moist, Severe Winter (D) type in all except two small areas off the coasts of the

higher middle latitudes in the Northern Hemisphere.

Finally, it should be noted that there is a much more regular belted arrangement of climates over the oceans than over the land. This reflects the facts already pointed out in the discussion of temperature and precipitation.

Further reference to climate over the oceans will be incidental for several reasons. In the first place, ocean climates are significant only

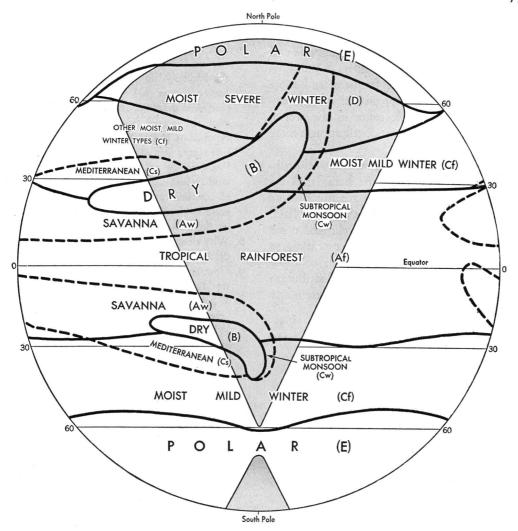

IIIB *GENERALIZED CONTINENT diagram, showing distribution of climatic types over the ocean as well as over the continent.*

as they affect water and air routes. In those instances, it is the climatic elements and controls rather than the climatic types that are significant. In the second place, there are no permanent sites on the oceans at which observations can be made. Our present knowledge is obtained by the study of records taken largely aboard ships which are moving from place to place. We have, therefore, no long-time observations for a large number of specific places. Consequently, our knowledge is inadequate to allow detailed statement. Any-

one who has sailed along the western coast of Africa southward from the Strait of Gibraltar knows very well that rain is an unusual phenomenon there. The deck of a steamer is covered by very fine dust particles even though the ship may be two hundred miles offshore. The wind is almost constantly from an easterly direction. All the meteorological observations point to the existence of a typical Arid (BW) climate along that coast. But, except for the occasional island site where long records may be kept, as in the Canary Islands, there is little to tell just what the extent of the Arid (BW) climate is.

Across the North Atlantic, thousands of ships, from the fastest ocean liners to the slowest "tramps," give more frequent and more massive evidence. There, on the most intensively used transoceanic route in the world, information about climatic distribution is more complete.

Though climatic maps may show the distribution over the oceans, the boundaries between one type and another are much more broadly generalized than those over the land. Realization of the fact that the climatic types are not confined to the land is essential; so also is the generalized distribution of those types; knowledge of their precise distribution over the sea is neither possible nor particularly vital.

....

CHAPTER OUTLINE

The world pattern of climatic types

Distribution of climatic types
The generalized continent diagram
    Distribution of major climatic categories
      Variations from the basic pattern
    Distribution of climatic types
Climate of the oceans

REVIEW QUESTIONS

1. Why is it more satisfactory to use a generalized continent diagram rather than a simple rectangular diagram to illustrate the distribution of climatic types over the earth?
2. What is the basis for the shape of the generalized continent diagram?
3. State in words the generalized distribution of the Dry (B) climates. Compare this statement with the facts as shown on the world map of Dry (B) climates (Fig. 33) and on Plate V. Account for differences between the generalized and the actual distributions.
4. Explain the position of the boundary between the Moist, Mild Winter (C) and the Moist, Severe Winter (D) climates on the generalized continent diagram. In what parts of the world does the actual boundary between the two types most closely approximate the generalized boundary? Why is the correspondence so close?
5. Illustrate, by reference to specific places, how land-surface irregularities and detailed position of coastline cause the actual distribution of climate to depart from the distribution as shown on the generalized continent diagram.
6. Why does the area of summer rain and winter drought lie in continental interiors?
7. How is it possible that certain parts of the world's oceans have Dry (B) climates?
8. What hinders the development of Moist, Severe Winter (D) climates over the oceans?
9. Why are climatic boundaries on the oceans more difficult to substantiate than those on the land?
10. Discuss the purposes of studying the generalized climatic pattern of the world.

SOME SUGGESTED REFERENCES

Blumenstock, David I., and Thornthwaite, C. Warren, "Climate and the World Pattern," *Climate and Man, Yearbook of Agriculture,* U. S. Department of Agriculture, 1941: 98-127. An excellent brief discussion of the generalized world climatic pattern; one of the best articles included in this volume which is practically "standard equipment" for the study of climate.

Köppen, W., and Geiger, R., *Handbuch der Klimatologie,* 5 vols. (not complete) Gebrüder Borntraeger, 1930- . A basic modern work in climatology; Volume I concerned with general climatology and other volumes with regional climatology; best available single source for climatological data; a few parts of volumes in English, remainder in German.

112 *ONE OF THE MOST SPECTACULAR landforms in the world: the Grand Canyon of the Colorado River. (Albert E. Burke)*

CHAPTER 10

Introduction to Landforms

....

The top of the earth's crust possesses an amazing variety of forms. It has been wrinkled, warped, broken, and worn into many shapes. Such shapes are landforms whether they be small or large, simple or complex. Their nearly infinite variety is barely suggested by such forms as volcanoes, canyons, fiords, sand dunes, plains, tablelands, and mountain ranges. It is to landforms, as the second of the physical or natural elements, that attention is now turned.

GEOGRAPHICAL SIGNIFICANCE OF LANDFORMS

Landforms are closely and intricately related to man's use and occupation of the land. Hence, even human geography finds landform study essential. In physical geography, landform study is essential in an even more direct sense, for the shapes of the earth's surface comprise conspicuous portions of the natural scene and they are intimately associated with virtually all other physical conditions, from climate and water to soil and vegetation. For such reasons, geography, regardless of the particular portion of its field under investigation at a given time, should not neglect the primary expression of the face of the land.

In the Human Scene

To illustrate the role of landforms in human geography the following examples are presented. The curved island of Honshu, largest of the Japanese islands, is hilly and mountainous to the extent of 85 per cent of its total area. The remaining 15 per cent, comprised of small, separated coastal plains and a few flat-floored mountain basins, represents nearly all of the land which can be used readily for buildings, settlements, routes of land travel, and agriculture. On these lesser portions are packed most of the fifty-odd millions of Honshu's inhabitants. The result is that a landform map of Honshu serves admirably as a map of the distribution of population; the predominant hill and mountain country represents blanks, or near blanks, and the scattered and miniature sections of nearly level land represent the densely settled portions (Fig. 113). In striking contrast are the northern and central portions of the state of Iowa. Part of an extensive plain which possesses only minor landform irregularities, the surface is such as to allow distribution of population, fields, pastures, woodlands, even the layout of lines of communication and transportation, to be arranged in most any fashion desired. This is particularly true in the central portion of the state, where the "ups and downs" of the land are decidedly minor—central Iowa

II3 *GENERALIZED LANDFORM and population patterns of the island of Honshu and adjacent parts of Japan.*

(Fig. 114) may not be as flat as a pancake, but compared to Honshu, it would seem to be.

As another example of landforms affecting human use of the land, one may think of the westward movement in the course of settlement of the United States. Where hilly or mountainous lands lay athwart migration,

II4 *THE FERTILE PLAINS of eastern Iowa, with a spring rainstorm approaching. This area has such low relief that only a practically horizontal view brings out the slight "roll" of the countryside. (U. S. Department of Agriculture)*

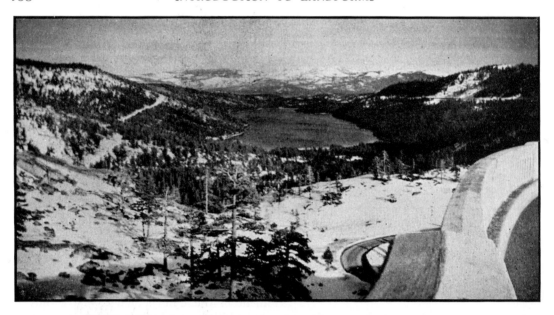

115 *WINTER SCENE at Donner Pass, Sierra Nevada, California, taken from the main highway bridge below Donner Summit. The highway seen below the bridge railing is the same highway that crosses the bridge. (John Nevins)*

travel was difficult and was funneled largely through a few corridors, gaps, and passes, such as the Hudson-Mohawk route in the north and Cumberland Gap farther south, or, in the Far West, through high saddles, such as Donner Pass in the Sierra Nevada of California (Fig. 115). Where landforms were more subdued, as along the Atlantic Coastal Plain or in the vast interior plains of the Mississippi Basin, relative freedom of movement was possible along many lines and in many directions. Further examples to show the close association between the lay of the land and human matters may be indicated by a few questions: Why, in both World War I and World War II, did the German forces attack through Belgium rather than directly across the French border? Why is access from the sea easier in Maryland than it is in California? Why is the problem of railroad construction much simpler in Indiana than it is in western Pennsylvania? To answer any of these questions it is necessary to refer specifically to the landforms of each area.

In the Physical Scene

As important as landforms are in the human portion of an area, they are even more significant in the physical setting. For one thing, landforms, of and by themselves, constitute a major part of the physical setting (Fig. 112). This is true even in plains regions, for the first thing one thinks in examining such areas is, "These are flat countries, aren't they?" (Fig. 114). And, in higher and rougher regions, landforms command the view to the initial exclusion of other features. In addition to such matters as general appearance and first impressions of a countryside, landforms are related to practically all of the other physical conditions, whether in immediately obvious fashion or not.

A bit to the northeast of Knoxville, Tennessee, in the famous Ridge and Valley country which lies between the Cumberland Plateau on the west and the Great Smoky Mountains on the east (Fig. 40), is the elongated backbone of Clinch Mountain. On the slopes of this ridge the soils are very thin and stony. This condition is related directly to the landform character, for the slopes are so steep as literally to shed their soils into the valleys which lie to either side. Contrariwise, the soils of the adjacent valleys, lying on nearly level land, are deep and nonstony.

In some areas landforms virtually control local climatic conditions. For instance, the land which lies at the eastern base of the Sierra Nevada is very dry. To the west of it lies the high and startlingly abrupt wall of the mountains. The major winds come from the west. To reach the land east of the mountain wall, the winds must rise over the mountain barrier and then descend 7,000 to 10,000 feet. Because of the descent, they become warm, thirsty winds; and so, instead of dropping moisture, they seek to pick up more of it (Fig. 116). The result is a dry climate. If the landform barrier were removed, the moist winds from off the Pacific Ocean would be less modified as they progressed eastward over the land and they would bring considerably more rain. In the same manner, removal of the coastal and near-coastal barrier of the southern Andes would result in more precipitation in the arid and semiarid portions of western and southern Argentina.

Again, without attempting to overexemplify the relationships between landforms and other physical elements, we may examine the drainage conditions of the Irrawaddy Delta. This large delta, in the southern part of Burma, is a land of sluggish streams, extensive swamps, and many coastal marshes, lagoons, and tidal flats. So low and featureless is the land that the abundant rains and the river waters which come from the north have little chance to drain away. To the west and northwest of the delta is a hilly and partly mountainous region, the Arakan Yoma. There, swamps, lagoons, and other types of "wet spots" are absent even though rainfall is more copious than in the delta lands. Slopes are so steep that the surface waters, whether in thin sheets, tiny rivulets, creeks, or rivers, drain away rapidly to the bordering lower lands.

LANDFORM CLASSIFICATION

Because one cannot comprehend all phases or conditions at one time, there is need for classification. For landforms, there is need for several types and degrees of classification, depending on whether landforms are being studied for the purposes of geology, geography, soil erosion investigation, or civil engineering. Nature provides no classifications; it is up to man, as he attempts to grasp the nature and meaning of phenomena, to make his own "working categories" and to shape them in such fashion as best to aid him in the attainment of his objectives.

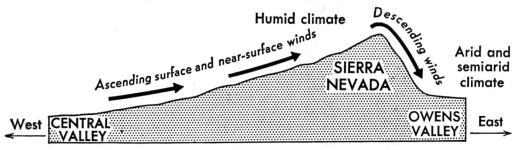

116 GENERALIZED PROFILE of the Sierra Nevada, California, and the effect of the Sierra on winds and moisture conditions.

117 *GENERALIZED THEORETICAL profile to show relationships among plains, plateaus, hills, and mountains.*

When one examines the shapes at the surface of the earth's crust, it is not long before he recognizes that some forms are relatively large, or *major landforms,* whereas others are comparatively small, or *minor landforms.* Together, all the large ones and all the small ones constitute the landforms of the earth. They occur in intricate patterns and in nearly infinite shapes, both over the exposed sweeps of the continents and islands and in the depths of the oceans. Our concern here is primarily with those of the continents and islands, although, at times, there will be reason to examine those which lie beneath the earth's waters, that is, the *submarine landforms,* as opposed to the *subaerial landforms.* The major landforms of the continents and islands are *plains, plateaus, hills,* and *mountains.* The minor landforms, almost innumerable, are *valleys, ridges, knolls, small plains,* and like features.

Major Landforms

PLAINS. Plains are comparatively level areas most of which lie relatively close to sea level (Fig. 117). More technically, they normally are regions of low altitude and low local relief. Low altitude means that they are not high above sea level, commonly less than 1,000 feet and in most instances less than 2,000 feet. A few plains exceed the latter altitude figure and they may be distinguished by the term *high plains,* particularly if they represent the continuation, without any major surface break, of plains of lower altitude, as do the Great

Plains of the United States (Fig. 118). Low local relief means that local differences in altitude are comparatively minor, often less than 100 feet and, in nearly all instances, less than 500 feet. The Gulf Coastal Plain of the United States (Fig. 118), for example, rises very gradually from the edge of the Gulf of Mexico; even at its most northern extent, where it touches southern Illinois, it is less than 500 feet above sea level. At the same time its surface is so nearly level that local differences in altitude (local relief) in excess of 100 feet are unusual. In contrast, in high mountainous regions, such as the Peruvian Andes, altitudes of 13,000 feet or more are attained within a few miles of the coast, and the altitudinal difference from the bottom to the top of a single canyon may be 5,000 feet, or more.

PLATEAUS. Plateaus are, in a sense, "plains up in the air." They are *tablelands* characterized by relatively high altitudes, usually in excess of 2,000 feet, and, unless their surfaces have been deeply cut by numerous streams, they are relatively level on top (Fig. 117). Local relief is usually less than 500 feet. The Colorado Plateau (Fig. 118), for example, has an average altitude of 7,000 to 8,000 feet above the far away tidewater of the Pacific, but the eye may wander across many thousands of square miles of its surface without encountering more than minor interruptions in the form of small canyons (Fig. 119). In the Grand Canyon section of the Colorado Plateau, the formerly tablelike surface has been cut up into very deep gorges and either flat-topped or knife-edged ridges. This section is a *dissected plateau.* If dissection is pro-

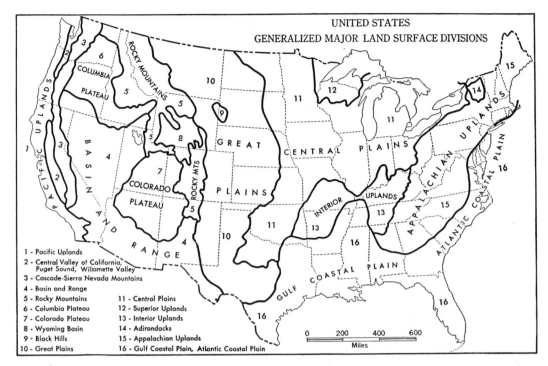

UNITED STATES
GENERALIZED MAJOR LAND SURFACE DIVISIONS

1 - Pacific Uplands
2 - Central Valley of California,
    Puget Sound, Willamette Valley
3 - Cascade-Sierra Nevada Mountains
4 - Basin and Range
5 - Rocky Mountains   11 - Central Plains
6 - Columbia Plateau   12 - Superior Uplands
7 - Colorado Plateau   13 - Interior Uplands
8 - Wyoming Basin   14 - Adirondacks
9 - Black Hills   15 - Appalachian Uplands
10 - Great Plains   16 - Gulf Coastal Plain, Atlantic Coastal Plain

118   *THE MAJOR LAND SURFACE divisions of the United States.*

119   *AIR PHOTO of the Colorado Plateau near Winslow, Arizona. This area is a tableland, only slightly dissected. The one canyon which does appear is famous Diablo
Canyon, about 225 feet deep and 500 feet wide. (Spence Air Photos, Los Angeles)*

nounced, and local relief is in excess of 500 feet, a dissected plateau warrants the name of hills. If dissection is extremely pronounced, and local relief exceeds 2,000 feet, a dissected plateau warrants the name of erosional mountains. Dissected plateaus not only possess much greater local relief than undissected ones, but they constitute barriers which are more difficult for man to cross.

Other characteristics of plateaus are found on their margins. Some, like the Colorado Plateau, have steep cliffs or escarpments on one or more sides but give way to hills and mountains on the other edges. Some, as the Bolivian Plateau or the very high Plateau of Tibet, are completely encompassed by high, rugged mountains.

MOUNTAINS. Mountain country has nothing in common with plains and little in common with plateaus, unless they be extremely and deeply dissected plateaus. Mountainous territory is marked by comparatively high altitudes (3,000 feet at the minimum), relatively high local relief (usually greater than 3,000 feet), long slopes, and small summit areas (Fig. 117). For example, the previously mentioned Sierra Nevada has crests and peaks which are 13,000 to 14,000 feet, or more, above sea level. Mount Whitney, highest peak in the United States, reaches an altitude of 14,495 feet above sea level. From one of the adjacent lower sections, just to the east of Mount Whitney, to the top of the peak itself is a rise of about 11,000 feet; this is one of the more extreme instances of great local relief to be found in the United States (Fig. 120).

Another trait, vertical zonation, is particularly useful in distinguishing mountains from hilly regions. True mountain lands usually are characterized by a marked and readily visible

120   *THE STEEP EASTERN front of the Sierra Nevada near Mt. Whitney. The immediate foreground is part of an irrigated ranch in Owens Valley. The low hilly ridge is fully separated from the Sierra front and is a local interruption in the floor of Owens Valley. (H. L. Kostanick)*

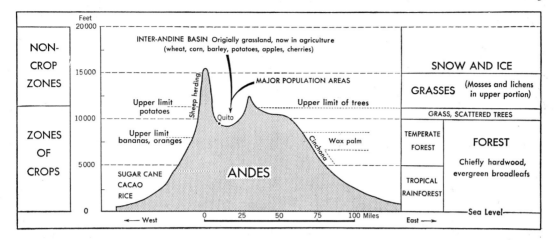

121 *GENERALIZED PROFILE of the Ecuadorean Andes at the latitude of Quito (0° 1'S.) showing some aspects of vertical zonation in tropical mountains. Information given on the sides of the diagram applies to the entire area, not just the side on which the information appears. This diagram is based mainly on information supplied by H. J. Bruman.*

vertical zonation of landscapes; hilly lands do not possess this condition. An instance of vertical zonation owing to altitudinal change in mountains is to be seen in the Mount Orizaba area of Mexico. This area lies in the southern part of the Eastern Sierra Madre Range, about on a line between Mexico City and the Gulf port of Veracruz. Much of the land up to an altitude of 10,000 feet is cleared and devoted to agriculture. In the lower parts are crops typical of the rainy tropics: rubber is grown up to 1,000 or 1,500 feet, sugar cane and bananas up to some 5,500 feet, coffee between 1,000 and 5,000 feet, and rice up to about 3,400 feet. In the upper portion of the agricultural area, or zone, are found crops typical of the mid-latitudes. Their presence is a reflection of the cooler temperatures caused by increased altitude. Wheat is raised from 6,000 to approximately 10,000 feet, apples from 6,000 to about 8,000 feet, and corn and beans are grown up to nearly 10,000 feet. Above the agricultural area, the land continues upward to a bit over 18,000 feet. Here, too, zonation is marked. Forests extend from 10,000 to 13,000 feet, with a transition from broadleaf trees in the lower parts to pines in the upper portion.

From 13,000 to about 14,500 feet is a zone of mountain meadows. Above the meadows is the zone of permanent ice and snow. Thus from bottom to top the Orizaba area is one zone after another; an agricultural zone divided between "tropical" and "temperate" crops, a forest zone, a zone of alpine meadows above the tree line, and a final zone of snow and bitter cold. It is almost as though one had journeyed from the tropical rainforest, through the mid-latitudes, and on into the polar lands.

In the Ecuadorean Andes, along the equator, is another excellent example of vertical contrast in mountain geography. Fig. 121 illustrates some of the typical conditions. It will be noted, again, that there is zonation of crops and natural vegetation alike.

HILLS. Hilly country is, in a loose sense, a baby edition of mountain country (Fig. 117). Altitude is appreciable (500 feet is an absolute minimum), and local relief is marked, but usually less than 2,000 feet, though more than 500 feet. Slopes may be as steep or steeper than mountain slopes, but they are much shorter. And, often, despite comparatively small summit areas, there is more relatively level land on the ridge tops than is characteristic of mountainous lands. However, there is no readily discernible vertical zonation. The Berkshires of western Massachusetts, the South China hill country, the southern Uplands of Scotland, or the Ridge and Valley area of the upper Tennessee Basin are typical examples of what is meant by hilly lands. Fig. 122 provides four views of hilly conditions.

Minor Landforms

The smaller shapes and convolutions of the top of the earth's crust are too numerous to count. It is they, with their host of varying combinations of slopes, which constitute the details of the major landforms and which provide highly localized individuality to the lay of the land. As noted before, all of the land which extends a considerable distance north from the Gulf of Mexico is composed of a wide variety of minor forms. Some of them are shore forms built and shaped by waves and currents, such as offshore sand bars, strips of sandy beach, and muddy tidal flats. Others are the low sprawling lands of the Mississippi Delta, marked by islands and tongues of land which rise barely above sea level and the levels of the many swamps and bayous. Farther up the Mississippi, north of the delta, are the steep, but low, bluffs which flank the alluvial plain of the valley bottom. Entering the valley bottom plain are many tributary valleys of several different shapes, and in between them are lands which vary from narrow and steep-sided ridges to broad, gently rolling slopes too subdued to call ridges. All of these features are a part of the local individuality which characterizes the surface configuration of the Gulf Coastal Plain.

Another example of local detail in the lay of the land is seen in Norway. This country, with only minor exceptions in the south and far north, is mountainous. Simply to call Norway a mountain country would not bring out the details of the surface which one travels across, or sees from a boat offshore or from a vantage point on the land. Many valleys, large and small, lead down and into, even under, the sea. Most of them are overhung by steep cliffs and marked by rocky steps which interrupt the otherwise fairly level valley floors. Because of subsidence of the land, the lower parts of these valleys are drowned by the in-reaching sea to give Norway its famous fiords (Fig. 123). At the heads of the fiords the in-tumbling streams have built little delta plains in the form of gently sloping fans. Between successive fiords rise high, sometimes tablelike, buttresses of solid bedrock. And, along the outer coast, are hundreds of solid rock islets, shaped much like eggs half-submerged in the salty waters.

SHAPING OF LANDFORMS

Primary Processes

Landforms do not just happen; each shape or combination of shapes, whether it be the Alps or a cluster of sand dunes, is the result of much work. Some landforms are shaped chiefly by processes operating from within the earth, others are shaped mainly by processes and agents working on top of the earth's crust. The shaping which is carried on from within the earth is accomplished by *diastrophism* and *vulcanism;* that carried on from without is the work of *weathering, erosion,* and *deposition.*

Shaping from Within

DIASTROPHISM. The earth's crust is under constant strain and stress. At times, and in certain places, it yields to these strains. When it does, the result is a change, major or minor,

A

CHARACTERISTIC *glacially rounded hills of northern Vermont. (Eagle from Standard Oil Co. [N. J.])*

B

HILLS along the shore of Lake Superior, northwest of Marquette, Michigan. (R. M. Glendinning)

C

CHAPARRAL-covered slopes of the Santa Monica Hills, Los Angeles County, California. (R. M. Glendinning)

D

NEARLY barren hills in the Mohave Desert, near Yermo, California. Creosote bushes dot the alluvial fan slope in foreground. (R. M. Glendinning)

123   *ONE OF THE many deep fiords on the rocky Norwegian coast. (Norwegian National Travel Office)*

slow or cataclysmic, in the shape of its surface.

Under certain conditions the earth's surface wrinkles, or folds, much like the skin of a drying apple. This *folding* may be simple and produce broad and open forms, like those of a gigantic corrugated iron roof, or it may be complex and result in tight folds, much like those of a closed accordion (Fig. 124A). In some regions, the folding has been so complex that the crustal corrugations have been tipped and laid at an angle on top of one another (Fig. 124B). Parts of the Alps show this latter condition, while the more simple type of folding is exemplified in several sections of the Appalachians. Regardless of the degree of complexity, each upfold is called an *anticline* and each downfold a *syncline*. Anticlines and synclines, as measured at right angles to the folds, may vary from a few feet to many miles.

Parts of the earth's crust yield to stress by *warping*. This is merely a bending, or flexing,

but not a folding, of the crustal materials. Examination of Figs. 124A and 124C will indicate the essential differences between warping and folding. Examples of warping on a large scale are found in the North Sea region and in the Lake Superior district. Crustal warping in the former has resulted in the slow drowning of what were formerly low plains. Within the period of recorded history, English shore villages and farms have had to be abandoned to the sea. The Lake Superior basin is being warped in such a manner as to raise the northern shore slowly and lower the southern. These movements are marked on the north by uplifted beaches and at places along the south shore, by submerged tree stumps and drowned river mouths.

When the crust neither folds nor warps, but still gives way to interior stresses, fracturing, or *faulting*, takes place (Fig. 124D). It is as though the crust were comprised of large and small earth blocks, each separated

124 (A) *and* (B) *TWO TYPES, or degrees, of folding in the upper part of the earth's crust.* (C) *Simple warping of the earth's upper crust.* (D) *Block faulting of earth's crust. Elevated blocks form block hills or mountains, depressed blocks form valleys or trenches.*

from the others by huge cracks along which the blocks are forced to move. Some blocks go up, some go down, and some move sideways. In fact, a given block, or earth compartment, may be moved up and laterally at the same time, or another moved both down and laterally during the same disturbance. As one block moves against another, a jarring, irregular set of tremors is induced and translated in the earth materials; these are *earthquakes,* the result, not the cause, of earth fracturing. When the movement of an earth block is only slightly upward only a very minor landform, such as a small *fault scarp,* may be produced; however, greater movements may result in huge blocky mountains like the Sierra Nevada, or if the movement is downward, in large trenches in the surface of the earth, like Death Valley (Fig. 2).

VULCANISM. The most readily recognized forms produced by vulcanism are volcanoes, especially those like Fujiyama or Vesuvius, which have been built by lavas and ashes into huge conical mountains (Fig. 125A). Others, low and broad, like the caldron form of Mauna Loa in Hawaii, while less conspicuous, comprise extensive landform features (Fig. 125B).

Vulcanism does not always produce volcanoes. Molten rocks simply may issue from great cracks and spread in huge laterally moving *lava flows* across the land. These molten *extrusions* may constitute extensive lava caps which cover thousands of square miles, as in the Columbia Plateau of northwestern United States (Fig. 118).

In other regions, the molten rocks, squeezed under tremendous pressures, may not reach the surface to construct either volcanoes or lava sheets. However, they move within the cracks and crevices of the crust as *intrusive* materials. Sometimes they are forced as layers, or *sills,* between the strata of other rocks, or they may rise and fill earth fissures to form *dikes,* or, again, they may simply collect in large subterranean masses. The fact that sills,

125 *TYPES OF volcanoes.*

dikes, and masses are not formed at the surface does not mean, necessarily, that they have no landform significance, for, later, as overlying materials are worn away, such intrusive features may be exposed at the surface as definitely visible forms (Fig. 126). In the instance of subterranean masses, whether they ever become exposed or not, rock layers above may be deformed by them to create *structural domes,* which do have expression in the surface scene (Fig. 127).

It is in such ways that forces working from below, whether diastrophic or volcanic, or both, change the face of the earth's crust.

Shaping from Without

WEATHERING. Just as paint on the sides of a house or the surface materials of a highway weather under exposure to the elements, so do the materials which comprise the upper portion of the earth's crust. This *weathering* is simply the breaking up of the rocks by chemical and mechanical means. If it is accomplished by chemical actions, it is called *decomposition;* if done mechanically, it is known as *disintegration.* Working together,

the two processes change exposed bedrock into pieces of rock, and then further weather the pieces into materials of progressively smaller and smaller size—essentially, it is a business of making little ones out of big ones. The resultant mantle is called *regolith.* It is thus that earth materials are made ready for the erosive agents such as running water, and made available, likewise, for evolution into soils.

Decomposition, or chemical weathering, is carried on by *oxidation, carbonation, hydration,* and *solution.* When rocks go to pieces by oxidizing, it is because oxygen in the air unites with certain elements in the rocks to form oxides. For example, iron may unite with oxygen to form iron oxides and provide the familiar rusty color which is seen in many earth materials. As this oxidation takes place, the original material is weakened and rotted. Under carbonation, certain elements unite in new combinations with carbon dioxide, the latter being common in natural ground water in the form of a carbonic acid solution. The element calcium, for instance, may join with carbon dioxide to form calcium carbonate and this action, or chemical reaction, weathers the rock apart in the process. Hydration is the

126 *STONE MOUNTAIN, Georgia, a huge mass of gray granite which has been exhumed by erosion to become a prominent local landform. The rounded form is largely the result of "leafing-off," or exfoliation, of the granite. (Hilliers from U. S. Geological Survey)*

Stream-cut gap in cuesta **Stream** **Cuesta - steep front and long, gentle backslope (formed by more resistant layer of sedimentary rock)**

GRANITE MASS

More resistant layers **Sedimentary rock layers**

1 2 7 *THIS GENERALIZED block diagram of the Black Hills, South Dakota, shows an eroded structural dome.*

taking on of water in chemical combination; the accompanying "swelling," or increase in bulk, causes the rocks so affected to "give" and fall apart. Solution represents the removal of materials which cement rock particles together. These materials, taken into true solution by the water in the ground as a teaspoonful of sugar is dissolved in hot coffee, leave behind rocks which are greatly weakened and often porous. Chemical weathering is at a maximum in those parts of the earth which are always hot and moist, as in the Congo Basin with its Tropical Rainforest (Af) climate. It is least effective in regions marked by extended cold and drought, as in the Bolivian Plateau with its cold Arid (BW) and cold Semiarid (BS) climates. While the foregoing processes have been given separate discussion, it must be remembered that they may all go on together in the same rocks at the same time; thus, the rocks of the Congo Basin are acted upon simultaneously by oxidation, carbonation, hydration, and solution.

Disintegration occurs when rocks are broken up by mechanical means. There is actual physical breakage, and while the ma-

terials are not normally pounded to pieces, as a brick may be broken by a sledge hammer, the results are much the same. One of the common means of disintegration is *frost action.* Water enters the cracks and crevices of rocks and then in freezing, expands to pry the rocks apart. If alternate freezing and thawing are the rule, as in high mountains and in Polar lands, the amount of regolith produced by frost action is considerable, and it is ordinarily comprised of sharp and angular fragments. Another type of mechanical breakdown is caused by *differential heating* and *cooling.* This results in unequal expansion and contraction of the rocks and causes them to be shattered. For example, a bedrock surface exposed to intense heating by the sun will expand, but the top materials will expand more rapidly than those underneath; something has to "give" and the materials are loosened. At night, or under a sudden, cooling shower, the materials will contract, but, again, the process is differential and the top rock will shrink at a faster rate than the rock directly underneath. Then further breakage occurs. Weathering of this type is not uncommon where rocks are exposed to Arid (BW) climates, especially to climate which is the hot Arid type.

Perhaps the grossest form of mechanical weathering is *diastrophic weathering*. In the formation of a huge anticline, for instance, the rocks at the top of the fold are severely cracked and broken by the stretching incident to the formation of the anticlinal crest; or, in vulcanism, lavas may force their way between rock layers or into cracks and split and pry the rocks apart. All such mechanical breakages as noted above, abetted by chemical weathering, are constantly at work weathering the bedrock into regolith and weathering the pieces and particles of the regolith into still smaller pieces.

Where plants and burrowing animals are present *organic weathering* operates. Expanding roots ferret out cracks and crevices and split the rocks; burrowing animals wedge, pry, and remove materials: working together, organisms may play a considerable part in rock breakage.

EROSION AND DEPOSITION. Erosion is, primarily, a process of "pick up and carry" of weathered materials. As earth materials are carried they may be used, further, as grinding and scouring tools to wear away and break up other rocks; this is *corrasion* or *abrasion*. For example, corrasion occurs when boulders and finer materials are rolled, bounced, and dragged against the bed of a stream and against one another. The *agents of erosion* are *moving water, moving air,* and *moving ice.* Accent is placed on motion, for without it the agents have no power to do work; stagnant water can cut no valleys, still air can carry no dust nor shift any sand, and stationary ice can move no regolith nor cut and scour bedrock surfaces.

Along the continental shores and over the vast stretches of the land, it is moving water which holds first place in erosive activities. This is true even in deserts as indicated by the very common occurrence of such water-cut or water-deposited forms as arroyos

(wadies) and alluvial fans (see pp. 251 and 253). The importance of water is greater in lands with humid climates and, hence, with a more abundant and reliable supply of water. As moving water carries on its work, it gnaws, batters, and etches the original landforms into new shapes. Following and accompanying such actions, it piles up, or *deposits* layer on layer, the transported materials to create still other shapes. The variety of water-eroded (*degradational*) or water-deposited (*aggradational*) forms may not be infinite, but it often seems so. Water-cut forms vary from wave-eroded cliffs and sea caves to deep canyons and broad, open valleys; water-deposited forms range from deltas and alluvial fans to wide blankets of river flood-plain materials and extensive coastal plains. Most anywhere, either in miniature or in large form, one can see shapes which have been dug out or built up by water "on the move."

Air in motion, or wind, has much less power to transport materials than does water or moving ice. Wind has the ability, however, to pick up fine dusts (*loess*) and, at times, sands. The dusts may be carried to great heights and scattered over extensive areas (Fig. 128), but the sands are seldom lifted more than a few inches or feet from the surface over which, or against which, the wind is blowing. In general, coarser materials such as sands or, occasionally, gravels, are rolled, bounced, and slid, rather than carried aloft. Yet, locally, the forms produced by wind erosion (*aeolian erosion*) and by the deposition of wind-blown materials may be conspicuous and dominant. Rocks are scoured and sandblasted (*wind corrasion*) into new and often fantastic shapes, and materials are removed to create depressions; where materials are deposited, they may form individual dunes or an entire sea of wavelike dune ridges (Fig. 129C). In several instances, it cannot be said that the results of wind work are purely local; here one may think of the North China Plain, which has received large loessal accretions for many thousands of years, as well as alluvial materials deposited directly by the waters of the Hwang Ho.

Small cakes of ice, grinding and rubbing against a beach or the base of a rocky cliff, produce minor erosion effects; ice moving in tongues or sheets over the land produces both minor and major forms. As soon as ice begins to move, a movement which is at snail's pace or slower, it carries on two kinds of work— one is erosion and the other is deposition. Both result in definite landforms. As "scour forms," one may cite the gouged-out valleys (*fiords*) of Norway, or the unequally scraped surface of Canada's vast Laurentian Shield (Fig. 130). On the depositional side, the curved ridges of loose glacial debris near Chicago or the plains comprised of out-washed materials in parts of southern Wisconsin will serve as examples (Fig. 190). Any area which has been "worked over" by moving ice presents a land surface that is drastically modified from that of the preglacial appearance.

ROCKS

The earth materials which are deformed by diastrophic movements and distorted and stacked up as a result of vulcanism, are rocks; so are the materials which are rotted and broken up by weathering and cut into or deposited by the agents of erosion and deposition. Over many parts of the continents, loose rocks and bedrock constitute a very conspicuous portion of the landscape, especially in deserts with their scant cloak of vegetation, in high mountains, particularly above tree line, and in regions of pronounced glacial scour, where the forest is much broken and even regolith is scarce (Fig. 151).

Composition of Rocks

All rocks are comprised of minerals. For example, common limestone is mainly the

128 *DUST STORM in Oklahoma. (U. S. Department of Agriculture)*

A

WEATHERED and wind-corraded sandstone on the exposed edge of a low bluff near Livingston, Montana. (Walcott from U. S. Geological Survey)

B

A DEPRESSION created by wind erosion in the Great Plains. The pedestal remnant provides a measure of the amount of material removed by the wind in creating this blow-out. (Darton from U. S. Geological Survey)

C

OBLIQUE air view of large sand dunes in southeastern Imperial County, California. The small dark spots are clumps of desert brush from four to six feet in height. (Spence Air Photos)

130   *AN AREA of differentially scoured bedrock in the Labrador section of the Laurentian Shield. Note the numerous ponds and lakes lying in "scour depressions." The
sinuous ridge which extends from lower left toward upper right is an esker which
has been deposited on the scoured bedrock surface. (Courtesy of the Geographical
Review published by the American Geographical Society of New York)*

mineral known as calcium carbonate plus, as
a rule, such other minerals as quartz and feld-
spar. Some rocks are comprised of only one
mineral: a piece of quartz, for example.

The minerals which constitute rocks are,
in turn, composed of chemical elements. In
quartz, two primary elements are involved,
namely, silicon and oxygen. Thus quartz is
mainly silicon dioxide although, if impure,
it may contain such other elements as iron,
gold, silver, and copper. It was noted that a
rock may consist of only one mineral; in the
same fashion, where elements occur in the
free, or pure, state, a rock may be composed
of only one element. A piece of pure copper
or a gold nugget are examples, for such pieces
are rocks, yet contain only one element each.
Table 13 shows the relationships just noted
and adds certain other information.

Rock Classes

IGNEOUS ROCKS. All rocks are either *igneous, sedimentary,* or *metamorphic* (Fig. 131).
Igneous rocks are those which are molten or
have cooled and become solid after being in
the molten state. Common examples are
granite, syenite (sometimes called "pink
granite"), lavas, and basalt. Such rocks are
formed within the earth, where temperatures
are so high as literally to melt solid rock.
These are the intrusive and extrusive materials which were mentioned in the discussion
of vulcanism. The intrusives, being buried,
cool very slowly. As they cool and solidify,
there is time for crystals to grow to relatively
large sizes and, hence, the rocks are usually
coarse-grained, like granite. The extrusives,
exposed to the air, cool more rapidly and they
are normally fine-grained like basalt. If igneous rocks contain a large amount of quartz,
they are usually light-colored. Thus, granite
is coarse-grained and light-colored. Those
igneous rocks which are high in the ferro-
magnesian minerals are dark. Thus, basalt is
fine-grained and dark-colored.

SEDIMENTARY ROCKS. These, as the name
implies, are comprised of sediments, or particles. They represent the accumulation,
through time, of layer on layer of deposited

Table 13   COMPOSITION OF ROCKS
(Read either from top to bottom or from
bottom to top)

ROCKS
(as limestone, granite, sandstone, etc.)

↑
↓

MINERALS
(as quartz, feldspars, ferromagnesians)

↑
↓

ELEMENTS
(as oxygen, silicon, aluminum, iron,
calcium, potassium, sodium, magnesium)

materials. Some are carried and laid down by the wind, others by moving water or glaciers. Most of them are finally laid down in the great accumulation basins of the oceans. Each depositional layer is a *stratum,* and a series of them are *strata;* hence, sedimentary rocks are normally referred to as *stratified.* The more common sedimentary rocks are sandstone, limestone, shale, and conglomerate. Sandstone is mainly comprised of grains of sand. If the strata are thin and waferlike, the sandstone is said to be *thin-bedded;* if the layers are thick, the sandstone is called *massive.* Limestone is chiefly an accumulation of small limy particles from skeletal remains of small sea organisms. It, too, may be thin-bedded or massive. Shale is a collection of particles of clay and silt, or muds. Conglomerate is, literally, a conglomeration of other rocks. The English refer to it, reasonably enough, as "puddingstone." It is comprised of boulders and gravels set in a filler, or matrix, of sands, silts, and clays. Pieces of it strongly resemble coarse, man-made concrete, both in color and textural variations.

METAMORPHIC ROCKS. These are rocks which have undergone marked change from their original condition. Most of the change is the result of heat and pressure incident to burial within the earth, abetted by the cementing action of underground waters and quite often, by crustal deformation. If granite, an igneous rock, is subjected to such conditions over a long enough period, it becomes the metamorphic rock known as banded granite, or gneiss. Sandstone, a sedimentary rock, will change slowly into quartzite; limestone becomes marble; and shale changes into slate. Thus, the common slate blackboard has had a long and eventful history. First it was mud; then the mud changed into sedimentary bed-

131   *SAMPLES of three kinds of rock:* (left) *igneous rock* (granite), (center) *sedimentary rock* (sandstone), *and* (right) *metamorphic rock* (hornfels). (American Museum of Natural History)

rock, or shale. The shale, acted upon over a long period by more heat and pressure, gradually evolved into the metamorphic slate. All this took many thousands, perhaps millions, of years; if great crustal deformation took place, the accompanying increased temperatures and pressures resulted in a relative speeding up of the change from shale to slate.

CONSOLIDATED AND UNCONSOLIDATED ROCKS. When earth materials are hard and compact to the point of being solid bedrock, they are called consolidated or indurated. If loose, *they are still rocks,* but unconsolidated or non-indurated. Actually, then, a handful of sand is rock, just as much as a piece of bedrock sandstone or a chunk of granite. In discussing rocks, or the landforms which they comprise, in part, there is need for careful distinction between the "consolidateds" and the "unconsolidateds." Obviously, it makes a difference whether a given deposit is mud, shale, or slate; it makes a difference whether a hill is a loose collection of sand grains or of massive sandstone bedrock; and, in terms of erosional accomplishments, it makes a difference whether a stream is cutting into loose clays or into solid, massive granite.

LANDFORM ANALYSIS

Types of Analysis

In dealing with landforms as part of the fundamental geography of an area, there are two methods of attack. One is simply to describe a given landform as it appears to the eye. The landform known as a *mesa* may be described as possessing a more or less circular flat top, encircling cliffs, and relatively gentle slopes which lead away from the base of the cliffs (Fig. 132A). This method shows the form, but it provides no understanding of how the form got to be that way. It is much

132 (A) *TYPICAL mesa profile.* (B) *One typical origin of a mesa, showing stages of development.*

as though one described the outer shape of a particular house, but did so with no indication of how that house was built, step by step, from foundation to roof.

Another, and much more meaningful, method is one which not only describes the form as it is at the present time, but indicates how the form was attained. Using this method, one may point out that the mesa mentioned above was once part of a plateau which possessed a hard cap rock (Fig. 132B). Streams gnawed their way back into the plateau in such a manner as gradually to isolate a portion of it from the rest. This resulted in a flat-topped remnant surrounded by cliffs which marked the existence of the hard cap rock. Materials falling from the cliffs and others washed down by rains slowly built up an "apron" which extended out, at relatively

133 *A DIAGRAMMATICAL east-west cross section of the Nashville Basin, Tennessee, and adjacent territory (see text for discussion).*

gentle slope, from the cliffs. Thus, the mesa was created (Fig. 132B). Examined from such a point of view, one appreciates that "mesa" is more than a form name; it is, also, a term which implies a certain kind of origin, or genesis. Involved in its genesis are different kinds and arrangements of earth materials, the processes which shaped them, and a given amount of work accomplished, step by step, by the processes.

Scientific Analysis

The second of the two methods discussed above is the scientific method. By means of it, any landform may be analyzed and comprehended, not only in terms of its present shape, but also in terms of each phase of its

evolution. Landform analysis of this sort involves consideration of *structure, process,* and *stage.*

STRUCTURE. Structure refers to the nature and arrangement of the earth materials which are being shaped, whether they be bedrock, unconsolidated rock, or a combination of both. In the instance of the mesa, the structure consists of layers of nearly horizontal sedimentary bedrock with the top layer hard enough to be relatively resistant to weathering and erosion (Fig. 132B).

Another example of the meaning of structure is to be seen in the Nashville Basin of Tennessee. Geologically, the region is a broad structural dome. It represents layers of sedimentary bedrock which, under crustal stress, were slowly deformed to create a shape somewhat similar to an inverted bowl (Fig. 133). As weathering and erosion went to work on this crustal "blister," they first wore away the higher portion. Working more deeply, they uncovered strata which are comparatively soft. These less resistant rocks (limestones) eroded to form the lowlands. Because the resistant rocks of the domal structure slant (dip) outward from the center, their steep margins form an encircling rim whose edges face inward toward the central portion. Thus, if one begins in the center and travels outward, he crosses a gently rolling plain (softer rocks), climbs up onto a steplike rim (harder rocks), and then, if proceeding eastward, makes another steplike ascent to a plateau surface (Fig. 133). Certainly, in a region of this sort, one cannot appreciate the character and geographic pattern of the landforms unless he understands the controlling part played by the structure.

PROCESS. Process refers to all the activities and agents which shape a given structure. To come back to the mesa, the processes involved are weathering, both disintegration and decomposition, and running water. Together, they are the shapers or carvers which have etched out the mesa form from the structure.

Process may be illustrated by reference to a

kind of sand dune. The dune has much the appearance of a breaking wave (Fig. 134). It owes its existence to loose sands which have been collected and shaped by winds. The winds slide, bounce, and roll the sand grains up one side, the gentle side of the dune ridge, where the grains drop and collect at a steep angle in the lee of the wind action. Such

ture is uniform, that all the materials into which the stream is cutting are essentially the same from top to bottom. At first, the stream will erode vertically to carve a valley which, in profile, has the shape of a V. The stream is greatly aided by the work of rainwash, which widens the valley by wearing away the slopes. This is the first major stage. When

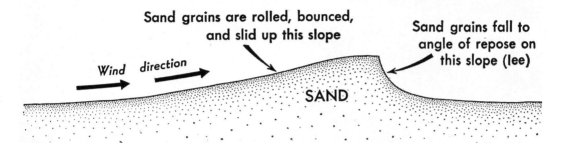

134 PROFILE of a "wave" dune. The angle of the slope is somewhat exaggerated.

action causes the dune to migrate, but it also causes it to retain the same form as it makes its slow journey over the land.

STAGE. Stage refers to the amount of work accomplished by the processes in the shaping of the structure. Inasmuch as all work cannot be done at once, it is accomplished in sequence, or in "stages." At first the mesa, for example, was only roughly outlined and partly separated from the parent plateau surface (Fig. 132B, parts 2, 3, 4). Next, it was definitely outlined and completely separated, as soon as stream valleys had been cut to form parts of its margin, and tributary valleys had been etched out "behind" to complete the isolation. Finally, the isolated and cliffed form was modified by regolith falling and being washed from above (Fig. 132B, part 5). Thus, there are, in a sense, three *major* stages which may be distinguished in the evolution of the mesa.

Further ramifications of the concept of stage may be illustrated by a stream valley created in a region of humid climate and, hence, by permanently running water. Let it be supposed, in this example, that the struc-

the stream has cut vertically as far as it can, it erodes sideways, or laterally. The lateral erosion widens the valley. The bulk of the lateral cutting takes place on the outside of each stream curve; deposition, marking the earliest beginnings of a river plain or a valley bottom plain, occurs on the inside of each curve. The cutting produces a bluff and the deposition creates a small valley flat. A valley which has attained this stage might be called a bluff-and-valley-flat valley. Further lateral erosion and rainwash, accompanied by more deposition, slowly create a relatively wide valley which possesses a definite and comparatively broad plain. This is the final stage in the genesis of the valley form. It might be called a river-plain valley (Fig. 135).

Later, when matters of landforms and the agents of erosion are treated in some detail, more will be said about stages of development of particular landforms and landform groups (Chap. 12). More pressing at the moment is a knowledge of the major landforms of the continents, their patterns of distribution, and their significance to man. These are dealt with in the chapter which follows immediately.

135   *AN EXAMPLE of a river-plain valley—a view of the Connecticut Valley in Massachusetts. (Parks, Standard Oil Co. [N. J.])*

CHAPTER OUTLINE

Introduction to landforms

Geographical significance of landforms
  In the human scene
  In the physical scene
Landform classification
  Major landforms
    Plains
    Plateaus
    Mountains
    Hills
  Minor landforms
Shaping of landforms
  Primary processes
  Shaping from within
    Diastrophism
    Vulcanism
  Shaping from without
    Weathering
    Erosion and deposition
Rocks
  Composition of rocks
  Rock classes

  Igneous rocks
  Sedimentary rocks
  Metamorphic rocks
  Consolidated and unconsolidated rocks
Landform analysis
  Types of analysis
  Scientific analysis
    Structure
    Process
    Stage

REVIEW QUESTIONS

1. Choose two examples, from your own experience if possible, to illustrate relationships between landform conditions and human conditions and activities. Discuss the relationships.

2. Choose two examples, from your own experience if possible, to illustrate relationships between landform conditions and other physical conditions.

3. What is the distinction between the terms "major landforms" and "minor landforms"? What is the difference in meaning between

"major landforms of the earth" and "major landforms of the continents"?

4. Name some typical minor landforms in the area in which you live.

5. In general, and in simple words, state the differences among plains, plateaus, hills, and mountains.

6. What processes account for the shaping of landforms? Which of them operate from within the earth and which operate "from without"?

7. Draw cross-section diagrams to show the difference between a structural basin and a structural dome.

8. What is the end result of weathering? Wherein is decomposition different from disintegration?

9. Name the chief agents of erosion.

10. Suggest what evidence there is to support the contention that, even in desert regions, moving water is the chief erosive agent.

11. Which of the following landforms are degradational and which aggradational? A sea cliff, the Grand Canyon, a delta, a gully, a sand dune, a loess plain, a fiord, an alluvial fan.

12. Give an example of a rock that is composed of one mineral; an example of a mineral that is composed of one element.

13. What is the difference between an igneous and a metamorphic rock? Give common examples of each.

14. Thinking of the rocks of the earth's crust as a whole, what are the chief elements which compose them?

15. Give examples, from your own experience if possible, of: (a) landforms of different structure, (b) landforms shaped by different processes, (c) landforms in different stages.

SOME SUGGESTED REFERENCES

(Attention is directed particularly, at this time, to the *photographs and diagrams* in the following references—photographs and diagrams which show the nature of many different kinds of landforms and, in many instances, the relationships between landforms and the use of the land by man.)

Finch, Vernor C., and Trewartha, Glenn T., *Elements of Geography: Physical and Cultural,* 3rd ed., McGraw-Hill, 1949. A standard college textbook providing a systematic treatment both of the physical and human elements (see illustrations, pp. 219-394).

Freeman, Otis W., and Raup, H. F., *Essentials of Geography,* McGraw-Hill, 1949. An introductory college textbook intended both for those who will continue in additional courses in geography and for those for whom the one course is terminal (see illustrations, pp. 199-253).

Lee, Willis T., *The Face of the Earth as Seen from the Air,* Special Publication No. 4, American Geographical Society, 1922. A pioneer book in the portrayal of geographical features on vertical and oblique aerial photographs (82 illustrations).

Light, Richard U., *Focus on Africa,* Special Publication No. 25, American Geographical Society, 1941. Africa in photographs, chiefly air photographs, along a route from Cape Town to Cairo (323 illustrations).

Lobeck, Armin K., *Geomorphology: An Introduction to the Study of Landscapes,* McGraw-Hill, 1939. A standard reference on landforms and their origins; profusely illustrated with diagrams, maps, ground photographs, and air photographs.

Rich, John L., *The Face of South America: An Aerial Traverse,* Special Publication No. 26, American Geographical Society, 1942. Parts of eastern and western South America portrayed by more than three hundred air photographs.

von Engeln, Oskar D., *Geomorphology: Systematic and Regional,* Macmillan, 1942. A standard textbook on landforms and landform genesis; contains many photographs as well as other types of illustrations.

136 *A SHEER DROP in the Half Dome area of the Yosemite Valley. (Albert E. Burke)*

CHAPTER 11

The Landforms of the Continents

··

MOUNTAINS

The major landforms comprise, continent by continent, some of the most basic and most conspicuous of all larger geographic features (Fig. 136). The patterns which they form are among the most fundamental of all geographical patterns. In North America, for example, no study, whether in such fields as botany, zoology, or climatology, or in other fields such as history, population, or transportation, can ignore the eastern hilly uplands, the vast north-south central plains, or the mountain, plateau, and hill complex of the West (Plate IV). Among the major landforms, whether in North America or elsewhere, no others are so noticeable or so "dictatorial" in their relation to other conditions as are mountains.

Mountain Regions

Mountains cover very appreciable portions of the earth's surface (Plate IV). Because so many of us live in lowlands and in lowlands far removed from most of the earth's mountainous regions, we are seldom aware of the extent, pattern of distribution, or variety of the world's highest and most rugged areas. No one knows, because of inadequate surveys, exactly what proportion of the land surface is truly mountainous. However, a study of the world map of major landforms will show that mountains occur in many and extensive areas, and that some continents are more mountainous than others. For example, Asia, despite vast areas of plains, hills, and plateaus, has hundreds of thousands of square miles of mountain lands, enough, in fact, to cover about all of Europe. Quite to the contrary, mountains are almost nonexistent in Australia, for only a small section in the southeast is sufficiently high and rugged to be considered mountainous. Perhaps it would be safe to say that about 10 per cent of the exposed face of the earth's crust is mountainous. This may not sound like a great deal, but it means that at least one out of every ten square miles of land is mountainous. In addition, there are the many more square miles of mountains which are drowned by seas and oceans. All except the completely submerged mountains stand as barriers to the movement of man and his goods, and most of them serve, at least to some degree, as human habitats.

THE PACIFIC RING. One of the conspicuous parts of the world pattern of mountains is the "ring" which encircles the Pacific Basin. If one examines a physical globe held in such a fashion that the view covers the Pacific Ocean, he sees a rim of high, rugged country which practically encompasses the broad Pacific waters (Plate IV and Fig. 137). Tracing from the far south, the jagged and nearly ice-drowned mountains of Antarctica are first.

Then, on the western margin of South America, other mountains extend high and unbroken from Tierra del Fuego and the Strait of Magellan to the shore of the Caribbean Sea. These are the famous Andes, the longest and most continuous belt of high country on Earth (Fig. 138). Possessing no low passes, the Andes constitute a physical barrier which even modern aircraft cross with difficulty. To this day, they act as a "separator" between the limited lowlands of the west coast and the major part of the continent. Were it not for the floors of occasional high-level basins which are tucked within the Andean ranges, no more than foothill portions of the Andes would be populated.

From South America, the Pacific ring continues in the mountains of the Central American backbone. Fortunately, this portion is broken by plains and hills, as in Panama and Nicaragua, and in Mexico's Isthmus of Tehuantepec, and the barrier effect is less pronounced than in the Andes (Plate IV). Again

there are some intermountain basins to serve as human abodes. These are welcomed not only because of the presence of comparatively level land, but because they are sufficiently high to provide more comfortable and more healthful living conditions than are to be found in the adjacent hot and damp tropical lowlands.

Northwestward from the Isthmus of Tehuantepec, is a major mountain knot which splits to form Mexico's Eastern Sierra Madre and Western Sierra Madre ranges, between which lies the Mexican Plateau. Because the heart of Mexico, in the sense of numbers of people and governmental establishments, is in the southern part of the plateau, the two Sierras act as barriers between the most densely populated area and the outside world. Likewise the Western Sierra rather effectively isolates the northwestern part of the country from Mexico City. Following a break in portions of northern Mexico and southwestern United States, high country again rises to

THE "PACIFIC RING" OF MOUNTAINS

137

THE *Pacific Ocean is ringed with mountains. On the east they are mainly on the continents; on the west they consist mainly of island arcs appreciably removed from the continents proper. In addition, there are many submarine mountains which do not appear above the ocean surface. See Fig. 138 for other world mountain areas which are not part of the "Pacific Ring."*

WORLD DISTRIBUTION
OF
MOUNTAINS

Compressed Sinusoidal
equal-area projection

138 *THE WORLD PATTERN of mountainous areas.*

form the Rockies and, closer to the ocean, such ranges as the Sierra Nevada, the Coast Ranges, and the Cascades. In addition to being "broken" in the south, the American Rockies are sufficiently separate in the Wyoming Corridor to allow routes to pass through without too great difficulty (Fig. 138). The southern "break" allowed the development of the Santa Fe Trail and the more modern transportation lines which were to follow; the Wyoming Corridor has played a similar role in connection with the Oregon Trail and today's highway and railway lines. Within the Rockies themselves, many valleys and local basins have become ranchlands and, here and there, in the higher sections, lumbering and recreation have become important. In some ways, the Sierra Nevada-Cascade backbone is much more of a barrier than the Rockies (Fig. 138). Its eastern face is very abrupt and there is no easily crossed pass all the way from the southern part of California to the gorges of the Columbia River.

Farther north, the Canadian Coast Ranges and the Canadian Rockies form a continuous series of unbroken barriers all the way to southern Alaska. There the Coast Ranges merge, without any easily crossed passes, with the great arc of the Alaska Range. The Alaska Range, with its 20,300 foot-high Mount McKinley (Fig. 139), rises as a complex wall between the Pacific and the interior of Alaska, thus making transportation difficult between such places as Seward and Fairbanks, as well as walling off the interior from moderating marine air masses. The western part of the Alaska Range slowly drowns itself to become first the Alaska Peninsula and later the Aleutian Islands. North of the Yukon country, the east-west trending Brooks Range stands as a continuous wall between the Arctic Coastal Plain and the interior. Because of mountains and their particular trends, the heart of Alaska is most accessible, in terms of ease of construction of land routes, from the east, and in terms of sea and land routes,

139   *MT. McKINLEY tops the snowy and icy wastes of the high Alaskan Range. Note the snow-covered streams of glacial ice, center and lower left. (U. S. Army Air Forces)*

from the west (Fig. 138). However, the isolation of northwestern Canada and of the Bering Sea have not encouraged the development of the routes which are easier from the standpoint of landform conditions.

The remainder of the Pacific ring lies on the western side of the Pacific. It extends, interrupted by drownings and by nonmountainous sections, from Kamchatka through the islands of Japan, Taiwan, the Philippines, New Guinea, New Zealand, and back to Antarctica. The mountains on the western side of the Pacific are much less continuous and barrierlike (Fig. 138) but, in general, they represent, latitude for latitude, the same radical changes from other landform conditions as are found on the eastern side of the

Pacific. In islands such as Honshu, New Guinea, and South Island of New Zealand, the mountains bulk large in the total geography, as scenery, as habitats, and as determiners of climatic distribution.

THE PAMIR MOUNTAIN HUB AND ITS SPOKES. The complex mountain node of the Pamirs, often referred to as the "roof of the world," lies in the extreme northerly tip of Pakistan and adjacent parts of Turkestan and Afghanistan. From it extends a triumvirate of broad and partly broken spokes which reach for thousands of miles across the earth (Fig. 138). This "hub" with its three "spokes" completes, together with the Pacific ring, the general plan, or pattern, of world mountain distribution. One spoke, trending northeasterly, stretches across the heart of Asia to farthest northeast Siberia. It includes such famous mountain lands as the Tien Shan, the Altais, Sayans, Yablonois, and the Stanovois. Beginning at the Pamirs, one could follow, with short interruptions, high mountain crests for a distance of nearly 5,000 miles. Actually there are a few breaks, as between the Tien Shan and the Altai Mountains and between the Sayans and the Yablonois, and these breaks long have been followed by caravan routes. To this day, the only rail line which crosses the "ridgepole" is the Trans-Siberian, which takes advantage of the break in the mountains near and southeast of Lake Baikal. Of course, the long-continued isolation of inner Asia reflects many things, such as great distances, scarcity of water, un-

friendly tribesmen, and so on, but much of it results from the presence and alignment of great mountains.

Another spoke, broader and more complex than the first, extends from the Pamirs. It includes the highest ranges on the earth's surface. Among them are the Karakoram, the Kunlun, the Altyn or Astin, and the famous Himalaya (Fig. 140). Along with others which reach to the edge of China's extensive hill lands, these ranges form the world's most impressive mountain bulwark. For some 2,000 miles, numerous peaks and crests attain altitudes of 27,000 to 29,000 feet. Between them, the lower parts are only comparatively lower, for there is no easily crossed pass from the Pamirs in the west to the edge of China Proper in the east. Thus, interior Asia and

140 *A GLIMPSE of the majestic Himalayas along India's northern border. (Burton Holmes from Fairchild Aerial Surveys, Inc.)*

India are effectively separated from each other, almost as though they lay in different continents. In addition, the bulwark blocks the movement of moisture-laden air masses from the south and thereby plays an important part in the creation of the "dry heart of Asia" to the north. Farther east, or rather, southeast, less continuous mountains occur here and there in Burma and French Indo-china and form the backbones of Sumatra and Java.

The third of the spokes which lead out from the Pamir hub extends to the west (Fig. 138). As far west as Turkey and southern Russia, there is no major break for the north-south flow of man and his goods. The lands of the Persian Gulf and Mesopotamia are separated from Russian Turkestan and southeastern Russia nearly as effectively as India is shut off from inner Asia. Scores of ranges comprise this vast mountain country, among them the Hindu Kush, Elburz, and Caucasus. West of Turkey and southeastern Russia, there are many large and small mountain regions. However, they lack the pronounced continuity noted in the high, rugged areas of Asia and Asia Minor. Among them and along their borders are plains and lowland corridors leading in many directions (Plate IV), and well within them are numerous fertile valleys quite in contrast to the arid conditions that border the major mountain regions of so much of Asia. Chief among the mountainous regions west of Turkey, that is, in southern Europe, are the Rhodope, Balkans, Pindus, Dinaric Alps, Carpathians, Alps, Apennines, and Pyrenees. The farthest west extension is found in the High Atlas Range of northwestern Africa. Many of these regions, such as the Alps and the Carpathians, offer favorable human habitats in lower and middle level valleys (Fig. 141) and all of them are conspicuously tied into the life of adjacent lowlands—whether in connection with passes or with such activities as summer grazing, lumbering, mining, recreation, or the generation of hydroelectric power.

OTHER MOUNTAIN REGIONS. In addition to those of the Pacific ring and the Pamir hub and its three major spokes, there are other mountain areas scattered widely over the earth's surface (Fig. 138). However, they are not as extensive or numerous as those already noted. In North America, comparatively small sections of the Appalachians constitute true mountain country, as in the Great Smokies of eastern Tennessee and the western Carolinas, in a part of the Adirondacks, and in portions of northwestern New England. The northern part of the rocky coast of Labrador is mountainous, as is much of the ice-free section of western Greenland. The Caribbean region, particularly in extreme southeastern Cuba and much of western Haiti, has a taste, here and there, of the earth's high and rugged lands. In South America, far east of the Andes, there is a considerable mountain cluster in eastern Brazil and one in and just south of the Guianas. In Europe, far north of most of the mountain areas of that "continent," occur the Norwegian mountains. Between Europe and Greenland, minor spots of mountain country appear in Iceland and Svalbard (Spitzbergen). The broad continent of Africa has comparatively few mountains. The High Atlas has been noted above, as the end of the complex mountain spoke extending westward from the Pamirs. In addition, there are the mountains of Ethiopia (Abyssinia), the scattered mountains of eastern equatorial Africa, southern Africa, and the heart of Sahara, and a few others. Australia has only one truly alpine area; this occurs in the southeast and it represents the highest and most rugged portion of the otherwise hilly Great Dividing Range.

Mountain Types

Mountains are not "just mountains," for, like other landforms, or like human beings, they have their own individual characteristics. Some mountains are narrow and jagged, some

141

AN INHABITED glaciated valley (the Lötschental) in the Swiss Alps in the winter. Note how the villages stand out in the snow cover on the valley floor, and the marked difference between the sunny side (adret) and the shady side (ubac) of the valley. (Swissair)

broad and generally rounded, some are blocky, and others are comprised of sharp, conical peaks. While they are all mountains, their individual characteristics help to provide great variety in the physical scene and are strongly reflected in human activities as man attempts to live in parts of them or to build his lines of transport and communication across or around them. There are many shapes, or forms, to be seen in mountainous regions, but four types stand out particularly: *folded mountains, fault-block mountains, dome mountains,* and *volcanic mountains.*

FOLDED MOUNTAINS. Mountains of this type have the general aspect of a corrugated iron roof expressed on a grand scale (Fig. 142). As was pointed out earlier, the earth's crust is under great strain and stress. In some regions, the stresses result in the folding of the crust into series of mammoth anticlines and synclines (Fig. 124A). Such diastrophic

activity does not necessarily produce alpine forms; it may not be pronounced enough to provide the required high elevations, but, instead, may result in hilly lands or nothing more than appreciable undulations in a plains country. However, when diastrophism occurs on a grand scale, and when uplift more than keeps pace with down-wearing, folded mountains are the result. Such mountains are represented by the Juras and the Alps, although the Alps as a whole look less like a series of great folds than do the Juras. The fact that certain mountains are classified as "folded" does not mean that other types of deformation are not present. It means simply that folding has been the dominant process in their formation. Where dissection, as by running water, has created many deep canyons and sharp ridges between canyons, folded mountains will have lost much of their corrugated appearance even though the underlying bed-

142

ONE TYPE of folded mountains: the Jura Mountains, which are located along part of the boundary between Switzerland and France. (Swissair)

rock, wherever exposed, shows the familiar upbends of anticlines and downbends of synclines.

FAULT-BLOCK MOUNTAINS. The origin of mountains of this sort is portrayed clearly in their outward appearance. They actually look like huge and jumbled blocks (Fig. 143). One can appreciate readily from their shape that the earth's crust where they occur has broken into mammoth blocklike compartments, some of which have been heaved slowly upward and, as a rule, tilted from the horizontal (Fig. 124D). There is no better example of this type of crustal disturbance than a mountain region which has been mentioned previously—the Sierra Nevada of California (Fig. 120). This entire range has the outward appearance of one huge block which has been upthrust and slightly tilted. The steep face of the block is toward the east and the gentle face toward the west. Just as folded mountains have undergone more than folding alone, so has the Sierra Nevada block been intricately folded and intruded with volcanic materials, but, nevertheless, the dominant mountain-building process responsible

for its present form is block-faulting. Other samples of fault-block mountains are found in the Charleston Mountains (Spring Mountains) near Las Vegas, Nevada; the Panamints, which border the western edge of the hot, arid trench of Death Valley; and several of the mountains of equatorial Africa.

DOME MOUNTAINS. The well-known Black Hills of South Dakota and Wyoming represent a doming of the earth's crust which has been pronounced enough to create a small area of mountain condition (Fig. 127). As their name implies, most of them are hills; but, in the central and higher section, one sees all the earmarks of mountain geography including the characteristic vertical zonation of landscape. The Black Hills are not primarily folded or faulted although both folds and faults may be seen in places where the bedrock has been exposed by weathering and stream erosion. Instead, they owe their existence and general shape to forces which produced a broad dome in formerly horizontal layers of sedimentary rock. Underneath the sedimentary strata is a mass of igneous rock which, in its upsurge, may have been the

143 *AN INDIVIDUAL fault-block mountain in southern Nevada. (R. M. Glendinning)*

cause of the blisterlike form. Down-wearing has exposed the igneous core and local dissection of the core has created high relief. Likewise, dissection of the domal structure as a whole has produced roughly concentric rings of in-facing ridges, or *cuestas*. The latter are typical of dissected domes, whether of mountainous scale or not, and each one marks the exposure of a dipping rock layer which is more resistant to wearing away than are the adjacent layers (Fig. 144).

Doming on a huge scale occurs in the Rockies, as, for example, in the San Juan Mountains of southwestern Colorado. Here the doming has been both broad and high. The result is that some of the higher spots, despite long exposure to the agents of degradation, are 13,000 to 14,000 feet above sea level and from 4,000 to 5,000 feet above adjacent lower areas. Examination of the rock structure of the San Juans indicates that rock members comprising the broad dome are in-

144 *A SMALL, eroded structural dome adjacent to Sinclair, Wyoming. Note the encircling and in-facing cuestas. (Balsley from U. S. Geological Survey)*

tricately faulted and folded, but the major action was domal upheaval; hence, the mountains are essentially domal, rather than folded or faulted.

VOLCANIC MOUNTAINS. One type of volcanic mountain is the cone-shaped volcano, like Fujiyama or Vesuvius. This type owes its being and form to the piling up of successive layers of materials which have issued from the earth by way of pipelike vents (Fig. 125A). The superheated materials, comprised of lavas, gases, and steam, are exuded into the open air, often with tremendous explosive force. At times of most violent erup-

tion, gases, steam, and rocks are hurled high into the air. The larger pieces fall as "volcanic bombs," while the smaller rock particles, the volcanic ashes, sift slowly downward. At the same time, flows of molten rock issue from the main vent, or subsidiary vents, and move over the surface. It is the alternate layers of lava and ash which, through time, build up the conical form (Fig. 145). If volcanic activity is sufficiently common, the cone may be built up to truly mountainous proportions. Occasionally, the conical type of volcano is so violently eruptive as practically to destroy itself. In 1883, Krakatoa, a conical island be-

145

CINDER CONE and lava of a young, active volcano: the famous Paricutin, near Uruapan, Mexico. (Pan American World Airways)

146 *SMALL CINDER CONES and "ropy" lava within the broad crater of Haleakala, Hawaii. (Mendenhall from National Park Service)*

tween Java and Sumatra, suddenly exploded with almost unbelievable force. Within a short time, only a blasted stump remained and the surrounding sea was thickly blanketed with ash and pumice. Volcanic dusts were hurled into the upper atmosphere where they circulated slowly around the earth. Very red sunrises and sunsets, resulting from the dust, occurred in places as far away as London, England. The noise of the blast was heard 2,000 miles away and great sea waves swept onto the beaches of neighboring islands to cause a loss of life estimated at 35,000 persons. Even when less violently active, the conical type of volcano may destroy life and property in surrounding areas, as witness the results of the many eruptions of Vesuvius, particularly the eruption which destroyed the cities of Pompeii and Herculaneum, and much of the nearby countryside in 79 A.D.

The other major type of volcano is known variously as the *shield type, caldron type, quiescent type,* and *dome type.* "Dome type" perhaps best describes its form (Fig. 125B). Each dome volcano represents a nonexplosive accumulation of lavas, sheet on sheet and flow on flow, which has created a great mass in the form of a huge inverted bowl. In the upper portion of each dome occur one or more shallow craters, or "caldrons." The lavas boil and bubble in these caldrons like hot fudge in a cooking dish. At times of pronounced activity, the "fudge boils over" and lavas move in fiery tongues down the flanks of the dome, there to cool and harden and thus add another bit to the mass of the volcano. The Hawaiian Islands themselves are excellent and famous examples of dome volcanoes. The islands owe their very existence to lava flows which have piled up on the bottom of the sea and then, with further addition, have pushed above the waters of the Pacific. On the island of Hawaii itself, the higher points are about 13,000 feet above sea level—but more than 20,000 feet above the sea floor where the initial construction began! One of Hawaii's craters, Haleakala, is known to thousands of tourists from all parts of the world (Fig. 146).

The occurrence of volcanic mountains, especially those of the conical type, is surprisingly widespread. They are most numerous in regions of very active diastrophism, particularly along the crests of sharply folded mountains. There, they arrange their steep cones in "marching" lines along the higher crests. Along such crests, the rocks of the earth's crust are being stretched and broken and it is relatively easy for the volcanic materials to escape. Typical "strings" of volcanoes are to be found over nearly the full extent of the Andes, the folded mountain section of Honshu, the alpine backbones of Java and Sumatra, the Alaska Range, and the island arcs of the Aleutians, Kurils, and Philippine group. Considerable numbers also are to be found in southern Europe, east-central Africa, Asia Minor, and the mountain heart of Asia, as well as in Iceland.

PLAINS

In turning from a discussion of mountainous lands to plains, one goes from the most conspicuous to the least conspicuous of the major landforms. Like mountains, plains occur in all the continents (Plate IV and Fig. 147). Some of them are small and some are extremely large; but, whether small or large, they are generally the earth's most productive, most easily traversed, and most densely populated regions. So large a proportion of the earth's inhabitants live in plains that the number supported in plateau, hill, and mountain country is comparatively negligible (compare Plates IV and VI). Likewise, the great bulk of the land, and even air, routes over which man moves himself and his goods lies on and over plains. What has just been said does not mean that all plains are highly productive, readily habitable, or easily traveled. For example, most of the extensive plains of Australia are steppes and deserts; the Arctic Coastal Plain of Alaska is so cold so much of the time that it can hardly be called a readily habitable land; the low plain of western

Siberia is so swampy as to make widespread use or transportation difficult. Yet, by and large, it is the plains regions which have had and will undoubtedly continue to have the greatest significance for mankind as a whole.

Plains Regions

NORTH AMERICAN PLAINS. Except for Europe and Australia, North America has proportionately more area in plains than has any other continent (Plate IV). The largest plain of North America sweeps all the way from the subtropical shore of the Gulf of Mexico to the cold waters of the Arctic Ocean, a distance of nearly 3,000 miles (Fig. 147). On the west, this vast interior plain is flanked by hills, plateaus and, most of all, by high mountains (Plate IV). On the east, in the southern portion, it reaches to the Atlantic and sends an ever-narrowing finger northeastward as far as southern New England. Farther north, the main mass of the great interior plain is largely cut off from the Atlantic by the Appalachian uplands and the higher and rougher portion of the Laurentian Shield. A notable corridor of appreciable width, the St. Lawrence Lowland, breaks through the eastern barrier to join the Great Lakes region with the Gulf of St. Lawrence. However, from the Gulf of Mexico to the Polar Sea, the plain is only slightly interrupted, even by low hills, and one may travel from the delta lands of the Mississippi to those of the Mackenzie without being forced to climb higher than 900 feet above sea level.

North America contains many lesser plains, even though some of them are of considerable size. The low, swampy plain of western Alaska is as large as Ireland. Alaska's Arctic Coastal Plain is nearly as large as Finland. Other plains, smaller, but much more hospitable than the two just noted, occur in the Puget Sound-Willamette Valley sections of Washington and Oregon, the Central Valley and the Coachella-Imperial Valley of California, and the lowland sections of Mexico and Central America. A perusal of the map (Fig. 147) will show still others such as those of Nova Scotia, New Brunswick, and Newfoundland.

All in all, North America is fortunate in its possession of so much territory that is easy to "lace" with routes, grow crops on, build great cities on, and, in general, to "spread out" on. To be sure, much of the plains land is a bit too dry, other parts are too swampy, and still others are cold and isolated. But there is plenty of good usable plains land left. If one thinks only of the major agricultural regions of the United States, he will realize that nearly all of the Cotton Belt, all of the Corn Belt, and all of the Winter Wheat and Spring Wheat Belts spread over hundreds of thousands of square miles of easily cultivated plains. Our resource of plains is of inestimable value. How different the United States would be if mountains, hills, and plateaus swept unbroken from the Atlantic to the Pacific!

PLAINS OF SOUTH AMERICA. In South America, as in North America, the lowlands are mainly interior plains and they have their greatest extent north-south (Fig. 147). Also, they are walled in to the west by high mountains and to the east by other types of uplands, chiefly hill and plateau combinations with some comparatively minor occurrence of mountains (Plate IV). The largest interior plain includes the Pampa and the Great Plains of Argentina and extends northward through the Parana Lowlands to join with the widest portion of the Amazon Plain. A relatively narrow lowland corridor connects the larger part of the Amazon Plain with the Atlantic. By following the course of this interior plain, one can travel from Buenos Aires to the mouths of the Amazon without ascending more than 900 feet above sea level at any point. Most of the plain is more isolated than the interior plain of North America. Part of this isolation, or comparative isolation, reflects such items as great distances,

147   *THE WORLD PATTERN of areas which are predominantly plains.*

unfavorable or relatively unfavorable climates, several occurrences of huge swamps and marshes, and lack of government in far interior holdings. The general isolation reflects, moreover, the landform conditions to the west and east. The Andes constitute a much higher and more continuous barrier than do the Rockies. Also, the eastern uplands are broader and less broken than those in North America (Plate IV). From Rio de Janeiro to the nearest part of Brazil's interior plain is 800 miles; from Rio to the Amazon Plain proper is nearly 2,000 miles—in between is little more than sparsely populated, undeveloped hill and plateau country.

The second largest continuous plain in South America is that of the floor portion of the Orinoco Basin. This extends from the Orinoco to the foot of the northern Andes, a distance of 1,000 miles. It is largely shut off from the Caribbean by the eastward arc of the Andes and from the Amazon country by the generally hilly and incompletely explored Guiana Highlands. Within itself it is handicapped by a type of climate which is too dry at one season and too wet at another.

The remainder of South America's plains are small and scattered. Those which lie outside of the hot, wet tropics have proved, at least so far, easier to live in and develop. The Central Valley of Chile and the coastal plain of Uruguay are instances.

EUROPEAN PLAINS. The major plain of Europe is very wide in the east and narrow in the west (Fig. 147). Its wider portion, known as the Russian Plain, extends from the Black and Caspian Seas to the Arctic Ocean. South of the hilly lands of the Urals, the Russian Plain merges with the plains of Russian Turkestan and the southern end of the West Siberian Plain. While extensive portions of the Russian Plain are arid and semiarid (in the extreme south and southeast) and other parts are cold and appreciably swampy (in the north), most of the plain is highly productive. This plain furnishes the Soviet

148   *A SEA OF WHEAT in a sea of plain: harvest time on the southern Russian Plain.* (*Sovfoto*)

149   *THE BASIN of Hungary is one of Europe's important plains regions. (Monk-meyer)*

Union with the bulk of its great agricultural strength (Fig. 148), and provides easy access to the Baltic region and the Black Sea region, as well as to Asia and the Arctic. West of Russia, the plain narrows. Part of it encircles the Baltic Sea and its fingerlike, westernmost extension curves through the Low Countries and western France to the base of the abruptly rising Pyrenees. The lack of mountains and any considerable hilly country between this latter portion and the Atlantic insures western Europe easy access to the sea (Plate IV). It also allows marine air masses to penetrate readily, thus providing relatively moderate, moist climates many miles inland.

Elsewhere in Europe are smaller plains important out of all proportion to their size. Among these are the plains portions of the British Isles, of the Po River in northern Italy, of the highland-enclosed basin of Hungary (Fig. 149), Romania, and Yugoslavia, and of the Walachian Plain of Romania. Others include the Rhone Valley of France and the Spanish plains in Aragon and Andalusia. Many minute plains lie between the sea and encroaching hills and mountains in Italy and Greece. On these sea-fronting plains developed the civilizations of Greece and Rome and the nuclei of empires.

PLAINS OF AFRICA. Such a small percentage of the total surface of Africa is plains that it might be referred to as the "plains-poor continent" (Plate IV). However, Africa is a large continent, and its plains, which appear insignificant, actually cover several hundred thousand square miles (Fig. 147). Perhaps most famous of African plains is that of the floor of the Congo Basin. It covers an area larger than France. Set well into the interior of the continent, the Congo Plain is surrounded by tablelike uplands which are in turn surrounded by hilly country (Plate IV). This situation, coupled with its hot, wet climate and dense forest growth, has caused it to be more than a little isolated. It reminds one, in many ways, of the wider portion of the Amazon Plain. Another large plain, of which little is heard, occurs in the western part of northern Africa. It extends along the coast for 1,500 miles, from the edge of French Morocco into Portuguese Guinea. Inland, it sends an angling and branching finger well into the Sahara. Rocky and, in part, sandy, this arid and windswept plain has little to offer man.

The remaining plains of Africa are smaller and much more elongated than the two noted above. Most of them occupy narrow coastal lowlands and send tentacles for various distances toward the interior. Some of them are dry lands, as those of southern Tunisia, Somaliland, and South-West Africa; others are hot and steamy, as those of the Niger Delta and French Equatorial Africa. Most famous of them all is the plains area of the delta and lower valley of the Nile (Fig. 205). Here, under desert conditions ameliorated by irrigation water from the Nile, flourished one of the earlier civilizations; here, today, is the densest population of all Africa (Plate VI).

PLAINS OF ASIA. Asia, largest of the land masses and nearly twice the size of North America, possesses one truly vast plain. This extends from the Caspian depression to the Arctic, a distance equal to the east-west extent of the United States (Fig. 147). It varies greatly in width, being widest in western Siberia and along the northern edge of the continent. Its southern portion is handicapped by aridity and its northern part, in addition to its long and severe winters, contains what is probably the most extensive swamp area on earth. In between, along and south of the Trans-Siberian Railway, the plain is more favorable to settlement and development is being pushed rapidly by the Soviet government.

Next in order of magnitude are the plains of India. These surround the triangular, generally hilly upland of the Deccan. The Ganges-Brahmaputra Plain, humid and fertile, sweeps from the head of the Bay of Bengal to the margin of the Punjab Plain of northern Pakistan. Cradled between the towering Himalayas and the much lower hill lands to the south, this plain supports more millions of persons than any other single physical division of India. Another major plain extends from the Arabian Sea northward nearly to the base of the Pamir mountain hub. This plain, usually referred to as the Plain of the Indus River, is comprised of hot desert in the southern half and semiarid

lands in the northern. The northern part, often designated as the Punjab Plain, merges with the plain of the Ganges. The Indus Plain allows relatively easy connection between the sea and the Punjab wheat region. Were it more bountifully supplied with water, it might possess the high population densities found in the Ganges Plain. The plains of peninsular India are narrow but highly productive; population densities are comparable to those of the Ganges region. On the west is the lowland ribbon which lies between the Western Ghats and the Arabian Sea. Its southern part is the Malabar coast, one of the famous coasts of the world. On the eastern side is a somewhat wider plain, from the southern tip of India to the Ganges Delta. It too has a famous coast, the Coromandel.

The plains of southeastern Asia lie chiefly in Burma, Thailand, and French Indochina. Less densely populated than those of India, they represent some of the few areas of the continent which can probably support much greater populations than are now present. In southwestern Asia, or Asia Minor, are the anciently settled plains of Mesopotamia. Most of them lie in the modern country of Iraq and they suffer from insufficient water although the Tigris and Euphrates rivers bring water from the Turkish mountains to modify the condition and allow irrigated areas to exist.

The major lowlands of eastern Asia lie in the northern portion of China Proper and in Manchuria. Although fertile, they are largely overpopulated. And, while they connect with the sea, they do not form great corridors extending into the heart of the continent (Plate IV). One of these plains is a series of basin floors reaching from the mouth of the Yangtze to the Yangtze Gorges at Ichang. Another, the extremely level North China Plain, arcs around the hilly land of the Shantung Peninsula and extends inland to the North China hill country. A third begins as a corridor-plain connecting with an embayment of the Yellow Sea and then widens to form the bulk of the Manchurian Plain. The northern part of the Manchurian Plain is the only portion of Greater China which offers any appreciable room for further settlement. Its gentle surface and rich grassland soils make it a much coveted area.

PLAINS OF AUSTRALIA AND NEW ZEALAND. Australia has more plains than it has higher and rougher lands (Plate IV). One continuous plain crosses Australia from the shores of the Great Australian Bight to the Gulf of Carpentaria and other plains occur along the eastern and western coasts (Fig. 147). How-

suffice to show what is meant. More than half of the ancient hard rock area which curves in a wide arc around Hudson Bay and reaches to the Arctic is an erosional plain. This is the plains section from James Bay and on to the northwest (Fig. 147). Within it there are some depositional plains, but it has become a plain mainly through the lowering and smoothing of a formerly higher and rougher surface by erosive action. First, stream action wore the surface down to a plain by picking up and carrying weathered materials. Next, within comparatively recent times, it was

150   *A SIMPLE expression of the main distinction between an erosional plain and a depositional plain.*

ever, this is not as favorable as it sounds for most of the plains, square mile for square mile, are either arid or semiarid. Australia has plenty of low and nearly level land but far too much dry country.

In New Zealand, there are limited plains on both North Island and South Island. Each has given rise to considerable settlement. There is no major problem of water supply, but nevertheless, the plains are dwarfed by hill and mountain country which is much more extensive.

Types of Plains

Like mountains, the many large and small plains of the earth are of several types. Some of them are the result of the wearing down accomplished by erosion while others are the result of the building up, layer on layer, of deposited materials. The former may be called *erosional plains;* the latter, *depositional plains* (Fig. 150).

EROSIONAL PLAINS. Examples of plains of this type are to be found in all continents. Two examples, taken from the Americas, will

smoothed by the glaciers—the great ice sheets of the Pleistocene Age. The combination—running water and moving ice—produced the erosional plains which cover much of Canada to the south, west, and north of Hudson Bay (Fig. 151).

In the broad plain of the western part of the Amazon Basin, we find another low and relatively smooth land which owes its form to erosion. Here, moving ice has played no part. Rather, running water, aided by weathering, has created the extensive plain. The streams cut their ways into the land and carried off the materials; rainwash ate at the sides of the ridges which the streams had created by digging their valleys and thus the interstream areas were lowered; the result is the plain of western Amazonia. The amount of the erosional accomplishment is shown by several higher remnants, known technically as *monadnocks,* which stand conspicuously above the stream-eroded plain. As the eye draws a line from the top of one monadnock to another, a line marking the general level of the former surface, one can begin to appreciate the tremendous erosional job done over the region as a whole.

151

A VERTICAL air view of the ice-scoured bedrock plain west of Hudson Bay. The darkest areas are lakes and ponds. (Royal Canadian Air Force)

DEPOSITIONAL PLAINS. Lowlands resulting from deposition are large and small and of many types. A very famous one, already mentioned, is the North China Plain (Fig. 152). It is mainly the creation of the silt-laden waters of the Hwang Ho (Yellow River). These waters, flowing from the mountains, plateaus, and hills to the west, have dumped their loads, century after century, into the shallow Yellow Sea and the Gulf of Po Hai. There the materials have collected, layer on layer, to create slowly a low, featureless plain built up from sea bottom. The river has been aided in its job of plain-building by annual accumulations of fine wind-blown dusts (loess) from the lands to the west. Another example of a river-built plain is found in the lower course of the Nile Valley (Fig. 205). This plain is a long ribbon of alluvial material in the bottom of the Nile trench and to either side of the Nile channel. It represents layers of silt deposited by many thousands of Nile floods.

A different type of depositional plain may be seen in Illinois and in states which lie adjacent on the east, west, and north. This gently rolling plain owes its existence to the work of glaciers. The glaciers dropped and spread a thick carpet of glacial debris over the entire region (Fig. 188). Glacially carried clays, silts, sands, gravels, and boulders smothered the previously existing landforms and produced a new kind of plain comprised of sandy flats, muddy swamps, low curving ridges of greatly mixed debris, and, here and there, small knobby hills.

The Atlantic Coastal Plain of the United States resulted from materials carried into and dropped in the shallow waters of the ocean. There they were spread and smoothed by waves and shore currents to produce an underwater surface of very low relief. Later, with slow uplift of the land, this smooth surface emerged to become the plain.

One more example may be taken to illustrate depositional plains, the triangular delta of the Irrawaddy River in southern Burma. It has grown and is still growing into the shallow waters of the Gulf of Martaban. The copious, mud-laden waters of the Irrawaddy provide a steady stream of materials for the job of delta-building. As the waters enter the gulf, their velocity is checked and the load is dropped at and near the seaward edge of the plain; as this goes on and on, the delta slowly pushes its marshy fringes farther and farther out to sea. In addition to those mentioned, there are several other types of depositional plains. For example, an alluvial fan (Fig. 181) is a type of depositional plain; so is a loessal plain.

PLATEAUS

Plateau lands are few and far between in some parts of the earth, as in Europe, but numerous and rather closely spaced in other parts, as in Africa (Fig. 153). Plateaus in Africa are so large, and cover such a major portion of the land mass, that any discussion of their world distribution should begin there.

Plateau Regions

AFRICAN PLATEAUS. From north to south and from east to west, the "Dark Continent" is mainly one huge upland platform. There are, as pointed out previously, a few large plains and many small ones, as well as a proportionately small area of mountains (Plate IV). In addition, there are large parts of the continent which are chiefly hilly regions.

However, as a study of the map (Plate IV) will indicate, Africa has about as much land in plateaus as it has in all other major landform types combined.

At this juncture, however, it is necessary to recall once more that a general, broad uniformity in landform condition does not mean geographical sameness or monotony. Nor does it signify an equality of habitat value. Some of Africa's plateaus are wind-swept, hot, and dry; others are hot and only semidry; still others are seasonally wet and dry savannas or perennially damp rainforests.

In general, the African plateaus range from 2,000 to 5,000 feet in altitude. Some sections, as in the Belgian Congo and Sahara, the latter being mainly plateau, are lower than 2,000 feet and others, as in Tanganyika, are higher than 5,000 feet. Most of the vast plateau area of northern Africa is comparatively low. Throughout, it is mainly desert and semidesert and it has little to offer man. Its interior portion is very isolated—an isolation resulting primarily from aridity and great distances. Most of it receives less than 10 inches of average annual precipitation; its central section is nearly 2,000 miles from the Atlantic Ocean and the Red Sea and nearly 1,000 miles

152

A VIEW of the North China Plain during a flood of the Hwang Ho. The flatness of the plain allows shallow waters to flood over extensive areas. (China International Famine Relief Commission)

from the Mediterranean. The central African plateaus fringe the Congo Plain and encircle Lake Victoria. Those of the Congo are hot, wet, and dense rainforests. Those around Victoria are high, comparatively cool, extensive savannas. The latter comprise much of the famous "big game country" of Africa. The south African plateaus cover much of the Union of South Africa, all of Bechuanaland and Southern Rhodesia, nearly all of Northern Rhodesia, and at least half of Southwest Africa. They are relatively high plateaus. To the west, they are mainly high steppes and to the east there are upland, as opposed to lowland, savannas. Partly tropical and partly subtropical, they offer, especially in the east, considerable opportunity for further settlement. They are "up" enough so that temperatures are comparatively cool, droughts are somewhat less severe, and conditions in general are relatively comfortable and healthful. The eastern and southeastern portions of the South African plateaus have been mentioned several times as possible resettlement areas for some of the "war-displaced" populations of Europe.

PLATEAUS OF EUROPE. In sharp contrast to Africa, the plateaus of Europe are few and small (Fig. 153). Actually there is only one of appreciable size, the Spanish Meseta. It occupies the upland heart of the Iberian Peninsula. On most of its margin, it gives way, downward, to hilly lands, but to the north and northwest it is flanked by abruptly rising mountains. The central part of the Meseta is semiarid, but the remainder is humid. The Meseta's interior position and the surrounding rougher lands engender a degree of isolation from the Atlantic and Mediterranean seaboards.

Elsewhere in Europe, small plateaus occur in eastern France, in western Germany and part of eastern Belgium, and in western Russia just northeast of the Carpathian Mountains. Other European uplands which are sometimes designated as plateaus, such as the Massif Central of France and the Bohemian Massif of Czechoslovakia, are so broken and dissected as to have the characteristic appearance of hill, rather than plateau, lands.

PLATEAUS OF ASIA. In Asia Minor are three famous plateaus. The largest—rocky, sandy, and arid—is the Arabian Plateau (Fig. 153). It tilts from a higher edge adjacent to the Red Sea to a lower, more or less cliffed, dropoff which fronts partly on the Persian Gulf and partly on the lowlands of Mesopotamia. Like its North African counterpart, it is sparsely populated and its interior is isolated. Next in size is the mountain-walled Plateau of Iran (Persian Plateau), which extends from Iran into both Afghanistan and Baluchistan. Its encompassing mountains make it a dry and greatly isolated region. The third of the major plateaus of Asia Minor is that of Turkey, or Anatolia. While the central part is semiarid, most of it is sufficiently watered to support much denser populations than are found in Arabia or Iran. It has access, between individual mountain areas and through bordering hilly lands, to the Black Sea and the Turkish Straits and the Aegean Sea. On the east and south, however, it is confronted with high and unbroken mountains.

Much of the heart of Asia is plateau (Fig. 153). Moreover, nearly all of it is desert and the remainder, steppe. Again, the combination of aridity, great distances, and hilly and mountainous borders means a land of few people and little connection with the outside world. The central Asian plateau extends from the eastern base of the Pamir mountain hub to the "big bend" of the Hwang Ho and the western border of Manchuria. This is a distance equivalent to that from Los Angeles to New York City. Within it is the Takla Makan (desert) of the Tarim Basin and the broad desert and steppe of the great Gobi. To the south of the Tarim Basin, but separated from it by some of the world's highest and most rugged mountains, is the Plateau, or, perhaps better yet, the several plateaus, of Tibet. Here are the most elevated tablelands on earth. They range in altitude from 10,000

153 *THE WORLD PATTERN of areas which are predominantly plateaus (table-lands), including intermont basins. Most of Greenland and practically all of Ant-arctica are ice plateaus.*

to 15,000 feet above sea level, but, even so, they are completely surrounded by mountains which rise from 10,000 to 15,000 feet higher. The high altitude of these plateaus, abetted by the moisture-excluding effect of the high mountains, makes them most inhospitable. They are so high as to have polar temperatures and so dry as to be deserts. The expression "frozen desert" comes close to describing them.

The remaining plateaus of Asia are comparatively small. One of them lies in the northwestern part of the Deccan and the other in China's Yunnan Province. The former is humid and quite fertile, and supports a dense population. The latter, humid but much higher and more isolated, supports populations of medium density.

AUSTRALIAN PLATEAUS. Most of the portion of Australia which is not plains is low plateau with several patches of interior high plateau

(Plate IV and Fig. 153). Nearly all of the huge plateau region is hot desert, from near the shore of the Indian Ocean to the geographical center of the continent, and from near the Great Australian Bight to the northern part of the country. There are no extensive plateaus in the islands to the north, the East Indies, nor in those to the east, including New Caledonia and New Zealand.

PLATEAUS OF THE AMERICAS. Plateaus are well represented and well scattered in South, Central, and North America (Fig. 153). Part of them are intermixed with mountains as is true of most of the Asiatic plateaus, and part of them stand more or less by themselves, as in Africa and Australia (Plate IV). The largest plateau areas of South America are in Brazil and Argentina. Those of Brazil extend in various shapes from the lower Amazon region to the southern boundary of the country and into the central part of Uruguay.

154 *A SMALL intermont plateau, or intermont basin, in Colombia. View of the city of Bucaramanga taken from the Cordillera Oriental. (Collier from Standard Oil Co. [N. J.])*

About half of the great triangle ordinarily designated as the Brazilian Uplands is plateau. To the north and west the plateau regions are comparatively low; to the east and south, they are much higher. The lower parts are mainly sparsely populated rainforests and grassy savannas; the higher parts support larger populations and are more in the nature of upland savannas, with scrub or thorn forests and, farthest south, pine forests and prairies. Argentina's major plateau is that of Patagonia. It extends from the Andean wall to the Atlantic and is a cold, windy desert of low habitat value. Other South American plateaus east of the Andes are in the heart of the isolated and little-known Guiana Highlands and in the equally isolated interior of southern Colombia.

The remaining plateaus of South America lie chiefly in the Andes (Fig. 153). Mostly small, but some comparatively large, they extend from central Colombia to northern Chile and Argentina. Largest and highest is the Plateau of Bolivia. The greater part of it is dry and wind-swept, much like the Plateau of Tibet. These plateaus were the centers of settlement and culture for the Indians of the tropical Andes, perhaps because they were cooler and more comfortable than the lowlands to the west and east. When the Spaniards appeared, they naturally set up their seats of government where most of the native populations lived (Fig. 154). To this day, a map of these intermountain plateaus is essentially a map of major human activities and of the distribution of population (Fig. 155).

North America's most extensive tableland stretches from Mexico City almost to the Canadian border, a distance of more than 2,000 miles (Fig. 153). It is chiefly semiarid, with patches of true desert. Many small mountain districts interrupt its surface. Here and there, great canyons have been cut into it. The Mexican Plateau portion is closed in on the south, east, and west by mountains (Plate IV). That portion in the United States is mountain-locked on the north and west, nearly so on the east, but relatively open on the southwest. With minor exceptions, it has remained an area to get across rather than

to settle in—most of it is still part of "the wide open spaces." Different names are applied to its major parts. To the north it is called the Columbia Plateau, to the south and west, the Great Basin, and to the east, the Colorado Plateau.

In Canada, between the Coast Ranges and the Rockies, are three other plateaus (Plate IV and Fig. 153). The southerly one lies mainly in the middle portion of the Fraser River drainage area; the central one partly in the upper drainage area of the Skeena River and partly in the upper drainage area of the Fraser; the third in the upper drainage of the

155 *A COMPARISON of the landform divisions and the population pattern of tropical Ecuador shows the close correlation of population with the intermountain plateaus (intermont basins).*

Yukon River. All three are "pocketed" in a broad mountain region and their isolation is extreme. So far, they are either unmapped or very sketchily mapped, and most of the information concerning them is derived from trappers' tales and meager reports from government agents and a few explorers.

From the distribution just given, it can be seen that North America, especially in the southwest, has its full share of plateau country. This is in sharp contrast to the eastern part, where major plateaus are lacking (Fig. 153).

POLAR PLATEAUS. Most of Greenland and Antarctica are covered by another kind of plateau. It is ice plateau. The Greenland ice plateau smothers valleys, ridges, and mountains alike (Fig. 156). Its snow-veneered surface extends mile after mile without perceptible slope. Only by careful measurements can it be shown that the surface does slope from its central area to outer edges; there it drops precipitously to the sea or to narrow margins of ice-free land along the coasts. Antarctica presents much the same wintry aspect, except that a considerable number of barren mountain backbones rise above the sea of ice to break the monotonous flatness.

Plateau Types

Plateaus may be classified in several ways. The particular classification used at a given time depends largely on whether one wishes to emphasize geographical location, bedrock structures, or stage of erosional evolution.

LOCATIONAL TYPES. In terms of geographical position, including extent and relation to other surface features, there are three chief plateau types. These are *intermont* or *intermountain plateaus, piedmont plateaus,* and *continental plateaus.* The Bolivian Plateau is an example of a relatively large and high intermont plateau (Fig. 157). It is "trapped" between the eastern and western ranges of the Andes. A much smaller example is the small intermont plateau in northeastern Colombia in which the city of Bucaramanga is located (Fig. 154). It, too, is completely surrounded by high mountain lands. The Plateau of Yunnan is a piedmont plateau for it lies in a piedmont, or foot-of-the-mountain, position in relation to the mountains of southern China (Plate IV). The plateau which extends eastward from the base of the Andes in southern Colombia is another example. The continental plateaus, so named because of their great

156

TEMPORARY camp of an exploring party in the interior of the snow-covered ice plateau of Greenland. (Courtesy of the Geographical Review published by the American Geographical Society of New York)

extent and the fact that they represent "continental platforms" largely unassociated with mountains, are best represented in Africa. The South African Plateau is a good example; so is the plateau portion of the Brazilian Uplands. A given plateau region may perchance be included in all of the locational categories just mentioned. For instance, the vast plateau area of western United States may be termed intermont, because it lies between the Rockies and other mountains to the west; it may be called a piedmont plateau, because many of the marginal portions are at the foot of mountains; or, because it is so extensive and platformlike, it may be considered a continental plateau (Plate IV). The choice of term depends on where one wishes to place emphasis for a given purpose.

STRUCTURAL TYPES. If a plateau is underlain by layers of bedrock which lie practically at the horizontal, it may be termed a *horizontal-rock plateau* (Fig. 158A). Examples are the Colorado Plateau and the Arabian Plateau. If tablelands are comprised of greatly deformed rocks which have been virtually beveled by erosion (and uplifted afterward), they may be called *deformed-rock plateaus* (Fig. 158B). The greater part of the Ardennes region of southeastern Belgium is a good example. In other regions, lavas have welled up through large earth fissures and spread over entire countrysides, thus smothering existing landforms and rock structures and creating *lava plateaus* (Fig. 158C). The Colombia Plateau is such a one; so is the Parana Plateau of southern Brazil.

DISSECTED PLATEAUS. There are many large and small sections of the earth which were formerly plateaus, but which have been changed in form by weathering and erosion

157   *A SKETCH map showing the Bolivian Plateau (altiplano) and the high mountains completely encompassing it. The plateau has an average altitude of about 12,000 feet; the surrounding mountain peaks, especially on the west, rise to altitudes of about 21,000 feet.*

until they no longer reasonably fit the plateau concept; no longer are they tablelike uplands of relative smoothness. Instead, they have been so deeply cut and etched by streams that their relief is marked. They are *dissected plateaus,* such as the Grand Canyon section of the Colorado Plateau. In some of them the pronounced ridges between canyons are still flat-topped and might be called miniature plateaus in themselves, but, in many others, the ridges have been sharpened until they resemble inverted wedges or steeply pitching roofs. Often the dissection has produced relief characteristics of hills or, if the relief so produced is extraordinary, mountains—hills and mountains created by erosion instead of by crustal deformation. For example, the so-called Allegheny Plateau of eastern United States has been so greatly dissected that, for

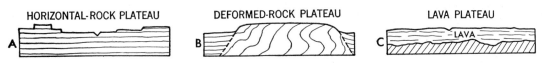

158   *PLATEAU (tableland) surfaces may develop on either simple or complex geologic structures, or they may result from extensive and thick lava flows (as in [C] above).*

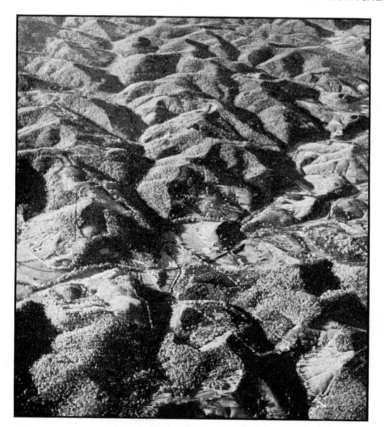

159

HILLY country in West Virginia. This is similar in appearance to many of the so-called plateaus (Allegheny-Cumberland) in Pennsylvania, West Virginia, and Kentucky. (Photo by J. L. Rich in the Geographical Review, Vol. XXIX, No. 4 [October 1939], published by the American Geographical Society of New York)

all practical purposes and in terms of appearance, it is a hilly region rather than a plateau (Fig. 159).

HILLS

The discussion of the major landforms of the continents has progressed from those which are highest and most rugged (mountains) to those which are lowest and least rugged (plains), and from there to the landforms which are comparatively high but non-rugged (plateaus). There remain extensive regions which are not plains, plateaus, or mountains. These are the earth's hill lands (Plate IV). Within these regions, both elevation and ruggedness are moderate, much of the land is in slopes, and little of the surface is flat.

Hill Regions

HILL REGIONS OF NORTH AMERICA. Study of the map (Fig. 160) will show that the hills of North America occur in many places from the Isthmus of Panama to the Arctic and from the Atlantic to the Pacific. There are others too small to show on a map of the scale of Fig. 160.

The great bulk of the North American hill region is in the east. As settlement crept inland from the Atlantic Seaboard of what later became the United States, hills, rather than mountains, stood in the way. A few passes became funnel lines and they witnessed the first trickles and, later, the full surge of the westward movement. Very important among them were the Hudson-Mohawk, the Potomac-Ohio, and the Cumberland Gap routes (Fig. 161). Farther north, the St. Lawrence Corridor served as another way through the

160 *THE WORLD PATTERN of areas which are predominantly hilly.*

hills, particularly for Canadian settlement. Otherwise, a broad hilly barrier stretched from central Alabama to the Hudson Bay entrance and beyond that to the far Arctic. To be sure, there are many local valleys within the hills, and scores of them served as new homes for the pioneers. But, by and large, the hill country was something to get through in order to reach the rich plains lands of the interior. It may seem strange to emphasize the barrier nature of hills inasmuch as they are lower in relief than are mountains. However, hill slopes are numerous, many of them are as steep or steeper than some mountain slopes, and they

161

THE HILLY lands of eastern North America constitute a barrier between the east coast and the interior. The St. Lawrence and Hudson-Mohawk routes are the only lowland corridors through the hilly barrier.

are just about as difficult to cross as are mountain slopes (Fig. 159). To this day, there are only a few major routes across this eastern hill country of the Appalachians.

In the west, hills lie along the eastern foot of the Rockies and continue northwest and, finally, west to occupy the wide interior of Alaska. Along the Pacific coast, the land is mainly hilly from the tip of the Peninsula of Lower California to northwestern Washington. Aided here and there by mountains, the hills provide a bold coast (Fig. 162), and one which has few gaps or routes to the immediate interior. The "break" through the Golden Gate is the only major one from the Tropic of Cancer to Puget Sound (Fig. 160). Another extensive hill area lies west of Mexico's Western Sierra Madre and reaches northwest into southern Arizona and southeastern California. Unlike those mentioned so far, this region is greatly handicapped by aridity. All of North America's western hill regions are closely associated with mountains and, in places, with high tablelands (Plate IV). The total combination has played a large part in separating the East from the West.

HILL REGIONS OF SOUTH AMERICA. Like its sister continent, South America has most of its hills in the east (Fig. 160). The various hill regions extend chiefly from Uruguay to the Orinoco River and are greatly interrupted by broad plateaus. To the north of Rio de Janeiro and in the Guiana Highlands, they are interrupted to some degree by mountains. The corridor of the lower Amazon is the only lowland pass in a north-south distance of 3,000 miles. Together with plateaus and some mountains, the eastern hill lands tend to separate the interior plains from the Atlantic even more effectively than in North America. They are dominantly tropical regions and most of their territory is savanna with some rain-forest and scrub forest. Except near the coast, the hill regions are sparsely settled and largely unexplored and unmapped.

In western South America, hills are prominent along the coast of Chile and on north well into Peru. Ecuador and Colombia have sizable hill regions which also lie close to the coast. Like the hills of the west coast of North America, those of western South America are caught mainly between the ocean and high mountains and they, too, provide an essentially bold coast with few harbors.

HILL REGIONS OF EUROPE. Outside of the Russian Plain, hills are prominent features in Europe (Fig. 160). Because most of them are neither too cold nor too dry and because of population pressure, they are used and permanently inhabited to a greater degree than in the Americas. In the British Isles, hills cover Scotland and Ireland except for central lowlands, most of northern and western England, all of Wales, and small sections of Cornwall. Partly forested and partly in grass and shrub, they furnish some lumber and large quantities of wool to the lowlands. Being relatively steep lands in a humid climate, they also supply considerable water power to the lower areas, many of which are highly industrialized.

On the Continent, most of the hill regions lie in the south. They extend, interrupted by mountains and plains, from the Atlantic to the Aegean and Black Seas and from the shores of the Mediterranean to central Germany and southern Poland (Plate IV). It is pertinent to note that the territories of several nations, such as Portugal, Italy, Yugoslavia, Greece, Bulgaria, and Czechoslovakia, are comprised more of hills than any other type of surface. Some of these nations also contain much land that is mountainous. With only constricted lowlands, nations of this sort have been forced to the development of "hill-land economies" marked by intensive use of valleys within the hills and by grazing and forestry on the slopes and ridge tops. Fortunately, the greater portion of the hill regions of southern Europe has a sufficiently mild and humid climate to allow such utilization. In many places, the lower parts of hills have been terraced in an attempt to provide level agricultural land where nature neglected to do so

(Fig. 163). A person from the hill regions of eastern United States would be amazed at the high degree of utilization of most of the hill country of Europe, whether in Greece and Italy, the Massif Central of France, or the southern half of Germany.

Northern Europe's hills are mainly in Sweden and parts of Norway and Finland. They form a long belt between the Norwegian Mountains and the Baltic Plain. Except in the southern part, they are less used than the hills of southern Europe. With their northern forests, numerous lakes and streams, and long cold winter, they remind one of the hill regions of eastern Canada, north of the Great Lakes and the St. Lawrence. In the far north, they are tundra rather than forestlands.

In eastern Europe, the long north-south stretch of the Urals forms a hilly "separator" between the Russian Plain and the plain of western Asia.

HILL REGIONS OF ASIA. Asia has more than its share of hills, just as it has more than its share of mountains (Plate IV). The hills of Asia extend from near the equator to the Arctic Ocean and from the Pacific to the far interior (Fig. 160). In a broad sense, they form a ring, only slightly broken around the mountain and plateau core of the Asiatic land mass. Because of their great extent, both latitudinally and longitudinally, they present many different aspects and degrees of habitability. They are all hills, but some are bleak tundras, others are part of extensive northern forests, others practically barren deserts, and still others savannas and tropical forests. In general, the warmer and wetter ones, such as the rolling hills of peninsular India and the knobby hill lands of southern China, support dense populations. Those which are dry or cold support only sparse populations. In eastern and southern Asia, where most of the plains are "bursting" with people, the hilly regions have been resorted to much more than

162   A SECTION of bold coast in southern California. Because of wave action and landslides, the coastal highway shown is very expensive to maintain. (Spence Air Photos)

they would have been if the plains with their resources had not been used to the hilt. Again, as in parts of southern Europe, the people have terraced many of the lower slopes, in an attempt to provide "plains in hills."

HILL REGIONS OF AFRICA. The hilly areas of Africa are rarely associated with mountains (Plate IV). Mostly, they join plateaus. In fact, the portions of this plateau continent which are not plateaus are mainly hills. The great bulk of the African hill regions occurs south of Sahara where they usually surround extensive interior plateaus (Fig. 160). The vast Saharan tableland is invaded by a curved finger of hills as a sort of hill-bridge which connects central Sahara with the hills which rim the northern margin of the Congo Basin.

Northwest of Sahara, hills are mingled with the plateau and mountain complex of the Atlas region. Among other hills are those which separate the Nile Valley from the Red Sea and those which extend from the mountains of Ethiopia to the northeastern "horn" of Africa.

Africa's hills, like those of other continents, vary in climate and vegetation cover. For example, the hilly lands to the east and north of the Congo Basin are rolling savannas. Those to the south are a part of extensive tropical scrub forest. Those to the west are clothed with dense, wet, tropical forest. Quite in contrast, the hills of desert regions rise gaunt and barren above equally barren plateaus.

163 *A PARTLY terraced hillside in southern France. (Webb from Standard Oil Co. [N. J.])*

164   *THE RIDGE AND VALLEY region northeast of Knoxville, Tennessee. Narrow cultivated valleys lie in between steep, largely forested ridges. (E. N. Torbert)*

HILL REGIONS OF AUSTRALIA AND NEW ZEALAND. Most of Australia's hill land is in the far east (Fig. 160). It acts as a separator between the humid east coast and the dry interior and forms the well-named Great Dividing Range. A few hilly areas lie to the west, partly in the interior plain and partly in the central and western plateau. These are steppes and desert hills, as opposed to the eastern hills, which are cloaked with a mixed forest. Tasmania is almost entirely hilly. Several hill regions occupy the bulk of North Island, New Zealand, as well as the northern end and southwestern corner of South Island.

Hill Types

It has been noted already that there are different types of mountains, plains, and plateaus. The same is true of hills: they, too, possess individuality and, while such regions as South China and eastern Kentucky are both hilly, the hills differ sufficiently in shape and arrangement to provide a different cast to the particular surface configuration, let alone their utilization by man.

STRUCTURAL HILLS. In some sections of the earth, the form and pattern of the hills reflect direct and strong bedrock control. For example, much of the hill country of Tennessee is underlain by strongly folded layers of sedimentary rocks whose axes have a pronounced northeast-southwest trend (Fig. 164). As weathering and erosion have worked on these materials, the hard rock portions have produced ridges and the soft rock portions have become narrow lowlands. The result is a hill country comprised of nearly parallel ridges and valleys with a northeast-southwest arrangement—the hill country resembles a series of huge "marching" waves. In an area of this sort, the pattern of land use is belted —strips of agricultural land occupy the valleys and strips of forest, the ridges. Travel is easy in the valleys, but difficult across the ridges; only where streams have cut narrow gaps, or passes, through the ridges is travel easy from one valley to another.

165 *THE LAURENTIDE hilly region between Quebec City and the Saguenay River, an area that has been shaped by glacial action. (R. M. Glendinning)*

EROSIONAL HILLS. The patterns of many hill regions show no immediate control by the underlying structure. This is particularly true where the rock layers are horizontal or where the "underlay" is comprised of masses of relatively homogeneous rock. The hill country of eastern Kentucky is the result of valley cutting by numerous streams in nearly horizontal rocks. So many streams have become established and have cut their valleys that virtually all the land between them has been sharpened into steep-sided ridges (Fig. 159). The stream patterns are treelike and hence so are those of the valleys. The ridges between the valleys merely fill in the areas between the trunks and branches of the streams. Along the southeast coast of Brazil, especially at and near Rio de Janeiro, are the famous "sugarloaf" hills. They are much different than the hills of eastern Kentucky. They represent hill types commonly produced in humid regions as a result of the weathering and erosion of granite. Their forms are knoblike and there is commonly level land around and among them. Despite their abruptness and steepness of slope, they do not constitute barriers as do hills which are primarily ridges. On the other hand, their slopes are so steep that they do

not support forests, let alone "sidehill" farms.

Still another type of hill country is seen in some of the regions which were "worked over" by continental glaciers. A typical section is the edge of the Laurentian Shield to the north of the St. Lawrence Valley (Fig. 165). Here are many ancient hills that have been shaped from solid bedrock partly by normal stream erosion and, more recently, by moving ice. Between the hills are broad troughs and shallow basins which also represent the erosional accomplishment of glacial ice. The result is a strongly rolling surface with enough "up and down" to create a hilly condition.

The foregoing discussion of different types of hills, or hill regions, is far from complete; it is not an attempt to classify and describe all hill types which might be distinguished. The chief point is that within the many hill regions of the earth there are several types of expression and condition, each having direct reflections in the form of the land and in the use of the land by man, and each adding another element to the infinite variety of the face of the earth.

The present chapter has focused attention on the continental patterns of the earth's major landforms. These patterns are seen in combinations on the world map in the front of the book (Plate IV). They are seen singly in several world maps contained in this chapter (Figs. 138, 147, 153, and 160). They are among the more basic of geographical patterns and, because of this, have been described in words and discussed, rather than leaving them to be "carried" by maps alone. Moreover, the chapter, by example and reference, has emphasized the important idea that parts of the earth are mountains or plains while other parts are plateaus or hills. Additionally, the chapter has given wide sampling of the many different types of mountains, plains, plateaus, and hills. The chapter which follows immediately deals with some of the details of the sculpturing of the earth's surface by the dominant erosive agents.

CHAPTER OUTLINE

The landforms of the continents

Mountains
  Mountain regions
    The Pacific ring
    The Pamir mountain hub and its spokes
    Other mountain regions
  Mountain types
    Folded mountains
    Fault-block mountains
    Dome mountains
    Volcanic mountains

Plains
  Plains regions
    North American plains
    Plains of South America
    European plains
    Plains of Africa
    Plains of Asia
    Plains of Australia and New Zealand
  Types of plains
    Erosional plains
    Depositional plains

Plateaus
  Plateau regions
    African plateaus
    Plateaus of Europe
    Plateaus of Asia
    Australian plateaus
    Plateaus of the Americas
    Polar plateaus
  Plateau types
    Locational types
    Structural types
    Dissected plateaus

Hills
  Hill regions
    Hill regions of North America
    Hill regions of South America
    Hill regions of Europe
    Hill regions of Asia
    Hill regions of Africa
    Hill regions of Australia and New Zealand
  Hill types
    Structural hills
    Erosional hills

REVIEW QUESTIONS

1. What is meant by the term "intermont basin"? Why are intermont basins apt to be comparatively more significant within the tropics than elsewhere?

2. "In some ways, the Sierra Nevada-Cascade backbone is much more of a barrier than the Rockies." Explain this statement.

3. Do mountain barriers act as barriers to other than the movement of man and his goods? Justify your answer.

4. Sometimes the same mountain region acts both as a barrier and as an important human habitat. Determine such a mountain region and discuss its dual function.

5. Account for the fact that active, or recently active, volcanoes are most numerous in such areas as the Andes, Japan, and Java.

6. Why does man live chiefly in plains areas? Does this mean that all plains are readily habitable? Discuss.

7. Both North and South America have extensive interior plains. Suggest why those of North America are characterized by greater populations and by a greater range of human activities than those of South America.

8. What might be some of the results if the plains of western Europe were walled off from the Atlantic Ocean by a high, continuous mountain region stretching from northern Norway to southern France?

9. The expression "Alpine Europe" includes what areas? What areas are included in "Plains Europe"?

10. Demonstrate that the importance of a plain is not necessarily dependent on large size.

11. What are the major handicaps for human use of Asia's largest single plains region? Are the handicaps ones which can be overcome? Discuss.

12. The North China Plain and the plains of Illinois are both depositional plains. If one were attempting to interpret these two areas to another person and were restricting the discussion to landforms alone, what else could one say about them?

13. Does the statement, "Africa is essentially a plateau continent," mean a general uniformity in Africa's geography? Discuss.

14. In what ways are the Bolivian Plateau and the Colorado Plateau dissimilar?

15. Wherein was the westward movement in the United States affected by hilly regions? Do the same hilly regions still affect the movement of men and goods? Illustrate.

16. Granting major settlement from the Atlantic seaboard, how do you think the penetration and settlement of the United States would have been affected if the major landform divisions of the country had been reversed so that the Appalachian Upland was in the Far West and the mountain, plateau, and hill complex was in the East?

SOME SUGGESTED REFERENCES

American Mountain Series, Vanguard Press. For example, Atwood, Wallace W., *The Rocky Mountains,* Vanguard Press, 1945. The Rockies from on foot, from the saddle, and from the air; described by an authority who knew them as a field of scientific study and a realm of beauty.

Atwood, Wallace W., *The Physiographic Provinces of North America,* Ginn, 1940. An authoritative text on the landform divisions (and their nature and origin) from Central America to the Arctic Ocean.

Cressey, George B., *Asia's Lands and Peoples,* McGraw-Hill, 1944. A textbook on the geography of Asia and the Soviet Union; many maps and photographs illustrative of landform conditions.

Fenneman, Nevin M., *Physiography of Western United States,* McGraw-Hill, 1931; and *Physiography of Eastern United States,* McGraw-Hill, 1938. Two essentially technical books dealing with the major and minor landform areas of the United States.

Fitzgerald, Walter, *Africa,* Dutton, 1945. A regional treatment of Africa's geography; many references to both small and large landform areas.

Gottmann, Jean, *A Geography of Europe,* Holt, 1950. A recent textbook organized essentially by countries, but containing general and specific references to Europe's landforms.

James, Preston E., *Latin America,* Odyssey Press, 1950. A standard textbook on the geography of Latin America, from the Rio Grande to Tierra del Fuego; contains many references to landforms and their significance.

Lobeck, Armin K., *Geomorphology: An Introduction to the Study of Landscapes,* McGraw-Hill, 1939. A much-used reference in landform study, with chapters on plains, plateaus, and mountains.

Peattie, Roderick, *Mountain Geography,* Harvard University Press, 1936. A book about physical conditions, man, and ways of life in mountainous regions.

Smith, J. Russell, and Phillips, M. Ogden, *North America,* Harcourt, Brace, 1942. A general geography of the North American continent; contains much discussion of landform regions, their nature, and their use.

von Engeln, Oskar D., *Geomorphology: Systematic and Regional,* Macmillan, 1942. A comparatively technical textbook on landforms and their origins (see, for example, the chapter dealing with the folded Appalachians).

CHAPTER 12

Landforms and the Agents of Erosion and Deposition

The agents of erosion and deposition help to shape the land surface in two major ways. First, they carve much as a sculptor cuts into stone. Secondly, they create new forms by piling up materials which they have transported. The first activity is essentially one of removal; the second is one of addition or accretion. For example, the deep gorge of the Grand Canyon and the low and nearly level delta of the Mississippi are both the result of work by running water; the gorge was created by erosion, the delta by deposition, layer on layer, of water-borne materials. Likewise, moving ice may scour out a valley to produce a fiord, such as the famous Stavanger Fiord of southwestern Norway, or it may lay a blanket of loose earth debris over the land, as in the glacial plains of Illinois. And, when wind carries on its work, one may find basin-shaped depressions, as among the knolls of the Sand Hills of Nebraska, or closely packed mounds and ridges, as occur in the White Sands of southeastern New Mexico.

In addition to the two ways in which each of the agents of erosion and deposition acts, it should be realized that each one creates its own distinctive forms. Often, too, several agents act collectively or in sequence. Thus there is created almost infinite variety in landform detail.

THE WORK OF MOVING WATER

The accomplishments of moving water are dominant over most of the earth's surface. Almost anywhere one looks, one sees water-cut or water-deposited features, whether it is the valley course of the Amazon, the gorges of the Yangtze, the Nile Delta, or the alluvial plains at the northern base of the Pyrenees. Even in the deserts and the semideserts, lands of little rain, the work of moving water is attested to by the presence of many landforms resulting from erosion or deposition by that agent.

The Work of Streams

As rain falls and snow melts, water begins to move over the land. At first, it moves down the slopes in thin sheets, but soon it is concentrated in small rills and creeks and, later, in large streams and full-flowing rivers. As soon as there is any degree of movement, there is capacity to do work. When there is only slight motion and little water, only the finest materials, as clays and silts, can be transported; when volume is greater and movement faster, coarse materials, such as sands, gravels, and boulders, can be moved. In extreme instances, huge boulders weighing many tons are shifted from one place to another, although their transportation is by sliding, bouncing, and rolling rather than by being picked up and carried.

VELOCITY. The ability of water to shape the land depends chiefly, though not entirely, on its velocity. Even a slight increase in velocity is accompanied by greatly increased power to do work. To put the matter technically, the transporting power of moving water varies as the sixth power of its velocity. This means that if the velocity of a stream is doubled, its capacity to transport sediment is increased sixty-four times! Knowing this, one can appreciate why flood damage by streams may be surprisingly great, even though the speed of the water may seem to have increased only slightly. Likewise, it is possible to understand why a minor increase in velocity results in a markedly greater ability to pick up and carry earth materials (Table 14).

there is a large volume of water flowing with only a slight load down a very steep gradient. Conversely, the smallest velocities are attained when a small volume of heavily loaded water is moving down a very gentle slope. Any change in one or more of the factors will immediately modify the rate at which the water moves. If a stream is flowing over solid bedrock and then, without any change in slope, flows across loose, easily eroded material, it will pick up more load and its velocity will decrease. If a stream issues from a steep mountain canyon onto a gentle plain, the change in slope will check its velocity, perhaps to the point where it will have to drop part of the load it carries. If a rain swells the volume of a stream, slope and load remaining constant, the water in the stream will move at a faster rate. Such changes, in affecting the velocity, produce significantly different effects on landforms. When the velocity is great, much material is transported, or, at least, the stream has a large capacity to carry materials; the result is normally an active cutting into the land surface. When velocity is

---

Table 14   RELATION BETWEEN STREAM VELOCITY AND ABILITY OF STREAM TO MOVE MATERIALS OF DIFFERENT SIZES

STREAM VELOCITY	SIZE OF MATERIALS MOVED
⅓ miles per hour	as large as sand
¾ miles per hour	as large as gravels
3 miles per hour	as large as small stones (2 to 3 inches in diameter)
6 miles per hour	as large as large stones (10 to 11 inches in diameter)
20 miles per hour	as large as huge boulders (16 to 17 feet in diameter)

The velocity attained by a stream depends on several factors; chief among them are *slope, volume,* and *load.* Slope is the angle, or gradient, down which water is moving. Volume is the amount of water which is "on the move." Load is the amount of material carried by moving water. Greatest velocities occur when

slight, capacity to carry load is small and built-up surfaces usually result. Thus, the velocity of a stream may determine whether it cuts a valley or lays down a blanket of alluvial material.

VALLEY STAGES. It may be recalled from earlier discussion (p. 199) that a stream

166 VIEW ACROSS Colorado high country, a portion of the San Juan Mountains. The peaks in the background have altitudes slightly in excess of 14,000 feet. (Cross from U. S. Geological Survey)

167 *EROSION cycle of a valley in a humid region.*

which is cutting a valley cannot do its work all at once but instead works in sequence or in stages. Each stage is marked by a particular valley shape. At first, the stream is attempting to cut its bed to the level of the body of water into which it flows. This level is called *base-level*. In its effort to reach base-level, the stream erodes vertically; then, when it has cut vertically as far as it can, it erodes laterally. As long as vertical erosion occurs, one type of valley shape exists; when lateral erosion becomes dominant, new shapes slowly emerge. Thus, there is an "erosion cycle," each stage of which is characterized by a typical valley form.

The first stage of the normal valley cycle is called *youth* and the valley is termed a *youthful valley*. A valley in this stage is recognized readily by the **V**-shape of its profile;

sides are very steep, there is no level land in the valley bottom, the stream occupies the entire lower part of the **V**, and the valley follows a relatively straight course across the land (Fig. 167A). Its shape shows clearly that the stream is still cutting vertically and has not yet reached the condition where valley widening by means of lateral erosion is possible, or the condition where rainwash down the valley sides has had the opportunity to widen the valley appreciably. As examples of such a valley type, one may turn to any ordinary small gully or, on a much grander scale, to any typical mountain gorge.

Mature valleys represent the second major stage in valley shape. The original **V**-shape has been modified by lateral erosion so the valley has the asymmetrical profile shown in Fig. 167B. Lateral erosion occurs on the outside of each curve of the stream where it produces a definite *undercut bluff*. On the inside of each curve, part of the load of the stream is deposited to form an arc-shaped *valley flat;* this marks the very beginning of a river plain. As a result of cutting on the outside of each bend and deposition on the inside, the stream widens its valley bottom and it curves or *meanders* more and more as time goes on.

The third major stage in valley form, an *old valley*, exists as soon as the work of lateral erosion, rainwash, and deposition has created a comparatively wide river plain, or *flood plain.* The flood plain is bordered by steep, but low, *valley bluffs.* These are steepest where migrating meanders are actively undercutting them, or where such undercutting has recently occurred (Fig. 167C). Within the flood plain, the stream swings in closely fitting meander loops which wander as though lost in the alluvial materials. Along the immediate banks of the stream channel are *natural levees* built up by successive deposits during times of flood. Swampy spots are common in the lowest places, near the valley bluffs or in the very shallow basins which are almost enclosed by the meander loops and the low, smooth forms of the natural levees. These wet spots are called *back marshes,* whether they occur back near the bluffs or in back of the natural levees. Old meander loops mark former positions of the stream channel within the flood plain; if they are largely filled with vegetation and in-washed sediments, they are termed *oxbow swamps;* if they are unfilled, except by water, they are *oxbow lakes* (Fig. 167C).

Thus, from the first small notch of youth to the broad plain of old age, valleys undergo drastic changes in form as streams cut their way into the land—first vertically, and finally in large meander sweeps which plane away the land and create broad alluvial plains.

SIGNIFICANCE OF VALLEY SHAPES. Whether a given area possesses youthful valleys, mature valleys, or old valleys, or a mixture of all three, makes a considerable difference in

the appearance of that area. More significantly, it makes a great deal of difference to man if he is attempting to live there. If there are a large number of youthful valleys, there is no level valley land available for use. If the valleys are so numerous as to lie extremely close together, there is practically no level upland in among them (Fig. 168A). In either instance, both travel and the transportation of goods are difficult and expensive. Cross-country highways need many bridges.

If valleys are largely of the mature type, and especially if they are deeply entrenched, the same difficulties of movement of man and his goods are present. Routes are still faced

A. YOUNG VALLEYS

B. MATURE VALLEYS

C. OLD VALLEYS

Stream   Settlement   ● Bridge or ferry
Woods   Main road   Pasture or cropland

168 *SOME effects of valley shape on land use in a region of humid climate.*

with steep valley sides and stream crossings, and they may have to follow even more devious lines than is true in an area of youthful valleys. This latter condition reflects the fact that the undercut bluff portions of mature valleys are too steep for roads or railroads; thus a given route will have to proceed down the more gentle side onto one of the valley flats, then turn, either upstream or downstream, to cross the river to the next valley flat, and then continue up another comparatively gentle slope. However, mature valleys provide more level land for man's use than do youthful valleys; at least there is level land in the form of the small valley flat which occurs on the inside of each river bend (Fig. 168B). Such features normally support one or more farms, depending on the size of the flat.

In an area of old valleys, there is a great deal of nearly level land. This is particularly true where flood plains are very broad and spaced closely together (Fig. 168C). Valleys of this sort, climate allowing, ordinarily support large farming populations, for the alluvial soils are normally of high productivity and they extend over many square miles with little interruption. However, there are some drawbacks; many sections of the flood plain are too swampy to use for crops although they may produce swamp forests and their margins may grow lush grasses suitable for feeding domestic animals. Moreover, there is the ever-present danger of floods, floods which may spread from one valley bluff to the other and destroy crops, settlements, roads, and railroads, even the inhabitants themselves (Fig. 169). Because of flood conditions, man often distributes many of his crops and settlements along the natural levees in the hopes that these slightly higher sections may stay above the floodwaters.

INTERFLUVE STAGES. At the same time that valleys are being etched into the land, areas between valleys are undergoing change. These areas are the ridges, or *interfluves*. Like valleys, certain normal interfluve types develop in definite sequence, each with its own characteristic form.

169 *MISSISSIPPI RIVER floodwater pouring through a break* (upper right) *in an artificial levee near Knowland, Arkansas. (U. S. Weather Bureau)*

The first stage in the normal erosion cycle of ridges is the *youthful interfluve*. It is a definite ridge, characterized by a nearly level top and steeply sloping sides. The top is part of the original upland surface as yet little eroded; the sides are those of the adjacent valleys (Fig. 170A). The exact condition of the sides will depend on whether the adjacent valleys are youthful, mature, or old. If they are youthful the sides of the youthful interfluves are, automatically, the steep sides of the **V**-shaped youthful valleys.

By the time weathering, soil creep, rainwash, and stream erosion have eaten into and sharpened the original youthful ridges, *mature interfluves* are created. At first, such ridges are very narrow and sharply crested. The form is essentially that of a steeply pitching roof (Fig. 170B). A bit later, the sharp crests are rounded as a result of weathering and rainwash, but they are still relatively narrow.

With continued wearing away, the pronounced ridge forms of maturity become *old interfluves*. Now they are so low and comparatively broad that they can hardly be called "ridges," but they still are "interfluves" (Fig. 170C). The lowness and smoothness are further enhanced by down-wash and the slow creep of soils until old interfluves are only gentle swells in the land surface. However, steep slopes may occur at places on their lowest and outermost margins where laterally eroding stream channels create abrupt drops. If, for example, two valleys adjacent to an old interfluve are in the stage of old age themselves, then the outermost edges of the old interfluve are the short, steep bluffs of the old valleys (Fig. 171).

A. YOUTHFUL INTERFLUVE

B. MATURE INTERFLUVE

C. OLD INTERFLUVE

170 *EROSION cycle of a normal interfluve in a humid region.*

SIGNIFICANCE OF INTERFLUVE SHAPES. As with the typical valley forms produced by running water, the type or types of interfluves in a given region are important in the general appearance and the use of the land by man. Where broad youthful interfluves are numer-

171 *PROFILE of old interfluves where adjacent valleys are also in stage of old age.*

ous, there is much nearly level land available for agriculture, settlements, and routes of travel. Transport lines can be laid out in almost any fashion desired (Fig. 172A).

A countryside comprised largely of mature interfluves is quite another matter. The ridges provide practically no level land. If the slopes are utilized for crops, great care is needed to prevent the soils, loosened by cultivation, from being washed away into the valleys. Where there are many mouths to feed, such slopes may be terraced to provide level land not available under natural conditions. This is common practice in densely settled portions of the Orient. In general, mature ridges are best used for forest or permanent and scientifically managed pasture. The same conditions which limit agricultural use make the laying out of routes difficult. Quite commonly, the major roads, as well as the distribution of dwellings, follow the crests of the narrow ridges (Fig. 172B).

In areas of old interfluves, there is relative freedom from limitations imposed by landforms. The gently rolling condition allows cropland to be widely spread. There is land suitable for villages, towns, and cities, and routes can be distributed in almost any pattern. In these respects, areas of old interfluves closely resemble those of youthful interfluves; both have a considerable amount of nearly level land, although there normally is more "roll" to the surface where interfluves are old (Fig. 172C).

VALLEY AND INTERFLUVE COMBINATIONS. The foregoing discussion dealt largely with valleys and interfluves as though they occurred without association with one another. Actually, they are inseparable and they occur in manifold combinations. Through use of the various terms which are applied to valleys and interfluves of differing stage and shape, a simple and meaningful description of local landforms becomes readily possible. Specific illustrations will serve to clarify what is meant.

There is a portion of the Cumberland Plateau in eastern Kentucky in which the landforms may be described simply and concisely as consisting of youthful valleys and mature ridges. This immediately gives a picture of a countryside with a surface profile somewhat like that of the teeth of a saw—the V's of the youthful valleys and the inverted V's of the mature ridges (Fig. 172B). In this instance, the saw-tooth profile is not on a mountainous scale for the vertical distance from ridge top to valley bottom is measured in hundreds instead of thousands of feet. Yet, nearly all the land is steeply sloping and the relatively sparse agricultural population is forced to use sidehill fields, in addition to what meager level land occurs along the narrow ridges and in the equally narrow creek beds.

In a similar fashion, the landforms of another area may be described as comprised of old valleys and old interfluves. Such a description brings to mind an entirely different kind of countryside than the one mentioned above. It is a countryside with very little "up and down" to it; valleys are level and relatively broad, the interfluves low and gently rolling (Fig. 171). It is an area where, as far as the dictates of surface are concerned, man has relative freedom to settle and work. Parts of the inner, and older, portion of the Atlantic Coastal Plain of the United States (see Fig. 118 for location) are thus hospitable to man.

There are, of course, many other possibilities of valley and interfluve combination. Some of these may be envisioned by means of a few questions. What would be the landform appearance of an area comprised of youthful ridges and youthful valleys (Fig. 172A) or one with youthful valleys and old interfluves—or mature valleys and youthful interfluves (Fig. 168B)?

STREAM-DEPOSITED FORMS. Not only does running water help to create landforms by carving valleyways and eating into and modifying interstream areas; it also produces new forms by actual construction. Some depositional forms have been noted already in connection with the formation of valley flats in mature valleys and flood plains in old valleys.

Other common examples, ones in which the entire form is depositional in origin, are the small cones and fans of alluvial material built up at the mouth of almost any little gully. On a much grander scale is the mammoth alluvial fan deposited at the northern base of the Pyrenees in part of southern France, known as Lannemezan. Another example is the almost unbelievably level land called the North China Plain, where the silt-laden waters of the Hwang Ho have filled in and built up an extensive plain in the shallow waters of a former sea. Other instances are to be seen in the large "birdsfoot" of the Mississippi Delta, which the muddy Mississippi River is still actively building into the waters of the Gulf, or in the arcuate delta which the Nile has constructed in the southeastern corner of the Mediterranean Sea.

The Work of Solution

Some landforms owe their existence and nature to solution by moving water. Solution goes on, as was mentioned in the discussion of chemical weathering, in practically all earth materials, both at the surface and to considerable depths. However, production of definite landforms by solvent action demands what might be considered as wholesale removal of materials by solution. Enough material has to be removed to affect the lay of the land. Accompanying such removal is the development of subterranean forms. These are not landforms, but, as the name implies, forms which occur under the land. Regions in which solution proceeds to a major degree are known as *karst* regions; they are areas which are underlain by soluble or partly soluble rock. The name derives from the Carso Plateau of Yugoslavia. Here both subterranean and surface forms of solution are highly developed, and here some of the more significant early studies of karst conditions were made. Other famous karst areas include the peninsula of Yucatán, the Mammoth Cave section of

Kentucky, the Shenandoah Caverns of Virginia, and the Carlsbad Caverns of New Mexico.

EVOLUTION OF KARST FORMS. As water works its way down the cracks and between the layers of soluble rock, it dissolves and carries away some of the rock materials. In time the vertical and oblique cracks, as well as the horizontal ones which separate the rock layers, are enlarged until they become small *solution channels.* With further work of solution accomplished, small channels become large ones and rock members are honeycombed with a completely developed, three-dimensional system of passageways. Here and there, where rock is more soluble, channels are expanded into *caverns;* these are the famous limestone caves. When caverns are

A. EXTENSIVE YOUTHFUL INTERFLUVES

B. NUMEROUS MATURE INTERFLUVES

C. EXTENSIVE OLD INTERFLUVES

≈ Stream   ⚹ Settlement   • Bridge or ferry
▨ Woods   ⊥ Main road   ‖≣ Pasture or cropland

172   *SOME effects of interfluve shapes on land use in a region of humid climate.*

numerous, and when they occur in lines at different levels, they are referred to as *galleries*. Fig. 173 shows, in cross section, an area in which the work of solution has proceeded to the point where solution channels, caverns, and galleries are fully developed.

By the time caverns are well formed, particularly near the surface, the work of solution is reflected in the landforms. As near-surface cavern roofs collapse, either slowly or suddenly, depressions called *sinkholes* are formed in the land. They are circular or oval

original surface, and marked by hilly or moundlike remnants of the soluble rock. Such remnants are greatly honeycombed and are known variously as *haystacks, hums,* or *magotes* (Fig. 174D).

DRAINAGE IN KARST. Conditions of drainage are normal in the initial phases of karst development. Of the moisture which falls from the skies, some sinks into the regolith, some is evaporated, and some collects and runs along low lines in the surface to form streams. But, as soon as solution channels, caverns, and

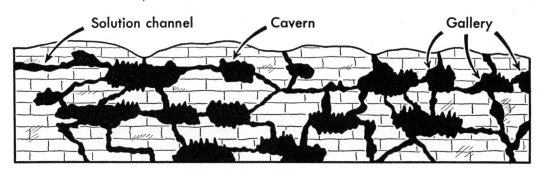

Solution channel   **Cavern**   **Gallery**

173   *LAYERS of soluble rock in which work of solution is well advanced.*

in ground plan and vary in size from a few feet to perhaps hundreds of feet across. In general, there are two types of sinkholes: one is funnel-shaped and is called a *doline* (Fig. 174A); the other is shaped more or less like a well and is known as a *ponor* (Fig. 174B). Where they are numerous, entire areas are literally pock marked with large and small depressions. If several caverns collapse along the same line or if the roof of an underground stream falls in, trenchlike forms are produced. These are *uvalas;* like sinkholes, they may be relatively small or may extend for several hundreds, or even thousands, of feet. Some of the uvalas in the karst of Yugoslavia are large enough to contain entire agricultural settlements. Part of Fig. 174 illustrates the general nature of uvalas.

After solution has continued for some time, the layers of soluble rock are almost entirely removed. If this has happened, there is a new level to the countryside, a level lower than the

sinkholes are present, the drainage condition is greatly modified. Water sinking into the regolith and on into the bedrock moves downward very rapidly through the honeycombed strata. Surface waters travel only very short distances before they disappear into the sinkholes and the underground channels which drain them. The lack of definite streams and the rapid removal of water to lower levels may actually produce "droughty" soils in regions which are climatically humid; in lands with Dry climates (BW, BS), the karst condition produces extreme drought (Fig. 175).

Some karst regions, depending largely on their degree of development, possess numerous small lakes and ponds. These usually reflect the blocking of sinkhole outlets so that each one acts as a reservoir to entrap local surface flow. Such ponds or lakes may drain away overnight if the outlets into the subterranean channels are freed of earth materials which block them. Thus, detailed maps of

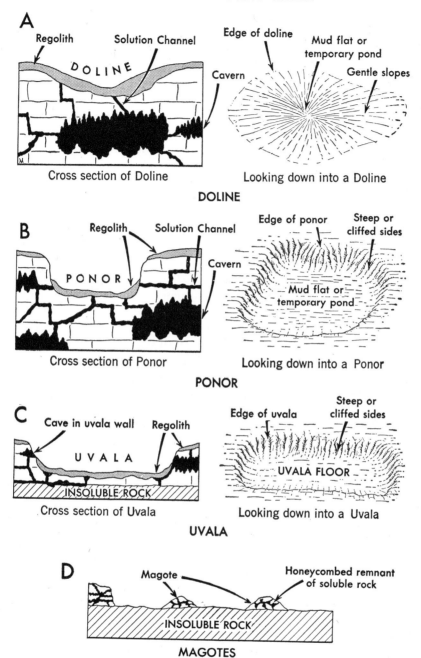

DOLINE

Cross section of Doline

Looking down into a Doline

PONOR

Cross section of Ponor

Looking down into a Ponor

UVALA

Cross section of Uvala

Looking down into a Uvala

MAGOTES

174 *GENERALIZED diagrammatic illustrations of some typical karst landforms.*

karst regions may show ponds and lakes which no longer exist as well as fail to indicate those which have come into being since the maps were made.

By the time the soluble rocks which comprise the karst are largely removed, drainage is again back at the surface and more or less normal drainage patterns are present. It is almost as though karst conditions had never existed in the region. As usual, there may be exceptions to this. For example, the soluble rocks in a given area may extend below sea level. If this is true, the final stages of karst witness extensive surface water channels and numerous ponds and lakes which are flanked and dotted with the remnants of the original rock.

STAGES IN KARST. The foregoing discussion of karst landforms and karst drainage shows a definitely sequential development of conditions. It shows, in a sense, the major steps in what may be termed "the karst erosion cycle." Obviously, the cycle is much different from that which occurs in connection with the evolution of stream-cut valleys and interfluves, but it is, nevertheless, a matter of stages. For this reason, it is often convenient to distinguish three major stages in the karst erosion cycle.

Youthful karst is characterized by a few sinkholes and predominantly surface drainage. *Mature karst* is marked by the presence of numerous sinkholes, a few or many uvalas, and drainage which is almost entirely subterranean. In the third major stage, *old karst,* drainage is back on the surface again, and all that remains to mark the area as karst are the scattered knobby and hilly remnants of the soluble rock. Each of these stages is represented in Fig. 176; a study of it will show how different a given area is from one stage to another.

SIGNIFICANCE OF KARST. In terms of habitation of an area by man, it makes a great deal of difference whether it is a karst or nonkarst region, and, if it is karst, whether it is in a youthful, mature, or old stage. In youthful karst, assuming a humid climate, water is abundant. Streams are on the surface and underground channels have not developed to the degree that they quickly rob the soils of necessary moisture. In addition, sinkholes are few and, thus, there are only minor interruptions to the surfaces of fields and only slight controls placed on the pattern of land routes.

By the time that uvalas and numerous sinkholes are present, habitat conditions are modified. Despite humid climate, water becomes a problem. There are no surface streams and soils may be deficient in moisture. This condition may be offset partly by the use of sinkhole ponds and lakes as sources of water for domestic animals. However, such water is of little use for man himself because it is usually dirty, stagnant, and unsafe to drink. In most karst areas, man has to collect rain water on the roofs of dwellings and store it in surface containers or in underground cisterns. Soils may be so dry as to support only drought-resisting crops or to demand special dry-farming methods. Moreover, the countryside is much interrupted by depressions, which affect the amount of land available for crops and exert strong limitations on the alignment of routes. Where sinkholes are of the doline type, more land is available for agricultural use; for example, the sides of the dolines may be used for pasture, and the ponds in their bottoms for water for stock, including such domestic animals as ducks and geese. If the

Surface stream   Surface stream disappearing into sinkhole   Lake in bottom of clogged sinkhole   Stream flowing across bottom of uvala   Stream disappearing into sinkhole   Surface streams flowing on insoluble rock   Remnants of soluble rocks (magotes)

Drainage in early stage of karst development (drainage chiefly on surface)
A

Drainage in well developed karst (drainage chiefly underground)
B

Drainage in last stage of karst (drainage again on surface, but at lower level than before)
C

175 *SKETCH maps to illustrate conditions of drainage in different stages of karst.*

176 *DIAGRAMMATIC expression of stages in the erosion cycle of a karst region.*

sinkholes are ponors, much land is wasted. The sides, usually cliffed, are too steep to use and any impounded water is not accessible to livestock. More than this, it is often necessary to construct fences around the ponors to prevent stock from falling in. In the same fashion, dolines place fewer limitations on the patterns of roads and railroads than do ponors; in fact, where dolines are very broad and relatively shallow they produce no more than a gently rolling country.

Areas which have reached the stage of old karst are little affected by karst conditions. Only remnants are left of the original soluble rocks. Streams are again on the land and soils are not losing their moisture to subterranean solution channels. However, in places, soluble rock remnants may be so numerous as to interfere with the use of fields and to cause marked deviation in the alignment of roads.

THE WORK OF MOVING WATER IN DRY LANDS

The surface features of the world's dry lands, like those of humid regions, are the result of the combined efforts of diastrophism, vulcanism, weathering, erosion, and deposition. By and large, they consist in forms ordinarily referred to as *hamada, erg, reg,* and *mountain and bolson.* A *hamada* is a rocky desert (Fig. 177). It often represents layers of sedimentary bedrock which have been uplifted sufficiently to provide a sort of slightly elevated benchland. Much of northern Libya is hamada. An *erg* is a sandy desert, best described as a sea of sand dunes (Fig. 177), as in the Grand Erg Oriental of Sahara, south of the eastern portion of the Atlas Mountains. A *reg* is an exceedingly level plain surfaced with gravels; it is a gravelly or pebbly desert, as opposed to a rocky or sandy one (Fig. 177). Many large sections of the heart of Sahara are of this nature. A *mountain and bolson* area is one of large and small basins which are rimmed and bordered by hills and mountains (Fig. 177). Most of the state of Nevada is like this, and so is much of the Mohave Desert of California.

While the major landforms referred to above comprise the broader view in dry lands, the closer and more intimate scene consists of much smaller forms, most of which owe all or part of their characteristics to the work of moving water. As stated previously, it is true, even in the regions of Dry climates (BS, BW), that running water is the chief agent of erosion. The valley forms which thread hamadas and cut the hamada surfaces into

177

DIFFERENT TYPES OF DESERT

(A) *Oblique air view of a small hamada. The table-top surface is a remnant of a once more extensive hamada. Southern Nevada, northeast of Las Vegas. (Fairchild Aerial Surveys, Inc.)*

(B) *A small erg area in the central section of the floor of Death Valley, California. (George A. Grant, National Park Service)*

(C) *The foreground of this photograph taken in Brewster County, Texas, illustrates a reasonably typical reg (gravelly desert) surface. (Hill from U. S. Geological Survey)*

(D) *Oblique air view of part of an extensive mountain and bolson region. The two light areas lying in the elongated bolson are playas, or "dry lakes," which are slowly being invaded by the alluvial fan slopes from the hills in the foreground and the hills and mountains in the background. Southern Nevada, southwest of Las Vegas. (Fairchild Aerial Surveys, Inc.)*

isolated segments are carved by water. The hills and mountains which encircle bolsons are lined and marked with deep canyons and sharp ridges which have been etched out by stream action. Ergs and regs are laced and intersected by usually dry stream courses. In lower portions of the drainage ways, other forms which have been built up by materials transported and dropped by water are common. Many of the differences in appearance

178

TYPICAL wadi, or arroyo (Mohave Desert, California). Note the boulder-strewn floor of the "washway" of the intermittent stream which has created the wadi. (R. M. Glendinning)

between the landforms of dry lands and those of humid regions result directly from the difference in the behavior of running water. In the dry lands, it is almost literally a case of "feast and famine," of freshet waters or no waters at all. In the western United States, one hears often about cloudbursts. The term is not only picturesque, but meaningful. Of course, clouds do not burst, but the fall of rain is commonly so heavy as to give that impression. Downpours of this sort create flash floods. Stream courses suddenly become raging torrents and then, almost as suddenly, dry up. Floodwaters carry heavy loads and exert a strong scouring action; then, quickly, as the waters dwindle and disappear, the loads are deposited.

Water-cut Landforms

No attempt will be made here to discuss all the surface features which are shaped entirely, or in part, by the intermittent waters of the dry regions. Instead, some of the more typical forms, those which are to be seen commonly in all deserts and semideserts of any appreciable extent, will be described.

WADIES. *Wadies* are the typical stream-cut valleys of the dry lands. They are known also as *washes, arroyos,* and *barrancas,* although the term wadi is most usually applied to them. A wadi may be shallow or deep, narrow or wide, but it is marked always by steep, normally cliffed sides and a nearly level bottom (Fig. 178). The shape is a direct consequence of the intermittency of water flow. When running water is present, it carves a more or less V-shaped valley at first, like the youthful valley of humid areas. As water disappears, the load is dropped to fill in the lower part of the V and create a level bottom. Succeeding water encounters a channel which is glutted with previously dropped materials; the flood spreads out over the wadi floor and actively undermines and steepens the valley sides. This procedure is repeated over and over again. Each freshet relays material farther downstream, leaves other material in its place, and erodes the banks to push them farther and farther apart. For these reasons a wadi, large or small, is maintained constantly with steep sides and level bottom. For the same reasons, its shape is different from that of the normal youthful valley in any humid area.

Where wadies are broad, their level bottom lands sometimes attract agricultural use under irrigation, and even settlements. The results are often disastrous, for the wadi bottom is the natural floodway, and fields, buildings, domestic animals, and human lives are apt to be wiped out by suddenly appearing walls of water. The fact that wadies are so numerous creates other problems. For example, roads and railroads must cross countless numbers of them. For roads, this means

Buttes as remnants of mesas

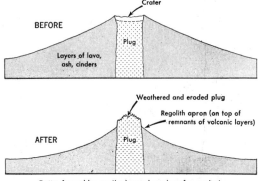

Butte formed by weathering and erosion of a conical volcano (more resistant plug becomes core of butte)

179   *TWO common origins of buttes.*

many expensive bridges or, the alternative, sections of highways temporarily blocked by floodwaters and deposited earth debris. Railroads have no alternative; they must build many sound bridges, and even then one of the large items of expense is the repairing of washouts and the clearing of debris from the channels underneath the bridges.

MESAS AND BUTTES. It may be recalled from previous discussion (see pp. 197-99) that mesas are etched out and separated from tablelands by streams which dig valleys around them (Fig. 132A). The same is true of many *buttes,* for they are often nothing more than sharpened remnants of former mesas (Fig. 179). However, they may consist of the weathered and pointed "plugs" which remain after conical volcanoes have been almost destroyed by weathering and erosion. An example of this is to be seen at Shiprock, New Mexico. The more common type, usually representing the "dying stages" of mesas, occurs in large numbers in the famous Monument

Valley region of northeastern Arizona, as well as in many other dry areas of the world. Suffice it to point out that a region marked with numerous mesas and buttes is like no other land surface expression, whether in dry or humid regions. The "monuments" dominate the scene, and whatever travel there may be must usually thread its way along their flanks and in among them, despite risk in following wadi-bottom trails and roads which are sandy and at the mercy of every flash flood.

PEDIMENTS. Many desert regions are of the mountain and bolson type. This means that there is much sloping land which is located along, or is comprised of, the bases of the hills and mountains. As floodwaters pour from hill and mountain canyons, they often spread out to carry on a considerable lateral, as well as vertical, erosion. If they do not spread out, but follow rather definite courses, the results are still much the same. A given channel becomes glutted as the floodwaters recede, and the next waters seek new channels and, hence, carry on further lateral erosion. Given sufficient time, the waters literally plane away the slopes to create a gently sloping *pediment* or *rock pediment* which descends, strewn with boulders, sands, and gravels, to the lower portion of a given area. Pediments become more extensive with time, for, as the hills and mountains are worn down and their fronts are planed away, the pediment sections grow in the direction of the higher crests (Fig. 180).

Water-deposited Forms

Landforms of water deposition in dry lands are not necessarily separate from those which are water carved. A wadi is primarily an erosional form, yet its floor is the result of deposition; a pediment, created by lateral cutting, is veneered usually with materials dropped by freshets. However, there are several characteristic landforms which owe their existence and shape to deposition alone.

ALLUVIAL FANS. If one had to choose the most characteristic minor landform developed under dry climates, it would be a tossup between the wadi and the alluvial fan. In most sections, one might, finally, choose the alluvial fan, because it is normally much more extensive than a wadi, and, being a built-up form, it is more readily visible.

The alluvial fan is well named for it is comprised of layer on layer of alluvial material and, when viewed from above, it has the shape of a fan (Fig. 181). If the waters which created it were permanently running, there usually would be no fan; instead, the materials would be carried into larger streams and, eventually, into the bodies of water into which the streams flowed. Again one sees the significance of the fact that dry-land waters are intermittent.

The origin of all alluvial fans is essentially similar. When floodwaters issue from a steeply sloping area such as a hill canyon, their velocity is suddenly checked by the change in gradient, and they drop their load of fine materials, sands, gravels, and boulders. Loss of water by evaporation and sinking into the ground further decreases the ability to carry load. A channel followed by water from a given flood is filled in and somewhat elevated when materials are dropped; the succeeding waters seek a new, lower line of flow and then drop their load along it. The same thing happens over and over again; slowly, but surely, the alluvial fan takes shape as materials are deposited by channels which swing through an arc of about 180 degrees as water issues, flood by flood, from the canyon mouth (Fig. 181). In general, finer materials are carried to the lower margins and the coarser left near the apex. However, some floods are more intense than others, and coarser materials are carried farthest at times when water is greatest in volume and velocity. Because of the manner in which deposition occurs, soils vary greatly, even within distances of a few feet. However, it is generally true that the bulk of the finer soils are to be found near

180 DIAGRAMMATIC expression of pediment development. Only a few of the previous stream channels are shown on the pediment area.

the lower margin of the fan and the coarser on the upper portion.

The slopes of alluvial fans are normally quite gentle. It is seldom that they exceed 3

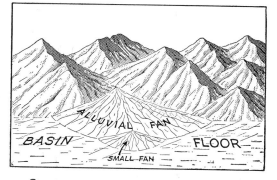

181 ALLUVIAL fan constructed at a canyon mouth. The apex of the fan lies back in the canyon. Some of the channels of intermittent water flow are shown on the fan surface.

182   *VIEW ACROSS the surface of a playa (dry lake) in the Harney Basin of Oregon,
east of the Cascade Mountains. As soon as the shore zone (foreground) is passed,
the playa surface is almost geometrically flat. (Piper from U. S. Geological Survey)*

or 4 per cent grade (3 or 4 feet of total vertical rise or fall in 100 feet of horizontal distance). Also, water may be diverted from the upper points of alluvial fans through about 180 degrees of arc, by means of simple and cheap gravity flow. For such reasons, alluvial fans are often used for irrigated farm or ranchlands. If water from the drainage basin in the higher area is abundant, an entire fan may be irrigated. If water is relatively scarce, irrigation is limited to the apex portion of the fan, and there may be enough of it to support only one farm. Of course, if the supply is too meager, no permanent use is possible. Moreover, some fans are too bouldery to use, and all of them are subject to torrential floods. In areas of Arid (BW) climate, however, their importance is great, for they provide places where water is most likely to be found.

PLAYAS. Playas are the beds of lakes which are dry most of the time. They are known not only as *playas*, but as *salars* and *dry lakes*.

The latter term commonly is used to designate such features in southwestern United States. A playa is comprised of fine silts and clays which are washed into the lowest spots in desert basins. During the short periods when lakes exist, the fine materials are uniformly deposited. Then, as the lakes dry up, they are exposed as extremely flat surfaces (Fig. 182). As long as the materials remain wet, they are very muddy, but when thoroughly dry, they become much like concrete floors. In this latter condition, they are useful as landing fields for aircraft and for automobile races and speed trials. Playa materials are high in mineral salts, so much so that their soils are useless for agriculture. Some playas contain so much alkali that they are completely surfaced with gleaming white salt crystals, as are the Bonneville Salt Flats to the west of Great Salt Lake in Utah and in the Devil's Golf Course of Death Valley in California.

The Dry-land Erosion Cycle

It is both possible and useful to distinguish an erosion cycle in arid and semiarid lands. The *youthful stage* of this type of erosion cycle is marked by unfilled basins or bolsons and by sharp, angular hills and mountains, as shown in the first part of Fig. 183. The *mature stage* is characterized by considerably worn down hills and mountains and appreciably filled basins. In this stage, alluvial fans are numerous, and large and small fans have joined one another laterally to form continuous *piedmont alluvial plains*. Out in the central portions of the bolsons, fans advancing from opposite directions are practically touching along their lowest margins. In the lowest spots between advancing fan fronts are numerous playas. The indices of maturity are illustrated in the second part of Fig. 183. The *stage of old age* represents the work of dryland weathering, erosion, and deposition, nearly completed. All that is left of the higher lands are rocky platforms, or hamadas. The former depressions are now almost completely filled with alluvial fan materials. Here and there are sand dune areas, as well as playas. This third stage, shown in the latter part of Fig. 183, has been described, and aptly so, as a "wind-swept desolation of hamada and erg." Dry lands in the stage of old age are normally exceedingly dry. There are few of the comparatively wetter hill and mountain regions present to furnish water to the lower sections, and what moisture does fall on the general surface is quickly lost in the loose, porous regolith of the filled basins. Such dry lands have exceedingly little to offer man, in terms of habitat value.

THE WORK OF WAVES AND CURRENTS

The bulk of the preceding discussion dealt with moving water which "runs." There is other water which is "on the move," but is not running; this is the water of waves and currents. Because it moves, it, too, has the ability to do work, and it affects the shores of humid lands and dry lands alike, whether the shores of Lake Michigan, the coast of Oregon, or the western edge of Sahara. Given sufficient

183

GENERALIZED diagrams illustrative of the erosion cycle in a dry-land area. (A) shows the youthful stage when mountains are bold and depressions are only slightly filled by alluvial fans. (B) represents maturity when mountains are less bold, depressions are more filled, and alluvial fans have coalesced to form continuous alluvial piedmonts. (C) shows old age when mountains exist as worn remnants and depressions are filled.

time, without any complicating movements of sea level or of the earth's crust, it actually would plane away the exposed land masses until the latter were no more than slightly submerged marine platforms. It is interesting to speculate on what sort of a world it would then be.

Erosional and Depositional Forms

SEA CLIFFS AND MARINE BENCHES. As waves roll and pound against a bold coast, they slowly eat their way into the land. Active removal of materials produces steep, usually vertical, forms called *sea cliffs* or *wave-cut cliffs.* The famous cliffs of Dover owe their shape to wave erosion. Portions of cliffs which are more resistant to wave action are isolated in forms of *stacks.* Other portions, much less resistant, develop *sea caves,* such as the famous Blue Grotto of the island of Capri near Naples, Italy. As the waves cut into the land, they also create slightly submerged platforms which occur at the base of the sea cliffs (Fig. 184). These are *wave-cut benches.* Some of the materials removed from the land are deposited directly adjacent to the wave-cut bench. They comprise *wave-built benches.* The two together constitute the typical *marine terrace,* as illustrated in part of Fig. 184. Other materials are carried by shore currents out into deep water or are moved along the coast, often to be deposited in bays which lie between rocky headlands.

BARS AND SPITS. Many coasts, instead of being bold and rocky, are low and subdued, and the waters offshore are shallow. This results in the development of quite different forms. Prominent among them are the various types of *bars* and *spits.* They represent the combined action of waves and currents. As waves break in shallow waters, they drag bottom to pick up materials which are then dropped as the waves break and topple over. This creates *offshore bars* behind which are *lagoons* (Fig. 185). Where bays are present, materials may be carried by shore currents and heaped up by wave action to create *bay-mouth spits.* Other currents, moving within bays, create spits in several bay-shore positions. Where spits develop curved ends, they are known as *hooks.* These are only some of the forms to be seen commonly along subdued coasts; some others, as well, are illustrated in Fig. 185.

Significance of Shore Forms

The general type of coast and the individual coastal forms play a large part in the appearance of the margins of the land masses and they decisively affect human activities. One

184   *WAVE-CUT and wave-built terrace and sea cliff.*

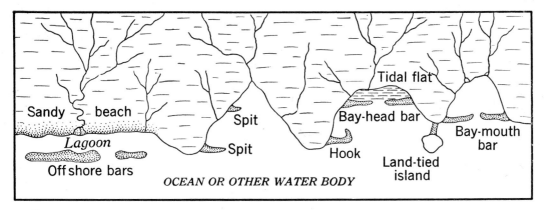

185   *SOME depositional forms common to shallow water and subdued coast.*

extreme is comprised of prominent, rocky cliffs interspersed with only limited beaches and, perhaps, no bays for the use of ships. Access to the land is difficult. Another extreme, marked by shallow waters, bars, wide beaches, and lagoons may offer much for resort purposes and for small, shallow-draft vessels, but little for easy use by large ocean-going ships. In between such extremes are many other combinations. One very useful one is the coast with prominent headlands and numerous deep and broad embayments. The headlands provide protection from storms and are often of such beauty as to attract vacationists. The bays provide deep anchorages for ships and reach far enough into the land, often into wide rivers, to tie the business of the sea and the land together. Then, too, many parts of the bay areas are ideal for resorts as well as for ports.

THE WORK OF MOVING ICE

Ice, like water, has to be moving in order to take part in the creation of landforms. Also like water, its movement results in two kinds of work, erosion and deposition, each with its own particular set of landform features. A little ice "on the move" will not transform a countryside, but comparatively large ice masses will eradicate or drastically modify previously existing landforms and substitute new and much different ones. Such masses are known as *glaciers*. The largest of them, as in Greenland or Antarctica, are *continental glaciers;* smaller ones, in valleys in Switzerland or the Rockies, for example, are *valley glaciers*. This twofold classification does not include all types of glaciers which may be distinguished, but for our purposes it is sufficient.

Continental Glaciation

GLACIER ORIGIN AND MOVEMENT. Contrary to popular belief, a glacier is not the result of water freezing into a large sheet of ice. Instead, glaciers are born of snow. Wherever more snow falls during the colder season of the year than melts during the warmer season, the result is an annual increment of snow crystals. As the older layers of snow become buried and are pressed down by newer layers, they slowly change into a coarse, granular snow. In time, the granular snow itself is transformed into solid glacial ice. If one visits the vast ice plateau of Greenland (Fig. 156), he sees little except mile after mile of snow, but, digging into the snow a few feet reveals the coarse granular material, and, a few feet below that, the ice mass itself.

186   *AT THE TOP is an example of the Greenland type of iceberg. Below is an example of the tabular Antarctic type of iceberg. (Both, U. S. Coast Guard)*

When appreciable thicknesses of ice have accumulated, movement begins. In continental glaciers, the motion takes place outward in all directions from the center. It is almost as though sand were being shoveled onto a pile and each successive shovelful forced the mass to move toward the outer edges of the pile. The movement is very, very slow, a snail's pace or less, because ice cannot flow like water even though in large amounts it does possess sufficient plasticity to

acquire a creeping and ponderous motion. Continental ice sheets which are still "alive" and advancing push their edges forward only a few feet each year. Even then, there are times when the rate of melting equals the rate of advance and the line of the "front" becomes stationary. There are other periods when the front retreats, *even though the ice itself is still moving forward.* This condition reflects a melt rate which is greater than the rate of forward motion of the mass. Still another situation arises when the supply, in the center of the accumulation area, is no longer sufficient to cause forward motion; then the ice merely lies in place until melting destroys it. Its last vestiges are to be seen in the places where it was thickest, or where great chunks of it were buried and insulated by earth debris.

If ice moves into the sea, its front breaks off, or *calves,* to form icebergs. Where it descends into the sea from considerably higher and rougher lands as in Greenland, the resultant bergs are sharply jagged in appearance (Fig. 186); where it moves in a thick, nearly horizontal sheet into the sea waters, as it does along much of the Antarctic shore, the bergs are flat and tablelike (Fig. 186). The flat bergs, moved by winds and currents, menace only occasional sealing and whaling vessels, or the still fewer ships of explorers, but the Greenland bergs, carried southward by the Labrador Current, menace the shipping of the world's busiest oceanic trade route—the North Atlantic (see p. 286).

LANDFORMS OF GLACIAL EROSION. When a continental glacier moves its billions of tons of ice across the land, it does an almost unbelievable amount of work. Loose soil or other regolith is picked up and carried in the subglacial ice and is used as scouring and grinding material to plane away and gouge into solid bedrock. Because the rock varies in hardness from place to place and because the local velocity and thickness of ice also vary, the stripping and scouring action is uneven. In some spots, the ice scours deeply, in others it merely scrapes a bit at the uppermost materials. Thus, when an ice mass has done its work and has disappeared, the resultant lay of the land is a series of "smoothed" ups and downs; pronounced if the countryside was formerly hilly, subdued if the former surface was a plain (Figs. 130 and 151).

The most conspicuous landform of glacial scour is the *roche moutonnée* (Fig. 187), a type of hill which has been shaped from solid bedrock by the erosive action of moving ice.

On the side from which the ice came it has a smoothed and relatively gentle slope; on the opposite end, it is rough and steplike. The steplike condition is the result of a plucking action whereby the lower ice carried away different sized blocks of the bedrock, later to become glacial boulders. *Roches moutonnées* occur in many sizes; some would fit into a small room while others are hundreds of feet in height and several miles in length. Regardless of size, their frequent occurrence gives a unique expression to a whole region. Less readily visible is another ice-shaped landform known as a *scour basin.* It has been scooped out of solid bedrock and its surface is just as hard, and sometimes as barren, as that of the *roche moutonnée.* However, because it is a depression instead of a hill, its surface is often partially buried by a thin veneer of loose glacial debris or covered by the water of a lake or the thick growth of a brush or tree swamp. The third of the more common landforms of glacial scour is the *glacial trough,* a gigantic groove which may extend across country for

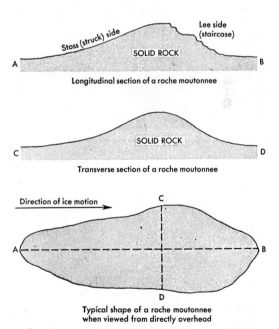

Longitudinal section of a roche moutonnee

Transverse section of a roche moutonnee

Typical shape of a roche moutonnee when viewed from directly overhead

187 *SKETCHES to show the general nature of a typical roche moutonnée.*

many miles. It usually marks the course of a former stream-cut valley which ran with the axis of ice motion. When this form is drowned, as where a trough enters the sea, it is known as a fiord; however, fiords are more common in connection with valley glaciation than with continental glaciation.

LANDFORMS OF GLACIAL DEPOSITION. The materials which are picked up and carried in the lower portion of the ice are eventually spread over the land in many forms. In some areas, the debris is laid down so thickly that all previously existing landforms are completely smothered and bedrock lies at considerable depths; in others, the debris blanket is thin and patchy, and bedrock, smoothed and grooved by ice scour, sticks through the unconsolidated materials. In general, the debris,

or *glacial drift,* is thinnest toward the centers of ice accumulation and thickest near the margins of the farthest advance of the ice.

Some of the more common and more readily visible features which have been shaped from the glacial drift are the *morainal forms* (Fig. 188). They are comprised of helter-skelter mixture of transported regolith which ranges from fine clays and silts on through sands, gravels, and boulders. In places, these unassorted materials have been deposited in the form of low rounded ridges which curve across country for many miles; in others, they comprise no more than gently and smoothly undulating plains. The occurrence of a morainal ridge marks the line along which the glacial front remained stationary for some time. The forward moving ice carried debris to this line

188

IN THE CENTRAL part of the top photograph appear two terminal moraine ridges resulting, in this instance, from deposition by mountain glaciers which have invaded a lower area. The lower photograph shows the gently undulating surface of a ground moraine area. (Cross and Pardee from U. S. Geological Survey)

189 *CHARACTERISTIC arrangement of typical landforms in a region of pronounced glacial deposition. The symbols shown in patterns of arcs and lobes mark successive positions of a stationary ice front.*

and stacked it up to form a ridge. Because the front of the ice had a scalloped or arc-shaped pattern, the morainal ridge took the same arrangement (Fig. 189). Moraines of this type which were laid down at the line of farthest advance of the ice are known as *terminal moraines;* those laid down elsewhere, each marking a stage in the recession of the line of the glacial front, are called *recessional moraines*. The only difference between them is a matter of geographical position, for they were formed in the same manner and from the same types of materials. Between the ridges of terminal and recessional moraines, or between two recessional moraines, the ice front was retreating and as it retreated it dropped a gently rolling carpet of *ground moraine*. Like the ridge moraines, it is comprised of materials ranging from silts to huge boulders.

Another landform fairly common in regions of glacial deposition is the *outwash plain*. It is well named for it consists of debris which was washed out from the glacial front by meltwater and deposited, layer on layer, to form a plain of very low relief (Figs. 189, 190). Such plains may cover an area the size of a few city blocks or several square miles. Tucked here and there against the outer edges of the morainal ridges, they present a sudden change in the lay of the land, even though the drop from the top of a morainal ridge to the surface of an outwash plain is usually only a few feet—perhaps 20 or 30 feet in some instances or as much as 75 or 100 feet in others. Outwash plains are notably sandy. Evidently the meltwater which flows more or less in a sheet from the ice front is not powerful enough to handle gravels and boulders, but it does have the ability to pick up and transport the silts, clays, and sands. As its power lessens, it drops the sands to build the outwash plain, while the finer clays and silts are carried on into the courses of glacial streams which lead out, at places, from the plain's margin.

190

THE SMOOTH *surface of a glacial plain with a low ridge of glacial debris in the background. (Wisconsin Geological Survey)*

Another important type of plain also occurs in glaciated areas. It owes its being to the previous existence of a glacial lake and is therefore called a *glaciolacustrine plain* (Fig. 191). A very large and famous plain of this sort occupies most of southern Manitoba province in Canada, and extends in an ever-narrowing finger across the border into northwestern Minnesota and the eastern edge of North Dakota. This area was once covered by the cold waters of glacial Lake Agassiz, waters which were caught between the wall of the ice front to the north and slightly higher land to the south. As long as the ice dam existed, materials, particularly fine materials, were washed into the lake's shallow waters and distributed very evenly over the lake floor. Later, when the ice dam disappeared, Lake Agassiz drained away to Hudson Bay, leaving behind a lake bed which is nearly as flat

as a billiard table and which constitutes some of the most productive soils of the world. These soils, fine textured and fertile, have proved capable of growing several varieties of high-grade wheat in tremendous quantities, and they comprise the basic resource of much of the major agricultural region known as the *Spring Wheat Belt* of the United States and Canada. The remnants of old Lake Agassiz are to be seen in the cluster of lakes comprised chiefly of Lake Winnipeg and Lake Winnepegosis.

Leading out from temporary glacial lakes, and hence from the low featureless plains which they left behind, are the ribbonlike forms of *glacial spillways*. They used to be the outlets for surplus lake waters; today some of them are valleys for streams, but others are simply elongated depressions floored with alluvial material and lacking streams.

Fine lake deposits
over glacial debris

GROUND
MORAINE

MORAINAL
RIDGE

TEMPORARY
GLACIAL LAKE

FRONT OF ICE

191   *DIAGRAM representing a possible origin of a glacio-lacustrine plain. After the disappearance of the ice dam and the lake formed in front of it, the lake deposits are exposed as a plain of very low relief.*

192 *A DRUMLIN. The steep end (direction from which ice came) is still wooded, while the less steep portions have been largely cleared for agricultural use. (R. M. Glendinning)*

Because they form low corridors, their courses are often used as routes for highways, railroads, and canals.

In addition to the major landforms already discussed, there are several minor features worthy of mention. In some areas, they are so numerous as to affect the general appearance of the land, as well as its use by man. One of these is the *drumlin* (Figs. 189, 192). A drumlin is a small hill that has the shape of an egg which has been cut in two longitudinally. The end which points in the direction from which the ice came is usually blunt and steep and the other, somewhat narrower, end is more gently sloping. Drumlins were formed underneath the ice sheet and their unconsolidated materials are normally high in clay content. They commonly occur in groups and, from high in the air, they closely resemble schools of half-submerged whales moving over the glacial plains on which they are placed.

Other minor forms include *eskers, kames,* and *kettle holes* (Fig. 189). An *esker* is a low, sinuous ridge which winds across country for a few rods, or, in some instances, for several miles (Fig. 193). The esker evidently represents a portion of a subglacial tunnel which was blocked with stream-borne materials; after the ice melted away, the mold of the tunnel was left behind as a low ridge. Because it is well drained, an esker often serves as a route for a trail or road. *Kames* are small, knobby hills; in single occurrence they are

193

AN ESKER traces its course across a glacially scoured portion of Canada's Northwest Territories. (Royal Canadian Air Force)

seldom conspicuous, but, when they occur in tightly packed groups, they create a sort of miniature hill country. *Kettle holes* are small funnel-shaped depressions. They mark places where blocks of ice were buried in glacial debris. As the blocks melted, the materials covering them dropped lower and lower until pits were created. They may be found almost anywhere in glacial debris. There are pitted outwash plains, pitted morainal ridges, pitted ground moraines, and the pits, or kettle holes, may be found in among clusters of kames (Fig. 194). Kettle holes, because of their shape, are often mistaken for sinkholes, but, obviously, there is no connection between a glacial kettle hole and a karst sinkhole.

GLACIAL DRAINAGE. When continental ice masses "work over" a region, they change more than the landforms. From preceding discussion, it is evident that soils are vitally affected, as in the instance of a sandy outwash plain, an old lake bed, or a bouldery and gravelly ground moraine. Partly evident, too, is the effect of the distribution of landforms on the pattern of routes. Even more important is the effect on conditions of drainage, for glaciation has played complete havoc with pre-existing stream patterns and stream behavior.

Whether in areas of scour or deposition, a *glacially deranged pattern* of drainage is created. The pattern is well named, for it is a "crazy" pattern without apparent rhyme or reason (Fig. 195). Lakes and ponds are numerous. They lie in the depressions created by unequal scour and by uneven deposition. Scattered among the lakes and ponds are many swamps, some of them representing former lakes and ponds which have been filled with in-washed materials and by the growth of dense swamp vegetation. Connecting lakes, ponds, and swamps are many large and small streams. They wander in a willy-nilly fashion as running water seeks the low lines in the glaciated surface and follows the varying tilt of the land. Their wanderings reflect the lack of sufficient time, since the ice disappeared, in which to carve definite and co-ordinated channels and patterns of drainage. Falls and rapids are the rule rather than the exception, although they are shorter-lived where streams are eating into loose glacial drift than where they are attempting to cut into solid bedrock.

194   *THIS IS a "kame and kettle" surface in a glaciated section of Wisconsin. The knobby hills are kames, and the more or less pitlike depressions in among the kames are kettle holes. (Alden from U. S. Geological Survey)*

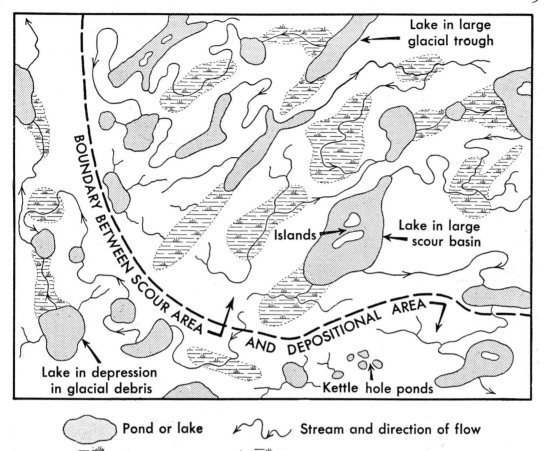

Pond or lake   Stream and direction of flow

Swamp   Stream course in swamp

195   *GLACIALLY deranged pattern of drainage in area of glacial scour (above dashed line) and in area of glacial deposition (below dashed line).*

SIGNIFICANCE OF CONTINENTAL GLACIATION. The achievements of the great ice sheets affect the appearance and nature of several million square miles of the earth's surface. Fig. 196 shows that the glaciers of Pleistocene times covered truly huge areas and that their much shrunken remnants are still present, chiefly in Antarctica and Greenland.

In Europe, the center of ice accumulation was on the edge of the Fenno-Scandian Shield, chiefly in what is now the mountainous backbone of Norway. From this elevated and somewhat elongated area, the ice pushed out in all directions. Much of it went to sea, but

at least half of it moved in such directions as vitally to affect the land. The British Isles were glaciated as far south as London, and the Continent was covered as far south as a line extending from the mouths of the Rhine, through central Germany, southern Poland, and on, in a northward curving arc, through the center of the Russian Plain to the northwestern corner of Siberia.

An even larger area was affected in North America. Here there were four centers of ice action. One, the Labrador center, lay about midway between the eastern shore of Hudson Bay and the coast of Labrador, and another,

196 *AN APPRECIABLE PORTION of the earth's land surface was affected by the continental glaciers of Pleistocene times, especially in North America, Greenland, Europe, and Antarctica. Large remnants of these glaciers still cover most of Greenland and virtually all of Antarctica.*

the Keewatin, was about midway between the western shore of Hudson Bay and Great Slave Lake. Along the "height of land," or drainage divide, between Lake Superior and the southern margin of Hudson Bay was the Patrician center. Far to the west, in the crest areas of Canada's high mountains, and on into Alaska, was the elongated Cordilleran center. From these four centers, the ice moved out in all directions until, at one stage, it covered prac-

tically all of Canada, parts of Alaska, and a considerable portion of northern United States. The last was glaciated as far south as a line extending, roughly, from Long Island across to the headwater section of the Ohio River, then along the Ohio and Missouri rivers to the northern portions of Montana, Idaho, and Washington. By the time the ice wasted away, it left nearly half of North America an inheritance of glacial landforms, glacial soils, and glacially deranged drainage. In terms of earth history, this legacy is so recent that it is as though the bequest had been made only yesterday. Only at the outermost margins of the oldest deposition has there been sufficient time for normal stream erosion largely to restore ordinary drainage conditions and create new, nonglacial landforms.

Elsewhere in the Northern Hemisphere (Fig. 196), ice sheets covered Greenland and adjacent Ellesmere Island, the Brooks Range of northern Alaska, and smaller areas in the American Rockies, the Cascades, and the Sierra Nevada. In Europe and Asia, they covered sections of the Alps, Pyrenees, the Sierra Nevada of Spain, the Caucasus, and many of the mountainous areas which stretch from the Pamir mountain hub to far northeastern Siberia. Noteworthy is the fact that most of Siberia was not then, and never has been, glaciated. Off the shores of parts of Europe and Asia, the ice affected, on more than local scale, such islands and island groups as Iceland, Spitzbergen (Svalbard), Novaya Zemlya, and the New Siberians.

In the Southern Hemisphere, the ice smothered Antarctica and pushed on into the sea, representing a glacial mass at least twice the size of the United States. South America's ice sheets, affecting only a relatively small part of that continent, lay mainly in the southern Andes with smaller occurrences in the central and northern Andes. Elsewhere in the world, small masses covered much of South Island, New Zealand, portions of Tasmania, and the southern part of Australia's Great Dividing Range. In Africa, there were minor glaciers in the higher levels of the central highland and lake district and, far to the northwest, in the High Atlas.

From the foregoing, it can be appreciated that the modifications wrought by continental glaciers are much more than matters of local geographic concern. It can be appreciated, also, that the present geography of Greenland and Antarctica, more than six million square miles of the earth's surface, is essentially an "ice geography"; in those regions there remains a "laboratory" for the study of the nature and behavior of continental ice sheets like those which moved over so much of the world during Pleistocene times.

Valley Glaciation

Quite in contrast to the extensive ice blankets of continental glaciers are the much smaller masses and tongues of valley ice. Each is born in a high valley head in those parts of mountains where more snow falls in winter than melts in summer. As soon as the accumulating snow has been transformed into ice and the ice has acquired sufficient mass to move, the glacier begins its slow journey down the valley. Again, motion means power to do work; by the time the work is finished and the ice gone, the typical V-shaped mountain valley has been changed to the typical U-shaped form of valley glaciation and much of the whole preglacial surface has been greatly modified (Fig. 197).

TYPICAL LANDFORMS AND DRAINAGE CONDITIONS. The first major job accomplished by valley ice is the creation of a *cirque*. This form is shaped in the valley head, where the glacier is born and where its ice is thickest. By a combination of scour and frost action, the valley head is carved into a type of small basin which has the form of an amphitheater, or the form of half of a bowl (Fig. 197). It is very steep on three sides and the fourth side is open in the down-valley direction. Where two or more cirques are formed close together in adjacent valley heads, the divides between them are sharpened into knife-edge ridges, or *arêtes*. If the ridges are lowered, mainly by frost action and the removal of materials at their bases by ice plucking, they become saddles, or *cols*, which mark low places in the mountain crests and which may be used as pass routes. Where at least three cirques have been created in a local area, the land between

A—Cirque   D—Horn

B—Arête   E—Hanging valley

C—Col   F—Ribbon falls

197   *A PORTION of a mountain region before, during, and after valley glaciation. Notice how greatly this process of valley glaciation has modified the landform and the drainage conditions in the region.*

may be sharpened into a pyramidal peak, known as a *horn* (Fig. 197), such as the famous Matterhorn of the Swiss Alps.

As the glacial tongue moves down the valley from the cirque basin, its strong erosive action steepens the valley sides and somewhat deepens the valley bottom, thus changing the V to a wide and irregularly shaped U. Also, there may be streams of ice in tributary valleys which are creating U-shaped valleys of their own, and which add their ice to the main glacial tongue. As a rule, the ice in tributary valleys, being less in volume and power, does not cut as deeply as the main ice flow and, hence, *hanging valleys* occur (Fig. 197).

Valley ice also builds landforms of deposition (Fig. 198). If the ice traveled the full length of the valley and emerged to fan out on a piedmont plain, a terminal morainal ridge is present. Because of its shape, it is called a *horseshoe moraine*. With retreating front, ground moraines are laid down, some of them out on the piedmont and some in the valley floor. Successive stages of stationary front are marked by the damlike forms of recessional moraines. Along the valley sides are hummocky ribbons of glacial debris in the form of *lateral moraines*. Where two valley glaciers join, the lateral morainal material which unites at the junction appears later as middle moraine, or *medial moraine*, in the main valley floor (Fig. 198).

A great part of the beauty of a glaciated valley results from glacially deranged drainage. The uppermost drainage feature is the *tarn*. This is a small lake which occupies the lowest portion of the cirque basin and sends its waters tumbling over the rocky edge of the cirque into the valley below. The lake waters are clear and cold and they make a perfect mirror which reflects the jagged pinnacles of the arête that stands against the sky hundreds of feet above. Farther down-valley, there is normally a series of small and shallow lakes which lie in local scour basins or are dammed behind deposits of morainal debris.

Out on the piedmont, if the glacier went that far, there is usually a marginal lake impounded by the curve of a horseshoe moraine (Fig. 198). Connecting all the lakes, from tarn to piedmont, are the alternately swift and sluggish waters of the valley stream. Where hanging valleys are present, the streams from them leap into space as misty ribbons of white water. A famous example of such *ribbon falls* is Bridal Veil Falls in the glacial trough of Yosemite (Fig. 199).

SIGNIFICANCE OF VALLEY GLACIATION. This type of glaciation has affected much smaller portions of the land surface of the earth than has continental glaciation. Yet, it occurs in literally hundreds of places from the high mountain valleys of South Island, New Zealand, and the southern Andes to those of the Brooks Range of Alaska and the Stanovois of Siberia. Likewise, it is to be found in such well-known alpine regions as the Rockies and Sierra Nevada of North America and the Alps, Pyrenees, and Caucasus of Europe.

Many of the earth's glaciated valleys, as in Switzerland, are greatly utilized by man. The valley ice created more level or nearly level land than was present before, thus providing more land suitable for crops, pasture, and settlements (Fig. 141). The glacially deranged drainage provides many natural reservoirs as well as falling waters to aid in the generation of hydroelectric power. And the total condition, marked by such features as tarns, arêtes, horns, hanging valleys, and ribbon falls, provides a scenic beauty which is the chief resource for recreational and resort industries. Perhaps it should also be pointed out that glaciated mountain valleys are important to lands which lie below, and sometimes miles away. The valleys, with their many natural reservoirs, collect waters which they release slowly. This not only minimizes dangers from floods in lower areas, but also insures a steadier supply of water for piedmont settlements, or, if the piedmont areas are in the dry lands, for irrigation.

THE WORK OF WIND

Compared to moving water and moving ice, the work of wind is relatively insignificant. Wind has carved no Grand Canyons, created no vast plains, nor changed the basic appearance of any Norways or Switzerlands. However, its work is of great local significance and it affects a few areas of appreciable size.

198

SKETCH showing the typical arrangement of glacial landforms and drainage features in the lower portion of a glaciated mountain valley. Here the ice not only reached the valley mouth but fanned out into part of the piedmont area.

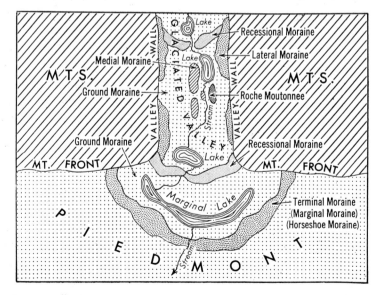

Like the other agents of erosion, wind does two jobs: one is the work of scour and transportation, the other the work of deposition. Most materials moved by wind action are fine in texture and light in weight. These are mainly dusts although at times of high velocity, sands, and even gravels, are moved. The last are moved chiefly by sliding, bouncing, and rolling, rather than by large-scale picking up and carrying, for wind does not constitute a powerful working stream in the same sense as a stream of water or a moving ice mass. As would be expected, wind accomplishes most in regions of Dry (BW, BS) climates. In these regions, the regolith is usually dry and subject to easy "blow," and it is not held firmly in place by the scant vegetation. Thus, some of the better places in which to examine the achievements of wind are in such areas as the Sahara, the Gobi of inner Asia, the Arabian Desert, or the Great Plains or the Mohave Desert of the United States.

There are places in humid lands, however, in which the work of wind is locally pronounced, mainly along the edges of bodies of water where wind sweeps across the water surfaces to blow sands and to shape dunes along the shore and near-shore sections. A good example is to be seen in the Indiana Dunes located at the southern margin of Lake Michigan. Also, there are many other spots, where man has overcultivated, or otherwise abused, the land, in which soils blow badly during the drier periods of the year. Recent examples of this have been reported from several sections in the United States Corn Belt.

Erosional Work

Those unused to dry-land conditions often complain more of the wind than they do of dryness and high temperatures. Wind seems ever-present and is most noticeable, as a rule, during the daylight hours. It dries the skin and nasal passages and it makes the eyes smart. It whips dust into the air and moves the sands (Fig. 128). During storms, as many as 16,000 tons of dust may be contained in one cubic mile of air; a storm covering an area 100 miles long and 50 miles wide has been estimated to pick up and carry some 20,000,000 tons of loess!

DEFLATION. The removal of materials from a surface by wind action is called *deflation*. If a given region were always subjected to large-scale deflation, its entire surface would be considerably lowered, perhaps even changed into a large and ever-deepening basin. However, deflation surfaces are more apt to be local and somewhat temporary. The winds which rob them of fine materials also bring replacement materials from other areas, and a reversal of wind direction may result in the return of dusts which were removed previously. Of course, an area which is so constituted and situated as ultimately to lose more than it gains becomes a more or less permanent deflation surface. Regs, mentioned earlier, represent one type of deflation surface. In them, the finer materials have been removed and the coarse pebbles and gravels have been left behind to comprise a "gravel desert" (Fig. 177).

Depressions known picturesquely as *blowouts* represent another type of deflation surface. Usually circular or oval in plan, they are formed by the blowing out of sands and finer materials from a given section until a type of basin results (Fig. 129). In southeastern Wyoming and adjacent parts of Nebraska, for example, they are sufficiently numerous to affect the general appearance and the use of the land. Blowouts may vary in size from a few feet in diameter to those which are large enough to contain a cluster of buildings eight or ten stories in height. They are marked commonly by strings of sand dunes which lead away from them on their lee sides.

SCULPTURE AND POLISH. Where rocks, boulders, or the bases of cliffs are exposed to sandblast, the softer materials are worn away and the harder left in place. The result is

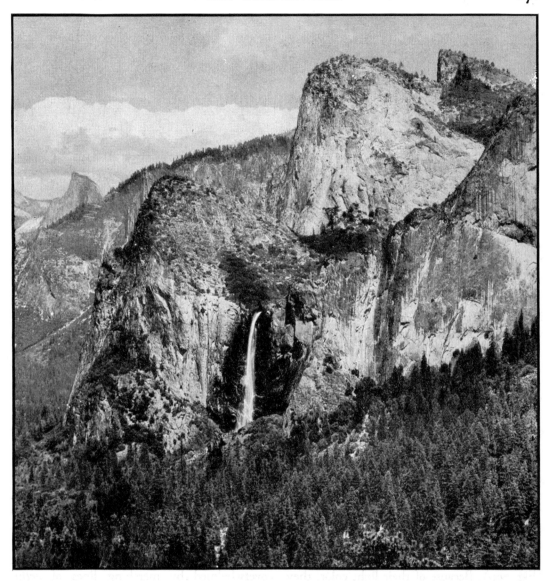

199   *A RIBBON fall, plunging from a hanging valley. This is Bridalveil Falls in the glaciated portion of the Yosemite Valley, California. (National Park Service)*

pockets, caves, flutings, and other intricately etched forms. Similar action, operating over finer materials and more level surfaces, scours and buffs rocks and pebbles until they acquire a high degree of *desert polish*. The smoothness and shininess of the pebbles, or other rock material, is enhanced by the dry air drawing moisture and dissolved chemicals from the inside to the outside surfaces; this moisture, in evaporating at the surface, leaves the chemicals behind as a crust which is baked by the sun and polished by wind-blown sands and dusts.

Depositional Work

Sands and dusts carried by winds are deposited in many different forms and at vary-

200   *A SHEET DUNE in the Colorado Desert, southeastern California. Strong winds have blown sand from the foreground area and have strewn it as a veneer up the ridge toward the saddle in ridge crest. In the foreground are numerous hillock dunes held by clumps of desert brush. (R. M. Glendinning)*

ing distances from points of origin. Sands, which normally do not travel far, are shaped into several types of dunes; fine dusts, which may be transported hundreds or even thousands of miles, are laid down in thin sheets which take the mold of the land on which they settle, or, if in large amounts, create extensive loess plains which are independent of the terrain smothered by them.

DUNES. Dunes assume many different shapes. Some of them are merely veneerlike sheets, or *sheet dunes,* which are spread over a surface like a blanket. They occur most commonly on flattish areas, but, in places, they are to be seen extending up the slope of a desert hill or draped over the nose of a ridge (Fig. 200). Because of their light color, they then may be seen for long distances. Other dunes may be no more than small knobs, or *hillock dunes,* formed where sands have collected around obstacles such as clumps of desert brush. If the brush succeeds in keeping its head above the sand, the queer appearance illustrated by the Devil's Cornfield of Death Valley is provided (Fig. 201). Some dunes, called *barchans,* are crescent-shaped in ground plan, very strongly resembling crescent moons superimposed on the general surface. Perhaps the most common type of dunes are those in

the form of wavelike ridges, the ridges being oriented at right angles to the major winds. Such *ridge dunes* may be a few feet high and long, or they may loom as high as 100 feet or more and extend in unbroken ranks for several miles. Where dunes cover many square miles, they comprise typical erg areas (Fig. 177); where locally developed, they may be thought of as miniature ergs.

Many dunes and dune regions pose problems for man. Their coarse sands provide no resource and their disconcerting habit of moving slowly and inexorably across a countryside often results in the covering and abandonment of man's establishments. Scores of oases, as in Arabia and northern Africa, have been overwhelmed by marching lines of *active dunes,* although, later, after the dunes moved by, they may have been reoccupied—even the same buildings as used previously. In humid lands, where migrating dunes are supplied from shores and river beds, fields, orchards, buildings, and even railroads and major highways may be smothered, or kept clear only at considerable expense.

LOESS DEPOSITS. Loess is fairly common in either small or large deposits throughout most of the dry lands. Strangely enough, many of the truly extensive loess deposits are to be found in regions of humid climates. Outstanding examples are found in parts of the Mississippi Valley, the North China Plain, and the Argentine Pampa. Large loess deposits are actually worth more than gold mines for they are highly productive, especially if they occur where nature supplies enough water for normal crop growth. In steppe regions, as the southern part of the Russian Plain, their inherent fertility warrants the use of dry-farming practices, at least temporarily. Moreover, loessal soils are comparatively retentive of moisture so that they are not as "droughty" under semiarid conditions as one might expect.

There is some argument as to the source, or sources, of the fine wind-blown dusts which have created the world's major loessal plains. It was thought formerly that they were derived entirely from steppes and deserts. Now much evidence has been gathered to show that a great deal of the loess originated within humid lands, particularly where broad river plains furnished winds with abundant fine material, and, more especially, where rivers carried exorbitant loads of fine glacial outwash which, after deposition, became important sources of supply of fine dusts. In any event, these wind-worked materials have provided man with several large, and many small, fruitful plains.

Loess is more than a matter of soil, for where dissected its presence is reflected in very steep valley slopes. The bluffs at Council Bluffs, Iowa, are loessal, and they are so steep as to form palisades. In the loessal hills of China, just west of the North China Plain, many of the roads lie in the bottoms of loessal trenches. For countless years, turning wheels and animal hoofs have stirred up the dust and the wind has blown the dusts away. Thus the roadways have sunk slowly into the loessal deposits. In the same area, man long ago wiped out the forests and allowed the summer rains to gully and channel the land; today, there are *badlands* which cover hundreds of square miles, and the inhabitants become

201

THE DEVIL'S Cornfield in the central portion of Death Valley, just south of the sand dune area shown in Fig. 177B. Xerophytic brush traps the blowing sand and then, as more sand collects, grows on top of the same mound to produce the effect of shocked corn in a field. (Dave Packard, Los Angeles)

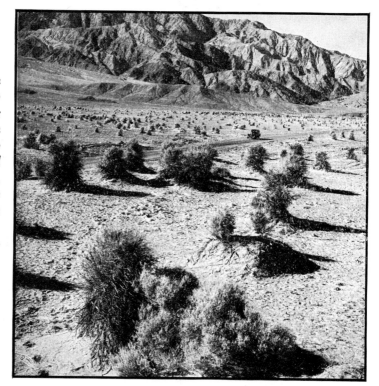

more and more desperate as they attempt to find and maintain enough level land for the production of vital crops (Fig. 202).

This chapter, in considering some of the aspects of landforms in relation to the agents of erosion and deposition has had much to say about water and conditions of drainage. It is apparent that land and water are inseparable, whether it be water which runs on the land, rests on its surface, gnaws into its shores, or is contained beneath its surface. Ensuing discussion, in the chapter which follows directly, provides further information on the nature and significance of the earth's waters.

....

CHAPTER OUTLINE

Landforms and the agents of erosion and deposition

The work of moving water
  The work of streams
    Velocity
    Valley stages
    Significance of valley shapes
    Interfluve stages
    Significance of interfluve shapes
    Valley and interfluve combinations
    Stream-deposited forms
  The work of solution
    Evolution of karst forms
    Drainage in karst
    Stages in karst
    Significance of karst
The work of moving water in dry lands
  Water-cut landforms
    Wadies
    Mesas and buttes
    Pediments
  Water-deposited forms
    Alluvial fans
    Playas
  The dry-land erosion cycle
The work of waves and currents
  Erosional and depositional forms
    Sea cliffs and marine benches
    Bars and spits
  Significance of shore forms
The work of moving ice
  Continental glaciation
    Glacier origin and movement
    Landforms of glacial erosion
    Landforms of glacial deposition
    Glacial drainage
    Significance of continental glaciation
  Valley glaciation
    Typical landforms and drainage conditions

202   *ERODED LOESS area in Shansi Province, China. (Frederick G. Clapp)*

Significance of valley glaciation
The work of wind
  Erosional work
    Deflation
    Sculpture and polish
  Depositional work
    Dunes
    Loess deposits

REVIEW QUESTIONS

1. Distinguish between sheet erosion and rill erosion.

2. Explain why a seemingly slight increase in stream velocity results in greatly increased ability to move materials.

3. What is the difference between grade and base-level?

4. Account for the shape of a youthful valley.

5. Explain the formation of valley flats in a mature valley.

6. Draw a surface profile to illustrate the landform nature of an area comprised of youthful valleys and youthful interfluves; of mature valleys and youthful interfluves.

7. If you were in the field in a typical karst area, what criteria would you use to determine whether the area was young, mature, or old?

8. Explain the development of galleries in karst.

9. If you were a farmer whose land was pitted with numerous sinkholes, would you prefer the sinkholes to be of the doline or ponor type? Why?

10. What is the basic reason for the differences in valley forms in dry lands as compared to those in humid lands?

11. Why is it that, even with continued erosion, wadies tend to maintain steep sides and essentially level bottoms?

12. Restate the following quotation in "plain English": "The hamada margin contains many deep wadies and its former extent is marked by numerous mesas and buttes. Nearby, in a lower area, are several small playas separated by miniature ergs."

13. Explain the origin of an alluvial fan.

14. What will a mountain and bolson region look like by the time it attains the stage of old age?

15. Discuss some of the problems of the highway engineer whose job it is to construct a modern highway across a large mountain-and-bolson region, or across a succession of ergs and hamadas.

16. Describe the landforms which are normally found along subdued, shallow-water coasts.

17. Consult a modern geology textbook for discussions of the theories of ice motion in glaciers.

18. Explain the origin of the Greenland icecap.

19. List as many reasons as possible why it makes a great difference whether a region was glaciated or not.

20. Distinguish between: (a) morainal ridge and ground moraine; (b) drumlin and *roche moutonnée;* (c) outwash plain and glacio-lacustrine plain; (d) kettle hole and sinkhole.

21. Compare central Indiana with the central portion of Ontario in terms of landforms, drainage, and soil conditions.

22. Describe the succession of landforms and drainage features which you would expect to see in traveling from the head to the mouth of a typical glaciated valley.

23. Just how has glaciation made certain rugged mountain regions more habitable and more useful?

24. What is meant by a surface of aeolian deflation?

25. Distinguish between loessal dunes and sand dunes.

26. Two areas are "covered" by sand dunes; one has a barchan surface, the other has a wave dune surface. What is the difference in appearance of the two areas?

SOME SUGGESTED REFERENCES

Antevs, Ernst, *The Last Glaciation,* Research Series No. 17, American Geographical Society, 1928. A technical book on continental glaciation (especially in eastern North America).

Bowman, Isaiah, *Desert Trails of Atacama,* Special Publication No. 5, American Geographical Society, 1924. A pioneer book in desert geography; deals with land, settlement, and problems in Chile's famous desert and contiguous territory.

Davis, William Morris, *Geographical Essays,* Ginn, 1909. A classic collection of educational and physiographic essays, ranging from discussions of the content of geography to discussions of landform evolution in humid and in dry regions.

Flint, Richard F., *Glacial Geology and the Pleistocene Epoch,* John Wiley and Sons, Inc., 1947. A detailed and comparatively technical treatment of glacial theory, ice forms, and glacially produced landforms and drainage conditions.

Gautier, E. F., *Sahara: The Great Desert,* Columbia University Press, 1935. An excellent translation of a famous systematic and regional analysis of the world's largest desert.

Johnson, Douglas W., *Shore Processes and Shoreline Development,* John Wiley and Sons, Inc., 1919. A standard text and reference on the nature and origin of coastal landforms.

Lobeck, Armin K., *Geomorphology: An Introduction to the Study of Landscapes,* McGraw-Hill, 1939. A standard reference on landforms and their origins.

Tarr, Ralph S., and von Engeln, Oskar D., *New Physical Geography,* Macmillan, 1926. A comparatively old, but still useful, textbook concerning many aspects of physical geography, including landforms and their development.

von Engeln, Oskar D., *Geomorphology: Systematic and Regional,* Macmillan, 1942. A major text on landforms and landform genesis, including separate discussions of the different erosion cycles.

203 *THE WATERS OF THE EARTH surround this coral isle in the Pacific, near Papeete, Tahiti. Here is much water and comparatively little land, as is true of the earth's surface as a whole. (Gendreau)*

CHAPTER 13

The Earth's Waters

....

The surface of the earth is chiefly water. This is a fact which we, as dwellers on the land, are apt to ignore or completely forget. The Pacific Ocean covers nearly one-third of the globe; moreover, it is of such great size that if *all* the continents were placed in it, there would still remain approximately eight million square miles of open ocean surface—an area almost as large as North America and more than twice the size of Europe. The combined areas of all water bodies, including oceans, seas, and lakes, add up to a total nearly three times that of all the lands of the earth; in other words, about 71 per cent of the earth's surface is water (Table 3, p. 20). In addition to the large expanses just mentioned, there are waters which run as streams on the top of the land and others which lie or move within the upper portion of the earth's crust. Likewise there is water in vapor and condensed form in the atmosphere. Thus, water is an important and practically all-pervasive element in man's habitat.

USES OF WATER

DOMESTIC. Water is most important for drinking purposes. Town and city dwellers, accustomed to obtaining drinkable water by the mere turning of a faucet handle, cannot fully appreciate this type of water use. How-ever, those who live in rural areas and have to spend much time in carrying water from a spring or stream, or pumping or lifting it from a well, know its significance fully. Even more aware are those who live in steppes and deserts, where drinking water is first among the necessities of life, not even second to food itself. Other home, or domestic, uses of water are many: for cooking, washing, bathing, and for lawn and garden. On the farm, water consumption amounts to 15 or 20 gallons for each person daily; in the city, the quantity is certainly greater. One can appreciate the problem of ordinary domestic water supply in a city of several million persons, particularly in those cities which have outgrown their local supplies and must send many miles away for the bulk of their water. Los Angeles, California, has two great aqueducts which reach out across hills, deserts, and mountains for some 300 miles (Fig. 204). So vulnerable is Los Angeles that major abandonment would quickly follow if the water supply were stopped. Other large urban centers, even those in more humid regions, are only slightly less vulnerable.

INDUSTRIAL. In town or city, wherever manufacturing and processing are going on, there is demand for water far in excess of domestic requirements. Water is needed to wash materials, to add to materials and goods, to flush sewage, to make steam in boilers, to cool or air-condition equipment and buildings,

PACIFIC

OCEAN

GREATER
LOS ANGELES AREA
WATER SUPPLY

0   100   200

Miles

204   *THE DOTTED LINES show the location of the two great aqueducts which bring "outside water" to the Los Angeles metropolitan area.*

and to serve many other purposes. A city the size of Chicago is said to use in excess of 300,000,000 gallons of water *each day,* the greater portion of which is used outside of the home. Just to supply Chicago with water is a big business in itself.

IRRIGATIONAL. Particularly in the dry regions, man also needs other than drinking and general household water. He needs water for stock and still more water where his econ-omy depends on the production of irrigated crops. Irrigation water may come from shallow or deep wells, from springs, from rivers, or it may be imported over long distances by means of ditches or pipes. The amount obtained determines, in general, the size of a given settlement, whether it is a small oasis in the coastal desert of Peru or an extensive and densely populated belt in the lower Nile Valley (Fig. 205).

205A

A VIEW of the Nile Valley showing the contrast between the irrigated land and the desert which borders it. (Hamilton Wright)

It should be pointed out, too, that the use of water for irrigation is not restricted to the regions of steppe and desert climate. Near large cities in humid lands great amounts are used to encourage a rapid and certain growth of truck crops for urban markets. In the extensive and humid ricelands of the Orient, the wet-land or *paddy* rice requires untold billions of gallons of slowly circulating irrigation water throughout the season of growth, even in those parts of the rainy tropics which receive very heavy precipitation.

POWER. Water is still used to turn mill wheels in most of the world's inhabited regions. In areas of modern industrial development, it is used to spin turbines which are connected to generators. The generators transform the water power into electric energy which is sent to home and factory by transmission lines. Numerous drainage basins

205B

A SMALL oasis in the coastal desert of Peru. The irrigated fields of cotton and sugar cane contrast sharply with the desert waste nearby. (Photo by George R. Johnson in his Peru from the Air, *published by the American Geographical Society)*

have largely been brought under control, from headwaters to mouth, for the particular purpose of generating great quantities of this type of electric energy.

TRANSPORTATION. Since primitive man first made a raft or hollowed out a log canoe, water has served as a highway, a highway built and maintained by nature and so buoyant that carriers using it can support and move burdens far greater than can be supported in land

food from the oceans as population increases and as much of the land is worn out by continued crop production. Seaweed, in addition to furnishing food, provides potash and iodine as well as stuffing for cushions and mattresses. Salt water furnishes salt and, recently, large quantities of magnesium. Then, there are other materials, from furs and hides to pearls and sponges. Many fresh waters likewise provide fish, shells, and furs.

206

ONE recreational use of water: sailing on Puget Sound, near Seattle. (Northern Pacific Railway)

or air vehicles. To this day, despite autotrucks, freight trains, and cargo planes, many of the world's water roads, whether the Rhine River or the North Atlantic, continue to prove highly useful.

FOOD AND RAW MATERIALS. Modern men are becoming increasingly aware of the resources contained in the many waters of the world. From the seas and oceans come foods in the form of fish, plants, and other marine life. Many persons believe that the world will become more and more dependent on

RECREATION. Whether seashore, tree-lined brook or river, small pond, or large lake, water is useful to swim in, to go boating and fishing on, or just to look at (Fig. 206). Many a small lake has proved to be a "gold mine" when developed for resort purposes, and many a piece of land has sold for a sum far above ordinary market price merely because it contained a bubbling spring or a small stream. Even the little lily ponds or artificial lagoons in a city park reflect the artistic or recreational value of water.

207 *GENERALIZED PROFILE of a section of the bottom of the Atlantic Ocean.*

WATER BODIES

Oceans and Seas

As previously noted, most of the earth is covered by interconnected bodies of water (see Chapter 2). Not only do these bodies vary greatly in size and depth, but also in the many patterns which they produce as they trace their edges against the land. To draw the outlines of the major water bodies is to delineate automatically the outlines of the land masses themselves.

NAMES AND TERMS. In order of decreasing size, the oceans are the Pacific, Atlantic, Indian, Antarctic, and Arctic (Table 3, p. 20). In places, the Antarctic is not distinguished separately from the southern portions of the Pacific, Atlantic, and Indian oceans with which it merges, or, in another sense, of which it is comprised. Also, the Arctic Ocean is sometimes referred to as a sea. However, the Arctic usually is considered to be an ocean and the Antarctic, despite the arbitrary nature of its northern boundary, normally is distinguished from the waters which lie farther equatorward (Figs. 10 and 11).

The term *sea* is indefinite. It is applied, in general, to bodies of water which are conspicuously smaller than the oceans and which are "tucked into" the land in such fashion as to leave only narrow oceanic connections or no connections at all. Thus, the term is applied to the Mediterranean and the Baltic, as well as to the Aral Sea and the Salton Sea. The term usually implies that waters are saline, but neither the Sea of Galilee nor the Great Lakes, which are often referred to as "inland seas," are salty. Table 3 lists some of the larger seas, and gives their approximate areas.

OCEAN BOTTOMS AND DEPTHS. Formerly, it was thought that the bottoms of the great water bodies were mainly comprised of smooth plains and monotonous plateaus. It was reasoned that sediments washed in from the land, materials dropped physically and precipitated chemically in waters far offshore, and the accumulation of skeletons of myriads of marine organisms would collect in low places until inequalities of sea bottom would cease to exist. It is now known that the floors of the seas and oceans possess landforms nearly as varied as that of the continents themselves. There are towering mountain ranges, broad plateaus, hilly regions, and plains of varying relief (Fig. 207).

In addition to the major landforms, there are countless smaller ones: conical volcanoes, cuestas, benches, deep gorges, broad valleys, and coral reefs, to mention only a few. Even the ancient notion of ocean basins has broken down partly. For example, we still speak of the Pacific Basin as though it were a washbowl whose sides slope uniformly downward to a central low spot. Actually, the Pacific contains many separate and distinct basins, both large and small, and their location, size, and shape have a great deal to do with varying conditions of water itself. The same is true of the Atlantic (Fig. 207) and other oceans.

The facts have been brought to light largely through the invention and use of the *sonic depth finder*. This instrument sends an impulse downward through the water and receives the echo of that impulse back at the instrument a bit later. The speed of the impulse through the water is known and by recording the time necessary for it to travel to the bottom and back, and dividing by two, the depth of the water can be calculated. The depth finder has been so perfected that a vessel traveling at full speed can make a continuous record of depths along its course. With thousands of soundings thus quickly and cheaply obtained, it is a relatively simple matter to prepare contour maps of the ocean bottom. Hitherto, the slow and laborious

method of using a weighted sounding line from a stationary vessel produced few and expensive data on the nature and shape of the bottom areas.

The average depth of the Pacific Ocean is about 14,000 feet, of the Atlantic about 13,000 feet, of the Indian about 13,000 feet, and of the Arctic about 4,000 feet. The average depth of the Antarctic Ocean is not yet known. Like so many averages, these have only limited usefulness. From man's standpoint, the depths which are of greatest meaning are those which are shallow. It is in shallow waters that man needs to know the actual depths in order to navigate his vessels safely; it is in the same waters that marine life which man seeks is especially abundant (Fig. 208).

As might be expected, most of the shallow waters are adjacent to the edges of the continents and large islands, although there are some which occur even in mid-ocean. The shallow waters next to the continents lie on the continental shelf (Fig. 209), a gently sloping extension of the continent itself and a reminder of the times when large shallow seas covered most of what are now the land

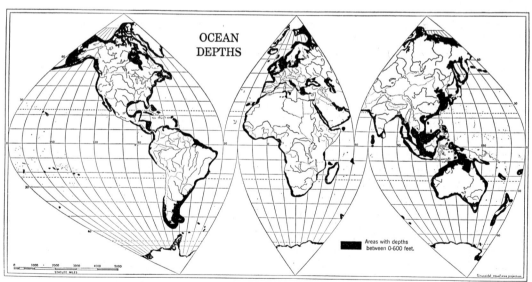

208 *OCEAN AREAS with approximate depths of 0-600 feet (0-100 fathoms) are particularly significant to man, both for navigation and for fisheries. Note especially the variable width of the continental shelves.*

masses, either in whole or in part at a given time. Depths on some continental shelves range from 0 to 60 fathoms, on others from 0 to 80 fathoms (1 fathom equals 6 feet), with the lesser depths inshore and the greater ones several miles at sea. Almost immediately beyond the 60-80 fathom line, the bottom drops away abruptly to much greater depths, often to 1,000 fathoms in a few miles. For example, the continental shelf as measured southeast from the coast of New Jersey is about 90 miles in width (Fig. 209). This means that the 80-fathom depth lies about 90 miles from the coast; but 15 or 20 miles seaward from there are depths as great as 1,000 fathoms or more, depending on exact position. It must be noted at this time, that major continental shelves differ greatly in width. Off eastern United States, for example, is a relatively wide continental shelf, but off the western coast the average width of the continental shelf is only 18 miles.

The oceanic regions of greatest depth have their bottoms so far below the surface that they are known as *deeps*. Those huge synclinal depressions which lie out in front of great mountain arcs are known as *foredeeps*. They owe their existence to the same crustal deformations which produced neighboring hills or mountains. One of them, the Mindanao Deep, which is located just to the east of the large island of Mindanao, has a record depth of about 35,000 feet. If Mt. Everest were placed in this trough, even its summit would be more than one mile below the surface of the ocean. The deepest section of the Atlantic, the Milwaukee Depth just north of Puerto Rico, has a depth of some 29,000 feet. The deepest parts of the Indian, Arctic, and Antarctic oceans, respectively, are about 23,000, 18,000, and 14,000 feet.

WATER MOVEMENTS. While one may think of the seas and oceans in only two dimensions, as "so long and so wide," they are actually three-dimensional. Their restless waters move not only horizontally, but vertically and obliquely as well. Some of these movements result in the transportation of significant amounts of water from one part of the ocean to another, like the flow of polar waters equatorward and of tropical waters toward the poles, or like the up-welling of deep waters and the slow descent of surface waters.

Other movements, such as storm, tidal, and seismic waves, do not result in any significant transportation. In tidal movements, the waters merely bulge in obedience to the mass attraction of the moon and sun (Fig. 6). Because the earth rotates, the bulges travel, but the water in them merely goes up and down and there is little, if any, transportation. Much the same sort of behavior occurs in seismic waves (*tsunami*). These are set up as a result of sudden and violent disturbances of a section of sea bottom, by block-fault movement or by volcanic activity. Some seismic waves are 50 feet in height and travel at speeds as great as 300 miles per hour. If they strike low and inhabited coasts, property damage and loss of life are heavy. One such wave, originating from crustal movements in the Gulf of Alaska, struck the Hawaiian harbor of Hilo in the spring of 1946 with disastrous results to persons, buildings, ships, and harbor installations. Yet, despite all the commotion they cause, seismic waves, like storm and tidal waves, do not cause waters to move from one region to another.

The movements which do result in transportation of large quantities of ocean water are called *currents*. These are of many sorts, some are cold and others warm, some are highly saline and others only weakly saline, some operate at great or intermediate depths and others move at and near the surface. Of them all, it is those at or relatively near the surface which are most significant geographically. It is these surface currents which affect ship navigation, the presence and numbers of commercial fish, and water and air conditions in shore and near-shore areas. Their effects on air (climatic) conditions have been mentioned previously in the discussion of climatic controls (see pp. 77 ff.).

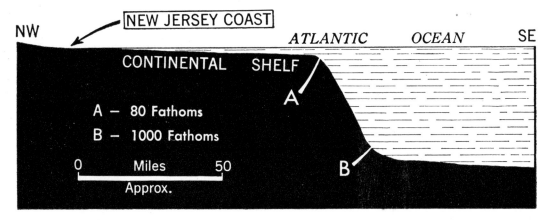

209 THE CONTINENTAL shelf off the New Jersey coast.

Within the tropics most of the surface currents and, hence, the greatest volumes of water, are moving steadily toward the west. This is in accord with the strong frictional drag of the Trades, which tends to pile up the surface waters against the eastern margins of the land masses in low latitudes (Figs. 71 and 72). This westward movement of tropical water is a twofold one, being comprised of the North Equatorial Current and the South Equatorial Current (Plate VIII). Between them is a smaller, reverse, compensating flow known as the Equatorial Countercurrent. In the part of the Indian Ocean from the equator to southern Asia there is a seasonal reversal of currents in accord with the behavior of the monsoon winds (Fig. 73).

The warm surface waters which move toward and tend to pile up against the eastern parts of islands and continental shores of much of the tropics are forced to turn poleward. This is primarily a reflection of their bumping into the land and secondarily the result of deflection incident to their movement on the surface of a rotating earth (see p. 103). The waters of the North Equatorial Current turn northward and those of the South Equatorial Current turn southward. As they travel, deflection to the right of their course in the Northern Hemisphere and to the left of their course in the Southern Hemisphere causes them to pull slowly away from

the eastern shores of the continents as they move poleward. By the time the middle latitudes are reached, rotational deflection and the force of the Westerlies, under whose influence they now come, cause them to take courses toward the east. This direction is just the reverse of their movements in tropical waters. The eastward journey carries them once more across the oceans where they split near the western margins of the land masses. Part of this split is the result of bumping into land and part is the result of deviation incident to earth rotation.

The splitting of the ocean currents in middle latitudes is well illustrated by the North Atlantic Drift, the offspring of the Gulf Stream (Plate VIII). This current, or slow drift, sends part of its water equatorward as the Canaries Current. The latter, in turn, flows into the North Equatorial Current previously mentioned. The other part of the North Atlantic Drift flows in a northeasterly direction between Norway and Iceland into the margin of the Arctic Ocean. It brings relatively warm temperatures to high latitudes and thus accounts for ice-free ports as far north as the Lofotens. It is responsible for a measurable portion of the climatic mildness characteristic of the British Isles and northwestern Europe.

On the opposite side of the North Atlantic, cold waters of Arctic Ocean origin, the

Greenland and Labrador currents, hug the eastern edges of the land mass as they move southward to encounter and slide under the warmer waters of the Gulf Stream. Associated with the cold water are the heavy and numerous fogs of the Newfoundland Grand Bank and other nearby areas. The cold waters also bring many types of small marine organisms which help to support commercial and other fish in the shallow waters of the continental shelf. Unfortunately, the Labrador Current also brings many icebergs to menace the heavily traveled lanes of the great North Atlantic route (Fig. 210). Particularly during the summer season, when the bergs are freed from the winter ice lock in Baffin Bay, do the floating ice mountains cause trouble. In summer, the lanes are actually shifted a bit farther to the south in order to avoid the areas of greatest berg concentration.

The picture of surface circulation in the northern half of the Pacific is strikingly similar to that of the North Atlantic (Plate VIII). However, the near junction of northeastern Siberia and western Alaska does not allow as free an interchange of waters with those of the Arctic Ocean. Instead, there is only a cold water stream passing from the Arctic to the North Pacific through narrow Bering Strait. This current, the Kamchatka-Oyashio, is the Pacific counterpart of the Labrador Current. There are, however, no icebergs, for there is no Greenland glacier to furnish them to the sea waters. Otherwise the two pictures are much the same; the general pattern of *clockwise* circulation occurs in both the North Atlantic and the North Pacific (Fig. 211).

The surface currents of the Southern Hemisphere, in the southern parts of the Pacific, Atlantic, and Indian oceans, are essentially the same as those in the northern, but the movement is counterclockwise (Fig. 211). There is interchange of polar and tropical waters, westward movement near the equator, poleward movement along eastern coasts, drift across the oceans in the middle latitude positions, splitting of currents in middle latitudes near west coasts, and generally rotary nature of the circulation as a whole.

ICE CONDITIONS. Some small icebergs are derived from local valley glaciers along mountainous coasts, as those of southeastern

210   *A LARGE GREENLAND iceberg which has been carried southward by the Labrador Current to menace the shipping lanes of the North Atlantic. The vessel is one of the cutters of the United States Coast Guard, whose job it is to share in the conduct of the International Ice Patrol. (U. S. Coast Guard Official Photo)*

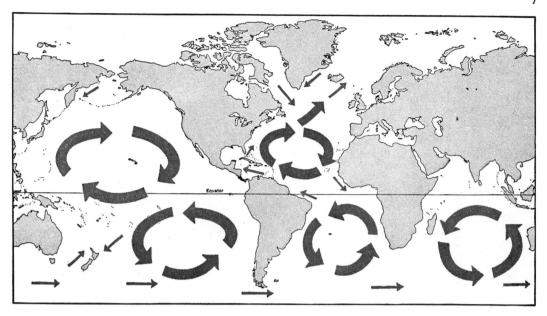

211 *EXTREMELY GENERALIZED expression of the clockwise circulation of major ocean currents in the Northern Hemisphere and the counterclockwise circulation in the Southern Hemisphere.*

Alaska, but they are short-lived and few in number. The bergs which are large and numerous come from the Greenland ice and from the vast ice layers of Antarctica. The tabular Antarctic bergs, unlike the jagged Greenland type (Fig. 186), do not menace any major shipping lanes, nor do they move as far from points of origin as do the Greenland bergs. Only the occasional whaling and exploring vessel must be on guard against them, particularly during fogs or storms. The equatorial limits, average and extreme, of iceberg occurrence are shown on Plate VIII.

Most of the ice which is found at sea is in the form of cakes (*floes*) and *fields* of salt-water ice (Fig. 212). These are monotonously flat except where huge cakes have bumped and ground together in such fashion that their edges have buckled and piled up to form shapes like those of miniature mountain ranges. Because the polar area of the Antarctic is a continent while that of the Arctic is an ocean, sea ice is much more prevalent in the Northern Hemisphere. It is the Arctic ice which threatens, entraps, and often crushes vessels attempting to develop sea routes and fisheries along the northern coasts of North America and Eurasia.

Ice of Arctic origin moves to some extent into the northwestern portion of the North Atlantic (Plate VIII). Packs, or fields, also constitute navigational hazards in the Bering Sea, Baffin Bay, and the Sea of Okhotsk. However, even in the Arctic Ocean, there is always open water. Contrary to popular belief, sea ice there never, even in the height of the coldest season, forms a continuous blanket from shore to shore. Storms, ordinary winds, and currents keep the ice broken up and shifting from place to place. One of the major problems of travel on such ice is the presence of open lanes and areas of water which are difficult for dogs, sledges, and men to cross. Another is that the ice may move at such speed and in such direction that an exploring party toils ahead for many hours, only to find that it is in the same location as before, as though it had been walking on a treadmill.

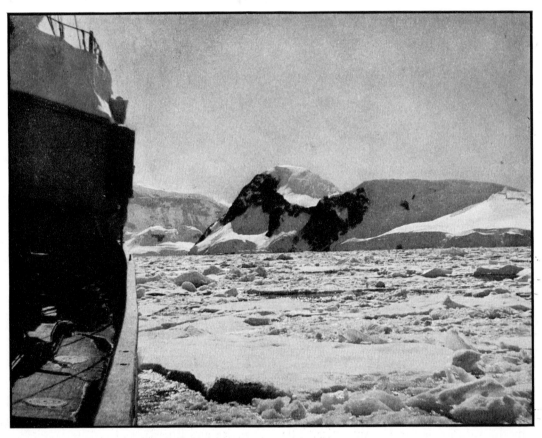

212   *FLOES OF SALT-WATER ice along the coast of the Falkland Islands. (British Information Services)*

Lakes

Compared to the great size of the seas and oceans, the smaller water bodies seem insignificant. However, significance cannot be measured by size alone. A lake, or group of lakes, may have a local or even an extra-local importance far out of proportion to the area or depth of water involved. Lakes may furnish domestic and industrial water, transportation, fish, and recreational opportunities. In such manner, they may be more truly and directly entwined with the lives of most people than are seas and oceans.

There are major portions of the several continents which do not possess lakes, except, perhaps, for one occasionally created artificially by man. A glance or two at the map will show how true this is (Plate III). For example, lakes in South America, at least lakes of any appreciable size, are conspicuous because of their rarity rather than for their large numbers. The same is true of Australia, most of Africa, and the bulk of Asia. Actually, conditions in nature work against the formation or long-continued preservation of any considerable number of lakes. The existence of a lake demands two things: some sort of basin which has no low-level outlet and enough water to fill such a basin or to flood part of it. Thus, lakes are largely ruled out of the earth's extensive dry lands. Where climates are humid and there are basins present, lakes are soon emptied as gnawing streams cut gorges into their rims and drain away the impounded waters, or they become filled with in-washed sediments and aquatic vegetation. It is possible that lakes are among the most short-lived of the earth's physical features.

In contrast to the vast regions with few or no lakes, there are others in which lakes are numerous. Most of the large regions with numerous lakes are areas of glaciation, chiefly of continental glaciation and to a lesser extent of valley glaciation (Fig. 196). In such regions, the characteristic unevenness resulting from both scour and deposition normally presents innumerable depressions which have no low-level outlet. It so happens that most such depressions are in humid climates so that there is abundant water to fill them. Streams are busily engaged in cutting through the rims, but there has been insufficient time since the glaciers disappeared for the streams to have drained the lakes of their waters or for the lakes to have become filled with plants and sediment. Some lake regions were not glaciated and lakes in them owe their origin to other causes. A few may be mentioned: the lake country of an appreciable section of equatorial Africa is the result of block faulting and damming by lava flows (Fig. 213); that of northern Florida is a result of certain karst conditions; and that of the lower Yangtze Basin is the result of variations in the deposition of river alluviums, plus, in part, some crustal warping. Beyond these, there are many other occurrences and possibilities of formation, but the original generalization, that lakes are most numerous in glaciated regions, especially those of most recent glaciation, is not destroyed by the exceptions.

THE GREAT LAKES. North America has the greatest number of lakes, from small and large ones at comparatively low elevations to small ones at mountainous altitudes. Of them all, whether Canada's Great Bear Lake in the far north or Lake Nicaragua in the tropics, the cluster known as the Great Lakes is the most conspicuous and the most important (Fig. 214). Not only does it provide the chief inland waterway of the earth, but it serves many other purposes, from water supply to commercial fishing and recreation.

213 *LAKE JIPE, one of the many lakes of the volcanic and block-faulted region of eastern equatorial Africa. (Photo by R. U. Light in his* Focus on Africa, *published by the American Geographical Society)*

Lake Superior is the largest of the lakes and the most extensive body of fresh water on the globe. It is about 350 miles in length and 160 miles wide. Its deepest section is about 1,300 feet, which places its bottom nearly 700 feet below sea level, while its surface is about 600 feet above the level of the sea. With an area of approximately 32,000 square miles, it is large enough to cover all of Belgium and the Netherlands and to extend over half of Denmark as well. A single outlet, the St. Marys River, connects it with Lake Huron. The "Soo" Canal, paralleling the rapids section of the upper St. Marys, allows vessels to move to and from the Lower Lakes (Fig. 215).

Lake Michigan and Lake Huron, lying about 20 feet lower than Superior, are connected by the Strait of Mackinac. The combined flow of Superior, Huron, and Michigan, except for minor diversion through the Chicago Drainage Canal to the Illinois River, moves by way of the St. Clair River into small and shallow Lake St. Clair. That, in turn, drains by means of the Detroit River into the western end of Lake Erie. At Erie's eastern end, the water forms the Niagara River which tumbles over Niagara Falls on its way to Lake Ontario. The Welland Canal, in Canadian Territory, makes it possible for vessels to move between Erie and Ontario. Lake Ontario is the smallest of the Great Lakes (little Lake St. Clair is not considered one of the Great Lakes), but even it is nearly as large as Massachusetts. From its eastern end pour the waters of all the lakes, waters which form the full stream of the St. Lawrence River. All in all, the Great Lakes cover an area the size of the United Kingdom or an area nearly a third greater than the New England states. The parts of the shorelines which lie entirely in United States territory are longer than the distance from New York to London.

The Great Lakes have been singled out for emphasis here because of their size, arrange-

214 *THE GREAT LAKES constitute the world's chief inland waterway.*

215 *LARGE GREAT LAKES vessels, the ore boats which carry iron ore "down-lakes," at the ends of the huge locks of the "Soo" Canal at Sault Sainte Marie, Michigan. The International Bridge, which connects the Canadian and American "Soos" and crosses above the rapids of the St. Marys River, may be seen in the right-hand background. (Editorial Associates, Ltd., Canada)*

ment, and commercial importance. More will be said about them in later chapters in this book. Were time and space available, it would be pertinent to discuss some of the other lakes of the world, such as Great Bear Lake, which has become famous for the uranium ores located along parts of its shore, or Siberia's deep and crescent-shaped Lake Baikal, or the lake districts of Switzerland and northwestern England, or of Maine. Interesting also, would be a discussion of the movements of waters in lakes. Like the oceans, they have their currents, and, again like the oceans, lakes are modifiers of climatic conditions in their shore and near-shore areas.

DRY LAKES. Maps of the continents and many smaller areas show by names and symbols numerous lakes which are not true and permanent lakes. Some examples are Lake Eyre (Australia), Lop Nor (western China), Shott el Jerid (Tunisia), and Muroc Dry Lake (California). These "lakes which are usually not lakes" are the playas or salars which were discussed on p. 254.

STREAMS

The lines of moving water which thread their ways across the surface of the land vary in size from mere rills and brooks to broad, full-flowing rivers. Where land masses and drainage basins are large and precipitation plentiful, streams are numerous and permanent; where drainage basins are small and especially where precipitation is meager, streams are small and intermittent.

The presence or lack of streams affects man's movements and settlements in a wide variety of ways. Primitive man camped at places along or near streams where water and fish were available and where he had a highway for his raft or crude boat. Man, primitive or not, has often settled on islands in rivers where the encompassing water provided a barrier against enemies. River junctions have been strategic points for the control of, and participation in, the trade which moved on the streams. River mouths, making union with the sea, gave access to ocean routes.

When industrial centers arose, the riverbank position provided large quantities of water for rapidly growing urban populations and supplied water for power and the processing of materials. In many areas, the fine dark alluviums of river flood plains attracted agricultural populations. In the eastern United States and to a lesser extent in the drier West, the bulk of the westward movement was locally carried and directed by the streams which floated men and their belongings. These are only a few of the ways in which rivers and men have been and, in many ways, still are related.

Humid-land Streams

In regions of humid climate, all except the smallest tributaries are normally permanently flowing waters. Their volumes may vary with seasonal differences in moisture reception. High and low stages represent ordinary behavior, but the streams are always there. In some streams, there may be little difference between highest and lowest water. This is true particularly where rainfall is of comparatively even distribution throughout the year and where waters are not partly locked up in the form of ice during the winter season. Variations in flow are significant as part of the physical picture of an area, but they are more significant in their relations to man and his activities. It is readily apparent that a permanent stream which is in high flood during part of the year and barely flows at another time is of much less utility than one which maintains a relatively uniform level.

GREAT RIVERS. Fig. 216 shows the longer rivers of each continent. All of them have their sources in humid lands, chiefly in rainy and snowy mountains, and most of them flow in humid regions throughout their courses. Exceptions to this latter condition are represented by the Nile and the Colorado, which run in dry areas for most of their lengths. Streams of this nature, unlike the Amazon

and the Mississippi, actually lose volume as they proceed mouthward; however, they receive sufficient water in the wet lands of their origin to carry them through steppes and deserts. Such streams are known as *exotic streams;* at least they are strange, or exotic, in the portions of their courses which extend through climatically dry regions. Exotic streams, like the Nile, Colorado, or Tigris-Euphrates, have played a large part in human history. They have supplied relatively abundant water to regions which otherwise could have supported only small and widely scattered settlements. They have encouraged, even forced, co-operation among peoples using them particularly in connection with the construction and maintenance of extensive irrigation works. Humid-land streams have also played much the same role, for the development of river transportation, the control of floodwaters, the generation of power, and the insurance of sufficient and proper supplies of domestic and industrial water have demanded co-operative, rather than individual, activity.

The longest of the great rivers is the Missouri-Mississippi. From its source in the northern part of the American Rockies to its mouth in the Gulf of Mexico is a distance of about 4,200 miles. Among its conspicuous features are a large number of tributaries, broad and fertile flood plains in its lower portion, and the wide delta which it is still building out into the Gulf of Mexico. Nearly as long as the Missouri-Mississippi and greater in volume is the Amazon. From its source in the high Andes, it flows eastward across the full breadth of the Amazon Basin to pour a wide and muddy stream into the Atlantic. So great is the volume and so heavy the load of fine materials that the Amazon can be detected as a dirty fresh-water stream for many miles out into the Atlantic, a sort of river in the ocean. Many large and small islands split its discharge area so that it has several mouths instead of one. The Amazon is the only stream which makes it possible for ocean vessels to steam nearly across a continent; such vessels, except for the larger ones, can travel all the way from the Atlantic to the town of Iquitos in Ecuador. Should the Amazon Basin ever become highly developed, this river probably will be one of the world's major arteries. The longest rivers of the other continents are the Nile (Africa), Ob (Eurasia), and the Murray (Australia). The latter, however, is not a "great river"; Australia, with its disproportionate area of dry climates and with only small drainage basins in the sections which are humid, has no large permanent streams.

STREAM PATTERNS. Study of maps which portray the lines of flow of surface waters will indicate many patterns. These are the particular patterns which individual streams have etched into the land as they have carried on their erosive work. That the patterns are very much a part of the actual geographic expression and not just features which have been unduly emphasized on maps is illustrated by almost any view which enables the observer to look down upon the land.

The most common stream pattern is the *dendritic pattern*. The term *"dendritic"* means treelike, and a stream system with this plan possesses a main trunk and branches which join it at acute angles. This pattern develops where the running water is cutting rocks, whether loose or consolidated, which are relatively uniform in their reaction to erosion. Thus, this pattern will occur in a region where streams are running on granite alone, or on a homogeneous sandstone, or wholly on loose clays, and so on. Fig. 218 presents the actual plans of some streams, large and small, which have the dendritic pattern.

Other major stream patterns are the *trellis, radial, annular, braided,* and *glacially deranged*. Over the land surface as a whole, they are much less common than the dendritic pat-

216

THE LONGER rivers (1,000 miles or more) of six continents.

NORTH AMERICA

Mississippi-Missouri 4000 mi.
Mackenzie 2500 mi.
Mississippi 2500 mi.
St. Lawrence 2100 mi.
Yukon 2000 mi.
Rio Grande 1800 mi.
Colorado 1650 mi.
Nelson 1650 mi.
Arkansas 1450 mi.
Ohio-Allegheny 1300 mi.
Columbia 1200 mi.
Saskatchewan 1200 mi.
Peace 1050 mi.
Churchill 1000 mi.
Red (U.S.) 1000 mi.
Snake 1000 mi.

SOUTH AMERICA

Amazon 3900 mi.
Parand-Paraguay 2450 mi.
Madeira 2000 mi.
Purus 1850 mi.
São Francisco 1800 mi.
Orinoco 1700 mi.
Tocantins 1700 mi.
Rio Negro 1400 mi.
Pilcomayo 1000 mi.
Uruguay 1000 mi.

EUROPE

Volga 2300 mi.
Danube 1700 mi.
Dnieper 1400 mi.
Ural 1400 mi.
Don 1100 mi.

ASIA

Ob 3200 mi.
Yangtze 3100 mi.
Amur 2900 mi.
Yenisei 2800 mi.
Lena 2800 mi.
Hwang Ho 2700 mi.
Mekong 2500 mi.
Irtish 2300 mi.
Salween 1750 mi.
Euphrates 1700 mi.
Indus 1700 mi.
Brahmaputra 1700 mi.
Si 1650 mi.
Ganges 1550 mi.
Amu Darya 1500 mi.
Irrawaddy 1250 mi.
Tigris 1150 mi.
Sungari 1100 mi.

AFRICA

Nile 4000 mi.
Congo 2900 mi.
Niger 2600 mi.
Zambesi 1600 mi.
Orange 1300 mi.

AUSTRALIA

Murray 2300 mi.
Darling 1150 mi.

Distances are approximate.

tern, but, in areas where they do occur, they are just as observable and significant. The trellis pattern is comprised of relatively straight lines which join each other at right angles (Fig. 217). This pattern occurs where there is a definite banding of the rocks or where a pattern of fault lines and their accompanying zones of weakness is rectangular. The radial pattern is found where there is a centrally located area of higher land from which the streams flow out in all directions like spokes from the hub of a wheel (Fig. 219). It also occurs in areas where there is a central low section and streams flow in from all, or many, directions. The annular, or ring, pattern occurs most frequently as a result of the erosion of structural domes (Fig. 219). Its plan reflects rock controls which are made

A

C

TRELLISED STREAM PATTERN
IN CUESTIFORM PLAIN

TRELLISED STREAM PATTERN
IN RIDGE AND VALLEY AREA

1 – Eroded anticlinal crest

2 – Synclinal ridge

B

1 – More resistant rock
(forms cuestas)

2 – Less resistant rock
(forms lowlands)

D

RIDGE
RIDGE
RIDGE

217 *TRELLIS DRAINAGE patterns and two of their characteristic relationships to landforms and rocks.*

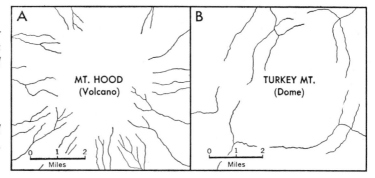

218

(Above) *Examples of dendritic stream patterns of a large, a medium-sized, and a small stream.*

219

(Right) *Examples of radial (A) and annular (B) drainage patterns.*

operative as soon as the domes have passed the initial stage in their dissection. In a sense, the annular pattern is a curved or bent trellis pattern. The braided pattern, characteristic of streams which are overloaded and have hence dropped materials to clog their former channels, is one of many joining and rejoining lines. Fig. 220 indicates, better than words, the nature of this pattern. The glacially deranged pattern has been discussed in the chap-

220

BRAIDED drainage pattern in the aggraded bed of the Platte River, Nebraska. Note the many interlocking stream channels. (Balsley from U. S. Geological Survey)

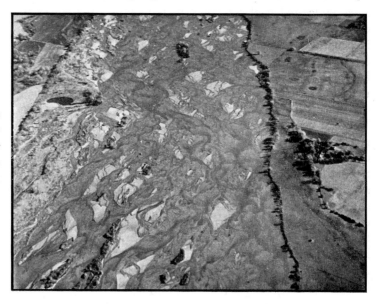

ter which includes mention of continental and valley glaciation (see p. 264).

Stream patterns are important in many ways. They provide part of the physical plan of a countryside and they affect the distribution of other physical features. One example is seen in the streams of Kansas; their patterns are largely dendritic and so are the patterns of the accompanying flood plains. Water is more abundant in the flood-plain soils and trees are able to maintain themselves there. Thus, fingers and lines of trees stand out in dendritic pattern and in sharp contrast to the drier, grassy interstream areas (Fig. 221). In the Ridge and Valley region of eastern Tennessee, the stream pattern is trellised and this is the key to distribution of the richer bottomland soils, as well as to the location of those types of natural vegetation which require more moisture than do the types on the ridges. These are only two examples, chosen more or less at random, but they serve to illustrate some of the relationships between stream patterns and other natural features.

When man comes to travel across the land, and to inhabit and use it, stream patterns are reflected in still other fashions. In the Amazon Basin, the stream pattern is dendritic in plan and many of the towns and small native villages are located at places along the top edges of valley bluffs. Thus, the population pattern is dendritic, although not solidly dendritic, for settlements are not continuous. It might be described as a broken dendritic pattern. In the northern part of the state of Mississippi, the streams likewise have a dendritic pattern. The best cornlands are found on the fertile, recent alluvium which borders the stream channels; hence, the pattern of corn distribution, at least of heavy corn yields, is the same as that of the streams. An annular pattern is characteristic of much of the drainage system of the Black Hills and the pattern of ranch lands follows in strong correspondence. In a large part of Pennsylvania, chiefly east of the Allegheny Plateau, the stream pattern is trellised and the individual parts of the pattern

mark the positions of the more level lands. These are the lands of densest settlement for that portion of the state and, thus, the population pattern there is essentially trellised (Fig. 222).

There are also significant relationships between road patterns and drainage patterns. How different the problems of road alignment and bridge construction in an area of glacially deranged drainage are from the same problems in a region of dendritic stream pattern. Again, the above are only a few examples of the relationships between stream patterns and cultural patterns, but they could be multiplied many times.

WATER POWER. There has been a growing emphasis on the development of power from streams. Particularly is this true of rivers in humid middle latitude regions or those which obtain enough water from humid areas to enable them to continue as streams through dry country.

The use of energy derived from running water is age-old. It began thousands of years ago in such areas as the Nile Valley and parts of India and China. Earlier installations were small and simple. They consisted of some type of wheel equipped with cleats or boards against which the water thrust itself to turn the wheel and its axle. Surprisingly enough, it is the simple type which is most common over the earth as a whole to this very day. With the coming of the Industrial Revolution and its demands for more and more power, much of the energy which at first ran the machines came directly from running water. Later, as man's knowledge of electricity and ways of producing it increased, part of the energy from running water was converted into electricity for running many of the machines. The large modern water-power establishments do not depend on the simple wheel; instead the water is dropped through huge pipes in which turbines are set. The down-rushing water turns the blades of the turbines at terrific speed and this mechanical energy is used to spin generators

Stream   Stream valley with forest

Short grass steppe   Tall grass prairie

K   A   N   S   A   S

0   100   200 Miles

2 2 1   *RELATION between stream pattern and natural forest vegetation in Kansas.*

Altoona

Harrisburg

Major streams only

Areas of denser population

0   50

Miles

2 2 2   *STREAM pattern and the more densely populated areas of a part of Pennsylvania.*

223   *A SCHEMATIC diagram showing the generation, transmission, and distribution of hydroelectricity.*

which transform the water power into electric power (Fig. 223).

The United States leads the world in the production of hydroelectricity, although on a *per capita* basis Norway holds first rank. If all possible water power were developed, the political unit of the Belgian Congo would lead and, among the continents, Africa would hold first place (Fig. 224). So far, the largest and most famous individual power plants are found in the United States and Canada. Among them are the Queenston plant on the Canadian side of Niagara Falls, the several plants of the Tennessee Valley, and the huge establishment at Hoover Dam on the Colorado River, as well as those at Grand Coulee and Bonneville on the Columbia River (Fig. 225). In addition to these power developments in the United States, there are other large plants and scores of small ones in California, the southern Appalachians, New England, and adjacent New York State.

Beyond engineering know-how, location in reference to markets, size of markets, and

the like, the generation of hydroelectricity has certain physical requirements. There must be a large volume of water of relatively steady flow, and a sufficient fall of that water. In addition, if artificial dams have to be built to improve natural conditions, there must be sites available where construction is safe and economically feasible. The sites must likewise be located in parts of valleys where sufficient amounts of water can be impounded. Thus, purely physical items such as nature of bedrock and shape of valley become significant. The physical conditions requisite to water-power production are most fully met in regions of continental and valley glaciation. It will be recalled that glaciated areas possess many natural reservoirs which insure large volume and steadiness of flow aided, of course, by humid climates. Many falls and rapids are present to insure sufficient water drop. Particularly in regions of glacial scour there are also many sites where dams can be easily constructed and safely anchored into the bedrock. Glaciation has helped to make possible

224

A COMPARISON of world water-power resources: (A) total world resources, (B) continents, and (C) political units. It will be noted in (A) that only some 10 per cent of available world water power has been developed. Africa leads the world in potential water power (B), but less than one per cent has been developed (D). The Belgian Congo

leads all political units in water-power potential (C) but practically none is developed (E). Note, also, that the U. S. and Canada combined produce nearly half the developed water power of the world (E), and that Europe produces very slightly more than North America (D). North America and Europe together produce nearly 90 per cent of developed world water power (D).

A WORLD WATER POWER

Devel-oped | UNDEVELOPED

0   20   40   60   80   100
Per cent

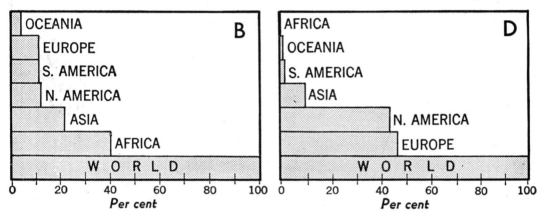

POTENTIAL WATER POWER

B
OCEANIA
EUROPE
S. AMERICA
N. AMERICA
ASIA
AFRICA
W O R L D

0   20   40   60   80   100
Per cent

DEVELOPED WATER POWER

D
AFRICA
OCEANIA
S. AMERICA
ASIA
N. AMERICA
EUROPE
W O R L D

0   20   40   60   80   100
Per cent

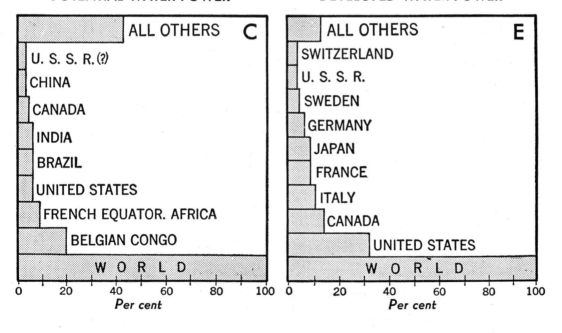

POTENTIAL WATER POWER

C
ALL OTHERS
U. S. S. R. (?)
CHINA
CANADA
INDIA
BRAZIL
UNITED STATES
FRENCH EQUATOR. AFRICA
BELGIAN CONGO
W O R L D

0   20   40   60   80   100
Per cent

DEVELOPED WATER POWER

E
ALL OTHERS
SWITZERLAND
U. S. S. R.
SWEDEN
GERMANY
JAPAN
FRANCE
ITALY
CANADA
UNITED STATES
W O R L D

0   20   40   60   80   100
Per cent

225

(Above) *Hoover (Boulder) Dam and a part of Lake Mead, Colorado River, Nevada-Arizona. The dark spots along the crest of the dam are automobiles, which give a notion of the gigantic scale of the dam. (William S. Russell)*

226

(Left) *A large dam on the Gatineau River in the Laurentian Shield just north of Ottawa, Canada. Sluice-way is provided for logs, some of which may be seen in the left foreground. (National Film Board, Canada)* the high per capita production of power in Norway. It also largely accounts for the power generated at places along the southern flank of Canada's Laurentian Shield (Fig. 226), as well as much of the water power produced in the northeastern part of the United States.

However, optimum physical conditions are no longer so important as they were in the past; greatly increased technical knowledge and abundant capital now enable man to make up in part for certain natural lacks. Hence, tremendous quantities of power can now be produced in sections where it would not have been possible, or feasible, a few years ago. Besides, streams today are controlled for other reasons, such as flood prevention, improvement and maintenance of navigation, and insurance of domestic and industrial water supply. Controls of this sort often result in the creation of proper conditions for power production. Thus power can be produced in many places more or less as a by-product of projects which are broader in scope. This is true in the Tennessee Valley, where a

separate governmental corporation, known as the Tennessee Valley Authority, was set up to control floods, improve navigation, and, in general, to help rehabilitate the run-down economy of the region. River control for the purposes of flood prevention and navigation entailed many dams and reservoirs (Fig. 227). These, in turn, provided several excellent possibilities for the steady generation of hydro-electricity.

Streams in Dry Lands

It has been noted previously that stream behavior in regions of arid or semiarid climates is much different from that in humid lands. The streams, except for those which are exotic, are intermittent rather than permanent and they are smaller and less numerous. Yet these intermittent streams present many vexing problems. They pour floodwaters onto settlements and play havoc with transportation systems (Fig. 228). Extensive flood pre-

227 *THE TENNESSEE Valley is now dotted with dams and reservoirs, potential sources of great quantities of hydroelectric power.*

228 *RESULTS of a flood on the intermittent Mohave River, Mohave Desert, California. Note breaching of the highway and the destruction of fields and homes. The town in the background is the desert railroad center of Barstow. (Spence Air Photos)*

vention works are necessary for the protection of towns and cities, as well as roads and railroads. It is somewhat paradoxical that floods and flood damage may be as severe in deserts as in lands of plentiful moisture.

The reasons for the difficulties lie basically in the amount and distribution of precipitation; that is, the problems are fundamentally climatic in origin. Because the water does not flow permanently, it drops flood-stage loads and channels are clogged. The next floodwater spreads out over wide areas, carving new channels soon glutted with debris as the water disappears. Except where wadies are deeply

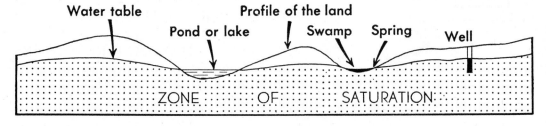

229 *ZONE of saturation, water table, and characteristic relation of water table to land surface.*

230

EXAGGERATED diagram of the three kinds of soil moisture: gravitational, hygroscopic, and capillary water.

Gravitational water (filling spaces between soil particles)

Film of hygroscopic water (thickness greatly exaggerated)

Soil particle (size exaggerated)

Capillary water (thickness greatly exaggerated)

entrenched, such behavior means that flood areas are usually broad and not too well defined; nevertheless, they are the natural drainways, and man must pay the penalty for settling in them and building his transport lines across them. Very often, he seems to know so little about stream behavior under such conditions that he fails to recognize that he is in the natural line of water flow.

GROUND WATER

A portion of the moisture derived from the air sinks into the upper part of the earth's crust to become *ground water*. Though not visible, it is just as important as surface water. From it come springs and well water and some of the moisture which is so necessary for the growth of natural vegetation and crops. As water moves downward from the surface, it fills the spaces among soil particles and also the crevices and cracks of the bedrock as far down as such exist in the earth's crust. The zone in which all spaces are filled is the *zone of saturation* (Fig. 229). The top of the zone is the *water table*. The water table follows, approximately, the profile of the land above, although it is closer to the surface in low places than in high places. Where it intersects the surface in low spots, the results are swamps, ponds, lakes, or springs. In general, the ground water table lies closer to the surface in regions of humid climates than it

does in the areas of arid or semiarid climates. Even in the latter areas, it may reach the surface in a few low spots and in these salt marshes are the normal result.

Soil Moisture

The amount of moisture present in the soil is a very critical factor in the growth of natural vegetation and crops. Soil moisture is of three kinds: *gravitational water, hygroscopic water,* and *capillary water* (Fig. 230). Gravitational water is the water which moves downward, under the pull of gravity, toward the zone of saturation. If gravitational water is too abundant, soils become waterlogged and useless for crops although such drowned soils are still capable of supporting several types of swamp vegetation. Hygroscopic water exists as an extremely thin film around each soil particle, somewhat as though each particle were "wrapped in cellophane." It is often referred to as "unavailable water" because plants cannot obtain it. Capillary water is the water which moves by capillary action, or attraction, in the same fashion that spilled ink may be drawn into and among the fibers of a blotter. Its ability to move even against the pull of gravity is significant for, as topsoils dry out, capillary water is drawn to the upper portion of the soil where it supplies the needs of plants. However, if such action is too long continued, particularly if the water is drawn all the way to the surface, soils become either weakly or strongly alkaline. If they are mildly

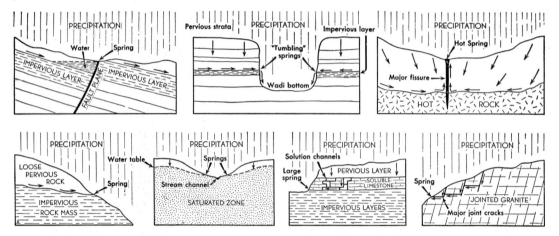

231A   *DIAGRAMS illustrating some of the conditions which lead to the formation of springs.*

231B   *SOME of the common methods of obtaining water from wells.*

alkaline, a few alkali-tolerant crops may be grown; with high alkalinity, no crops can grow although a few especially adapted types of natural vegetation (halophytes) may be able to exist. Soil becomes alkaline when the water is drawn to the surface, is evaporated, and leaves its minerals behind. If there is insufficient precipitation to wash the minerals, or mineral salts, back down into lower parts of the soil, permanently alkaline soils are created.

Springs and Wells

SPRINGS. When ground water issues at the surface it creates either springs or seeps. Whether in deserts or in lands of plentiful

rain, springs and seeps are very useful to man and animals alike. If they are hot springs or are heavily charged with certain minerals, they may be used for health baths and general resort purposes. A spring in the desert usually makes possible an oasis settlement; and a line of springs, as along the base of a range of hills or mountains, allows a string of oasis settlements to exist. Springs on farms or ranches may constitute the drinking water supply and may be covered by small structures, called springhouses, to serve as cool, damp places for the storage of milk and other perishable products. While some springs are safe for human use, others, especially those which draw their water supply too directly from local surfaces, may be seriously polluted and may become sources of severe epidemics. The underlying causes of springs are many; Fig. 231A indicates a few of the more common possibilities.

ORDINARY WELLS. Wells, with one exception which will be discussed below, do not bring their waters to the surface. Man must dig and drill until he reaches below the water table and then must contrive some method of lifting the water to the surface. There are many ways which have been devised to bring the water up where man can use it; some of these are shown in Fig. 231B. The problem of water supply from wells is a relatively simple one where the water table is close to the surface, but difficult and expensive to solve where the distance to the zone of saturation is great. The cost of "bringing in" water from a well 100 or 150 feet deep may run into hundreds or even thousands of dollars, and this does not include the cost of pumping, which will continue as long as the well is in use. One small well drilled recently in the Mohave Desert, and drilled entirely in unconsolidated alluvium, cost about $900 for a drill depth of 75 feet. This included the cost of drilling and the large pipe which is used to line the drill hole.

ARTESIAN WELLS. These are wells of a special and important category. The conditions necessary for such wells are illustrated in Fig. 232. There must be slanting (dipping) layers

of rock, the ends of which are exposed at the earth's surface. At least one of the dipping layers must be porous enough to absorb and collect water from the surface, taking the water in at the end which is exposed to precipitation and surface flow. In addition, the porous, water-collecting layer must be capped by a relatively impervious rock layer, otherwise its water will be lost through the several rock layers. As water fills the porous layer, or *aquifer,* considerable pressure is built up in that layer, especially in that part which is far removed from the intake area and is receiving the push of all the water which has collected on the up-slope of the dipping stratum. By drilling into the part of the aquifer where the water is under great pressure, man may obtain a flowing or gushing well (Fig. 233). If the pressure continues sufficiently, man receives the artesian water without the bother and expense of pumping. However, if the drilling of a well or, perhaps, too many wells causes the pressure to drop, then the water must be pumped to the surface. It is still artesian water, but the well is not a flowing well. Artesian wells occur in many parts of the earth, in dry as well as humid regions. Obviously, they are apt to be most significant in the dry regions, for they may mean an excellent water supply even in those parts of deserts which are so arid that no springs are present. Australia is particularly famous for its resources of artesian water, the bulk of which lies in steppe and desert.

232   *DIAGRAM showing conditions necessary to produce an artesian well. Here the water supply of the intake area is insufficient to fill completely the aquifer. Also, the aquifer is trapped between impervious layers, instead of being only "capped" by an impervious layer.*

SOME WATER PROBLEMS

The preceding discussions have shown that man is confronted with many problems as he attempts to use or to protect himself from the earth's waters. Some of the problems are more numerous and serious than ever before because man himself has created many of them and has often made those of natural origin more pressing.

Oceans

Since the days when trade on the oceans first assumed real importance, there has been an international struggle for control of the sea lanes. History is replete with such references as "Britannia set out to rule the waves," "The War of 1812 was a war for the freedom of the seas," "Mussolini attempted to make an Italian lake of the Mediterranean," "Russia desired access to ice-free ports," or "The Japanese fishermen must be driven from Alaskan salmon waters."

To suppose that the struggle for the seas and oceans is over is to be unrealistic, especially with the growing comprehension on the part of many nations of the extent and value of the food and other resources of the vast salt-water areas. Also, even the largest water bodies have ceased to function as effective barriers against fast ships, speedy aircraft, and unbelievably swift rockets. The question of how much of the Atlantic should be owned or controlled by the United States, for example, is a vexing one. Should it be the area within 10 miles, or 20 miles, of the shore —or should it be the area within a line drawn from Greenland to include Bermuda and the Caribbean islands and on to northeastern South America? In view of modern weapons, any line drawn for protective purposes may be of no consequence, but how about the resources of the sea and their use in both peace and war? Should the Russians or the British control the Mediterranean—or should control rest in the United Nations? Should fishermen from California have free access to the rich waters which lie off the western coast of Mexico? These and scores of other questions which might be asked present issues that are far from being settled; one can only hope that they will be answered peaceably and that the solutions will bring benefit to the largest possible numbers of the earth's people.

Streams

These are both friend and enemy to man: friend in that they serve so many of his needs; enemy in that they go on rampages of destruction or change their courses and thus confuse property limits and political boundaries, or become polluted and carry filth and disease.

FLOODS. The problem of high water is acute in densely populated regions, especially where the presence of fertile flood plains and strategic trade and manufacturing foci has lured large populations not only into the lower areas but to the very edge of the low-water channels. It has been said that the problem is not so much to keep the rivers away from the people as to keep the people out of the rivers. The magnitude of the problem is partly indicated by the fact that one serious flood on the Mississippi may take scores of lives and cause hundreds of millions of dollars in damage (Fig. 169). A major flood on the Hwang Ho, called "China's sorrow," may drown thousands of persons and cause untold damage to fields and sorely needed crops, not to mention the famine and pestilence which ride hard on the heels of such a flood (Fig. 152).

The control of river waters to the point of preventing serious floods is neither easy nor inexpensive. Normally it requires careful study and artificial controls of entire drainage basins from uppermost tributaries to stream mouths and the costs run into millions of dollars. Also, it requires the co-operation of many agencies and of the public as a whole. Yet it may be cheaper to pay for proper controls than to pay the bills for flood damage, particularly if men continue to crowd the rivers. The price of stream control is only part of the cost for cutting away the forests, breaking the sod of grasslands, running cultivation furrows up and down the slope instead of aligning them with the contours, and settling in the natural drainways. Remedies lie in reforestation, regrassing, contour plowing, strip cropping, construction of large and small dams—in general, in wise land-use policies operating throughout entire drainage areas, including suitable adjustments in the use of areas of flood hazard.

SOIL EROSION. There is always a certain amount of erosion under perfectly normal conditions, but it is seldom, except in dry regions, that normal erosion causes any widespread difficulties. It is when natural balances are upset and waters speed unchecked that erosion rises far above normal. Land, soils, and the works of man are then destroyed. It may be possible to rebuild rather quickly the works of man, whether bridges, highways, or homes, but destroyed soils cannot be replaced for many generations and, in most instances, they are gone for all time. When one realizes that soil is the most valuable of all the resources from the earth itself—coal, iron ore, and others not excepted—it is startling to learn that we in the United States already have allowed erosion to steal about one third of our best topsoil (Fig. 234). That, to use a very trite expression, "is something to think about." It is also a situation to do something about.

SHIFTING COURSES. Streams, regardless of size, are wont to change the positions of their channels unless valleys are of such a shape as to hold them rigidly within bounds, as in normal youthful valleys. In old valleys or where braided channels are common, shifts in stream courses occur frequently. One common example is the cutting off of a meander loop in an old valley (Fig. 235). The stream then flows directly across the neck of the for-

mer meander and the land inside the meander loop finds itself on the opposite side of the river channel. If the water channel is designated, as has so often been the case, as a property line or a political boundary, disputes arise as to who owns the land and as to its political affiliation. Or, a stream may be shifting its channel very gradually as a result of lateral

233 *A FLOWING artesian well in the San Luis Valley of southern Colorado. (Siebenthal from U. S. Geological Survey)*

erosion. As it eats on one side, it deposits on the other. Again, if the shifting stream channel is a boundary of some sort, arguments arise as to land ownership and political position (Fig. 235).

The behavior of the Rio Grande in the lower portion of its course created problems international in scope. The lower course crosses a broad floodplain which contains many braided channels. The international boundary between Mexico and the United States had been defined as the main channel of the river, but, under such conditions, which channel is the main one—and where is it located? It was finally necessary for an international commission to study the problem and to reach an agreement on a boundary which would "stay put." The result is a boundary defined by fixed points, on the basis of latitude and longitude, and not by capricious river channels.

WATER RIGHTS. In regions where water is naturally scarce, or, in humid areas where demands on surface and ground waters are especially heavy, there arise many conflicts over rights to water. The majority of such conflicts revolve around stream water. In the "old days," the disputes were normally settled by force; today they are settled in court and in terms of laws and procedures which have become very complicated. It is not unusual for litigation of a given dispute to continue for several years or even for decades. Problems of water rights are particularly complicated in connection with streams which flow through two or more states or in more than one country. California and Arizona are still not in agreement over the disposition of Colorado River water. Also, many persons and groups in California believe that Mexico has been guaranteed too much of the flow of the Colorado River; especially in view of the fact that there is greater need for the water in California and that the cost of expensive controls, such as Hoover Dam and other works, have been borne by the United States rather than Mexico. There has been, and will probably continue to be, much argument on both sides.

NAVIGATION. Navigable streams which lie entirely within one country fall under the jurisdiction of the national government of that country. Streams which flow through two or more countries fall under different political control in different sections of their courses, as in the instance of the Rhine and the Danube. Under such circumstances, reciprocal agreements often cover the navigational use of the rivers. For some time, there has been a strong movement afoot to internationalize

234   *SHARP CONTRAST: eroded and noneroded farmland near Maysville, Oklahoma. (Rotkin from Standard Oil Co. [N. J.])*

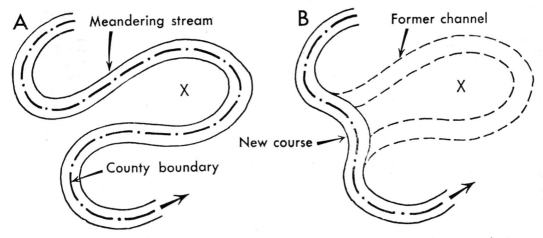

Instance of stream channel designated as a political boundary. After the stream has cut through the meander neck, the land area X lies in a different country.

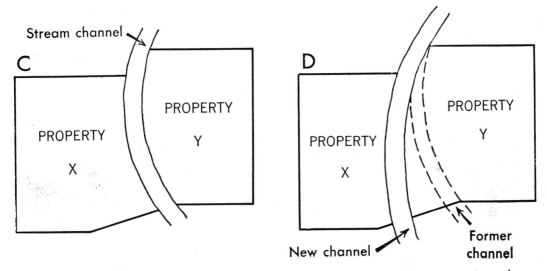

Instance of stream designated as a boundary between two pieces of property. Lateral erosion has resulted in a shifting stream channel: property Y has gained area at the expense of property X.

235 *TWO EXAMPLES of boundary problems created by shifts in position of stream channels.*

rivers like the Rhine and Danube, the idea being to provide a "freedom of the rivers" in much the same sense as "freedom of the seas."

Navigable streams present many other problems, most of which are physical in nature. Dams and reservoirs are often necessary to insure a sufficient and steady flow; if the dams are located in navigable sections, they must be equipped with expensive locks to allow the passage of vessels (Fig. 236). Channels must be dredged and marked and, usually, artificial embankments must be con-

236

TOWBOAT and barges "locking through" Fort Loudoun Dam, one of the several dams on the Tennessee River. (Tennessee Valley Authority)

structed to prevent shifting of channels. Interestingly enough, portions of some rivers, the Mississippi for example, in its main channel through the delta, are made to dredge themselves. Jetties (Fig. 237) force the flow of the river through narrower channels, thus increasing the velocity of the water and, hence, its ability to move its load. The result is that the river literally sweeps its bed clean.

POLLUTION. Countless streams formerly clean and attractive have already been polluted by man. This results not merely from increased loads of sediment coming from man-induced erosion of the land, but also results from dumping sewage, trash, and industrial wastes into the nearest convenient stream. The problem has become so serious and widespread that laws to prevent pollution of streams have been adopted in many regions. Such laws are, however, too few in number, and they are honored more in the breach than in the practice. Until industrial wastes and domestic sewage are properly treated, far too many of our streams will continue to resemble moving cesspools.

Underground Water

Some of the dangers already noted apply to waters within the earth as well as those on the surface. The destruction of natural vegetation cover, abnormal erosion, and rapid water loss affect the amount and character of ground water as well as the behavior and nature of streams. When surface waters are not conserved, it is only a short time before the water table is lowered and springs and wells diminish or dry up entirely. Indiscriminate pumping also may drain the ground water reserves and lower the water table to the point where pumping costs are prohibitive (Fig. 238). This can happen even in humid areas. In parts of Ohio, the uses of water from the ground have become so heavy and numerous that industrial expansion is severely handicapped. This is no reflection of climate, for the annual rainfall has not changed. What it does reflect is a tremendous withdrawal of water from the ground, followed by discharge of that water into streams which carry it rapidly out of the area. What

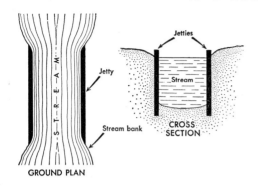

237 *USE OF jetties to confine stream flow within narrower bounds, thus increasing the velocity of the water and enabling it to "sweep its bed."*

is seemingly needed is the dumping of used water onto broad "spreading grounds" where it will have an opportunity to sink back into the earth to replenish underground reserves. Another problem is the pollution of ground water. The same practices and lack of foresight which cause stream pollution are apt to render ground water unpalatable and unsafe. This is particularly true in karst regions where water can run "unfiltered" in myriad solution channels.

● ●

CHAPTER OUTLINE

The earth's waters

Uses of water
  Domestic
  Industrial
  Irrigational
  Power
  Transportation
  Food and raw materials
  Recreation
Water bodies
  Oceans and seas
    Names and terms
    Ocean bottoms and depths
    Water movements
    Ice conditions
  Lakes

    The Great Lakes
    Dry lakes
  Streams
    Humid-land streams
      Great rivers
      Stream patterns
      Water power
    Streams in dry lands
  Ground water
    Soil moisture
    Springs and wells
      Springs
      Ordinary wells
      Artesian wells
Some water problems
  Oceans
  Streams
    Floods
    Soil erosion
    Shifting courses
    Water rights
    Navigation
    Pollution
  Underground water

REVIEW QUESTIONS

1. What "waters" are included in the term "the earth's waters"?
2. List the major uses of water.
3. Why is per capita consumption of water so much greater in urban than in rural areas?
4. Explain the statement, "Heavy use of water for irrigation is not limited to arid and semi-arid regions."
5. What is meant by saying that water bodies should be considered three-dimensionally?
6. What is the landform nature of ocean bottoms?
7. Distinguish between currents, tidal waves, and tsunami.
8. Discuss the general circulation of major ocean currents. Include causes in the discussion.
9. What would be some of the direct and indirect results if ocean currents moved counterclockwise in the Northern Hemisphere and clockwise in the Southern Hemisphere?
10. Why does the surface of the Arctic Ocean not freeze completely from shore to shore?
11. In what portions of the world are lakes most numerous? Why?

12. Explain the statement, ". . . conditions in nature work against the formation or long-continued preservation of any considerable number of lakes."

13. Determine as many possible origins of lakes or lake regions as you can.

14. What are the component parts, including natural links or connections, of the Great Lakes?

15. Give a number of examples to show relationships between settlements (and spread of settlement) and water features of different sorts.

16. Show that stream patterns affect the distributional pattern of other geographic features.

17. Describe the nature and explain the origin of a trellis drainage pattern.

18. Distinguish between "single-purpose" and "multiple-purpose" control of rivers and drainage basins on the part of man.

19. How do you account for flood damage in arid regions?

20. Distinguish between gravitational, hygroscopic, and capillary water.

21. Why is it that many areas which developed on the basis of artesian water are now suffering water shortages?

22. Certain amounts or degrees of flooding are

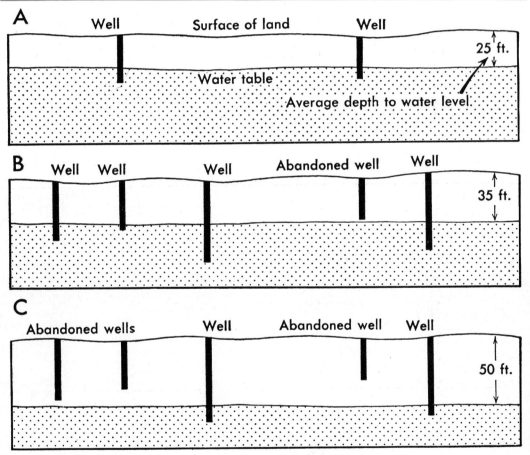

238 WHAT OFTEN *happens in an area where withdrawal of ground water exceeds natural replenishment. In* (A) *water table is little affected by wells. In* (B) *there are too many wells: withdrawal exceeds natural replenishments; water table has "dropped" slightly. In* (C) *water table has been greatly lowered: most wells are abandoned: pumping costs are very high for wells still in operation. The time lapse between* (A) *and* (C) *was approximately 25 years.*

naturally common to river valleys. What are some of the major reasons for abnormal flooding in areas inhabited by man?

23. What are some of the human implications of shifting stream courses?

24. Give a definite example of a dispute over the control and use of water.

25. What is the nature and degree of seriousness of water pollution in the area in which you live? What are the remedies?

26. Why is it that problems of water supply are serious in many areas of continuously humid climate?

27. The statement, "The world is running out of water," is commonly read and heard today. Is there justification for this statement? How can a world with so much water in it "run out of water"?

SOME SUGGESTED REFERENCES

Bird, John A., *Western Ground Waters and Food Production,* U. S. Department of Agriculture, Miscellaneous Publication No. 504, 1942. A simply written, illustrated pamphlet emphasizing ground water and its use; includes a section on ground water law.

The Colorado River, U. S. Department of the Interior, 1946. An extensive report on the development and use of Colorado River water for irrigation, power, etc.; many maps and photographs.

The Columbia River, U. S. Department of the Interior, 1947. Same type of report as that noted directly above.

Davis, Darrell H., *The Earth and Man: A Human Geography,* 2nd ed., Macmillan, 1948. An introductory college textbook with emphasis on man and his activities in different environments; see especially Chapters 17 through 21, and Chapter 25, which discuss waterways, power, irrigation, water supply, and oceans and coasts.

Finch, Vernor C., and Trewartha, Glenn T., *Elements of Geography: Physical and Cultural,* 3rd ed., McGraw-Hill, 1949. See Chapter 22 of this textbook.

Freeman, Otis W., and Raup, Hallock F., *Essentials of Geography,* McGraw-Hill, 1949. See Chapters 15, 16, and 20 of this introductory college text.

Hatcher, Harlan, *The Greak Lakes,* Oxford University Press, 1944. Discovery, history, and development of the Great Lakes from the days of the canoe and bateau to the days of the great freighters.

Headwaters Control and Use, U. S. Soil Conservation Service and others, U. S. Government Printing Office, 1937. A well-illustrated and only partially technical treatment of water behavior and control in headwater areas of different sorts.

Irrigation Agriculture in the West, U. S. Department of Agriculture, Miscellaneous Publication No. 670, 1948. A simply written booklet dealing with several aspects of water supply and land use in the 17 western states.

Parkins, Almon E., and Whitaker, J. Russell, editors, *Our National Resources and Their Conservation,* John Wiley and Sons, Inc., 1939. A standard textbook on resources and their use; see Chapters 12 through 15 which discuss water supply, power, waterways, and floods.

Person, H. S., *Little Waters,* U. S. Government Printing Office, 1936. A small, illustrated booklet which presents in simple style many aspects of water in relation to man's use of the land.

Rivers of America Series, Rinehart. For example, Havighurst, Walter, *The Upper Mississippi,* Rinehart, 1944. A popular treatment of the upper part of the Mississippi River, including its role in human affairs.

Sverdrup, H. U.; Johnson, Martin W.; and Fleming, Richard H., *The Oceans: Their Physics, Chemistry, and General Biology,* Prentice-Hall, 1942. A comprehensive technical treatment of the oceans; see especially Chapters 2, 11, 14, 15, and 19 which discuss ocean basins, currents, waves and tides, water masses, and organic production in the sea.

Thoreau, Henry D., *Walden: or Life in the Woods,* Dodd, Mead and Co., 1946. An American classic in an illustrated edition; contains many references to water and water behavior, especially in connection with Walden Pond itself.

Twain, Mark, *Life on the Mississippi,* any edition. Another American classic; deals with a great river and ways of life on its surface and along its shores in the "early days."

von Engeln, Oskar D., *Geomorphology: Systematic and Regional,* Macmillan, 1942. See especially Chapter 3 of this textbook on landforms and landform genesis.

239 *THE MARKS of intelligent selective logging are hardly visible in this ponderosa pine forest of the Pacific Northwest. Mt. St. Helens is in the background. (Eagle from Standard Oil Co. [N. J.])*

CHAPTER 14

Natural Vegetation and Animal Life

Outstanding variety in the human habitat is created by differences of vegetation cover from place to place. A forest landscape is distinctive, whether the land is flat or gently rolling, whether it is hilly or even mountainous. Lands with grassy cover look and are different from similar surfaces that are forested or barren. Woodland which is green throughout the year contrasts vividly with an area in which the trees lose their leaves during one season. From such easily observed characteristics comes some realization of the greater or lesser habitat value to man of one area as compared with another. For example, the forests of the Amazon Basin look and are different from those of Mediterranean Europe. When the Portuguese and Spanish encountered the Amazon forest during their exploration and colonization of South America, they found it to be a barrier which, to them, proved insurmountable. It was nothing like the forests they knew and used to their advantage in the Iberian Peninsula. For them, the Amazon forest had no habitat value.

Animal life, too, presents a further measure of habitat value. On the East African Plateau, the big game country, wild animals are an ever-present hazard both to human life and to property. Similarly, in Panama, the yellow-fever mosquito created an inhospitable and dangerous habitat for man. Not until this insect pest was destroyed was it possible to construct the canal which links the Pacific with the Atlantic. Conversely, use of the northern forested area of Canada or of northeastern European Russia depends in large part upon the relatively dense population of fur-bearing animals.

Native vegetation cover and animal life were originally the direct bases for all human existence. They supplied the essentials of food and clothing. Both have been profoundly altered by human use of the land, particularly where men have congregated in large numbers. Certain plants provide food, others supply raw materials for commerce and industry, and some simply beautify the setting in which men live. Others have been removed. In densely populated regions, the selected few that have been retained or introduced from other areas may be only a pitiful reminder of a once luxuriant variety. Similarly, animals have been tamed to provide food, raw materials, labor, and even companionship. Others have been killed off, greatly reduced in numbers, or forced to migrate to areas less desired by man.

Where man's inroads have not been extensive, plants and animals stand as visible and direct indicators of the physical equipment of an area for human living. This is more obvious in the instance of vegetation, for plants are immobile. Their whole nature is determined by the combination of elements of the setting in the specific place in which they grow. Temperature and moisture, qualities of soil, and even details of surface all restrict the type of vegetation, so that actually

TYPICAL steppe, with its short grass vegetation on the High Plains of Kansas. The circular depression in the foreground is a buffalo wallow. Note the wheel tracks stretching straight across the surface to the buildings in the background. (W. D. Johnson from U. S. Geological Survey)

the plant cover is the observable result of the combination of all.

Yet, in the broadest sense, climate exerts the principal influence on natural vegetation. Over large areas, the particular kind of plants is determined largely by temperature and moisture, both of which are primarily elements of climate. In more restricted areas, the nature of the soil may be an effective control. While a climate may be suitable for one characteristic plant cover, the soil may be so porous or so infertile as to prevent the growth of the expected types and to allow the growth of others in their stead. For example, a Semiarid (BS) climate has, in general, enough precipitation to support a continuous cover of grasses though not enough for trees. Yet, there are many areas of Semiarid (BS) climate where the soil is so porous that it retains too little of the moisture which falls upon it to support even grass. In such places, desert plants take over. The vegetation is thus *edaphically* (of or pertaining to the soil) rather than climatically determined.

Animals are less accurate indicators of the physical equipment of an area for most of them can move about beyond the confines of any one small region for the food and water necessary to them. Animals therefore provide only an approximate measure of the quality of the setting. Our primary concern, then, is the world distribution of natural vegetation. This offers not only the most obvious clue to essential differences among habitats, but also a gauge of their desirability for human living.

MAJOR CATEGORIES OF NATURAL VEGETATION AND ANIMAL LIFE

Plant Associations

From a world-wide viewpoint, there are three main plant associations. These are *forest, grassland,* and *desert* (Figs. 239, 240, and 241). The number of specific plants which make up any one of these associations is almost infinite. However, it is on the dominant type of vegetation rather than on individual plants that attention must be focused when the world pattern is the desired end. To be sure, trees are the dominant plants in a forest association, but there are likewise many woody shrubs, grasses, and other ground-covering forms included in the association. Grassland is characterized, as the name implies, by grasses and other nonwoody plants, but there are included numbers of shrubs and even some trees. Similarly, desert associations often include many of the grasses and occa-

240B

A MAN-MADE prairie. Second-year stand of a grass similar to the original prairie cover, near Mankato, Kansas. (U. S. Department of Agriculture)

sionally a few trees, but these are the exception rather than the rule.

Vegetation cover in some areas appears to be neither forest, grassland, nor desert. It consists of a thicketlike growth of low, woody plants, like the *chaparral* of California. Detailed studies would, of course, recognize in this type of cover a distinct association, *scrub* or *shrub*. But on a world scale, the common practice is to include this kind of vegetation within the forest association and to refer to it as *scrub forest*.

FOREST CHARACTERISTICS. The larger plants which make up the forest association demand more moisture than those of either grassland or desert. Water must be present in the soil in large enough amounts to satisfy the needs of the trees. This necessitates relatively large amounts of precipitation. Likewise, water must be present in the soil in a liquid state, rather than frozen, so that the plant roots may make use of it.

Plant growth generally ceases when air temperature drops below 42° F. Where temperatures that low or lower persist throughout most of the year, forest is usually lacking, either because the amount of precipitation common to areas of continued low temperature is too little for tree growth, or because the growth period (above 42° F.) is too short.

Variations in moisture and temperature are reflected in certain outstanding differences among trees. Some trees retain most of their foliage at all times. They do drop leaves, but only one by one and never all at the same time. Such trees are known as *evergreens*. In contrast to these, there are other trees that lose all of their leaves at one season and acquire new ones at another season. Trees which show this seasonal rhythm are known as *deciduous* trees.

Where temperatures are always high and precipitation is heavy throughout the year, trees are evergreen, like the live oak and the red bay in the Gulf Coast region of the United States. Where there is a deficiency of moisture for an appreciable part of the year, either through lack of precipitation or through lowering of temperature so that the moisture is ice-locked and hence not available to the plant roots, a period of rest from growth is introduced into the annual cycle. Under these conditions, trees may be deciduous, like the maples, elms, and hickories of northeastern United States.

Though the existence of a period of rest from growth may induce the deciduous habit just described, plant structures may be such as to make possible the retention of foliage despite periodic lack of moisture. Reaction to dryness is often indicated by leaf form. A tree may be either *needleleaf,* like the pine, having leaves that are very narrow in proportion to their length, or *broadleaf,* like the maple, having leaves that are relatively wide in proportion to their length. Most needleleaf trees lose and add leaves regardless of the season, but they do not lose all of their leaves at any one time. Thus, they are evergreens. Broadleaf trees may be either evergreen or deciduous.

The more common needleleaf trees develop their fruit in the form of woody cones. They are, therefore, commonly referred to as *conifers* or *coniferous trees.*

On the basis of the characteristics described above, four main kinds of trees may be distinguished. These are: broadleaf evergreen, broadleaf deciduous, needleleaf evergreen, and needleleaf deciduous. There are whole forests dominated by each of the first three types. For example, the forests in areas of Tropical Rainforest (Af) climate are made up predominantly of broadleaf evergreen trees; those in areas of Humid Continental climate with hot summers (Dfa and Dwa) of broadleaf deciduous trees; and those in areas of Subarctic (Dfc and Dfd) climate, of needleleaf evergreens. But trees of the fourth type, needleleaf deciduous, do not commonly occur as a distinct forest type. Needleleaf deciduous trees, like the larch, occur rather as individuals within forests dominated by other kinds of trees.

GRASSLAND CHARACTERISTICS. Grassland (Fig. 240) has typically a smooth cover of vegetation only occasionally interrupted by isolated trees. In some places, low woody plants are intermixed with the grass, but nowhere are they so numerous as to dominate. The grasses vary in height from a few inches to several feet, depending largely upon the climate and soil. Most of the individual plants are *perennials;* that is, they continue their growth from year to year. A few of them are *annuals* that complete their life cycle during a single growth season, but leave seeds which reproduce the cycle the next season.

Grass needs less moisture than trees do; hence it forms the normal vegetation in drier parts of the world. But, as dryness increases, as along the boundary between the Semiarid (BS) and Arid (BW) climates, grassland gives way to desert vegetation.

DESERT CHARACTERISTICS. In contrast to forests and grasslands, the vegetation of the deserts, both the deserts of dryness (Fig. 241A) and those of continued cold, is relatively light or almost entirely lacking. There is no continuous cover like that formed by the grasses and there is no close crowding of plants as in most forests. Yet the desert, except for the icy wastes of the Arctic and Antarctic, is seldom without some vegetation. Very little of the world's land area is completely barren. An absolutely bare, sandy waste—the popular concept of a desert—is infrequently encountered. To be sure, there are some areas where sand and rock seem to exist without any plant cover, but close examination normally reveals the presence of at least a few specially adapted plants. Individual plants are widely scattered and many of them are dormant throughout the greater part of the year, but, following one of the irregular rains which characterize desert regions, the barrenness is soon dispelled. Plants in profusion burst into active life, hurrying to complete the growth cycle while moisture is available.

All the plants in the desert association are *xerophytic;* that is, they are plants that are structurally adapted to a limited supply of water. Both *perennials* whose growth period may be short or even intermittent and *annuals* that are able to complete their cycle quickly are included. Particularly striking are the many *succulents,* or watery-tissued forms, like the cactus, capable of storing moisture for long periods of dryness.

Included within the desert association are the *tundras* (Fig. 241B) which fringe the poleward edges of the forest association. Tundra is the name applied to the particular group of plants like mosses, lichens, sedges, some

241A

TUNDRA on the Colville River Delta in Northern Alaska. Note the flowering plants (marsh marigold) which fringe the small pond in the foreground while ice still covers the larger pond in the background. (Urban C. Nelson from U. S. Fish and Wildlife Service)

grasses and bushes, and even stunted trees that exist where continued low temperatures produce extremely adverse conditions of growth. It should be noted that the word tundra is often used to mean the area where this kind of vegetation is found as well as the vegetation association itself. During most of the year, water is present only in the form of ice and is hence not available to the plants. During the very short period of temperatures high enough to allow plant growth, there is usually an excess of water resulting primarily from poor drainage and low evaporation. Slopes are commonly very gentle in tundra regions and this hinders rapid surface drainage; temperatures are rarely high enough for a sufficiently long period to bring about thawing of the subsoil so that underground drainage is impeded. Excessive water about the plant roots retards the growth processes with much the same result as too little water. Though for different reasons from those applicable in the dry deserts, most of the individual plants which make up the tundra vegetation, or *cold desert*, are xerophytic. It is mainly for this reason that tundra is classed as part of the desert association.

Natural Vegetation Types

The major plant associations are composed of distinctive *types,* or minor associations, indicated in Table 15. Each type will be characterized and its distribution outlined later in this chapter.

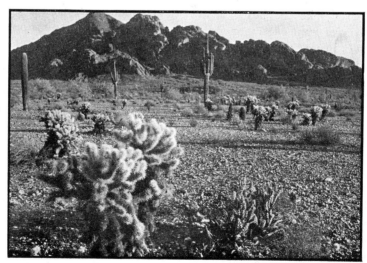

241B

DESERT vegetation near Phoenix, Arizona. (Trans-World Airlines)

Table 15 NATURAL VEGETATION TYPES

I. Forest association
  A. Tropical forests
    1. Tropical rainforest or selva
    2. Tropical semideciduous or monsoon forest
    3. Tropical scrub or thorn forest
  B. Middle and high latitude forests
    1. Mediterranean scrub forest
    2. Broadleaf and mixed broadleaf-conifer forest
    3. Coniferous forest
II. Grassland association
  A. Tropical grassland or savanna
  B. Middle latitude grasslands
    1. Steppe
    2. Prairie
III. Desert association
  A. Desert shrub and barren desert
  B. Tundra

Within mountainous regions, there is usually a combination of several of the vegetation types listed in Table 15. The expression *mountain vegetation* is used to convey this idea despite the fact that the combination changes from one mountain area to another. In a sense, mountain vegetation forms an added type.

Native Animal Types

As has been previously suggested, any attempt at fixing exactly the distribution of native animal life is seriously handicapped by its mobility. Though animals are usually limited to certain rather broad ranges within which they find the necessities of life, most of them do not remain fixed in any one small region. Their distribution can be suggested only roughly as a sort of adjunct to that of natural vegetation.

Most animals can be divided broadly into two main groups: the *herbivores* and the *carnivores*. Herbivores, or herbivorous animals, are those that secure their food directly from plants. Ground animals of small size like the rabbit, larger ones like the deer, and tree-living (*arboreal*) forms like the monkey are plant-eating animals, herbivores. It is obvious that they must live where the plants upon which they depend for food grow. A monkey would find it difficult to live in a grassland just as a horse would in a desert. Often, also, animal distribution is limited directly by climate. While the monkey is an arboreal animal, he would be unable to withstand the rigors of a Subarctic (Dfc) climate even though that climate normally is a forest-producing one. In a general way, there is a certain degree of correspondence of the pattern of animal distribution to that of vegetation types. For example, the giraffe, as a native animal, is seldom found outside tropical grasslands, or *savannas*. This is not to say that the giraffe is common in *all* savannas.

The flesh-eating animals, or carnivores, like lions, tigers, and wolves, depend upon herbivores for their food supply. Consequently, the distribution of carnivores mirrors not only that of the herbivores, but, indirectly, that of the natural vegetation types.

Many animals are *omnivorous;* that is, they eat both plants and other animals. Frequently, the struggle for adequate food makes them omnivores; when there is a plentiful food supply, they are entirely herbivorous or entirely carnivorous. Most of our domestic animals are omnivorous, but, in their original wild state, this was true only under great stress. The dog may prefer meat; he belongs to the same general group as the wolf. Yet more often than not, the dog is fed items which are made from plant products; seldom does he have an entire meat diet.

Birds, insects, and reptiles all add their bit to the various habitats of the world's land surface; so do fish and other water-living forms to the earth's waters. Only loosely is there a correlation between their distribution and that of certain vegetation types for, like other animals, they are mobile. The migration of many of the northern forest animals poleward onto the tundra during the summer and back again to the forest during the winter is paralleled by the seasonal migration of many birds. The appearance of the robin in New England in early spring gives indication that the long winter is over, just as a high, southward flight of geese in perfect V formation on a snappy, clear fall morning presages the coming of winter. The furious buzz of the June bug against the screen is an indicator of early summer just as is the stinging attack of the mosquito or the irritation engendered by the ubiquitous housefly. In climates without great seasonal change, the presence of many of these animals is a permanent part of the physical scene; where seasonal change is noticeable, the animals come and go.

VEGETATION TYPES AND THEIR DISTRIBUTION

Tropical Forests

One of the heavier forest covers to be found anywhere in the world exists in the regions of Tropical Rainforest (Af) climate. Constant heavy precipitation and constantly high temperatures, the two characteristics of the Tropical Rainforest (Af) climate, provide the condition for a vast "natural greenhouse" in which the forest is evergreen and broadleaf. As one proceeds away from the regions of Tropical Rainforest (Af) climate through Tropical Monsoon (Am) and Savanna (Aw) zones, the optimum conditions for forest development vanish. Increased prominence of the dry season over the rainy season soon removes the possibility of broadleaf evergreen

forest. Smaller and smaller amounts of precipitation compel a thinning of the forest and a decrease in the size of the individual plants until finally a limit is reached beyond which it is too dry for trees. Even in sufficiently wet areas, the existence of definite cool and hot seasons beyond the margins of the Tropical Moist (A) climates brings about a change in species which make up the forest so that the whole aspect is altered. In such areas, the tropical forest is supplanted by a middle latitude forest.

Three major forest types may be recognized in tropical regions. Transition from one to another is gradual and often the types are intermingled along wide zones rather than cut off sharply. Nevertheless, marked distinctions set them apart from one another. The three specific types of tropical forest are *tropical rainforest, tropical semideciduous forest,* and *tropical scrub forest.* These are often called *selva, monsoon forest,* and *thorn forest,* respectively. In addition to the major types, there are three associated secondary ones. These are *mangrove, jungle,* and *galeria forest.* Each of the three major types will be treated separately while the secondary types, usually occurring in such small areas as not to be possible of illustration on world maps of the scale used in this book, will be treated only in reference to the others.

TROPICAL RAINFOREST OR SELVA. Selva is the most luxuriant of tropical forest types (Fig. 52). From the air, it resembles a turbulent green sea. Tall trees crowd so closely together that their crowns form a dense irregular canopy through which very little sunlight penetrates to the ground. On close examination, the crowns are seen to be arranged in layers or stories. The lowest lies at about seventy-five feet above the ground, the second at about one hundred feet. Above that second story extend the upper trunks, branches, and foliage of the forest giants rising to one hundred and twenty-five feet or more. Yet, except where the forest has been removed, the canopy of leaves is unbroken. As a result, the interior of the forest is dark and the air in it is still and moist. Trunks rise straight and branchless to the crowns, which are always green, for water is continuously available to the tree roots. So plentiful is the moisture supply that the trees are usually shallow rooted and they depend largely on buttresslike ridges at the base of the trunks for their support. The trees are broadleaf hardwoods and, though a tremendous number of species is included, rarely are there sizable stands of any one species. Where the forest is undisturbed by man, it is unusual to find more than three or more individuals of any one species in an acre of forest.

Though the forest is evergreen, there is constant loss of leaves from each tree throughout the year. On the tree, there is equally constant leaf replacement. Thus, a steady supply of dead and decaying matter falls to the forest floor and it might be expected that litter would accumulate in large amounts. However, the rapidity of decay under such hot, moist conditions as prevail within the forest and the activities of insects like termites and wood beetles are so great as to remove most of the material almost as it falls. Consequently, the floor of the selva is remarkably clean. In addition, the absence of sunlight prevents the growth of much underbrush. Movement through the forest is, therefore, little restricted.

Characteristic also of the selva is the unusually large number of *epiphytes* and *parasites*. Epiphytes grow on other plants, but do not secure their food from them; parasites grow on and do secure their food directly from other plants. In great profusion, both sorts hang ropelike from the tree crowns or jut out from the trunks. Many of them are brilliantly flowering, like the orchids, which are epiphytes. Together with the density of the trees, they convey the impression of superabundant plant life. This kind of forest is often incorrectly called jungle.

Jungle is dense undergrowth or second growth in tropical forest areas. It occurs only where sunlight can penetrate to the forest floor. In most selva, the shading of the forest floor is so complete that only removal of the tree crowns will admit the sunlight necessary for heavy ground-plant growth. This occurs characteristically in three kinds of places.

Where man clears the forest or where lightning strikes and burns it, dormant plant seeds are quick to germinate and the struggle toward the sun begins. Thousands of plants in a tangled thicket vie with each other for the space left by the fallen giants which preceded them. This is ordinarily *dry jungle* (Fig. 51), so called because the plants rise from relatively dry and firm ground. Eventually, the faster growing and larger specimens crowd out the others and the spot of jungle disappears.

The second characteristic location of jungle is on steeply sloping land where the sun's rays can penetrate between the tree trunks and thus come to the forest floor. This is also dry jungle. In such a location, it is often more permanent than that which springs up in clearings, for the trunks of the trees provide less shade than do interlocked crowns.

The third location of jungle is in the wet spots of the tropical forests: along the banks of streams too wide to be completely shaded by the crowns of the forest giants on either side, on the flood plains of mature and old age rivers, on shelving lake shores, or near the seaward edges of low coastal plains. This is the *wet jungle*. The dense tangle of vegetation rises directly from shallow water or from deep mud. It is difficult to tell "where the land begins and the water leaves off." Myriads of insects and many reptiles make the wet jungle a place to be avoided. Wet jungle is much more permanent than dry jungle, for the places in which it occurs are usually too moist for most of the tree species found in the selva.

It is the wet jungle which gave rise to the idea of jungle as the usual vegetation type in equatorial regions. Early explorers penetrated the land along great rivers. Their way lay between jungle-fringed banks. Seldom did this jungle stretch back from the river for more than a few hundred yards, but to most explorers attempting to find a route away from the stream, the dense vegetation seemed to continue without end. From this came the inference that jungle persisted throughout in these latitudes. Actually, once the jungle fringe is breached and the forest attained, undergrowth usually becomes relatively light.

Another of the secondary types, *mangrove*, is found where tropical forest comes down to the sea or to a tidal inlet. Mangrove is sometimes spoken of as a kind of wet jungle. It becomes established on very shelving, muddy coasts where there is no strong current and only moderate fluctuations in the level of the sea between high and low tide. At low tide, tripodlike prop roots rise out of the mud flats, the roots of one individual interlocked with those of the next to form a close-knit wall. Well above the place where the roots rise out of the mud, and just above the level of high tide, heavily leafed branches bush out. At high tide, the fringe of green may stand a considerable distance out from the shore. The roots are then entirely covered by water. So thick is the barrier formed by mangrove that sediments brought from the land by the rivers are held close to the shore. A mangrove fringe thus acts as a "land builder" along shelving tropical shores.

Where rivers cut deeply into the land, selva is often confined to valley sides or levees, and lighter forest dominates the interstream spaces. If the band of selva along either bank is narrow, quite distinct from the lighter forest of the lands back from the river, and if the tree crowns meet over the stream, the impression is created of a green tunnel through which the river flows. This type of forest is known as a *galeria* forest. Most commonly it occurs where the river flood plains make moisture available to the trees despite a climatic dry season. In other words, the long stringers of tropical forest which reach into tropical grassland are the ones to which the term galeria is most commonly applied. It is equally applicable, though not so easily noticeable, where narrow bands of selva penetrate into regions clothed with tropical semi-deciduous or tropical scrub forests.

Animal life in the selva is primarily arboreal, or tree-dwelling. Ground animals are few and of small size, for food is difficult to secure on the floor of the forest. There, only myriads of insects add their constant hum to the gloomy, dripping wetness. High above in the crowns of the trees, brilliantly colored birds, monkeys and other similar animals, insects, and reptiles seeking sunshine make up for the quiet of the forest depths. Most of the tree animals are herbivorous, but there are a few small carnivores. Colorful and profuse as this tree life is, it offers relatively little to man as an added resource of the forest.

Selva constitutes one of the most extensive types of forest remaining in the world. Destruction and alteration of it have been great in a few localities, as in Java and in India, but elsewhere little of the selva has been entirely removed. Where clearings have been made, regrowth is rapid unless measures are taken to restrict it. Rubber, cacao, cabinet woods like mahogany and ebony, many gums and resins, and both edible and commercial nuts are all derived from trees native to the selva. Many tropical fruits have local use and some, like the banana, are significant items of world trade. But throughout the selva, there is one great handicap to intensive utilization. The trees of any one species are widely scattered and, unless some device like the creation of an artificial forest similar to those of the Malayan rubber plantations is resorted to, small-scale forest industries cannot operate efficiently or without great cost. In lumbering, for instance, selective logging, rather than "over-all" logging must be practiced. Distance from world markets and from large supplies of labor add materially to the difficulties of exploitation. It is generally suggested by foresters and lumbermen that, with large-scale operations, it is possible to assemble

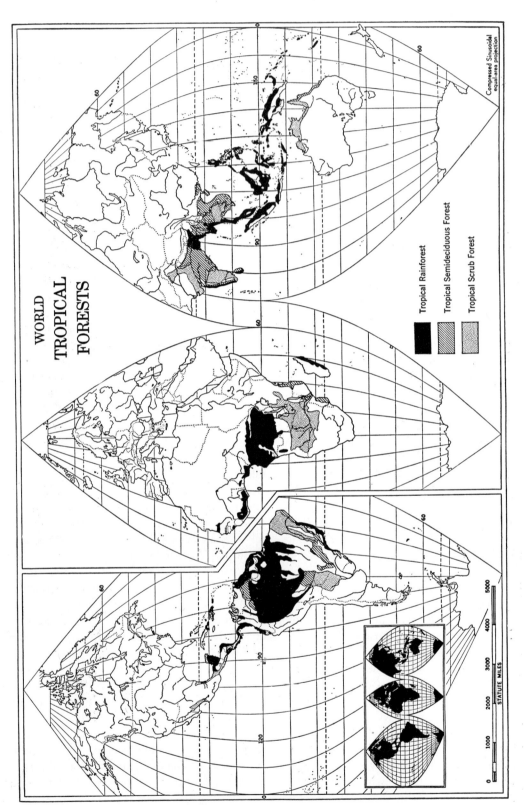

WORLD
TROPICAL
FORESTS

Tropical Rainforest

Tropical Semideciduous Forest

Tropical Scrub Forest

Compressed Sinusoidal
equal-area projection

STATUTE MILES

0   1000   2000   3000   4000   5000

242   *WORLD DISTRIBUTION of tropical forest regions.*

many different kinds of wood instead of carrying on selective logging and thus to exploit tropical forests economically. Despite this suggestion, selva products, except for a few items like Brazil nuts or chicle, an important ingredient of chewing gum, remain luxury goods.

The largest areas of continuous selva occur in South America and in Africa (Fig. 242). Less extensive areas of this type of forest are to be found in Middle America, southeastern Asia, and the East Indies.

There is close correspondence between the distribution of selva and Tropical Rainforest (Af) climate, as can be seen from a comparison of Plates VII and V. Nevertheless, there are certain departures from absolute sameness, like that in Liberia for example. There, the vegetation is selva, but the climate is Tropical Monsoon (Am). Here, even though there is a period of less rain, soil moisture is never insufficient to satisfy the needs of the forest. Minor discrepancies of this sort result from many causes; prominent among them are edaphic factors (factors concerning the soil), lack of numerous long-time climatic observations, and lack of exact information regarding the detailed distribution of vegetation types. Despite such minor discrepancies, the similarity of climate and vegetation patterns on a world scale is pronounced. This applies not only to the selva and Tropical Rainforest (Af) climate, but to all of the natural vegetation types and the climates in which they characteristically occur.

TROPICAL SEMIDECIDUOUS OR MONSOON FOREST. Beyond the limits of Tropical Rainforest (Af) and the wetter portions of Tropical Monsoon (Am) climate, increased severity of the dry season enforces more and more strongly a period of rest in plant growth. The forest becomes lighter, the individual trees more widely spaced, and the low undergrowth heavier. The forest is semideciduous. Pure stands of one species are common, like the teak forests of Burma. The dry season prevents most of the trees from being evergreen.

Some of the trees do retain their foliage, but by far the greater part of the forest is dry and brown throughout the nearly rainless period. Many of the species common to the selva are found likewise in this monsoon forest, but a large number of them that are evergreen in the selva are deciduous in the monsoon forest.

Jungle is more truly typical in monsoon forest than in selva because of the wider spacing of the big trees. As a result, passage throughout this forest is much more difficult than it is through the selva. Only here and there, particularly on low river flood plains or on low-lying coastal strips, is there a sufficient number of broadleaf evergreens so that sunlight is cut off from the forest floor and jungle is thereby eliminated. Mangrove is a characteristic coastal fringe and narrow stringers of galeria point out the river courses across low-lying plains.

Areas of monsoon forest are generally more easily cleared by primitive groups because of the smaller size of the ground plants. Consequently, there are fewer and less extensive areas of it remaining. Commercial operations to recover forest products are easier than they are in the selva for the more frequent stands of one individual species make possible economic utilization of the resource. Among the trees of this forest which are of great commercial significance is teak, which is particularly desirable because of its strength and durability.

Tropical semideciduous forest is generally found in areas of Tropical Monsoon (Am) and in the wetter parts of areas of Savanna (Aw) climate. Its greatest extent is on the continent of Asia (Fig. 242), where it stretches, with some interruption from other vegetation types, from the Western Ghats of India to the northeast coast of Australia. Other areas of tropical semideciduous forest occur in Africa, South America, Middle America, and the West Indies.

TROPICAL SCRUB OR THORN FOREST. As the annual rainfall decreases, and as the dry season becomes longer within areas of Tropical

Moist (A) climate, the forest changes not only to a lighter and an entirely deciduous type, but it even acquires characteristics which are definitely xerophytic. Low-growing trees with thick bark, smaller leaves, and thorns replace those of the semideciduous forest or selva (Fig. 243). Undergrowth increases in density and many thorny plants replace soft-tissued ones. The forest looks almost like scrubby second growth. In some places, it is so scattered and grasses take over so much of the space between trees and bushes that the name forest hardly seems applicable. In other places, a dense tangle of gigantic brambles with many low trees jutting above it seems, during the wet season, to be fully as luxuriant as, though lower than, in the selva, while during the dry season the leafless, thorn-covered branches intertwine to form a brown, impenetrable wall.

Along river flood plains galeria forest makes a break here and there in the scrubbiness of the cover, much of which may justly be called jungle, though of a dry sort. Mangrove forms a characteristic green fringe only infrequently in areas where thorn forest comes to the sea.

In both the tropical semideciduous and the tropical scrub forests, ground animals are numerous. Many large herbivores, like the elephant in Asia and Africa or the giraffe in Africa, live on the margins of these forests where they give way to tropical grasslands. The larger carnivorous forms like the lion and the tiger likewise make the lighter woodland fringes their usual home, migrating with the movements of the herbivores out onto the grasslands and back into the forests. Arboreal animals, birds, insects, and reptiles are even more numerous than in the heaviest selva. The forest-grassland margin in the tropics supports the world's densest remaining native animal population. This is especially true where human beings are few as in central Africa, but even in the heavily peopled regions of Asia, destruction of life and property by animals is so common as to provide a serious handicap to the maintenance of human settlement.

The areas of tropical scrub forest (Fig. 242) lie adjacent to the other types of tropical forest in Africa, Asia, Australia, and South America. The tropical scrub forest is actually a transition belt between the denser forests and the grasslands.

Tropical Grassland or Savanna

Within areas of Savanna (Aw) climate, the total amount of precipitation decreases as one moves poleward toward the dry lands and as one moves from east coasts toward the interior. Decrease in total annual precipitation means less and less moisture for the support of tree cover. At the same time, there is an increase in the length of the dry season which likewise produces conditions unsuited to tree growth. First, as we have seen in the discussion of the tropical forests, the trees acquire the deciduous habit; then they become of smaller stature and are more and more widely scattered. As trees cease to be the dominating forms, first bushes and then grass take over. Eventually, the land is characterized by grass cover rather than by forests. These are the tropical grasslands, or *savannas,* and they extend generally from areas of drier Savanna (Aw) climate well into the regions of Semiarid (BS) climate. Along their drier margins, these grasslands are sometimes spoken of as *tropical steppes.*

The grasses of the savannas (Fig. 244A) are coarse and rank-growing. Most of the plants grow singly, though some grow in clumps or tufts. In either instance, there is considerable bare ground between the plants; no turf or sod is formed. At the beginning of the rainy season, young blades of a dull green color, looking something like oats, shoot up rapidly. As the plants mature, the blades become stiff and sharp-edged; eventually they attain a height of from two to twelve feet. With the coming of the dry season, the grasses dry out to a dusty brownish color and slump to the ground.

243

THESE two views from Brazil suggest the variety to be found in the tropical scrub forest: (Above) a wet phase, known as the campo cerrado, *north of São Patricio in the State of Goiás, Brazil; (below) a dry phase, known as dry* caatinga, *west of Campina Grande in the State of Paraíba, Brazil. (Preston E. James)*

It is almost impossible to set any precise limit to the wet edge of the savanna for the forest dies out irregularly and spottily. Where savanna abuts upon selva, there are grass-covered openings within the forest on one side of the boundary and clumps of selva trees scattered irregularly through the grass on the other side. When clumps of trees are dotted through grassy plains, the cover is called *park grassland*. Where savanna joins tropical semi-deciduous or scrub forest, a scattering of grassy openings within the forest gives way to a dotting of low trees and bushes through the grass, and the cover is known as *scattered tree savanna*. Another common type, espe-cially in Africa, finds the continuity of the grass broken by the occurrence of flat-topped acacia trees (Fig. 244B); this is called either *acacia-tall grass savanna* or *acacia-desert grass savanna,* depending upon the luxuriance of the grass mantle between the trees. In some places, the land is covered by grasses unin-terrupted by either trees or shrubs and the grasses may be higher than a man on horse-back. All gradations from what is almost a forest through to the surface which has no continuous cover are included under the broad heading of savanna or tropical grassland just so long as grass is the dominant plant form. It is a vegetation type which reflects limited available water combined with constantly high temperatures.

Because the savannas provide easily accessible food for many herbivorous animals, both from the grass and from the foliage of the low trees, they generally have a large native animal population. Numerous herbivores obviously attract a large population of carnivores, insects, and reptiles. Grass and brush offer optimum conditions for insect life, especially during the steamy dampness of the rainy season. Termites, mosquitoes, and other insects like the tsetse fly, carrier of the dreaded sleeping sickness, abound. Large numbers of reptiles and birds find ample food in the form of insects and small ground animals.

The animal population of the savannas benefits and increases also because of the absence or infrequence of great numbers of humans. The difficulty, for primitive peoples, of clearing the land of its heavy cover of grass, of overcoming insects or the danger of destruction by carnivorous animals, of adapting to seasonal water deficiency or seasonal flood destruction—all these make the savannas less desirable as human habitats than many other regions of the world. Thus these difficulties help to preserve native animal life.

There are tropical grasslands in Africa, South America, and Australia (Fig. 245), where they abut upon or are enclosed by some type of tropical forest (Plate VII). On

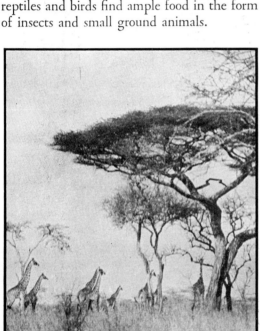

244A

ACACIA-TALL grass savanna on the Serengetti Plains, Africa. (American Museum of Natural History)

244B

THE savanna of northeastern Colombia. Note scattered clumps of trees in the lower, wetter sections. (Collier from Standard Oil Co. [N. J.])

their dry sides, the savannas give way to desert.

Though the vegetation map of the world (Plate VII) shows a sharp boundary between the tropical forests and the tropical grasslands, there are actually many fingers of galeria forest reaching out into the grasslands along the rivers. Similarly, many small clumps of forest trees interrupt the grassland. But both the galeria forests and the clumps are too small to be shown on maps of this scale.

Desert Shrub and Barren Desert

Only xerophytes can find sufficient moisture to form a thin and scattered vegetation in the drier parts of the low latitudes and on into the drier middle latitude areas, the areas of Arid (BW) climate. Some places are even so dry as to prevent the precarious foothold of stunted bushes and bunch grass and, in those places, sand and rock wastes, seemingly interminable, stretch without a vestige of plant cover. Actually, little of the surface is absolutely barren, but only along occasional watercourses or close-grouped about the infrequent springs is the vegetation even temporarily heavy. Over most of the land small patches of short grass or isolated bushes gain a foothold. Most of the time they are brown and lifeless, but when water becomes available, a bright green coloring makes sharp contrast with the soft browns and yellows or the brilliant reds of the rock and sand. Desert vegetation begins where dominant grass cover ends; both on the equatorward and on the poleward sides, grass borders the desert (Plate VII).

Most of the world's deserts extend from tropical west coasts inland and poleward. In all of them, the plants are xerophytic and sparse. The greatest of all deserts is the Sahara, which has its beginning on the west coast of Africa (Fig. 246) and stretches 3,500 miles across the northern part of the continent. Throughout its whole length, it is seldom less than 1,000 miles wide. From the Red Sea, desert continues, with occasional interruptions, into the heart of Asia. Other less extensive deserts exist in Africa, Australia, South America, and North America (Fig. 246).

Middle Latitude Grasslands

Except where it comes to the sea, desert vegetation normally gives way to grass. As along other vegetation boundaries, the change is a gradual one. As one passes to wetter and wetter regions, grass becomes more and more luxuriant until it, in turn, gives way to forest. Through the zone in which grass is dominant, two distinct types, *steppe* and *prairie,* are recognized: *steppe* is a short-grass cover in which individual plants usually form a continuous mat some four to eight inches in height, and *prairie* is a tall-grass cover, equally continuous, but with a height of from one and a half to two feet on the average. The boundary between the two corresponds roughly to that between the Semiarid (BS) climates and the humid types like Humid Subtropical (Cfa) and Humid Continental (Dfa). Most of the steppe lies in areas of Semiarid (BS) climate and most of the prairie, on the drier margins of the humid types, as in the Great Plains of the United States.

STEPPE. The term *steppe* as here used is applied to short-grass areas within the middle latitudes (Fig. 240A). Sometimes, the expression *tropical steppe* is used to describe the drier margins of the savanna. The drier margins of the savanna are characterized by relatively short grass to be sure, yet there are frequently included many scattered xerophytic shrubs and even a few spindly, stunted trees. In this way, the tropical steppe differs radically from the middle latitude short-grass areas. In the latter, the matlike carpet of grassy plants extends mile after mile without

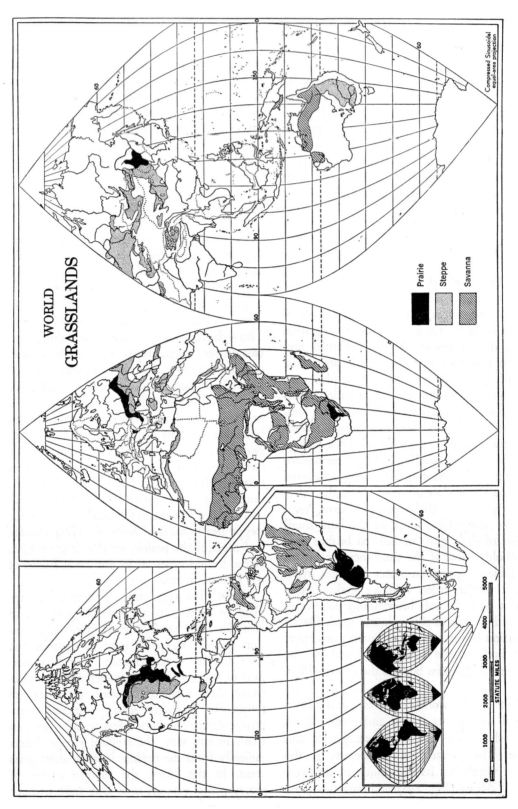

WORLD GRASSLANDS

Prairie
Steppe
Savanna

Compressed Sinusoidal
equal-area projection

STATUTE MILES
0   1000   2000   3000   4000   5000

245   *WORLD DISTRIBUTION of regions that are predominantly grasslands.*

246 *WORLD DISTRIBUTION of regions that are predominantly desert.*

noticeable interruption by trees or shrubs except near some wet spot or along a stream.

Like savanna, steppe once provided a suitable habitat for herbivorous animals, though, since the cover was less heavy, fewer individuals could be supported by it. Carnivorous animals too were originally present, but they were fewer than in savanna. Lower temperatures and a smaller animal population supported a reduced insect and reptile life; for this reason, the steppes were even more habitable for some animals than were the savannas. Floods and droughts were less severe because rainy and dry seasons were less pronounced than in areas of Savanna (Aw) climate or in areas of Semiarid (BS) climate adjacent to Savanna (Aw). But, because of this very desirability, man could and did make greater inroads upon the steppes. Native animals like the American buffalo were killed off or driven out and much of the land was brought under the plow. Except in the African and possibly the Australian steppes, man,

with the plants and animals he has domesticated, now dominates.

The distribution of steppes over the world is shown in Fig. 245. It should be noted that steppes fringe the edges of the deserts in the middle latitudes (Plate VII).

PRAIRIE. Most of the world's prairie has been destroyed either by being plowed up in the advance of agriculture from wetter lands, as in the westward spread of settlement in the United States, or by being invaded by domesticated plants, as in the Argentine Pampa.

Prairie is a distinct type of middle latitude vegetation (Fig. 240B). Its most extensive development was found in the Americas (Fig. 245) before the coming of the white man. Spreading out from the face of the southern Canadian Rocky Mountains, it formed a crescent which extended eastward to Winnipeg and crossed into the United States in North Dakota and western Minnesota. It widened southward to include central Illinois and a small portion of Indiana, and then narrowed to pinch out in central Texas. Outlying bits fringed the Gulf coast of Texas and Louisiana. In South America, the Argentine Pampa and the Argentine Mesopotamia, the whole of Uruguay, and the southernmost part of Brazil formed the world's second largest prairie region. In Africa, a small triangle of prairie occurred in eastern Orange Free State and Basutoland, where it occupied an unusual position as a transition from steppe to savanna (Plate VII). Its occurrence there resulted primarily from lower temperatures induced by the considerable elevation of this portion of the South African Plateau. In Europe, the Hungarian Plain, the Walachian Plain, Bessarabia, and a wedge-shaped strip through south central Russia to the southern end of the Ural Mountains were comparable prairie regions. The only extensive area in Asia was that of the Manchurian Plain. Elsewhere on that continent, the transition from steppe to forest was so rapid or so poorly marked that no true prairie regions can be said to have existed.

Middle and High Latitude Forests

Outward from the desert interiors of the continents, one passes through a definite sequence of vegetation types from desert to grassland to forest. Within the tropics, where the temperatures are constantly high, the sequence is determined almost solely by the availability of water. In the middle and high latitudes, the sequence still depends on the availability of water, but it is further modified by marked seasonal fluctuation of temperature. All of the climates of the middle latitudes aside from the Arid (BW), the Semiarid (BS), and the drier margins of the Moist, Mild Winter (C) and Moist, Severe Winter (D) types have ample available moisture to provide for a forest cover. There is considerable variety in the forest cover, however, due to contrasts in seasonal distribution of precipitation or in severity of the winter. There are three principal forest types in the middle and high latitudes: *Mediterranean scrub forest, broadleaf and mixed broadleaf-coniferous forest,* and *coniferous forest* (Fig. 247).

MEDITERRANEAN SCRUB FOREST. The Mediterranean forest is dominantly broadleaf and evergreen despite the fact that it occurs in areas of pronounced seasonal drought. Mediterranean (Cs) climates have sufficient precipitation to support a forest, but the smaller part of this precipitation comes during the period of highest temperatures, the season when plant growth would ordinarily be expected to be most active. In the tropics, where a dry season prevails, the trees are adapted to the dry season by their deciduous character. In the Mediterranean forest, the plants are not commonly deciduous; they are adapted to drought in a variety of other ways. They are markedly xerophytic. Trees are generally low with gnarled, thick-barked trunks. The root systems spread wide laterally and reach deep into the ground. The leaves are small, thick, and waxy. Evergreen oaks, particularly cork oak, olive, and chestnut are common trees. A mild seasonal rhythm makes the plants look gray or brown, almost blending with the color of the soil from which they grow, during the height of the summer. With the fall comes the sprouting of new leaves and, through the winter, the greenness prevails, reaching its peak with the flowering of early spring. This is gradually succeeded by fading and apparent lifelessness during the summer. Yet, at no time are the plants completely dormant. Then, too, the trees are widely spaced and between them grows a ground cover of stunted trees and low bushes, densely packed in wetter areas and very sparsely sprinkled over the land in the drier regions. This low brush growth is called *maquis* in the European areas and *chaparral* in the California region. There are many sections where maquis takes over entirely and grows so thick as to form an almost hopelessly tangled barrier fit only for the pasturage of a few goats. Grass is not common despite the relatively large spaces between the trees and bushes. Only in the Californian areas of this type of vegetation is there any considerable amount of grass intermixed. Sprinkled through the dominant broadleaf evergreen woodland are many conifers like the Bishop pine and the Monterey cypress of California and the maritime pine in Europe.

247   (Upper left) *A remnant of Mediterranean forest which surrounds the former royal residence at Bussaco, about 125 miles north-northeast of Lisbon, Portugal. Note the patchy distribution of forest and brush on the hills in the background (Casa de Portugal, New York).* (Upper right) *Mid-latitude mixed hardwood forest in Indiana (W. H. Shaffer from U. S. Department of Agriculture).* (Lower left) *Characteristic virgin Douglas fir forest in British Columbia (Eagle from Standard Oil Co. [N. J.]).* (Lower right) *A stand of loblolly pine in the southern pine forest, South Carolina (B. W. Muir from U. S. Department of Agriculture).*

WORLD
MID-LATITUDE
FORESTS

Mediterranean Scrub Forest

Broadleaf and Broadleaf-Conifer Forest

Coniferous Forest

Compressed Sinusoidal
equal-area projection

STATUTE MILES

0   1000   2000   3000   4000   5000

248   *WORLD DISTRIBUTION of Mid-latitude regions which are predominantly forested.*

Most Mediterranean forest regions have been so long settled that the vegetation has been markedly altered by man. The greater part of what remains is the scrub form, maquis or chaparral, rather than true forest. It is possible that these forms do not represent the original cover, but rather a second growth which developed following the destruction of the forest. Whatever changes have been wrought, the Mediterranean forest is unique in that it is still basically a broadleaf evergreen type in an area of seasonal drought.

The distribution of Mediterranean forest is shown in Fig. 248. Of all the major vegetation types, this forest is the least extensive.

BROADLEAF AND MIXED BROADLEAF-CONIFEROUS FOREST. Where the tropical forests come to the margins of the low latitudes east of the dry continental interiors (Plates VII and V), they are succeeded poleward either by broadleafs of a somewhat different type or by a forest of conifers. Climatically, these areas have sufficient moisture for tree growth and the winters are not cold enough to enforce a rest period. The forest is therefore broadleaf evergreen. The individual trees belong to different species than those of the selva; they are less closely crowded, and the forest undergrowth is usually more dense. Epiphytes and parasites are common. The whole forest looks like a miniature selva.

Where poor sandy soils occur, conifers replace the broadleaf evergreens. Here are dense, forest-covered swamps dominated by cypress, which frequently pushes its rounded head to a height of one hundred feet from a buttress-rooted base, in the lowlands (Fig. 249A). Within these swamps, a dense tangle of low bushes and trees, interlocked with epiphytes and parasites, creates a gloom and dankness reminiscent of the wet jungle.

Where the winter season is more severe, as in the higher middle latitudes, the forest changes to one of broadleaf deciduous trees with scattered conifers (Fig. 247). Seasonal rhythm becomes well established with budding, flowering, and leafing in spring, a full greenness in summer, and the brilliant change of leaf color with the coming of the first frost. Then the bare branches of the broadleafs, contrasting sharply with the dark green of the conifers, form the distinctive winter scene. Many of the broadleaf species, the oaks for example, are the same as those which are evergreen farther equatorward, but in this middle latitude forest, the profusion of secondary plants is missing. Undergrowth is usually heavy, but is largely composed of small specimens of the trees which dominate the forest. The accumulation of litter on the forest floor from the seasonal dropping of leaves and the occasional fall of branches and trunks is great. It is not rapidly destroyed for, under the climatic conditions which exist, the rate of decay is slow. Hence, much of it remains to furnish soil-enriching material.

In this woodland, pure stands of broadleafs like maple, oak, and hickory cover areas of better soil while similar stands of conifers like pine, fir, spruce, and hemlock are to be found on poorer soils. Here and there, grassy openings break the continuity of the forest. Edaphically dry localities produce a low bushy cover in which plants like heather form a woody mantle. To these areas the name *heath* is given. Edaphically wet sites are clothed in a similar low vegetation in which many of the ground mosses combine with heather and similar plants to form the *moors* or *moorlands* (Fig. 249B). *Meadows* of tall grass and *canebrakes,* thickets of large jointed-stemmed grasses, edge the rivers where wide flood plains have developed.

Of all the forest types in the world, this mixed broadleaf-coniferous type has suffered the most destruction by man. A broadleaf, deciduous woodland once covered much of the British Isles; today, less than five per cent of it remains or has been replanted. In the eastern and central United States, less than one-tenth of the original forest has been preserved. In China, only vestiges give evidence of the luxuriant forest that once must have spread over the whole land. After the supply

249A

TYPICAL cypress swamp on Weeks Island, Louisiana. (Collier from Standard Oil Co. [N. J.])

249B

MOOR in the Northwest Highlands of Scotland. Hills rise to about 2,700 feet above sea level. Note complete absence of trees. (British Information Services)

of broadleafs was exhausted, scattered conifers provided a convenient source of softwoods. They likewise have largely been removed. The plentiful game and fur-bearing animals that formerly inhabited these regions disappeared with the forest. Indiscriminate killing threatened to exterminate many species and nearly succeeded in doing so before hunting regulations were imposed. Other species migrated to the forests farther poleward.

Last to be attacked of the middle and higher middle latitude forests were the coniferous forests of the southeastern United States (Fig. 247) and the equatorward edge of the northern coniferous forests like those of the Pacific Northwest (Fig. 239) or those of Sweden and Finland. This is less through man's design

than through the distance of the forests from densely settled regions which demand their products.

Ruthless destruction has left a host of problems for man to solve. One of the greatest of these is soil erosion. Forest removal makes little, if any, change in precipitation; yet more moisture is available as an agent of erosion. Less moisture filters into bare soil than into forest-covered soil; runoff is thus increased by forest removal. Gullying and sheet erosion produce surfaces unfit for cultivation where remedial measures are not taken, and too often such measures are taken only too late. A large proportion of the rainfall flows over the surface of the ground to the streams, carrying with it an increased load of sediment. Formerly ample stream channels can

250

A MUSKEG-fringed pond in the northern coniferous forest. Stunted trees rise out of a water-logged mat of grassy and bushy vegetation which is encroaching on the pond and which will eventually fill it. (E. A. Preble from U. S. Fish and Wildlife Service)

no longer handle flood loads and control works are necessary to preserve the valley lands from destruction. This is only a suggestion, all that can here be made, of the significance of widespread forest removal. Some other problems growing out of forest removal will be mentioned in the discussion of lumbering in Chapter 26.

The world distribution of broadleaf and mixed broadleaf-coniferous forest areas is shown in Fig. 248. The main Northern Hemisphere areas correspond roughly to regions of high population density. It is within these areas that forest removal has been greatest.

CONIFEROUS FOREST. Mixed forest continues poleward approximately to the boundary between Humid Continental climate with hot summers (Dfa) and that with warm summers (Dfb) (Plates VII and V). There, a coniferous forest takes over. This high latitude forest is ordinarily called the *boreal forest* or *taiga* (Fig. 250). In these latitudes, increased coolness and shortness of the growing season provide a climatic environment in which few of the hardwoods thrive. Some of the broadleafs like birch, poplar, alder, and willow are numerous, but the great bulk of the trees are needleleafs. Needleleaf trees like pine, cedar, spruce, hemlock, and fir do not grow more satisfactorily in this setting because it is ideal for them; rather they dominate because the hardwoods are less well adapted and therefore provide less competition. The forest is tall, dark green, and close-packed along its equatorward margin, but it becomes more and more stunted and scattered as its poleward edge is approached. Frequently, there are extensive swampy interruptions in which tamarack, cedar, and spruce dominate, or in which excess of water produces a quaking bog of low-growing, leathery-leafed bushes, mosses, and grasses which form a spongy mattress between stunted trees. This is the northern *muskeg* (Fig. 250). In some sections, as in Siberia, the amount of precipitation is so slight as to rule out forest as a complete cover. In such places, steppelike grass often extends over wide areas between thin, scattered patches of conifers. Also, in regions of pronounced glacial scour, as in the Laurentian Shield, extensive and numerous outcrops of bedrock as well as many glacial ponds and marshes make the northern forest a very patchy affair. Where the original cover has been removed, broadleaf deciduous trees are most numerous in the second growth. Low, thin-trunked saplings rising from a thicket of stunted brush form an almost useless covering which the conifers replace very slowly.

In addition to the taiga, there is one dominantly coniferous forest which should be noted. It is found on the margins of the low latitudes in southeastern United States (Fig. 247). It differs markedly from the taiga for it is a sparse woodland of pine almost unmixed with broadleafs. Tall, thin trunks rise unbranching to light, spreading crowns from a sparsely covered forest floor. Undergrowth is light; only here and there in small areas of good soil is there a heavy tangle of deciduous bushes to interrupt a scanty ground cover of grass.

The native animal life of the boreal forests is probably more abundant than that of any middle latitude forest. Streams, lakes, and ponds support a varied fish life represented by such species as bass, pike, pickerel, muskelunge, and trout. In the forest itself are many animals both large and small. Common examples, as in the Canadian taiga, are moose, caribou, deer, bear, wolf, fox, beaver, mink, marten, muskrat, weasel, and rabbit. In addition, there are many birds such as loons, geese, ducks, partridge, owls, song sparrows, and chickadees. Some of the wild life is migratory; caribou move into the protecting forest by winter and northward onto the tundra in summer; ducks and geese spend their winters in warmer climates far to the south, returning to the northern forest in summer. However, most of the animals remain in the taiga the year around.

Any mention of native animals should include insects, more particularly flies and mosquitoes. Though short-lived because of the long season of cold, they constitute a scourge to man and beast alike during the short summers. They do not carry diseases like their counterparts in warmer lands—one need have no fear of malaria or yellow fever—but their bites and stings are a severe trial. It has been said that the great drawback to life in the taiga is not the short summer, nor the long bitter cold winter, but the flies and mosquitoes.

Wild animal life is a major resource of the boreal forest except in scattered farming and mining localities. From the forest have come, and still do come, many prime pelts to the great fur markets of Europe and North America. As a wood resource, the boreal forest is less valuable than is commonly supposed. Its patchy and broken distribution and the small size of most of the trees mean that the total board-footage is comparatively small. Only on the warmer margin, where trees are larger and more easily accessible, does the forest furnish much lumber. As a pulpwood resource, however, the boreal forest offers much greater possibility.

Extensive coniferous forest is limited to Northern Hemisphere areas (Fig. 251). Taiga occurs only in regions of Moist, Severe Winter (D) climate, and it will be remembered that Moist, Severe Winter (D) climates are developed only in the Northern Hemisphere. The Southern coniferous forest of the United States is essentially edaphically determined and has no true counterpart in the southern continents.

Tundra

North of the boreal forests, tundra forms the final fringe (Fig. 251). Since the tundra is of such little significance to man, no distinction of variety is made on the vegetation map. Near the forest margin, it is heavier than elsewhere and is actually intermingled with stunted forest specimens, some so small as almost to belie the fact that they are trees. Trunks about the size of an ordinary lead pencil with other features in proportion represent many years of exceedingly slow growth. Further from the forest margin, woody plants and bushes are absent, and the grasses, mosses, lichens, and sedges form an even mat over the whole surface. Still farther poleward, the cover is reduced to isolated patches of these plants with much bare ground between. And finally, all signs of vegetation disappear and bare rock or ice forms the surface. The transition is in many ways similar to that which is encountered in crossing from the forest through grassland into desert.

The great areas of tundra are those of the Arctic fringe of North America and Eurasia, from which long fingers stretch southward along highland zones. In the Antarctic, tundra is almost entirely lacking, for the icecap extends over almost the whole of Antarctica.

Mountain Vegetation

In the mountains pronounced vertical zoning of vegetation corresponds to the vertical zoning of mountain climates. The sequence of types approximates the sequence from the equator to the poles. In a middle latitude mountain region, the lower slopes are clothed with deciduous broadleafs, followed in succession by zones of coniferous forest, a tundra-like cover known as *alpine meadow,* bare rock, and even, near the high peaks, a zone of permanent snow. In tropical mountains like Mount Ruwenzori in east central Africa, the sequence includes tropical forest, broadleaf evergreen forest similar to that of the middle latitudes, broadleaf deciduous forest, coniferous forest, alpine meadow, and finally no vegetation. The particular zoning depends first upon the type found at the base of the mountain. The number of zones in the sequence decreases as one gets away from the equator.

251 *WORLD DISTRIBUTION of northern latitude regions which are predominantly coniferous forest and tundra.*

But this zoning is not always present with diagrammatic simplicity. It will be remembered that in mountain climates, details of position and exposure result in a spotty distribution of climatic types. Similar spottiness is reflected in the details of vegetation. Because of local dryness, the expected pattern of forest zones may be broken by the occurrence of a grassland or a desert vegetation type, or a broadleaf forest may be interrupted by a needleleaf variety. While the general sequence can be stated, local departures from it frequently are so great as to appear to upset the whole pattern. For that reason, the collective expression, mountain vegetation, provides a category which includes all of the types previously discussed. No attempt is made to indicate on the world map the detailed distribution from place to place. The outline of regions of mountain vegetation (Plate VII) is the same as that which appears on the climatic map and on the surface map.

....

CHAPTER OUTLINE

Natural vegetation and native animal life

Major categories of vegetation and animal life
  Plant associations
    Forest characteristics
    Grassland characteristics
    Desert characteristics
  Natural vegetation types
  Native animal types
Vegetation types and their distribution
  Tropical forests
    Tropical rainforest or selva
    Tropical semideciduous or monsoon forest
    Tropical scrub or thorn forest
  Tropical grassland or savanna
  Desert shrub and barren desert
  Middle latitude grasslands
    Steppe
    Prairie
  Middle and high latitude forests
    Mediterranean scrub forest
    Broadleaf and mixed broadleaf-conifer forest
    Coniferous forest
  Tundra
  Mountain vegetation

REVIEW QUESTIONS

1. Give some examples, drawn from different parts of the world, to indicate the significance of natural vegetation in man's habitat.
2. In what ways does native animal life contribute to or hinder human use of an area?
3. Natural vegetation may generally be considered as visible evidence of the climate of an area. Why? What causes major departures from this generalization?
4. Suggest, from your own experience if possible, examples of each of the main plant associations.
5. What are some of the basic differences between evergreen and deciduous trees? between needleleaf and broadleaf trees? Give examples of each type.
6. Why are tundras included under the heading of deserts? Explain.
7. Explain the difference between a major plant association and a natural vegetation type.
8. In what kind of tropical forest would life be easiest for an agricultural people? In your answer, consider only the kind of the natural vegetation and animal life. Present a reasoned discussion supporting your choice.
9. Why is it that the word "jungle" is so often erroneously used to mean almost any type of tropical forest?
10. Suggest a reason, from the point of view of human activity, for recognizing the kinds of places where jungle is likely to occur.
11. Of what conceivable importance is mangrove?
12. The statement is made: "The forest-grassland margin in the tropics supports the world's densest remaining native animal population." Why should this be so? Discuss fully.
13. If the savannas have as many trees as their descriptions imply, why are they called grasslands?
14. Why is the area in northern South America which is known as the Llanos of the Orinoco not one of the world's greatest cattle countries?
15. In terms of location, what is the relation be-

tween deserts and other natural vegetation types?

16. Much of the world's prairie and steppe is today surplus grain-producing land. Present a reasoned discussion why this should be.

17. Why is the Mediterranean scrub forest the least extensive of all the natural vegetation types?

18. The mid-latitude forests of the world have suffered heavy destruction in Europe, North America, and Asia. Suggest some of the reasons for this.

19. Do the mid-latitude forests offer the same problems to human activity as do the tropical forests? Explain fully.

20. Why are there no areas of taiga in the Southern Hemisphere?

21. Explain the vertical zoning of vegetation in mountain areas. Give examples from your own experience if possible.

SOME SUGGESTED REFERENCES

Cain, Stanley A., *Foundations of Plant Geography,* Harper, 1944. A technical reference work; concerned with concepts and methods of interpretation of plant distribution rather than with descriptive plant geography.

Forester, C. S., *The Sky and the Forest,* Little, Brown, 1948. Like this same author's *The African Queen,* this novel contains vivid, accurate description of tropical forest and primitive life within it.

Lillard, Richard G., *The Great Forest,* Knopf, 1948. The story of the forests of the United States from the coming of the Europeans to the present; describes the original forests, their uses and abuses, and some of the conservation advances;

well documented; nontechnical and for the general reader.

Schimper, A. F. W., *Plant Geography upon a Physiological Basis,* Oxford University Press, 1903. Still the basic reference (along with the German edition which appeared in 1898) on the vegetation cover of the world.

Shantz, H. L., and Marbut, C. F., *The Vegetation and Soils of Africa,* Research Series No. 13, American Geographical Society, 1923. The standard technical account of the vegetation and soils of the African continent; one section deals with land classification; illustrative on a continental scale.

Transeau, Edgar N., "The Pattern of Vegetation," Chapter 8 in *Global Geography,* ed. George T. Renner, Thomas Y. Crowell Co., 1944. An especially clear, though brief, account of the world vegetation cover.

Weaver, J. E., and Clements, F. E., *Plant Ecology,* 2nd ed., McGraw-Hill, 1938. A standard reference and text on vegetation classification.

Grass: The Yearbook of Agriculture 1948, U. S. Department of Agriculture, 1948. One of the famous series of yearbooks; a mine of information about grasses in the United States and its territories, from species of grasses to problems of grassland management; many useful tables, bibliography, and illustrations; written for the general public.

Trees: The Yearbook of Agriculture 1949, U. S. Department of Agriculture, 1949. Another of the famous series of yearbooks; a well-conceived and splendidly executed collection of articles by over 100 leading American students of forests and their problems, especially in the United States; well illustrated, bibliography, useful reference appendices; written for the general reader.

252   *MODERN WAYS of using soil. Contour and strip farming, Berks County, Penn-*
sylvania, extends man's control over the soil. (Gendreau)

CHAPTER 15

Soils: Their Formation and Distribution

There are very few people who have not recognized in a casual way the rich brown coloring of one newly plowed field, the shiny blackness of another, or the yellow or red stickiness of a third. But this common observation is usually passed over, certainly by city dwellers, as of minor importance. Both the landforms and the plants which clothe the surface are so conspicuous that they force themselves upon our attention. Climate, though not visible, is rendered conspicuous through the other senses. Soils are not like this. Indeed, they are so lacking in prominence that they are often forgotten as constituting one of the great essentials of life. Without some covering of soil, plants could not exist; man would have no plant or animal products from the land. Even the seas and oceans would have little to offer, for it is water coursing over the land and carrying soil particles to the water bodies that supplies much basic food to marine life. Though their functions are indirect, soils are just as fundamental to human life as are air and water.

Variations in soil quality from place to place provide differences in habitability just as do variations in climate, surface form, natural vegetation, and animal life. The way in which man uses or misuses the soil frequently determines the relative success of settlement and the sustained productivity of one area as compared with another. No world survey should omit at least a brief consideration of soil as a vital element in the human habitat.

SOIL CHARACTERISTICS

All too frequently, soil is considered to be simply a collection of weathered rock material at the surface of the earth, or as "so much dirt." It is far more than this. Even the most finely divided rock is not soil. *Soil* is a mixture of mineral and organic matter with air and water. It may cover the earth's surface to a depth of only a few inches or it may be several feet deep. In a few places, as on rocky mountain crests, it is lacking altogether. Sometimes, the mineral element dominates; in other soils, organic matter, both living and dead, constitutes the bulk. Regardless of the proportions, both are present, and with them are air and water.

The soil is constantly evolving. Time, parent material, slope, climate, vegetation, and bacteria all contribute to this evolutionary process. So do man and other animals, both large and small. Every conceivable gradation from weathered rock, not soil by itself, to the most complexly altered covering can be observed in detailed study. Yet, from a world point of view, certain great groups of similar soils can be distinguished. Within each one of these groups, all of the soils have certain characteristics in common. These reflect dominantly the controls of natural vegetation and climate. It is upon the nature and distribution of these types that attention is here focused.

Soil Profile

By far the larger part of the earth's soils are developed from weathered rock. As noted previously, when rock is exposed at the surface, it is subjected to both weathering and erosion, which create a mantle of unconsolidated material, known as *regolith*. Into the spaces between the individual particles in the mantle, water and air penetrate; plant roots secure a foothold; and life forms, represented by small burrowing animals, ants, earthworms, and bacteria, become established. The evolution of soil begins when organic forms start their existence in the upper part of the regolith.

The major obvious result of the soil-forming processes is the development of definite layers within the regolith. These layers are called *horizons*. Though they stand out markedly from one another, they have a common origin. Each of them is characterized by certain physical and chemical peculiarities and, within each, certain of the processes which bring about the evolution of regolith to soil are dominant. A cross section through all of the layers is called a *soil profile*.

The uppermost layer is called the *A horizon* (Fig. 253). This is the zone from which materials are being removed either in solution or in suspension. It is often referred to as the "zone of robbery." In addition, it is considered to include organic debris which is either freshly accumulated upon the surface or partially decomposed. A walk through any wooded area will reveal the sort of material actually lying on the soil, but generally considered to be included in the A horizon. The fallen leaves in a deciduous woodland form a brown matting, loose and rustling if dry, sticky and soggy if wet. When these leaves are kicked or scuffed up, blackened forms of older leaves are uncovered and, below them, a black mass in which the original structure has been obliterated. Beneath that is the part of the soil which is mainly mineral fragments. Similarly, the A horizon of a pine forest has a matting of brown needles often many inches thick and below, a thin band of black, decayed and partially decayed, older needles. The black material is called *humus*. Upon the chemical reaction and amount of the humus depend many of the specific qualities of the underlying soil. It is important to note that humus is *partially* decayed organic matter; if decay is complete, there is no humus, but only a residual mineral ash.

Below the A horizon, there is a more compact zone in which much of the material removed from the upper layer is deposited. This layer, known as the *B horizon,* is a "zone of accumulation." Together with the A horizon, it constitutes the soil proper.

The third layer, known as the *C horizon,* is the weathered parent material from which the soil is derived. Within it, there are sometimes found accumulations of chemical compounds, like white calcium carbonate or bluish-gray ferrous iron, which indicate peculiarities of soil drainage. Below the C horizon is rock material, either consolidated or unconsolidated, which is unaltered by the soil-forming processes. To this layer, the name *D horizon* is sometimes given. Weathering proceeds downward into it, and thus produces the regolith from which the overlying soil is developed.

The boundaries between soil horizons may be either sharp or indistinct. They may also be smooth or irregular. Furthermore, not all of the horizons are present in all soils. In some places, as on a slope without vegetation, surface erosion may remove the A horizon altogether. In other places, the B horizon may extend downward practically to the unweathered rock so that no C horizon exists.

Soil Color

Each horizon or part of a horizon has certain features of color, texture, and structure peculiar to itself. Perhaps the most easily observed of these features is color. In itself,

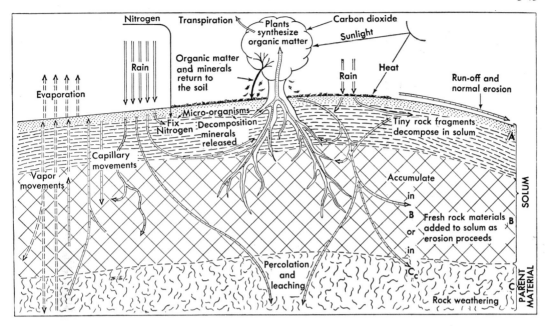

253   *SCHEMATIC DIAGRAM of the principal dynamic processes in a soil, much simplified. (From Charles E. Kellogg)*

color is not a complete index to soil nature. Yet it is usually a "key" to the differences between one type and another.

In part, color indicates organic content. Decomposed organic matter has a blackish coloring. Where there is a large amount, the soil is black or very dark brown. As organic content decreases, the color changes through the darker browns to lighter ones. The contribution of organic coloring decreases to the point of grayness in soils where the content is low.

Chemical change in the mineral parts of the soil is responsible for other colors. Iron contributes either a reddish or a yellowish color under certain conditions. Occasionally it produces a bluish-gray mottling. Most other chemical salts are white.

The precise color of any one horizon depends upon the detailed actions of the soil-forming processes. The whole range from black to white can be obtained by differing mixtures of each color contributor. Usually, the upper part of the A horizon is the dark-est part of the soil. Downward through the A horizon, color lightens. Ordinarily it becomes deeper again in the B horizon, though it is seldom as deep there as in the upper part of the A horizon.

Soil Texture

Soil particles show a wide variety of sizes which in turn produce a wide variety of textures. When the individual particles are larger than a grain of corn, they are not considered to be true soil particles. Rather they are gravelly or stony fragments included in the soil. Below that size, several categories are recognized. The major ones are sand, silt, and clay. Arbitrary sizes have been set in terms of the diameter of the particles. In sand, the individual grains have a diameter between .05 millimeter and 1 millimeter; in silt, between .002 millimeter and .05 millimeter; and in clay, below .002 millimeter.

No soil exists in which all of the grains

have the same size. Hence, certain classes have been established based upon relative proportion of grains of each size (Fig. 254). Sand is the coarsest and clay, the finest. Between the two, in increasing order of fineness, are loamy sand, sandy loam, loam, silt loam, silty clay loam, clay loam, and silty clay. These in turn are modified by descriptive adjectives so that a wide variety of gradations

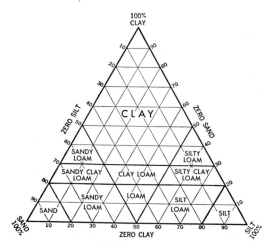

254   *THE SOIL texture triangle. Classes of soil texture are determined by the proportions of sand, silt, and clay particles. For example, "loam" is the textural name applied to a soil in which the proportions are 30 to 50 per cent sand, 30 to 50 per cent silt, and 10 to 20 per cent clay.*

are recognized. There are, for example, very fine sandy loams or stony sandy loams.

Texture has important effects upon the ability of the soil to retain moisture and to make the necessary foods available for plants. Fine-grained particles expose more surface than do coarse-grained ones. Hence, hygroscopic and capillary water (see p. 303) perform their functions more actively in silty or clayey soils than they do in sandy ones. Thus larger feeding areas for plant roots are provided in fine soils and smaller ones in coarse soils.

Within most well-developed soils, the texture of the A horizon is generally coarser than that of the B horizon. This is brought about largely by the removal of the smallest soil particles from the A horizon by gravitational water, which deposits them in the B horizon.

Soil Structure

Individual soil particles may group themselves in the soil in various ways. To these arrangements, the term *structure* is applied. Within each horizon in any one soil, a particular structure is characteristic. The particles may stick together in thin horizontal plates. The structure is then said to be *platy*. They may combine into more or less rounded forms of varying size. Then the structure is said to be *granular*. Many other specific arrangements have been observed, but occasionally there is no grouping of particles. Then the soil is said to be structureless, either *single grain,* when the particles are large like sand, or *massive,* when the particles are fine like clay.

While texture is more or less fixed for any one horizon, structure may vary from time to time depending, for example, upon the moisture content. A simple example is provided in the collection of silt in a mud puddle. During a rain and for such time afterward as water is present, a thin, fine-grained deposit lines the bottom of the puddle. After the water has drained away or has been evaporated, the silt dries out and cracks appear. Careful examination will show that the silt particles are then arranged in thin scales or plates. The change of structure in the silt of a mud puddle under differing moisture conditions is a miniature of the same process in soil. On a large scale, this same variety of change may be seen in any granular soil which has been excessively plowed and cultivated. After a time, such a soil loses its granular structure. Then, when water is applied to it, it becomes a "soupy mud," only to dry out into hard crusts or clods.

AGENTS AND PROCESSES OF SOIL FORMATION

Soil-forming Agents

The evolution of soil is brought about by four main agents: water, air, plants, and animals. Though each of these performs certain functions, the resulting soil reflects their combined action. Soil in one place differs from that in another because the contribution of each agent varies.

WATER IN THE SOIL. Three things may happen to water which falls upon the earth. It may run off the surface and be conveyed by streams to lakes or oceans. It may be evaporated and returned to the atmosphere as water vapor. Or it may sink into the ground and become hygroscopic, capillary, and gravitational water (see p. 303). While the effect of hygroscopic water is negligible, capillary and gravitational water are vital agents in soil formation.

Capillary water acts as the major source of plant moisture. Its amount depends upon the number and size of the spaces between soil particles as well as upon the total amount of water available to the soil. In finely divided soils, it is abundant; in coarse ones, it may be almost lacking. As the surface dries out, capillary water from the lower horizons may move upward if the soil spaces are small enough. In this manner, moisture necessary to plants is made available in periods of protracted drought. Where the movement toward the surface is pronounced and long-continued, it often causes a concentration of chemical salts, some of which may be injurious to the plant life (see pp. 303-04). In this way, capillary water is an agent of soil evolution.

Gravitational water produces the most striking results within the soil. It is the major agent of color, texture, and structure changes in both the A and B horizons. It is thus responsible for easily observed differences between the parts of any soil profile.

Two of the major changes produced by gravitational water are physical. As the water moves downward through the A horizon, it tends to pick up minute soil particles. These exceedingly fine bits of matter are carried downward out of the A horizon as the water moves through it. The process of removal of the fine particles from the upper horizon is called *eluviation*. The result of this process is a coarsening of the texture of the A horizon, particularly in its lower part. Structure is generally altered and the spaces between the particles are increased in size. Consequently, less water is retained as capillary water, for capillary water exists only in fine, hairlike spaces. Thus the A horizon becomes less suited as a medium for plant roots.

As the gravitational water moves downward toward the water table, its ability to carry the load of fine particles becomes less, just as a river's ability to carry alluvium becomes less as it nears or enters the body of water into which it is flowing. Eventually, the fine particles are deposited in the spaces of the B horizon. The texture and structure of the B horizon are thereby altered. The layer becomes more compact. Hygroscopic and capillary water are both increased in amount. The action may be carried on to such a degree that, in combination with certain chemical changes, a very stiff, impervious layer, called *hardpan,* may be formed. This retards soil evolution and harms plant and animal life locally.

The third of the major functions performed by gravitational water is chemical rather than physical. As water moves downward through the A horizon, it tends to dissolve the more soluble of the chemical elements. This process is called *leaching,* and it, also, may change both the texture and the structure of the soil. Very definitely, it changes the chemical composition and thus it alters the value of the A horizon as a source of plant food materially.

The exact nature of chemical change varies with the reaction of the water. If the water is mixed with large amounts of carbon dioxide from the air or if it seeps through a heavy layer of humus, it becomes a weak organic acid. Then chemical reactions between this acid water and the soil particles differ from those produced by "purer" water. Leaching always tends to increase soil acidity.

Various chemical changes frequently affect the soil color. When the action is such as to leave the iron compounds in the A horizon, a reddish or yellowish color results. When the iron is removed, a grayish or whitish color prevails. When the water is strongly affected by the humus through which it passes, it often imparts blackish or brownish coloring to the A horizon.

Elements which are leached from the A horizon are frequently concentrated in the B horizon. Thus the passage of water through the soil effects changes in both horizons.

AIR IN THE SOIL. The presence of some air in the soil is essential for plants and for soil animals. Life processes cannot go on without an adequate supply of oxygen and though some of the plants and a few of the animals can secure it in ways other than directly from the air most of them are unable to do so. Their survival depends essentially upon air which is present in the spaces between soil particles, spaces which are not permanently filled with water. In addition, when the soil air is charged with water vapor or with carbon dioxide given off by the plant or animal life within it, it is capable of bringing about a certain amount of chemical change by solution. The air is thus a direct agent of soil change.

In most soils, there are times when little air is present. This is true particularly during and after heavy precipitation. Then gravitational water occupies practically all of the openings, but it soon drains away and is replaced by air.

ORGANIC MATTER IN THE SOIL. Both plants and animals live in the soil and are agents of its evolution. When plant roots establish themselves, they draw water and absorb as food many of the chemical elements in the soil. Under the influence of sunlight and carbon dioxide from the air, the items drawn from the soil are converted into various new compounds, known as *organic* compounds. These are the direct foods on which the plants live and from which they develop their structures. The plants in turn provide food for animals. When the plants and animals die, both organic and mineral substances are returned to the soil either at the surface as in the accumulation of leaves, twigs, branches, and trunks in a forest or in the form of dead root fibers within the soil itself. The processes of decay convert the organic matter to humus. At the same time, many of the mineral elements in the decaying structures are released to the soil.

Small animals, like the earthworm, feed upon humus and carry it downward into the soil. Large numbers of bacteria feed upon it, often converting it to other forms, and mix it with the mineral parts of the soil. Fungi, plants without green color, likewise feed upon it and in turn produce other organic compounds. The bodies of all of these plants and animals alike provide a further source of organic matter when they die. Certain of the bacteria have the ability to take nitrogen directly from the air and to transform it so that it can be used by plant roots. The presence of nitrogen-fixing bacteria in large numbers insures high fertility.

The mixing process and the downward movement of altered organic compounds is furthered by the action of water. Some of the compounds are extremely soluble and are hence rapidly leached away; others are quite insoluble and remain to provide black coloring to the soil.

Organic matter, either living or dead, makes for greater soil fertility and for ease of soil cultivation; normally, the more humus, the greater the friability, or "workability," of the soil. In general, where soils are well drained, high humus content implies high fertility and low humus content implies low fertility.

Principal Soil-forming Processes

Soil is formed from regolith as a result of the combined activity of all the agents so far suggested. No one of these is alone responsible. At the same time, it is obvious that the combinations are not everywhere the same. In some places, water is plentiful and its functions can be carried on continuously, as in areas of Tropical Rainforest (Af) climate. In other places, water is infrequently available, as in areas of Arid (BW) climate. Accumulation of organic matter is rapid in some regions, in the middle latitude grasslands, for instance. In other regions, like the deserts, it is slow. Earthworms are important soil "cultivators" in some regions, but are absent in others. Despite infinite variety of possible combinations, the soils produced may be summarized in terms of three processes: *laterization, podsolization,* and *calcification.* One process alone or any of them in combination may be involved in the evolution of any one soil. The world-wide soil types, or major soil groups, depend upon the balance between all three which exists over different parts of the earth.

LATERIZATION. The laterization process is one in which leaching and eluviation are very highly developed. It occurs only where there are large supplies of moisture at temperatures which allow soil formation to continue throughout the year. Because it is continuous, soils in which laterization is the dominant process are deeper than others. The whole profile often exceeds 25 feet in depth. Under the most extreme conditions, as represented in areas of Tropical Rainforest (Af) climate, bacterial life is plentiful and prevents large accumulations of humus in the upper part of the A horizon. Organic matter is rapidly converted into a form which is quickly and easily leached away. Most of the soluble minerals are removed likewise. Leaching is so strongly developed that even much of the silica is removed. Only iron and aluminum oxides remain in the A horizon. Eluviation is likewise at a maximum; the A horizon becomes extremely coarse textured and porous while the B horizon becomes compact and clayey. One prominent indicator of the process is color; the iron oxides give reddish or yellowish colors to the soil.

PODSOLIZATION. The podsolization process is the summation of the effects of soil agents under quite different conditions from those which produce laterization. Acid organic matter collects at the surface and decomposes very slowly. Bacterial life is meager and soil animals are few in number so that there is no intensive conversion or mixing of organic elements and the mineral parts of the soil. The A horizon is leached of its iron and aluminum compounds and what remains is dominantly silica. It thus presents an ashy color. The B horizon is compacted by the deposit of leached and eluviated materials from above. The process occurs in humid areas with pronounced cool season and consequently does not continue uninterrupted throughout the year. Soils developed by it are generally very shallow, with an average depth of only 14 or 15 inches.

CALCIFICATION. The process of calcification is best developed under grass rather than forest cover. Grass feeds on large amounts of calcium brought by the roots from the lower parts of the soil. When the grass dies, calcium is returned to the upper soil layers. Grass roots and leaves provide heavy mats of organic matter. Bacterial life is plentiful. Water is not sufficient in amount to cause heavy leaching or eluviation. In contrast to soils in which laterization and podsolization dominate, those in which calcification is the most important process are not acid in their reaction.

A summary of the more prominent effects of each of these three processes is given in Table 16.

CONTROLS OF THE SOIL-FORMING PROCESSES

The end product in the evolution of any one soil is determined by which of the three processes, laterization, podsolization, or calcification, dominates and by the rate at which the process operates. Five controls, in turn, determine the dominant process and its rate. These controls are (1) climate, (2) vegeta-tion, (3) parent material, (4) slope or lay of the land, and (5) time. The first two are world-wide in their effects. The third and fourth are of extreme importance locally. The fifth control is important in all soil evo-lution, whether world-wide or local.

Control by Climate

Because water and air are such significant agents in the soil-forming processes, climate

---

Table 16 SUMMARY OF MORE PROMINENT EFFECTS OF SOIL PROCESSES

EFFECTS ON "A" HORIZON

Laterization	Podsolization	Calcification
1. Most chemical elements except iron and aluminum removed.	1. Most chemical elements except silica removed.	1. Only the most soluble chemical elements removed.
2. Fine particles removed producing coarse texture.	2. Fine particles removed producing coarse texture.	2. Only very finest particles removed leaving texture moderately fine.
3. Almost no humus accumulated on surface or mixed through horizon.	3. Moderately large amount of humus accumulated on surface, but little mixed through horizon.	3. Large amount of humus accumulated on surface and well mixed through horizon.
4. Considerable depth developed.	4. Only shallow depth developed.	4. Moderate depth developed.

EFFECTS ON "B" HORIZON

Laterization	Podsolization	Calcification
1. Elements leached from A horizon concentrated.	1. Elements leached from A horizon concentrated.	1. Calcium and magnesium concentrated in form of carbonate nodules.
2. Particles eluviated from A horizon concentrated producing heavy clay texture.	2. Particles eluviated from A horizon concentrated producing clayey texture.	2. Texture little changed by particles eluviated from A horizon.
3. No humus mixed through horizon.	3. Little humus mixed through horizon.	3. Humus well mixed through horizon.
4. Considerable depth developed.	4. Little depth developed.	4. Little depth developed.

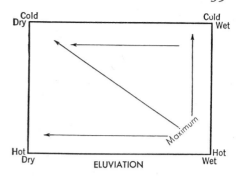

255 SCHEMATIC representation of the relations of the leaching and eluviation processes to climate. Effectiveness of each process decreases in the directions shown by the arrows. Corners of the rectangles represent climatic extremes.

exerts the most important single influence on soil development. A large amount of precipitation means a large amount of soil water. The continued presence of moisture in the soil depends largely upon the distribution of precipitation through the year. Temperature is also very significant, for the effectiveness of water as a soil agent depends upon it.

In a Tropical Rainforest (Af) climate, with constant high precipitation evenly distributed throughout the year and with regular high temperatures, there is a large amount of water available for both leaching and eluviation. Not only is the amount large, but it can continue its functions throughout the whole year, for there is no period when temperatures are low enough to freeze the water, thus reducing its activity. In addition, air and water temperatures are relatively high and solution proceeds more rapidly at high temperatures than at low ones. In sharp contrast to such conditions are those under an Arid (BW) climate. Water is extremely small in amount and it comes at irregular intervals. Hardly any of it can sink far into the ground before evaporation has dried out the surface. Then capillary activity allows what has sunk in to rise again toward the surface. Leaching and eluviation under such a climate are at a minimum. Similarly, in a Polar (E) climate, water is seldom present in large amounts in a liquid state. When water is present in the form of ice, the proc-esses which it carries on under warmer temperatures cannot take place.

Some of the relationships between climate and the processes carried on by water are shown in Fig. 255. The arrows point in the direction of decreased effectiveness of water as a soil agent.

Control by Vegetation

Control by vegetation is exerted largely through its influence on the supply of organic matter. The largest amount of humus is accumulated under grass cover and the next largest under forests. Transfer of this humus to the soil is dependent mostly upon living organisms. As previously pointed out, some climates favor plentiful soil life while others discourage it. Similarly, some types of vegetation produce organic material which can be converted readily while others do not.

In the tropical rainforest, the production of dead organic matter is enormous and continuous, but the climate is such that bacterial life is plentiful. The bacteria decompose the plant products rapidly and they are reduced to a form in which living plants can use them. Hence, there is no considerable humus accumulation on the soil nor any great permanent incorporation of organic compounds in the soil.

In a northern coniferous forest, the cool, moist climate fosters the accumulation of a thick layer of dead organic matter on the surface, but the formation of humus is very slow. It develops in a form which is easily leached out of the A horizon. Climate, along with acid reaction of the A horizon, discourages the presence of many earth animals. Hence, organic matter is not made easily available to plant roots in a form which they can use. Despite this, much of it is actually carried downward into the B horizon.

When the combined influence of climate and vegetation is recognized, a definite relationship between them on the one hand and the dominating processes on the other can be made out. In areas of Tropical Rainforest (Af) climate and vegetation, laterization is at its height; in areas of Humid Continental (Df) climate and boreal forest, podsolization is paramount; and in regions along the wet margins of Semiarid (BS) climates and prairie grass, calcification dominates. As is indicated in Fig. 256, laterization decreases toward cold areas and toward dry ones. Podsolization decreases toward hot and toward dry areas. Calcification decreases toward both hot and cold wet areas and toward both hot and cold dry areas.

Control by Parent Material

As one travels through any small area, it is easy to see differences between soils, especially when fields are being plowed. Some soils may be yellowish and sandy, blowing with every wind; some may be sticky, red clay; some may be yellowish-brown and rich looking. Often, these differences can be traced to differences in underlying rock, the *parent material* from which the soils are derived.

Parent material obviously contributes to the nature of the soil. Unless the parent material contains certain chemical elements, the soil must of necessity lack them. If the prod-

ucts of weathering are fine-grained, then the soil also can be expected to be fine-grained. Parent material provides the specific combination of chemical elements in the regolith and greatly influences its texture. Those traits are passed on to the soil.

Differences of this sort induced by parent material may be of tremendous significance locally and regionally. They provide the finer, the more detailed, patterns. But, though local differences may be of great significance in detail, they are of little service in a study on a world scale. From a world point of view, the controls of climate and vegetation combine to establish certain major climax types toward which all soils are developing. The controls of climate and vegetation thus mask that of parent material when the world is the object of view rather than a locality or a region.

Control by Slope

Slope induces local and regional variation just as does underlying rock. On steep slopes, runoff is rapid and large in amount. Not only does it have effective force as an agent of erosion; it diminishes the water available to sink into the ground and to carry on the soil-forming processes. Frequently, slope lands are so badly eroded that an A horizon is lacking altogether. In extreme cases, the whole profile may be lost and the slope may be soilless, clothed in parent material or in coarse rock fragments.

Slope likewise may induce poor drainage. Undrained depressions may exist where the water table is so close to the surface as to prevent the downward percolation of water and thus to eliminate air from the soil spaces. The normal processes of leaching and eluviation cannot go on under this condition. Soil evolution is stopped.

Over wide areas of gently sloped surface, the effect of the lay of the land is minimized; the other controls operate more strongly.

Control by Time

Time is the prime requisite in the production of all soil. On a world scale, differences of parent material and of slope can be overcome, given sufficient time. Under each climate and vegetation cover, a major variety of soil will develop. Just how long a time is necessary cannot be stated with any meaning in terms of human life. Observations are plentiful to indicate the basic importance of this control, however. On the steppes of European Russia, deep black soils occur clear across the zone of grass which follows the wet margin of the Semiarid (BS) climate. Under these soils lie crystalline rocks in some places and sedimentaries in others. Some of the surface was covered with glacial debris and some was not. But the soil cover shows similarity throughout. A long enough time has elapsed so that the controls of climate and vegetation have left their unmistakable imprint.

SOIL CLASSIFICATION

As in the study of climate, landforms, and natural vegetation, it is necessary to recognize certain groupings of soils in order to compare one part of the earth with another. Major categories are erected upon the basis of soil traits which reflect the controls of climate and vegetation. These controls, as we have seen, are operative over large areas and the soil traits due to them therefore provide the most obvious means of world comparison.

The major categories are really the *mature* types toward which all soils under the same climatic and vegetational controls are developing. They are the end products which may be expected of the action of soil-forming processes through long periods of time.

Because the controls are operative over great areas or zones of well-drained and gently sloped land, the major categories are called

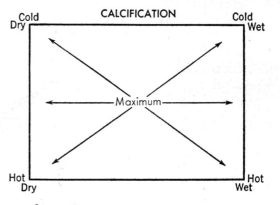

256 SCHEMATIC *representation of the relations of the soil-forming processes to climate. Effectiveness of each process decreases in the directions shown by the arrows. Corners of the rectangles represent climatic extremes.*

zonal soils. Within the extent of any one zonal soil, local controls of relief, parent material, or detailed differences of climate and vegetation all may produce variations. Some of the variations occur in areas of more than one zonal soil; these variations are therefore called *intrazonal*. For other soils there has not been enough time to produce characteristics determined either by climate or by vegetation. Soils in which this is true are called *azonal*.

As was true of the controls of the soil-forming processes, attention must be directed either to the world-wide pattern or to the local or regional pattern. It is the zonal soils which provide the usable world pattern. Though intrazonal and azonal soils are matters of great significance locally and regionally, they are of little service in a study on a world scale. Therefore, attention is here directed to the zonal soils alone.

Zonal Soils

The great zonal soils, often called the *great soil groups,* of the world have both internal and external features reflecting the controls of climate and vegetation. Where they are well developed, they occur over many kinds of parent material. Their profiles are the result of long-time action by soil-forming processes which operate over wide areas. Five principal types are recognized. Where the process of laterization is dominant, the resultant soils are known as *lateritic soils.* At the opposite extreme within forested and humid areas, podsolization is the principal process and the soils are called *podsols.* Where calcification is the prime process, the resultant soils are called *chernozems.* In arid regions where all soil-forming processes proceed at a very slow rate, the soils are spoken of as *desert soils.* Where continued cold persists and all processes are slowed, *tundra soils* are found. Between these extreme forms, there are many gradations, certain of which are sufficiently pronounced to warrant recognition as distinct

zonal soils. Thus, as one passes from areas of lateritic soils to areas of podsols, laterization becomes less and less significant and podsolization more and more so. One zonal soil is recognized in this transition, the *gray-brown podsolic soils.* Lateritic soils, gray-brown podsolic soils, and podsols are all formed in forested regions.

As one proceeds from regions with these types toward areas of chernozems, one passes through a zone in which the dark brown or black coloring under grass cover indicates a kind of balance between the three processes of laterization, podsolization, and calcification. Under such conditions, *black prairie soils* develop.

On the dry side of the chernozems, decreased effectiveness of the soil-forming processes is evidenced by increased shallowness of profile and lightening of soil color. Calcification occurs throughout areas of grass and desert vegetation, but it is less intense in the drier areas. Between the chernozems and the desert soils, one final zonal type is recognized, the *chestnut and brown soils.*

A check list of the zonal soils follows:

1. Lateritic soils
2. Gray-brown podsolic soils
3. Podsols
4. Black prairie soils
5. Chernozems
6. Chestnut and brown soils
7. Desert soils
8. Tundra soils

In summary, it should be reiterated that zonal soils are the fundamental types, the *mature soils,* toward which all types are developing. Climate and vegetation are the outstanding controls in zonal soil evolution. The close relationships which exist between climate, vegetation, and zonal soils can be represented schematically as in Fig. 257. In each rectangle, the corners represent climatic extremes; cold dry in the upper left-hand corner, cold wet in the upper right-hand, hot dry in the lower left-hand, and hot wet in the

257

SCHEMATIC representation of the distribution of climatic types, natural vegetation associations, and zonal soils. Corners of the rectangles represent climatic extremes. Comparison suggests the interrelationship of these three elements of the physical setting.

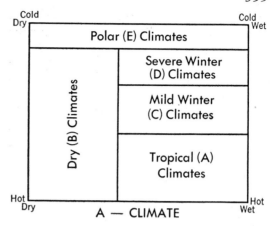

A — CLIMATE

lower right-hand. It should be noted that part A of Fig. 257 is a repetition of Fig. 106 in Chapter 9.

Other Categories of Classification

In detailed soil study, further division is made within each of the zonal types. Of great local importance is the soil *series*. A soil series is a group of soils having profiles similar in their major characteristics and all developed over the same kind of parent material. The series is broken down into *types*, determined largely on the texture of the A horizon. The types are further differentiated into *phases* which represent features of significance in soil use, such as slope, stoniness, and the like. Table 17 illustrates the foregoing classification for a specific soil.

While all of these categories are of major significance in detailed examination, they do not clarify the world picture. We speak of

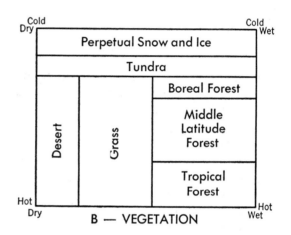

B — VEGETATION

Table 17 CLASSIFICATION OF ONE SPECIFIC SOIL

GROUP—gray-brown podsolic
SERIES—Hillsdale
TYPE—sandy loam
PHASE—gravelly phase

Soil is referred to as a *Hillsdale sandy loam, gravelly phase.* This is recognized as being within the gray-brown podsolic zonal soil group.

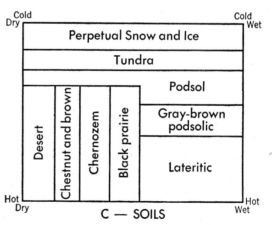

C — SOILS

(After Blumenstock and Thornthwaite, "Climate and the World Pattern," in Climate and Man, U. S. Dept. of Agriculture, *1941)*

broadleaf, deciduous forest just as we speak of gray-brown podsolic soil; we do not list the many kinds of trees which make up the forest, nor should we try to consider the many series, types, and phases which make up the gray-brown podsolic soils. Our attention must be focused upon the same degree of detail in all the features of the physical setting recognizing, at the same time, the generalizations necessarily implied.

NATURE AND DISTRIBUTION OF ZONAL SOILS

Each zonal soil is really a group or family of soils some of which have developed mature profiles and others of which are immature. The following descriptions of the characteristics of each zonal soil apply to the mature profile. It is very important to realize that mature soils are rare in many areas, as in Kentucky and Tennessee, for example. On the other hand, it must be remembered that all soils with immature profiles are evolving, under the controls of climate and vegetation, toward one or the other of the mature forms.

Lowland Soils

LATERITIC SOILS. Reddish and yellowish color and considerable depth are among the earmarks of all lateritic soils. The profiles of all of them show only a thin covering, if any, of organic matter (Fig. 258A). In the most completely laterized forms, the A horizon is reddish, coarse textured, and very porous, while the B horizon is deeper red in color and relatively fine textured. A depth of eight to ten feet is not uncommon. In areas where there is some evidence that podsolization is active, red and yellow lateritic soils take the place of the extreme forms. In the former,

the thin surface layer of organic matter is underlain by yellowish-brown highly leached material. In the B horizon, the color becomes a deep red. In the latter soils, the A horizon is grayish-yellow and highly leached. It grades into a yellowish, clayey B horizon.

Throughout all areas of lateritic soil, the intensity of leaching and the small accumulation of humus tend to produce soils which are relatively infertile both from the point of view of mineral and organic plant foods. Continuous heavy cropping is impossible without heavy fertilization. Likewise, the porosity of many of them makes irrigation a necessity in areas of protracted seasonal drought.

The great zone of lateritic soils is the forested region of the tropics and of the lower middle latitudes. In the Americas, these soils extend from the Amazon Basin southward into southeastern Brazil and northward through Middle America into the southeastern United States (Plate IX). Central Africa, the southeast coastlands of that continent, and the lowland portion of nearby Madagascar form a second large region. Southeastern Asia and the southwest Pacific Islands constitute the third great region. The soils of the Mediterranean fringe of Europe and of the southern peninsulas of Australia are so generally similar that they too are included in this zone.

GRAY-BROWN PODSOLIC SOILS. Poleward from the regions of lateritic soils and still within forested regions, the soils show marked features of podsolization. The surface accumulation of humus is still relatively thin, though thicker than in the lateritic soils (Fig. 258B). Below the humus, a grayish-brown, rather heavily leached A horizon gives way to a dark brown, fine-textured B horizon. The whole profile is shallower than that of the lateritic soils, usually reaching a depth of about four feet. Leaching is less in these soils than in those of the tropics and subtropics, and more organic matter is incorporated in them. Consequently, the gray-brown podsolic soils are of medium fertility and are much more retentive of moisture than the lateritic soils.

The great areas of gray-brown podsolic soils are three in number (Plate IX). Northeastern United States is the single important area in the Americas. In Europe, a wedge stretches inland from the Atlantic coast to the heart of European Russia. In Asia, interior and northern China, Korea, and northern Honshu in Japan have similar soils. It should be noted that all of these are areas of relatively high population density and that they are important agricultural regions. That agriculture still remains prominent in all of them is in large part a reflection of careful human management.

PODSOLS. These soils develop mainly under coniferous forest in relatively cool climates. A thin layer of humus lies upon a coarse-grained, whitish or ash-gray, heavily leached horizon (Fig. 258C). This in turn breaks sharply to a dark brown layer which is very compact. The whole profile is very shallow, usually less than two feet in total depth. The natural fertility of podsols is low.

These soils dominate in the northern forested lands of North America and Eurasia (Plate IX). In North America they extend uninterruptedly from central Alaska eastward past the northern Great Lakes to come to the Atlantic coast from eastern Maine to southern Labrador. In Europe the podsols begin on the wetter and cooler sides of the British Isles. They pick up, after a short break, in southern Norway, Denmark, and northern Netherlands to spread in an increas-

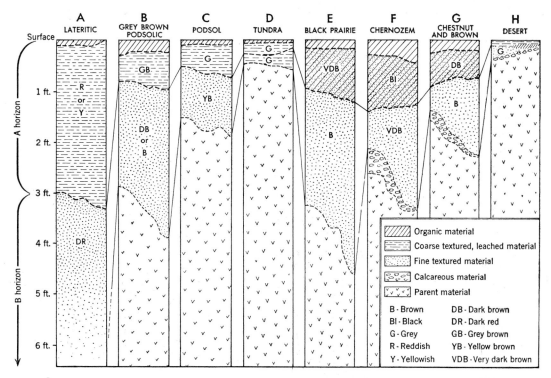

258 SCHEMATIC, comparative profiles of the eight zonal soils. The scale at the left applies to all eight profiles. The lines between profiles connect the bottoms of the respective A horizons and the bottoms of the respective B horizons. Note that individual horizons vary in depth; change from A horizon to B horizon, or from B to C, does not necessarily occur at exactly the same depth everywhere in any one soil.

ingly wide belt across northern Europe and Asia to the Pacific shores.

TUNDRA SOILS. Poleward from the zone of podsols (Plate IX) and also in many high mountain areas, the surface is covered by a mat of dark brown, partially decayed vegetation (Fig. 258D). Under this in more favorable locations, grayish horizons are observable from a few inches to a foot or so in thickness. Under these layers, there is usually a permanently frozen mass. Actually, very little evidence is present to indicate that the more common soil-forming processes have acted upon the parent material. There is considerable mixing of mineral and organic materials through the alternate actions of freezing and thawing. Where the soil has sufficient depth, where the growing season is long enough, and where the soil dries sufficiently to allow cultivation of even the most meager sort, natural fertility often surpasses that of the podsols.

BLACK PRAIRIE SOILS. Under a tall grass cover in a region of humid climate, a soil of high fertility develops. A thick mat of grass roots gives way to a very dark brown horizon (Fig. 258E). This grades through lighter browns to a light-colored parent material. The whole profile varies from three to five feet in depth. The high percentage of available organic matter and the relatively slight leaching leave ample plant food.

One of the most important areas of black prairie soils occurs in the United States (Plate IX). There it forms a belt along the dry margins of the lateritic soils, the gray-brown podsolic soils, and the podsols. Through southeastern Europe and in isolated spots through central Asia, these soils occupy similar positions with respect to the other types. Other areas include a strip through Paraguay, northern Argentina, northern Uruguay, and southeastern Brazil in South America and two prominent patches in the Sudan of Africa.

CHERNOZEMS. These soils are found on the dry margins of black prairie soils. They show a thick mat of grass roots at the surface, grading downward into a black A horizon (Fig. 258F). With depth, the color shades through the browns to a lighter-colored parent material. At a depth of from two to four feet, there is a layer of whitish nodules which are accumulations of calcium. Chernozem is only slightly leached, it has a high organic content, and it has large amounts of available calcium. Consequently, its natural fertility is high. However, it is not well suited to the production of plants which demand large supplies of water for it occurs on the margins of the humid climates. Nevertheless, the chernozem belts have become the great surplus wheat-producing regions of the world.

In the Americas, there are two chernozem belts (Plate IX). One stretches from the Peace River country of Canada southeastward through the Dakotas to central Texas. The other forms a northward-jutting wedge from the Pampas of Argentina and of southern Uruguay. In Eurasia, the chernozem belt extends from southern European Russia past the southern end of the Ural Mountains into southwestern Siberia. Surrounding the lateritic soils in Africa are narrow zones of soils so nearly like chernozems as to be called by the same name.

CHESTNUT AND BROWN SOILS. On the dry side of the chernozems, the soils are lighter in color and the layer of white nodules is closer to the surface (Fig. 258G). A thin mat of grass roots is underlain by slightly leached horizons which grade through lighter and lighter brown down to the calcium layer. In the chestnut soils, this layer may be as deep as three feet below the surface; in the brown soils, it may be as shallow as one foot.

The outstanding areas of chestnut and brown soils are those of the United States just east of the Rocky Mountains (Plate IX), those of Argentina just east of the Andes Mountains, and those of Australia forming the fringes of that continent's desert heart. In Russia, chestnut and brown soils form a border for the chernozems from the Caspian shores to Lake Balkhash. In Africa, the greater part of the Sudan and the wet margin of the Kalahari have soils of this type.

DESERT SOILS. Where desert soils exist, they are very shallow. Seldom are they more than a few inches from the top to the bottom of the profile (Fig. 258H). Grayish and only slightly altered parent material is closely underlain by a zone of calcium nodules. Because of the slight degree of leaching, desert soils are often of quite high fertility when water is made available to them.

The distribution of desert soils repeats the facts of Arid (BW) climates and of desert vegetation (Plate IX, Figs. 93 and 246).

Upland Soils

Because of the significance of slope in their development, the soils of mountain regions show less distinctly the controls of climate and vegetation. In some parts of mountain areas, soils do attain some of the characteristics of the zonal types, but distribution is spotty just as it is with mountain climate and mountain vegetation. Consequently, no attempt has been made to indicate the detailed variations on a world scale. The outline of the area of mountain soils (Plate IX) is the same as that of mountain climate (Plate V), mountain surface (Plate IV), and mountain vegetation (Plate VII).

MAN AND SOILS

The discussion of soils so far has largely omitted consideration of man; it has stressed what may be called the "natural" agents and processes of soil formation and the resultant nature and distribution of zonal soils. Nevertheless, it must not be forgotten that, in many parts of the world, man has altered and continues to alter the environment in which soils develop. Among other things, he has changed the rate at which natural processes operate; some of them are speeded, others are retarded, and still others are made completely inactive. He has likewise affected the agents of soil formation; water has been increased or decreased in amount, humus has been destroyed or added, and soil life has been altered. Such actions have not destroyed the general world pattern of zonal soils but, locally, they have made profound changes.

In detail, no single human act produces the same result in all soils; each soil reacts to man's efforts in its own way. Yet, certain common practices have definite general results in all soil evolution.

Some Changes in Soil Environment Induced by Man

VEGETATION REMOVAL. When man begins to cultivate land, his first action is to remove the cover of natural vegetation or as much of it as he can. Many of the primitive peoples, like those of the Amazon forest, burn off the smaller plants and girdle the larger and taller ones so that they die. Other more advanced peoples cut down the forest and remove the stumps. Pastoral peoples are also indirectly responsible for vegetation removal through the feeding habits of their animals. Up to a point, this removal may not be serious. On the other hand, when too many animals are pastured in a given area or when they crop the grass too closely in their feeding as sheep often do, bare surface is exposed. Gradually, the original vegetation is either completely destroyed or is in part replaced by other types.

Whether it is in forest or grassland, destruction of vegetation removes one of the natural controls of soil formation. Likewise, it removes a major soil constituent, humus. The balance of the whole soil environment is upset. With that comes a change in soil life and a change in erodibility of the soil itself.

CULTIVATION. When soil is brought under cultivation, both its texture and its structure are modified. Digging and plowing may bring the B horizon to the surface and may bury the A horizon beneath it. Constant working, as with a hoe or cultivator (Fig. 259), alters soil structure by breaking up the grouping of soil particles at the surface. In consequence, natural processes of soil formation are materially altered. For example, a mixture of coarse particles from an A horizon with fine particles from a B horizon decreases the size of spaces between individual particles near the soil surface. The effect of this is to retard the downward movement of gravitational water and, at the same time, increase the supply of capillary water. Both leaching and eluviation are thereby reduced.

Beyond mechanical changes which accompany cultivation, there are those which result from the growing of a new cover. The new plants may have a different root structure as, for example, that of a grain crop compared with a forest. This means different feeding habits; grains derive most of their food from the soil proper, whereas trees obtain a large share of theirs from parent material. Also, the absence of roots following extensive clearing, as of a forest, alters the environment for soil life. Then too, when the crops are harvested, the greater part of the plant cover is removed. Thus, the chemical elements on which the crop feeds are permanently removed and, unless they are artificially replaced, the soil is impoverished.

Again, continued cultivation of the soil makes it easily susceptible to increased surface erosion by both running water and wind. When vegetation is heavy and the upper surface of the soil is not broken, individual particles are not easily removed. Runoff of rain water is reduced by plant cover and downward percolation is increased. Without plant cover, runoff is large in amount and power of erosion is therefore great. Plants also protect the surface from the sweep of wind. A cultivated surface with fine soil particles laid bare facilitates removal by both water and wind.

MANAGEMENT. When man uses soil to produce the plants which he desires, he may follow certain practices which are calculated to make the soil more suitable for the plants he wishes to grow; this is called *soil management*. For example, an area may be cleared for the purpose of cultivation. After it is cleared, it may be discovered that the soil, for one reason or another, is too moist for the desired use. Drainage must be improved, either by ditching or by some other means. In another locality, soil may be so coarse as to have excessive drainage. Then, some procedure must be adopted which will make up for the lack of moisture. In many areas where moisture is deficient either climatically or edaphically, irrigation must be instituted before the soil can be made to produce. Whatever man does by management alters the action of the soil environment.

Some Problems Arising from Man's Use of the Soil

SOIL IMPROVEMENT. There is a distinction between soil fertility and soil productivity. Fertility implies the presence of the chemical elements necessary for specific plant growth in adequate amounts, properly balanced with the other elements, and readily available to the plant roots. A soil which is extremely fertile for potatoes may be quite infertile for wheat. The potato needs certain chemicals in relatively large amounts while wheat needs others. Productivity, on the other hand, implies not only the proper constitution of the soil, but its proper management as well. By management, man can alter productivity materially and rapidly. He can therefore improve it from the point of view of his own use. He can supply more water to it or remove excess water from it; he can change structure by tillage; he can rotate crops so that certain soil minerals are replenished and proper balance insured; and he can add to

259

THE VERY act of plowing may cause profound changes in all soil characteristics; likewise, plowing subjects the soil to active erosion. (Parks, Standard Oil Co. [N. J.])

the humus content by growing cover crops and plowing them under. Similarly, he can change the rate of surface erosion by planting certain crops to hold the soil in place. All of these practices come under the head of management. By good management, man can improve soil locally.

SOIL EXHAUSTION. All too commonly, man has brought about the destruction of soil either by exhausting its fertility or subjecting it to accelerated forces of surface erosion. Soil exhaustion, or loss of fertility, does not occur rapidly when natural forces are unhampered. Admittedly, heavy leaching and eluviation remove chemical elements from the A horizon and change the texture and structure of the soil. But there is constant return of chemical elements from soil organisms and from the plants which clothe the surface. Growing plants take chemicals directly from the soil. When these plants die or lose leaves and branches, the chemicals are, in large part, returned to the top of the soil. From there, they are eventually reincorporated into the soil proper by the action of water and soil organisms. In the same way, the soil organisms themselves are part of the cycle.

When man clears land and plants a certain crop on it, he is indirectly removing part of the soil. In growing, the crops use certain chemicals just as the natural vegetation did. But at harvest, there is nearly complete removal of the plant cover; plant remains are not left to be reincorporated in the soil. If the process is repeated time after time, and if no procedure is established to replenish the elements lost, the soil becomes exhausted so far as those elements are concerned. Even if the weathering of the underlying rock releases a new supply, the natural replenishment rate is slow. From man's point of view, this results in smaller and smaller crop yields until, eventually, it is uneconomic to continue planting and harvest. In the past, the solution has frequently been land abandonment rather than corrective management, and a resource is lost.

SOIL EROSION. Abandonment of exhausted soil leaves an opening for accelerated erosion, especially if the soil is an upland one. Without man's intervention, there normally is erosion of all upland soils and deposition of soil material in lowland areas. Youthful streams cutting into an interfluve wear away soil and carry it downstream perhaps to be deposited on the flood plain of an old valley or in a delta. But this normal process is slow. Among other things, it is partially restrained by vegetation cover. If man uses land until the soil is exhausted and then abandons it, if he manages it poorly, or if he simply removes the vegetation as in lumbering operations and abandons it, the work of running water and of wind is greatly speeded. Rills or sheet erosion developing on bare sloping fields during every rainstorm wash away a large part of the A horizon (Fig. 260). Repetition soon creates gullies through which much of the B horizon is removed. In some instances, these gullies cut down through the C horizon to underlying rock (Fig. 261). The soil is thus lost through "man-induced" erosion.

No process that man yet knows can speed up creation of new soil from rock. The relatively slow process of weathering followed by the alteration of the regolith by water, air, and living organisms produce soil only through very long periods of time. Once destroyed by man, this great resource is, for all practical purposes, irretrievably lost. By good management, flexibly applied for each soil, man can do much to conserve soil and to increase and sustain its productivity (Fig. 252). Yet, in so doing, he does not break the broad pattern created by the zonal soils, the great soil groups of the world.

....

CHAPTER OUTLINE

Soils: their formation and distribution

Soil characteristics
  Soil profile
  Soil color
  Soil texture
  Soil structure
Agents and processes of soil formation
  Soil-forming agents
    Water in the soil

Air in the soil
Organic matter in the soil
Principal soil-forming processes
  Laterization
  Podsolization
  Calcification
Controls of the soil-forming processes
  Control by climate
  Control by vegetation
  Control by parent material
  Control by slope
  Control by time
Soil classification
  Zonal soils
  Other categories of classification
Nature and distribution of zonal soils
  Lowland soils
    Lateritic soils
    Gray-brown podsolic soils
    Podsols
    Tundra soils
    Black prairie soils
    Chernozems
    Chestnut and brown soils
    Desert soils
  Upland soils
Man and soils
  Some changes induced by man in soil environment
    Vegetation removal
    Cultivation
    Management
  Some problems arising from man's use of the soil
    Soil improvement
    Soil exhaustion
    Soil erosion

REVIEW QUESTIONS

1. In your own words, describe the significance of soil to man.
2. Explain how horizons are developed in soil.
3. What is the real significance of soil profile?
4. Suggest some reasons why the boundaries between soil horizons are sometimes sharp and sometimes indistinct.
5. Is color a good clue to major soil differences? Has soil color anything to do with soil fertility? Explain.
6. Account for the fact that soil particles vary

260 *PERMANENT PASTURE which shows severe gullying and sheet erosion in south-central New York. Snow lies in the gullies. (U. S. Department of Agriculture)*

261

GULLIES in this south-central New York cornfield have cut so deep that they have eaten into bedrock. (W. W. Reitz, Soil Conservation Service, U. S. Department of Agriculture)

in size. Just how does this create different soil textures?

7. If you were a farmer, would it make any difference to you whether the soil in a particular field was massive or granular? In what way?

8. How does eluviation differ from alluviation?

9. It is common for both farmers and home gardeners to speak of hardpan. Do they use the term correctly? Is it possible to tell whether a soil is likely to have a hardpan before it is plowed or dug? Under what conditions might a hardpan be expected to be present?

10. Why is air essential in the soil? What would result if all air were excluded from all soils?

11. Suggest some ways in which organic matter is important as a soil component.

12. Is there any way in which leaching can be stopped? Would a soil benefit, from the point of view of fertility, if leaching did not occur?

13. Construct a chart or diagram to show the relationship between the soil-forming processes: laterization, podsolization, and calcification. Base the chart or diagram on the relative importance of leaching, eluviation, and humus accumulation in each of the three processes.

14. Choose one of the zonal soil types and analyze the part played by each of the "controls of the soil-forming processes" in its development.

15. Can all of the material at the surface of the earth be called mature soil? Illustrate your answer by reference to specific examples.

16. Are the majority of the world's soils zonal, intrazonal, or azonal? Explain your answer fully.

17. Why is it necessary, or even desirable, to recognize further division within the zonal soils?

18. What zonal soil is found in the Amazon Basin? in central Iowa? Give the major reasons for its existence in each area.

19. It is sometimes said, "Soil erosion might be a blessing in disguise for some areas in the rainy tropics." Is there any basis of fact for this statement? Propose a line of reasoning to support this contention.

20. Is it true that use of the soil by man always means its impairment or destruction?

21. If you were a farmer in the United States, in which of the zonal soil areas would you choose to have your farm? Discuss.

22. Of what significance is it that soil exhaustion be checked? that soil erosion be checked?

23. Soil erosion in the United States alone actually costs the people of the country billions of dollars per year. Suggest some of the ways, direct or indirect, in which these losses occur. Is the problem as severe in all parts of the world? Discuss a few remedies.

SOME SUGGESTED REFERENCES

Bennett, Hugh H., *Soil Conservation,* McGraw-Hill, 1939. The standard reference on soil erosion and its control.

Glinka, K. D., *The Great Soil Groups of the World and Their Development* (translated from the German by C. F. Marbut), Edwards Brothers, 1927. A reference work upon which many of the present ideas concerning soil classification and soil geography are based.

Jenny, Hans, *Factors of Soil Formation: A System of Quantitative Pedology,* McGraw-Hill, 1941. An advanced textbook in theoretical soil science; treats of soil-forming factors and processes of soil genesis.

Kellogg, Charles E., *The Soils That Support Us,* Macmillan, 1941. An engagingly written book describing soils, their development, and the problems arising from their use; includes maps, outlines, bibliography, and glossary; primarily for the nonprofessional reader.

Mickey, Karl B., *Man and the Soil,* International Harvester Company, 1945. A brief, readable account of the significance of soil conservation and of conservation methods; for the general reader.

Soils and Men, Yearbook of Agriculture 1938, U. S. Department of Agriculture, 1938. One of the extremely valuable series of yearbooks issued by the Department of Agriculture; articles included range from discussions of the fundamentals of soil science to the development and implementation of soil conservation programs.

CHAPTER 16

Coal and Petroleum: the Chief Sources of Industrial Energy

So far in this book, attention has been focused primarily, although not entirely, on the surface of the earth. For another important part of the physical complex it is necessary to go beneath the surface, into the upper portion of the earth's crust. Here are the minerals which have played and are playing a major role in man's material and cultural progress. From raft to ocean liner, from wooden hoe to tractor and gang plow, from foot and horseback to streamliner and airplane, from home workshop to mammoth factory, man's story is inextricably entwined with minerals. Even his very leisure, so essential to progress, reflects the manner in which resources from within the earth have helped to free him from unending drudgery. Among these resources none have proved more important than coal and petroleum.

COAL

It has been said that "coal is the lifeblood of modern industry" and that "no modern nation has become a world power unless it has had abundant coal." Neither statement is exaggerated. Coal is so vital to the highly industrialized parts of the world that any insufficiency in supply creates serious problems; sudden and complete stoppage of supply brings quick paralysis. Why this is so may be appreciated readily by considering the uses of coal.

Uses

No one knows when man first discovered that certain "black stones" would burn, and provide more heat, more lasting heat, than wood. One authority believes that coal was used to smelt copper in Manchuria as early as 1100 B.C. If that is so, it probably was used for domestic purposes long before that. Coal cinders are contained in the remains of a Roman wall constructed near Manchester, England, about 100 A.D. Newcastle, England, had a coal mine in operation as early as 1238 A.D. Even the American Indian knew of coal and used it slightly. From him, the colonists learned about the existence of some of the coal deposits of eastern Pennsylvania.

The beginning of the Industrial Revolution (about 1750) marked the real start of commercial coal production. This was in the British Isles, where man first turned from the making of goods by hand at home to their manufacture by machines in factories. Machines needed power, and coal was the answer. Burning it under boilers supplied steam and steam ran the machines. As the Industrial

Revolution spread to Europe and the United States, so did the mining of large quantities of coal. By 1850, the United States was on its way to become the world's leading coal producer, a position it attained about 1900. In

Europe, at about the same time, Germany surpassed Britain in coal mining and soon came to rival the United States.

Today, on the basis of tons consumed, there are five definitely major uses of coal. The two chief ones are the use of coal to run locomotives and to run factories. In the United States, the former consumes about one-fifth and the latter about one-quarter of the amount mined. The other major uses of coal are: the making of coke, the heating of homes and public buildings, and the generation of electricity. Minor amounts are used in mining and as "bunker" or "steam" coal for ships. The extent to which coal enters into the production of particular materials and goods is partly indicated in Table 18.

Table 18   SELECTED LIST OF PRODUCTS OBTAINED FROM COAL

COKE	HEAVY OIL
Blast-furnace coke	Carbolineum
Smelting coke	Carbazole
Foundry coke	Anthracene
Domestic fuel	Anthraquinone
Industrial fuel	Phenanthrene
Briquette coke	
Carbon dioxide	GAS
Water gas	Fuel gas
Boiler gas	Illuminating gas
Calcium carbide	Naphthalene
Carbons	Cyanogen
Electrodes	Sulphur
Graphite	
Washing soda	HARD PITCH
	Insulation
AMMONIA	Electrodes
Pyridine	Core compound
Nitric acid	Pitch coke
Nitrous oxide	Pitch gas
Ammonium phosphate	
Ammonium sulphate	SOFT PITCH
Ammonium chloride	Roofing
Ammonium carbonate	Waterproofing
Ammonium nitrate	Paving
	Batteries
LIGHT OIL	Paint
Benzene	
Solvent naphtha	TAR ACIDS
Benzaldehyde	Phenols
Benzyl alcohol	Cresols
Carbon disulphide	Carbolic acid
Varnish	Flotation agents
Toluem	Naphthalene

Comparative Importance

Coal is the main source of energy for the industrial nations of the world as a whole, although there are some exceptions, such as Norway, Switzerland, and Italy. In those countries, lack of coal has stimulated the use of electricity obtained from water power. In the United States, coal is nearly as important as all other energy sources combined (Fig. 263). So far, petroleum is coal's major rival and it is a very close second at present. In fact, if natural gas is included, it will be found that petroleum (plus, then, natural gas) has slightly exceeded coal in importance as a source of energy in our country. Hydroelectricity also has made great gains in recent years, but its energy output is still far behind that of coal or petroleum and natural gas. It is well to remember that in the United States, and in the world as a whole, far more electricity is produced from the burning of coal than from the use of water power—despite the tremendous increase in production from hydroelectric plants within the past twenty-five to thirty years. It seems evident that coal, even with increasing competition from other energy sources, will continue to play a major

262   (Above) *MINERS OPERATING a cutting machine in the working head of a coal mine (National Film Board, Canada).* (Below) *Oil field near Oklahoma City, Oklahoma. One of the wells in the foreground is out of control and is a temporary "gusher" (Standard Oil Co. [N. J.]).*

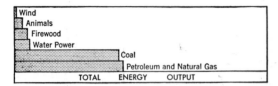

263   *THE chief sources of energy in the United States. The relative importance of each in relation to the total energy produced is shown.*

part for a long time to come. What may happen if atomic energy is successfully harnessed for industrial purposes is anyone's guess. Also, more efficient mining and utilization of coal will enable it to meet competition more effectively. A significant recent development is the perfection of the coal-burning gas turbine, which uses finely powdered coal and can consume coal of low as well as high quality. It is said that a locomotive powered by the gas turbine is three or four times as efficient as the older coal-burning steam locomotive. In the face of diminishing reserves of petroleum and natural gas, such an invention may have far-reaching consequences and may cause coal to increase, rather than decrease, in significance. Still another probability is the use of coal as an important source of gasoline.

Origin

Coal represents a long evolution from plant remains to the "black rock" which we know today. It began its existence in extensive swamps where lush tropical vegetation grew. As plants died, muds and water prevented their complete decay. Running water carried other muds and sands into the swamps, to bury and press down upon the layers of organic material. The result was alternate layers of plant remains and earth materials. As time went on, pressure from overlying earth materials, plus the heat derived from those pressures and from deeper burial, caused the organic materials to evolve into some kind, or stage, of coal. Instrumental, too, were the

great pressures and high temperatures which accompany deformation of the earth's crust. Such deformation did not occur in all areas where coal was being formed, but, where it did take place, it speeded up the evolutionary process. When sufficiently severe, it produced types of coal that could not otherwise have come into existence.

Stages

Each kind or type of coal represents one stage in the evolution of plant remains. The first stage is *peat,* as the peat of the bogs of Ireland. Peat is not truly coal, but it may be called "incipient coal." Acted upon through time by heat and pressure, it slowly changes into *lignite* or *brown coal.* Lignite is soft, woody, high in water content and volatile gases, and low in carbon or "fixed carbon" (Fig. 264). Its low quality and low value normally limit its use to local areas and to simple domestic purposes. However, Germany has made important use of her lignite deposits for industrial and manufacturing purposes. This has been done at large expense in time and money, for it involves special processing as well as mixing of the lignite with coals of higher quality.

When lignite was subjected to further metamorphosis, it became *bituminous coal,* the exact type and quality depending primarily on how far the evolution was carried. Bituminous coal is higher in fixed carbon and lower in water content than lignite. It is also hard enough to stand shipment without too much breakage. Bituminous is the coal of major use. The higher the grade of bituminous, the less are the wastes in ash, water, and volatile gases (Fig. 264), and, in general, the greater are the possibilities of use. Some grades of bituminous are of "coking quality." This is important, for the manufacture of iron from iron ore demands large quantities of coke for use in the blast furnace. Inasmuch as steel is made from iron, coke is thus essential to the steel industry. Coke is coal that has been baked in "coke ovens" until part of the volatile gases have been removed, leaving material which is high in fixed carbon. The volatile gases, formerly wasted, are carefully collected and used as "artificial" gas in homes and factories. Nations which, like the United States, possess large tonnages of bituminous coal, including that of coking quality, are richer than they would be if they owned, instead, all the gold mines of the world.

Some coal evolved to the stage in which it is very hard, shiny, and comprised largely of fixed carbon. This is *anthracite*. It is clean, slow-burning coal. Its "dustless" and "smokeless" nature makes it an excellent fuel for the heating of dwellings and public buildings in cities. Such use is greatly encouraged because it decreases the smoke pall or smog which distresses large urban areas. However, anthracite is a very expensive coal. It occurs in few places in the world, and it is so interbedded with complexly folded and faulted rocks that mining costs are high.

In a few places, coal evolved to the point where it is no longer coal. So great was the change that virtually all volatile matter was eliminated, leaving little more than carbon, or graphite. The "graphitic coals" are insignificant commercially.

Geologic and Geographic Location

Many things determine the usefulness of a given coal deposit—and of deposits of other minerals as well. Very important among them are geologic and geographic location. Geologic location refers to the actual position of the coal layers, or seams, within and among other rocks and to distance from the surface of the ground. Some coal seams are near or at the surface and are arranged horizontally or nearly so. If the seams are also thick and of high

264 *COMPARISON of the composition of lignite, medium bituminous coal, and anthracite coal.*

quality, conditions for mining are optimum. Cheap strip-mining methods can be used; the regolith or, in some instances, solid rock is removed by power shovels and draglines, and the coal is scooped up and loaded into trucks or railway cars (Fig. 265). Much of the Illinois coal is mined in this manner.

Most of the world's coal is not so conveniently located. It occurs in layers at various depths and in various degrees of deformation. Often the coal seams outcrop on the sides of valleys and the easiest way to obtain the coal is to make tunnels or "drifts" which reach back, following the given seam, into the valleyside. Tunnel mining demands supporting timbers to prevent cave-ins, proper aeration and drainage, and small tracks and cars for hauling the coal out of the mine. Much of the Appalachian coal of the United States is mined in such fashion (Fig. 266A). Obviously, it is much more expensive than strip mining. Some coal seams are intricately folded and faulted and, in part, deeply buried (Fig. 266B). This is particularly true of the anthracite coal seams of eastern Pennsylvania. In attempts to follow the weaving, broken seams into the earth, a combination of shaft and tunnel mining is necessary. Coal has to be lifted through the shaft to the surface by elevators and the deeper the mine, the greater is the cost of getting the coal up. Thus, purely geologic location is an especially prominent factor in the price of anthracite, or any other type of coal which is similarly placed.

Geographic location simply refers to where coal is in the world, as in western Germany or southern Wales. This is just as important as geologic location. There are large deposits

265 *STRIP MINING of coal, like open-pit mining or iron ore, is less expensive than shaft or tunnel mining. Here a steam shovel both digs and loads the coal. (National Film Board, Canada)*

of high-quality bituminous coal in Antarctica, but they are in the wrong place to be utilized. Much the same is true of Alaskan coal and of many deposits in the interior of Asia. However, a region does not necessarily remain inaccessible. There was a time when the Illinois coal was inaccessible, but the westward spread of industrialization and improved methods of transportation greatly changed the picture. A few years ago, the coal of the Kuznetsk Basin, in Siberia, was inaccessible. Now it is being actively mined. However, the mining of Kuznetsk coal is not simply a matter of transportation, railway coal cars, and availability of miners, but a matter of government as well. The Soviet Union runs the mines and the operations do not have to be "economical"; they do not have to meet open commercial competition from other coal mines in the U.S.S.R. or in foreign countries.

Thus, it is sometimes difficult to state which coal deposits are favorably located in a geographic sense and which are not. The same applies partly to geologic location, for governments may order that certain coal deposits be mined, regardless of mining difficulties. Granted all this, the optimum conditions occur in those areas where thick, high-quality seams lie horizontally near the surface and within, or with easy access to, large markets.

Major Coal Fields

Coal occurs in all continents and in nearly all countries, but most of it is in the Northern Hemisphere and the richest deposits are in only a few countries (Fig. 267). These are the United States, Germany, the United Kingdom, and the U.S.S.R. The order given

266   *CROSS SECTIONS showing positions of coal seams among other earth materials. Part A is fairly typical of the Appalachian bituminous coal fields; Part B is representative of the Pennsylvania anthracite fields.*

is that of rank in coal mined within recent years, but prior to World War II. Germany is still in the postwar reconstruction period. Whether she regains her former position remains to be seen. In any event she has the largest deposits of high-quality coal to be found in all of Europe.

UNITED STATES. This nation possesses, despite previous heavy withdrawals, the largest and richest coal deposits of any country. Their

distribution, including low-quality bituminous and lignite, is shown in Fig. 268. The coal fields of the eastern (Appalachian) province extend from northern Pennsylvania to the Birmingham district of Alabama. Most of the coal is high-quality bituminous, including abundant coking coal. The world's chief anthracite deposit occurs in eastern Pennsylvania, in the Scranton-Wilkes-Barre district. The eastern province is the world's outstand-

267   *THE NORTHERN Hemisphere is the coal hemisphere.*

ing example of "enough of the right kind of coal in the right place." The interior province extends from Michigan to central Texas. It, again, is comprised of bituminous coals. So far, the chief mining areas are in Illinois and parts of adjacent Indiana and Kentucky, areas which are most favorably located in terms of market and where the coal is in the more favorable geologic positions. The remaining provinces are more broken and scattered and definitely inferior in quality of coal, although the tonnage is tremendous. The Gulf province is a lignite province. The Great Plains province is chiefly lignite. The Rocky Mountain province, very much scattered, contains bituminous and subbituminous coals. The Pacific province is more a name than an actuality (Fig. 268).

The world leadership of the United States, beginning about 1900, is based on the coal in the eastern half of the country, most particularly in the Appalachian region. The chief coal-mining states, in order of production, are Pennsylvania, West Virginia, Illinois, and Kentucky. Pennsylvania and West Virginia produce about 65 per cent of United States coal and Illinois and Kentucky produce about 20 per cent.

EUROPE. The major coal fields of Europe are in Germany, Belgium, Poland, the U.S.S.R., and the United Kingdom. Small and scattered fields are found from the Mediterranean to the Baltic and from the Atlantic to the Urals (Fig. 269).

The United Kingdom held first rank in world coal production from the beginning of the Industrial Revolution until about 1900. If lignite is excepted, she still holds second rank; if lignite is included, Germany is second. British coal fields, although heavily mined for a century and a half, are not exhausted. Reserves are said to be sufficient for several hundred years. However, the coal which remains is much less accessible and, as mines

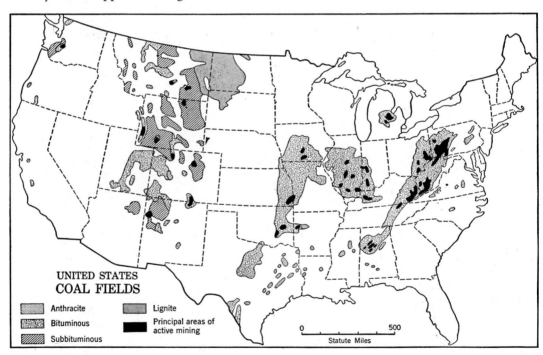

268 *THE UNITED STATES is a coal-rich nation. Active mining, especially in the fields east of the Mississippi River, account for this leadership in world coal production.*

EUROPE'S
COAL FIELDS

0   500   1000
Statute Miles

RUHR

UPPER
SILESIA

DONETS

WALES

SAMBRE
MEUSE

SAAR

269

EUROPE has a few large and many small coal deposits. Ruhr Valley coals lead in both high quality and great quantity.

are pushed deeper and deeper, mining costs increase. The chief fields lie among the margins of the Pennine Chain and in southern Wales. Significant deposits also occur in the Central Lowland of Scotland (Fig. 269). The Welsh coal has been particularly useful in Britain's sea-borne commerce, not only to fuel her merchant marine, but also as an item of foreign trade. The coal is high in quality and is located practically on tidewater. Welsh coal is to be found on the wharves of most of the earth's major seaports. When one recalls the world position of the United Kingdom in manufacturing and trade, it is easy to appreciate the role of coal in the British economy.

Germany's rapid rise to power was based as much as anything else on plentiful bituminous coal, including coking coal. While she has several small fields, the bulk of her production comes from the famous Westphalian fields in the equally famous Ruhr Valley (Fig. 269). From 1870 until 1914, Germany possessed both the Ruhr coals and the Lorraine iron ores, two major sinews of modern

industry—and of modern warfare. Following World War I, Lorraine was returned to France, but Germany still retained the Ruhr coals as well as important fields in Upper Silesia, next to the southwestern border of Poland. At the end of World War II, Germany lost the Upper Silesian fields to Poland, and the Saar Basin coal field which is located along the Franco-German border next to Luxembourg. She continues to hold the Ruhr, or Westphalian, field, largest and richest on the Continent.

The European coal fields of the U.S.S.R. are mainly in the Donets Basin, in the southern part of the Russian Plain and a bit to the north of the Sea of Azov (Fig. 269). They are chiefly bituminous; some of them are of coking quality, but not of highest coking grade. Other fields are the Tula field, just south of Moscow, and several small ones at the southern end of the Urals. The former is comprised of lignite and low-quality bituminous; the latter contain bituminous of noncoking nature. The U.S.S.R. "came out of nowhere" in terms of world coal production. In 1918, its name did not appear on the list of important coal-producing nations; by 1939, at the start of World War II, it held fourth place. The sharply rising curve of its coal production practically coincides with the curve of Russian industrial progress. As will be noted later, a significant part of Russian coal is now mined in Siberia.

Belgium and France share coal fields which extend roughly east-west through central Belgium and barely into northern France. They are the Sambre-Meuse fields (Fig. 269). Smaller fields occur in northeastern Belgium and in several parts of France, chiefly around the edges of the Massif Central. The Sambre-Meuse coals are excellent for most purposes, but they have to be mixed with imported coals in order to manufacture high-grade coke. Both France and Belgium have had to depend greatly on coal from the Ruhr and the United Kingdom. France now controls the Saar Basin fields, but the coal obtained has to be mixed with higher-grade coking coal from the Ruhr.

ASIA. The coal of Asia extends in a sort of broken ring around the margins of the upland heart of that continent (Fig. 267). Most of it is in Siberia, China, and India. Lesser amounts occur in scattered fields in the Japanese islands and elsewhere.

Some of the significant activities in world coal mining and utilization have taken place recently in Soviet Asia. Chief among them is the use of the coal of the Kuznetsk Basin. This region is located in the southeastern part of the Ob River Basin, in the foothills of the Sayan Mountains and a bit south of the main line of the Trans-Siberian Railway. Here and nearby are several new industrial centers which draw on Kuznetsk coal. Other important coal fields, some of them being utilized, occur across much of southern Siberia, from the region north of Lake Balkhash nearly to the Pacific Ocean. Still others, about which we yet know little, lie in central Siberia and on the fringe of the tundra region.

The bulk of the coal of China lies in the North China hill country, west of the North China Plain, in the provinces of Shansi and Shensi. The coal has been only slightly utilized; it is expensive to mine, hard to reach, and far from the market. Unless China becomes much more industrialized, the Shansi-Shensi coal deposits will remain chiefly as untapped resources. Actually much more coal has been mined in southern Manchuria than in any other part of China. However, Manchurian reserves are meager compared to those of China Proper.

Japan's coal fields are small and scattered. Hokkaido has the largest reserves, followed by Kyushu and Honshu; Honshu is a poor third in coal resources. Japanese coals are bituminous of medium quality, but Japan has had to import coking coal for its iron and steel industries from southern Manchuria. At the beginning of World War II, Japan was the leading coal producer of Asia with production that rivaled that of Belgium and of France.

Most of the coal fields in India lie to the west of Calcutta, partly in the Ganges Plain and partly in the hills of the northeastern portion of the Deccan. Other important ones occur in the Godavari Valley section of the Deccan. Lesser fields are found in far eastern and northwestern India. India's coal, particularly that to the west of Calcutta, is enabling her to make significant strides toward an industrial economy.

SOUTHERN HEMISPHERE. Coal fields are "few and far between" south of the equator (Fig. 267). Australia has the lion's share in both tonnage and quality. Some of Australia's coal is of coking quality and is unique in this respect among Southern Hemisphere coals. The chief fields occur near the important ports of Sydney and Brisbane. Newcastle, a bit northeast along the coast from Sydney, is the chief coal center. It takes its name from a more famous Newcastle, the ancient coal-mining city in England.

South Africa has coal of medium grade in parts of Natal and Transvaal. This coal can be moved readily to Port Natal and less easily by longer "hauls" to Cape Town. Its importance rests largely on the fact that it is excellent for railway and steamship purposes and that no other coal is available within thousands of miles.

South America is "coal poor." Only in the southern part of middle Chile is there coal which is both accessible and of good quality (Fig. 267). Even then, reserves are small. Some high-grade coal exists in the Peruvian and Colombian Andes, but it is so isolated as to be of little use. Southern Brazil possesses coal, but of low quality. Most of the large cities of South America are seaports. They find it easier to use British coal from southern Wales than to search out and develop the generally scattered and inferior fields of their own continent.

PETROLEUM

The commercial uses of petroleum are both old and new. In certain places, where the "rock oil" seeped from the ground, it has undoubtedly had minor use for thousands of years. Historical records mention it as early as four centuries before the birth of Christ. In early trade, it was a rare and costly substance.

Uses

Primitive man used crude petroleum obtained from "seeps" to caulk small boats, to waterproof dwelling roofs, to dress his hair, and to anoint his skin. Later, as in the trade of the Middle Ages (roughly 500-1500 A.D.), it was used as a medicine. Petroleum derived from coal and oil shales began to serve importantly for lighting purposes by 1800, gradually replacing whale oil and tallow candles. Modern production from drilled

wells started just prior to the American Civil War and increased by leaps and bounds after 1900. Accompanying the rapid upsurge in production there was great progress in drilling and refining methods as well as in transportation and marketing.

In recent years, the story of petroleum parallels that of automobiles, airplanes, and modern ships. It is a story of tremendous demand for petroleum and petroleum products to run and to lubricate engines and machines. In addition, petroleum is used to supply paraffin, vaseline, cleaning fluids, kerosene, dyes, and scores of other products. Table 19 indicates most of the present-day uses. Looking at this table, one can appreciate why world production has risen from less than 7,000 barrels in 1859 to about 3,000,000,000 barrels at the present time and why production in the United States, major home of the automobile and the airplane, rose from 2,000 barrels in 1859 to 63,000,000 barrels in 1900, 1,350,000,000 barrels in 1940, and approximately 2,000,000,000 barrels at present.

Comparative Importance

Petroleum and petroleum products now furnish much of the energy used in the United States (Fig. 263). Petroleum has become so important that any sudden stoppage of supply would paralyze the nation almost as quickly as would lack of coal. Not only is it necessary to a peacetime economy, but it is extremely critical during time of war. Air fleets, mechanized armies, and navies require huge quantities of fuel oil, gasoline, and lubricants. In World War I, it was said that the Allied nations "rode to victory on a sea of oil." This was doubly true in World War II. Considering the significance of petroleum in peace and war, one can easily understand why there has been, and still is, a "world struggle for oil." Nations with little or no oil struggle to insure themselves supplies from foreign countries. Thus, the United King-

Table 19 SELECTED LIST OF PRODUCTS OBTAINED FROM PETROLEUM

NATURAL GAS	Flotation oils
Domestic fuel	Transformer oils
Industrial fuel	Lubricating oils
Butadiene	Waxes (paraffins)
Butylene	
Acetylene	**RESIDUES**
Ethylene	Greases
Methyl alcohol	Lubricating oils
Formaldehyde	Fuel oils
Chloroform	Road oils
Carbon tetrachloride	Waterproofing oils
Carbon black	Oil coke
	Medicinal oils
HYDROCARBON GASES	**REFINERY SLUDGES**
Fuel gas	Sulfonic acids
Petroleum ether	Sulphuric acid
Liquefied gases	Asphalts
Solid carbon dioxide	Binders
Carbon black	Wood preservatives
Light naphthas	Fuel oil
	Fuel coke
WHITE, INTERMEDIATE, HEAVY DISTILLATES	**SPECIAL USE PRODUCTS**
Naphthas	Penetrating oils
Refined oils	Skin and hair oils
Kerosene	Colored smokes
Signal oil	Skywriting smokes
Diesel fuel	

dom is vitally interested in the rich oil fields of Iraq and in protecting the pipe lines and sea lanes which bring the oil to the British Isles. Other nations, temporarily rich in petroleum, seek large supplies for use in the future or to help conserve their own deposits. This partly explains why a nation like the United States is vitally concerned with the huge oil reserves of faraway Arabia. It likewise partly explains the interest of the U.S.S.R. in the affairs of Iran. When two strong nations are attempting to gain control of oil in the same foreign country, the possibilities of conflict, even open warfare, are great. Iran is a case in point, for both Russian and British interests are strong there, and Iran itself is, in a sense, "caught in the middle." Someone has said that the worst thing that can happen to a weak, undeveloped country is the discovery of large and rich oil deposits within its boundaries.

Geologic Occurrence

Petroleum is found in only very restricted portions of the earth's crust. First of all, it is limited to regions of sedimentary rocks. Thus there is no possibility of its discovery in such vast areas as the Laurentian Shield of North America, the equatorial uplands of eastern Africa, most of western Australia, and many other areas. Even in regions of sedimentary rocks there are few deposits, at least in commercial quantities. Either the oil was not formed, or it was lost as a result of seepage, erosion, or extreme diastrophism.

For petroleum to exist in commercial amounts, in the form of oil "pools," special rock structures are required. These must trap and hold the oil particles as they migrate within sedimentary rock layers. Fig. 270 illustrates some of the more common possibilities. It will be noted in each example that the rocks are so arranged, because of folding, faulting, or both, that any oil particles which may be present are literally trapped in a portion of the structure. Here the particles lie, under great pressure resulting from the weight of the rocks above and from the natural gas which is usually entrapped with the oils. When an oil prospector locates a "pool" and drills into it, the oil and gas usually rush up the drill hole with great force, often with a roar which can be heard for several miles. Such oil wells are "gushers." They must be capped in order to control the flow of oil and gas and to prevent complete loss. Later, as pressures lessen, such wells must be pumped.

Geographic Distribution

UNITED STATES. The United States has the largest, richest, and most actively exploited of all the world's known petroleum deposits. Commercial production began in 1859, when the initial well was drilled near Titusville, in northern Pennsylvania. This was the first drilled oil well in the world. Oil was obtained at a depth of only 69 feet. As equipment improved, it was possible to tap deeper-lying pools, both in Pennsylvania and elsewhere (Fig. 271). Today, man is able to reach far into the earth for petroleum: a well drilled recently in California is nearly 17,000 feet deep—more than three miles! In recent years, the United States has produced from 60 to 65 per cent of the world total. For the future, she has the largest proved reserves of any single country. However, the greatest group of reserves appears to be in the Near East, in Arabia, Iraq, and Iran.

The petroleum fields of the United States are sufficiently scattered to insure most of the nation easy access to the oil and the products derived from it (Fig. 272). Moreover, petroleum and its products are relatively easy to transport, whether by pipe line, tank car, tank truck, oil barge, or ocean-going tanker. Most of the refineries, about five times the number found in all the rest of the world, are located at the junctions of major pipe lines and at points where foreign oil arrives at the seaboard. The greatest single refining district is located between New York and Baltimore. Much of the crude oil used there comes by tanker from Venezuela and many of the refined products travel by water to western Europe. Other major refining centers are at the southern end of Lake Michigan, along the Texas-Louisiana Gulf coast, and in the south coastal section of California.

U.S.S.R. Russia became an important producer of petroleum about 1873. In some years, Russia actually produced more than did the United States—not, however, since 1901. Russia's total production to date has been only about one-fifth that of the United States. Russian oil reserves are estimated to be only

PETROLEUM

270 SOME of the types of geologic structures which trap petroleum: (A) anticlinal trap; (B) fault trap; (C) trap in a lens structure; (D) traps formed by deformation of strata by a volcanic "neck."

271   OIL FIELD south of Oklahoma City. The wide spacing of wells is in accordance with modern conservation practices, which allow recovery of greater quantities of oil. Contrast this picture with Fig. 262B. (Rotkin, Standard Oil Co. [N. J.])

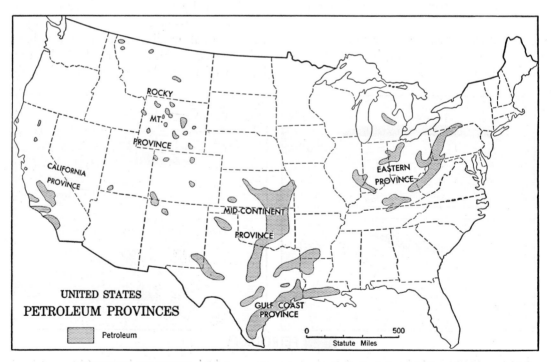

272   UNITED STATES petroleum deposits are well distributed. By use of pipe lines and other conveyances, petroleum products, including natural gas, are readily made available to most sections of the country.

MAJOR
PETROLEUM
PROVINCES

Compressed Sinusoidal
equal-area projection

0 1000 2000 3000 4000 5000
STATUTE MILES

273   THE WORLD *pattern of known petroleum provinces.*

about one-third as large as those of the United States; hence Russia is vitally interested in acquiring control of foreign oil, as in neighboring Iran.

Practically all of the oil of the U.S.S.R. occurs along the northern and eastern margins of the Caucasus Mountains (Fig. 273). The Baku fields, located where the Caucasus meets the Caspian Sea, are the most important. Other fields occur at the northeastern edge of the Caspian and in the southern Urals. Eastern Siberia reportedly has considerable petroleum resources to offer. Outside of the Caucasus area, Romania has the only other oil fields of significance in all of Europe and these, producing about 3 per cent of the world total, are under Russian control.

Present Russian petroleum production is about one-sixth that of the United States. However, this is sufficient to give her either second or third place in world output, probably third. If Soviet statistics on petroleum production are accepted without question, the U.S.S.R. holds second rank; if not, then Venezuela is second. In any event, Venezuela and the U.S.S.R. are in a close race for second position.

VENEZUELA. It was not until 1919 that Venezuela entered importantly into the world petroleum scene; yet, by 1928, she was in second place, although producing only slightly more than one-eighth as much as the United States. Today, as discussed above, she may still be in second place, producing about one-sixth as much as the United States and roughly one-tenth of the world total.

The rapid increase in Venezuelan oil output largely reflects improved technology. By the time her pools were discovered, the petroleum industry had developed modern techniques for drilling, pumping, and transporting oil in large quantities. In addition, American capital was readily available and there was a great world demand for the oil.

Although there is some production elsewhere, as in the lower Orinoco Basin, most of

274

PIPE lines carry crude oil across the desert. This is the line between Dhahran and Abqaiq in the El Hasa section of Saudi Arabia adjacent to the Persian Gulf. (Corsini, Standard Oil Co. [N. J.])

the Venezuelan oil comes from the Lake Maracaibo fields (Fig. 273). Shallow-draft tankers carry the oil out into the Caribbean to the nearby Dutch islands of Aruba and Curaçao. There some of the oil is run through mammoth refineries (Fig. 275) and shipped to the United States and Europe; the remainder, pumped into large ocean-going tankers, proceeds to refineries located on our Gulf and Atlantic coasts and to those located in Britain and adjacent sections of western Europe. Venezuela enjoys the distinction of exporting more petroleum than any other nation. Her proved reserves, probably about one-third those of the United States, are the second largest in all the Americas and are comparable to those of the U.S.S.R.

NEAR EAST. The countries of Iran, Iraq, and Arabia together now produce between 6 and 7 per cent of the world's crude petroleum. Iran alone produces close to 4 per cent. Iranian output was important by 1910 and it has increased steadily since then. For many years Iran has held fourth rank in world output. Iraq's oil became significant in world markets by 1928. She now produces about 2 per cent of the world total. Arabia, or more technically Saudi Arabia, is the real newcomer in oil production. So far production is compara-

tively small, but is increasing very rapidly. American capital is developing Arabian oil and indications are for great expansion in the near future.

Iran's oil fields lie close to the Persian Gulf and only slightly removed from the southeastern corner of Iraq (Fig. 273). New discoveries have been reported in the north, near the border of the U.S.S.R. Iraq's fields are well into the northern interior of the country, chiefly around Kirkuk. Most of the oil exported from Saudi Arabia comes from the island of Bahrein, in the Persian Gulf. However, new oil fields are rapidly being developed on the mainland.

The real significance of the oil of the Near East lies in the future, and, evidently, the near future. Recent information indicates that the Near East possesses at least 40 per cent of the world's remaining reserves of petroleum. This is a greater reserve than in the United States, or in all of North America. In fact, it is nearly as great as the total reserves of all the Americas, North, Middle, and South. Much of the reserve, particularly in Saudi Arabia and Iran, is located close to cheap water transportation and even more of it is so placed that the oil can move to the sea's edge by means of relatively short pipe

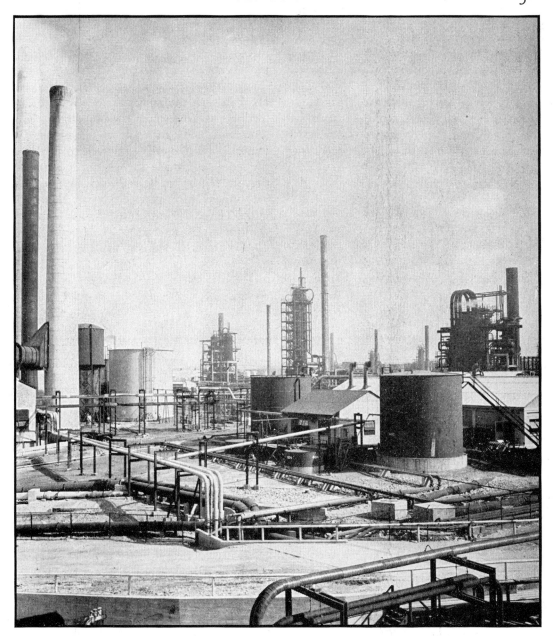

275   *PART of a large oil refinery on the island of Aruba, Netherlands West Indies.
(Morris, Standard Oil Co. [N. J.])*

lines. Long pipe lines are already in use to transport Iraq's oil to the eastern end of the Mediterranean and new ones will soon carry oil to the Mediterranean shore from new fields in northern Arabia (Fig. 274).

OTHER AREAS. The countries and fields noted above produce nearly 90 per cent of the world's petroleum and possess about 90 per cent of the petroleum reserves. Thus world oil production will continue to be associated primarily with the United States, the U.S.S.R., Venezuela, Iran, Iraq, and Saudi Arabia, with the last three gaining in prominence. However, production will continue for some time in other areas. These appear in Fig. 273. Chief among them are Mexico, Romania, Indonesia, and Colombia. Others include Trinidad, Argentina, and still lesser ones such as Japan, Burma, and Canada.

The Future

Recent estimates of petroleum reserves on the land areas of the world indicate that there is enough petroleum to last about 160 years at the current rate of production. To this total should be added the reserves of the continental shelves, which are less easily estimated and certain to be more costly to develop than reserves not covered by sea water. The estimated oil reserves of the United States are probably sufficient for another twenty-five to thirty years, although their duration will depend on such things as correction of wasteful methods of production, development of new sources of motor fuel, and on the amount of imported oil. It is very significant that most of the products which are obtained from petroleum can be made from coal, although, as yet, only at much greater expense. With definitely limited petroleum reserves and the world's largest reserves of coal, perhaps the United States should begin to turn more and more to new phases of coal utilization. This might also mean fewer chances of foreign conflict involved with the "world scramble for oil."

CHAPTER OUTLINE

Coal and petroleum: the chief sources of industrial energy

Coal
    Uses
    Comparative importance
    Origin
    Stages
    Geologic and geographic location
    Major coal fields
        United States
        Europe
        Asia
        Southern Hemisphere
Petroleum
    Uses
    Comparative importance
    Geologic occurrence
    Geographic distribution
        United States
        U.S.S.R.
        Venezuela
        Near East
        Other areas
    The future

REVIEW QUESTIONS

1. Why is coal so important in this so-called Age of Electricity?
2. See if you can determine how important coal is in the community in which you live.
3. Discuss the origin and the "stages" of coal.
4. Distinguish between geologic and geographic location of coal.
5. Identify coal fields now actively mined which were formerly unused because of unfavorable geographic locations. What happened to make their use possible?
6. Is it possible to overcome a poor geologic location of coal? Explain.
7. What is the relative position of the United States among the nations as far as possession of high-quality coal is concerned?
8. List the major coal fields of Europe. Which one of them will undoubtedly be exhausted last?
9. What are some of the major reasons why China's Shansi Province coals have been mined so little?
10. Compare the Northern and Southern Hemispheres as to quality and quantity of coal.
11. Account for the comparatively sudden large demands for petroleum.

12. Explain the statement, "Petroleum may be one of the major causes of future wars."
13. In recent years, much has been heard about petroleum discoveries in Canada. What would your attitude be if you were asked to invest money in exploration for petroleum deposits in the interior of Quebec? Give the reasons for your attitude.
14. Is the geographic location of petroleum in the United States favorable or unfavorable? Explain.
15. Compare the mining and transportation problems of coal and petroleum.
16. What is the world position of the United States in petroleum production and reserves?
17. Why is there so much argument about how long the world's petroleum supplies will last? Why do estimates as to the amount of petroleum in the world, or in individual countries, vary so greatly?

SOME SUGGESTED REFERENCES

Encyclopædia Britannica (1943 edition). See section on Coal and Coal Mining, and on Petroleum; also, *Britannica Book of the Year,* section on Coal and on Petroleum.

Energy Resources of the World, U. S. Department of State, 1949. An illustrated monograph dealing with types of energy, energy utilization, and trends, both for individual countries and for the world as a whole.

Fanning, Leonard M., *Our Oil Resources,* McGraw-Hill, 1945. A recent evaluation of our petroleum supplies and their utilization.

Fanning, Leonard M., *The Rise of American Oil,* Harper, 1946. The story of the discovery, development, and use of our petroleum.

Glover, John G., and Cornell, William B., *The Development of American Industries,* Prentice-Hall, 1946. A book on the history and present economic significance of our basic industries; see especially Chapter 15, The Petroleum Industry.

Jeffrey, Edward C., *Coal and Civilization,* Macmillan, 1925. A rather full consideration of the part which coal has played and is playing in man's affairs.

Lovering, Thomas S., *Minerals in World Affairs,* Prentice-Hall, 1944. A book dealing with the history, economics, geology, and geographical distribution of the important minerals; see Chapter 6, Coal, and Chapter 7, Petroleum.

Minerals Yearbook, U. S. Bureau of Mines. An annual report on mineral production and mineral industries in the United States.

Pratt, Wallace E., and Good, Dorothy, *World Geography of Petroleum,* Princeton University Press (published for the American Geographical Society as Special Publication No. 31), 1950. The most recent treatment of world petroleum.

276 *OPEN-PIT IRON ore mine at Hibbing, Minnesota, located in one of the great iron ranges of the world. Electric shovels scoop up the ore and load it onto the cars which then "spiral" up out of the pit. (U. S. Steel Corp.)*

CHAPTER 17

Iron Ore and the Ferroalloys

IRON ORE

No iron ore, no iron; no iron, no steel. Thus, briefly and directly, may be stated the significance of iron ore in the present-day world. While coal and, to a lesser extent, petroleum, run most of the world's machines, the machines themselves are made chiefly of iron or of steel, which is itself made from iron. The same is true of common tools from knife and ax to saw and hammer. When it is remembered that iron is one of the more abundant elements in the earth's crust, it would seem that no country, region, or district need lack for iron. But such is not the case.

Chief Ores

Iron has practically no "free" or pure occurrence in nature. It exists in many compounds which, in turn, are greatly mixed with other rock materials. Most of the iron compounds do not constitute ores; that is, they do not occur in sufficient quantities or in sufficient purity to bear the expense of commercial development. Thus, there is much iron in the earth, but there are relatively few deposits of iron ore.

The chief ores of iron are *hematite, magnetite, limonite,* and *siderite.* They are mainly compounds of iron, oxygen, and carbon, plus, of course, varying amounts of impurities. The first three ores named are oxides, whereas the last is a carbonate. If impurities, such as phosphorus, are present in too great amount, the ores are inferior or, perhaps, unusable. Iron ores vary considerably in the proportion of iron per ton of ore. Some "run" as high as 60 or 70 per cent, others as low as 30 to 40 per cent. A few countries, such as the United States and Sweden, have been fortunate in the possession of large tonnages of ore high in iron content. Others, like France, have large tonnages of low-grade ore. Still other countries, such as Poland and Italy, have little or no iron ore.

To date, the chief iron ores have been commercially mined mainly in five nations. They are the United States, the U.S.S.R., France, the United Kingdom, and Sweden (Fig. 277). Together, they have, in recent years, produced nearly three-quarters of the world's annual output. Other significant producers are Germany and Luxembourg. All remaining nations combined produce only about one-quarter of the annual total and no one of them mines as much as 2 per cent of that total. Some of the earth's major iron ore deposits as yet produce very little, or none at all. Important among such prime reserves are those in Brazil, Newfoundland, Canada, and the central portion of southern Siberia (Fig.

277). Possibly another prime reserve is that which is undergoing development in Venezuela. Brazil is reputed to have the largest deposit of high-grade iron ore in the world; her production today is much less than 1 per cent of the world's annual production.

Iron Ranges of the United States

Districts containing usable iron deposits are known as *iron ranges*. There is no necessary connection between iron ranges and ranges of hills and mountains. Some occur in hilly areas, as do the iron ranges of northern Sweden and northeastern New York State; some are found on the flanks of or within mountainous country, as are those near Bilbao in northern Spain and near Melilla in Spanish Morocco; but many, like those of the Cleveland district in England or the Dnieper Basin of Russia, are located in plains.

The chief iron ranges of the United States are located in northeastern Minnesota and northern Michigan. Other important ones lie in central Alabama, northeastern New York, southeastern Pennsylvania, and northern Wisconsin (Fig. 278). All of them, from Minnesota to New York and south to Alabama, are either in or close to the margins of the northeastern manufacturing region of the United States—the greatest manufacturing region in the world. In addition, the major iron ranges have easy access to cheap water transportation on the Great Lakes. Lesser ranges, scattered and isolated, occur in Wyoming, Utah, Colorado, New Mexico, and California.

LAKE SUPERIOR RANGES. Located in a broken arc around the western margins of Lake Superior are the large, high-grade deposits which have given the United States first rank in the

277   *WORLD distribution of the chief producing iron ranges, plus major iron ranges of potential importance.*

278

THE LARGEST movement of iron ore in the world flows from the upper to the lower ports of the Great Lakes. It moves chiefly to the margin or into the Appalachian coal fields and, thus, into the heart of the world's largest manufacturing region.

Legend (within map):
- Major iron ranges
- + Other iron ranges
- Major flow of iron ore from upper lakes
- Approximate boundary of major coal regions
- Approximate boundary of the Northeastern Manufacturing Region

mining of iron ore (Fig. 279). These ranges normally account for about 80 per cent of United States output and nearly a third of that of the entire world. Ordinarily, from 40,000,000 to 60,000,000 tons of iron ore travel the Great Lakes each year, chiefly to those blast furnaces and steel mills strung from Chicago to Buffalo and from the southern margins of the Great Lakes to the Ohio Valley. During part of World War II, the annual output was almost 100,000,000 tons! But there are warnings in the air. We have drawn so heavily on the Lake Superior ranges, both in peace and in war, that the readily procured reserves of high-grade iron ore may be exhausted by 1970. The period of the richest harvest is about ended. To be sure, there are tremendous reserves of low-grade ore, but they will demand expensive processing and, perhaps, the importation of high-grade foreign ores to be mixed with them as "enrichers."

The iron ore of the Lake Superior country

was discovered in the Upper Peninsula of Michigan in 1844; this was in the section which soon became known as the Marquette Range (Fig. 279). Movement of ore from this range to eastern manufacturing districts was greatly facilitated by the opening, in 1855, of the "Soo"—Sault (pronounced "soo") Sainte Marie Canal. The Menominee Range came into production in 1872 and the Gogebic Range in 1884. Then, in 1892, the greatest of them all was opened— the world-famous Mesabi Range, which lies in northeastern Minnesota, within short and easy rail haul of the ports of Duluth and Two Harbors (Fig. 279). In recent years, this range alone has supplied more than half of all iron ore mined in the United States. When other Minnesota ranges, the Vermilion and Cuyuna, came into production, Minnesota far outdistanced Michigan as an iron ore producer.

The importance of the Mesabi Range is based on more than tonnage of high-grade

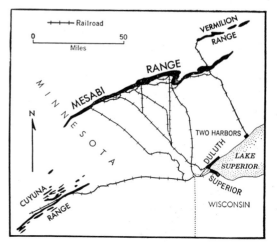

279

(Above) *LOCATION and names of the Lake Superior iron ranges, including Canada's Michipicoten Range;* (right) *main rail lines which connect Minnesota's iron ranges with the Lake Superior shipping ports.*

ore. "Geology was kind" to the Mesabi: the high-grade ore lies at and near the surface and in continuous deposits which are so soft that they can be mined with power shovels (Fig. 276). Quite to the contrary, the ores of the Michigan ranges occur mainly in tortuous, faulted, and deep-reaching veins and pockets within masses of hard rock (Fig. 280). Thus, while Minnesota ores are mined by relatively cheap open-pit methods, the Michigan ores demand the use of slower and more costly shaft-mining procedures (Fig. 281). Shafts, often 2,000 feet deep, reach down into very hard rocks and from the shafts several tunnels or drifts extend out to intersect the weaving and pockety ores. Special equipment is needed to operate elevators or lifts, to pump out water, and to supply a steady flow of clean, cool air. When demand for iron ore is high, the shaft mines operate at a profit; when demand is low, they must close or

operate at a loss. Thus, the Mesabi continues to produce during years when most of the shaft mines are closed. To be sure, the open-pit operations cease for three, four, or five months each year, depending on the severity of the winter, but the ore is not perishable and enough can be mined during the "open season" to fill each year's orders.

ORE ON THE GREAT LAKES. It is hardly possible to discuss the Lake Superior iron ranges without mentioning the Great Lakes. These great bodies of water effectively connect our richest iron ores with our most useful coal deposits (Fig. 278). Over these lakes, from April to December, move the long ships, called ore carriers or ore boats, which transport the reddish ores "down-lakes" and the black coal "up-lakes" (Fig. 282). Then, when blizzards blow and cold strikes, violent storms sweep the lakes and thick ice forms in the canal locks at the Soo and in the harbors of the

280   *DIAGRAMMATIC expression of the occurrence of ore in the Lake Superior iron ranges. Part A is typical of the Mesabi Range; Part B is typical of the Marquette Range. In B, the bedrock is both intricately folded and faulted.*

281
(Right) *SHAFT HOUSE, crusher, and iron ore stock pile in the "Iron Country" of northern Michigan, and* (below) *one of the tunnels in a "hard rock" iron ore mine. (Cleveland-Cliffs Iron Co.)*

upper lake ports. As the winter season progresses, large ice packs shift back and forth over the lakes, blown first one way and then the other by the winds. This is the "closed season" and during this time the ore carriers are tied up in long rows in several ports of the lower lakes. There they await the "spring breakup" which again will send them shuttling back and forth in long processions between such ports as Duluth and Buffalo, and Escanaba and Gary (Fig. 278).

To reach the carriers, iron ore must travel short distances by rail. It moves in open-topped cars which are hauled to tall and massive ore docks at Duluth and Two Har-

bors in Minnesota, Ashland and Superior in Wisconsin, and Marquette and Escanaba in Michigan. Cars are hauled up long ramps to the tops of the docks; there the bottoms of the cars open to drop the ore into huge cylindrical bins embedded vertically in the sides of the docks. Ore boats move into position below the bins and the ore slides from the bottoms of the bins into the holds of the boats by means of long metal chutes. Most carriers can contain about 10,000 to 11,000 tons, although a few of them are capable of transporting as much as 15,000 tons at one time. One boat, recently built, has a capacity of nearly 20,000 tons! The happy combination

282 *LOADED ore-carrier leaving the harbor at Duluth, Minnesota, to begin its journey down-lakes. (Bubley, Standard Oil Co. [N. J.])*

of short rail haul, mass handling, and cheap lake transportation is basic to the ability of the United States to produce iron and steel in such great quantities and at such low cost.

After loading, the boats begin the long journey down-lakes. Some of them go to the Chicago-Gary district at the southern end of Lake Michigan, but most of them proceed to ports located along the southern shore of Lake Erie. Chief among the latter are Toledo, Cleveland, and Ashtabula, all in Ohio; Buffalo in New York; and Erie in Pennsylvania. The most lengthy haul is from Duluth to Buffalo, a distance of approximately 1,000 miles, requiring about four days' travel time. From the Lake Superior ports to those of the lower lakes, the ore vessels make use of Lakes Superior, Huron, St. Clair, and Erie. In addition, they must "lock through" the Soo, follow the narrow and winding St. Marys River and the straight and full streams of the St. Clair and Detroit rivers. Much of the ore shipped out of Escanaba moves over Green Bay and then south to the southern end of Lake Michigan; the remainder proceeds, via the Strait of Mackinac, into Lake Huron and thence down-lakes to Lake Erie.

At either upper or lower lakes ports, most of the ore carriers are unloaded by machines (Fig. 283) located on the edges of the wharves. However, some vessels carry their own unloading machines, which are permanently fastened to parts of their long steel decks. Unloading may require from four hours to half a day, whereas the original loading by means of chutes took only two or three hours. The ore may be placed in huge stock piles on the wharves, close to the blast furnaces, or it may be dumped into railway cars and shipped to Pittsburgh and other iron and steel manufacturing districts. Whether the ore is used at the ports or at inland centers, the flow of ore down-lakes has no parallel in any other part of the world.

BIRMINGHAM DISTRICT. Second only to the Lake Superior iron mines, albeit a poor second, is the string of iron mines which lies immediately east of Birmingham, Alabama, and extends southwest to nearby Bessemer and Woodstock. Most of the ore is mined by shaft methods, although there are a few small open-pit mines near Woodstock. Birmingham ore varies considerably in quality, but there is enough high-grade ore to mix with that of low grade to bring the resultant mixture up to blast furnace standards.

283

UNLOADING coal from a lake vessel at Duluth, Minnesota. (Bubley, Standard Oil Co. [N. J.])

The Birmingham district is unusual and fortunate in that both coking coal and limestone lie close together near the iron ore (Fig. 284). This is significant because the blasting of iron ore to make iron requires coke as a fuel and limestone as a purifier. In addition, some of the Birmingham ores actually contain enough lime to make them self-purifying or self-fluxing. Mainly because of the proximity of vital raw material, the Birmingham district can produce metallic iron cheaper than any other part of the United States although it has no local markets comparable to those of Pittsburgh, Cleveland, Gary, or the many other cities which lie along or near the Great Lakes.

OTHER RANGES. The relative insignificance of the other iron ranges of the United States can be appreciated when it is pointed out that all of them combined mine less than 10 per cent of the United States output. These other ranges are scattered here and there from New York to California. Chief among them are the iron-mining districts of the Adirondacks and the ridges and valleys of eastern Pennsylvania.

Iron Ores of Europe

European iron ores occur in many places, but the major deposits are in France, the U.S.S.R., Sweden, and the United Kingdom (Fig. 285). Other important deposits are located in Luxembourg, several small districts of Germany, and northern Spain.

284 *THE BIRMINGHAM district of Alabama, showing the general distribution of coal, coking coal, iron ore, and limestone.*

FRENCH ORES. France possesses the largest deposit of iron ore in Europe. This Lorraine deposit is in the northeastern part of the country, close to the German border (Fig. 285). Some of the ore extends into Luxembourg and a small, but important, section of Belgium. France has other iron ore deposits in several places, but they are comparatively insignificant. It was the Lorraine ores, plus Ruhr Valley coal, which largely made possible the industrialization of the Continent. From the time of the Franco-Prussian War (1870) to the end of World War I (1918), Germany had both the Ruhr coal and most of the Lorraine ores. The combination enabled Germany to become a world power. Since 1918, France has again controlled all of the Lorraine ores, but is still greatly dependent on Ruhr coking coal.

As mentioned earlier, French iron ores are low grade. They contain only 30 to 40 per cent of metallic iron, in contrast to the Lake Superior ores of the United States, which run in excess of 50 per cent iron—some as high as 60 and 70 per cent. Then, too, French ores are high in phosphorus, so that they had to await the invention of special processes before they could be used fully. In 1880, the *open-hearth* method of steel-making appeared. This process allowed ready use of iron derived from high-phosphorus ores. As a result, the value of the Lorraine ores increased immeasurably. Germany, however, was the first to profit, for the open hearth came into use only ten years after she seized the deposits.

For many years the mining of Lorraine ores has given France leadership in Europe and has enabled her to hold either second or third place in world production.

RUSSIAN ORES. Much of the startling industrial progress made by the Soviet Union is based on the relatively recent exploitation of Russian iron ores. At present, the Soviet Union ranks second only to the United States in tonnage of iron ore mined, although only a few years ago Russia was not even mentioned among important iron ore producers.

Most of Russia's iron ore is obtained from two districts, Krivoi Rog in the Dnieper Basin of the southern Ukraine and the district near Magnitogorsk in the southerly portion of the Urals (Fig. 285). Krivoi Rog is by far the more important. Its ores are high in iron and low in phosphorus, and are in such a geologic position that the relatively inexpensive open-pit method of mining is used. These advantages, coupled with government ownership and operation and the manner in which the government can force production regardless of ordinary economic considerations, have brought Krivoi Rog to a high position among the world's iron ranges.

SWEDISH ORES. Sweden's dominant iron range lies in her north country, in that inhospitable region where the northern forest gives way to the tundra. The district is known as Kiruna or Kiruna-Gellivaara (Fig. 285). The ores are hard and phosphoric, but they are surface-mined. They are rich in iron—rich enough so that, despite geographical position and the rigors of the long winters, they are much sought after in western Europe. They have been exported primarily to Germany and secondarily to England, Czechoslovakia, Belgium, and France. During the summer, the ores move to the Gulf of Bothnia by rail and thence to ports in west central Europe and the British Isles. In the cold season, their chief outlet is the Norwegian port of Narvik, for that port remains open while the Gulf of Bothnia is in the grip of thick ice. Strange as it seems, the major iron-ore shipping port for Sweden actually is the Norwegian port of Narvik.

Other Swedish iron ore, roughly 25 per cent of the country's output, is mined near and northwest of Stockholm, chiefly in the Grangesberg district. This ore is the basis for Sweden's small iron and steel industry. The latter is world-famous for quality, but total production is meager. There is no lack of iron ore, but coking coal is not available. This lack forces Sweden to use charcoal in place of coke for smelting iron ore in the blast furnace and hydroelectricity as a source of energy in the manufacture of "electric-furnace" steel. The end product is the excellent "Swedish steel," but quantity is small and production costs are relatively very high.

BRITISH ORES. The iron ores of Europe were first commercially used in England and Scotland. There the "ironstone," along with coal and coke, furnished the sinews for the Industrial Revolution which was to sweep into western Europe and, a bit later, into the United States. Because of many years of mining, the best of the ores have been used up and Britain finds herself forced to import about 40 per cent of her requirements. The imported ore comes mainly from the Bilbao district in northern Spain, from several small districts in the Atlas country of northwestern Africa, and from northern Sweden.

Today, the bulk of British ore is mined in the Cleveland district of Yorkshire (Fig. 285). Lesser amounts come chiefly from the Midlands area at the southern end of the Pennines. Most British ores average only 30 per cent iron and are high in phosphorus. Mining costs are high, partly because the ores are so situated that open-pit methods cannot be used, although there are a few places where "ironstones" are quarried. Despite all this, Britain still furnishes about 60 per cent of her iron ore needs.

THE FERROALLOYS

Steel cannot be made from iron alone. To the iron must be added other ingredients in order to obtain steels of wide commercial use. Because such ingredients will unite or "alloy" with iron, they are called iron-alloys or, more properly, ferroalloys. Chief among the ferroalloys are manganese, chromium, tungsten, molybdenum, vanadium, and nickel. Each imparts some particular quality to the final steel and enables the production of many types of steel for many different uses.

285 *EUROPE possesses many small and scattered iron ranges and a few major ones. The major ones are named on the map. The Krivoi Rog range of the U.S.S.R. is the most recently developed. The iron range near Magnitogorsk in the southern Urals lies off this map about 1,000 miles east and a bit north of the Krivoi Rog.*

Manganese

This ferroalloy has been called "the Achilles heel of the steel industry." Without it, truly useful steel cannot be made. On the average, 14 pounds of manganese are required for each ton of steel manufactured. In addition, larger amounts are needed to purify the materials as they "cook" in the steel furnace.

In one way or another, the steel industry consumes about nine-tenths of the world's production of manganese. About 5 per cent is used to mix with other metals, such as copper and nickel, and another 5 per cent is used in the manufacture of paints, varnishes, glass, disinfectants, and batteries.

As a purifier in the steel furnace, manganese cleans the molten steel of oxides and sulphur. This use accounts for the bulk of manganese consumption. The part which remains in the final steel is essential in providing the vital qualities of hardness and toughness. If larger amounts are purposely kept in the steel, the resultant metal is particularly resistant to shock and abrasive wear; such manganese steels are very useful for heavy-duty steel rails, railroad switches, digging and crushing equipment, and many types of tools.

Like iron, manganese occurs widespread in the rocks of the earth's crust, but, also like iron, it is found in commercial deposits in relatively few places. It is important to realize that the United States, leading steelmaker of the world, produces little manganese. The interest of United States steel manufacturers in foreign manganese ores can hence be readily appreciated.

The Big Three of world manganese production are the Soviet Union, India, and the Gold Coast of west Africa (Fig. 286). The major Soviet deposit, largest in the world, is in the Caucasus region; another important one lies just to the north of the Black Sea, close to the Krivoi Rog iron ores. These two deposits usually produce at least as much as the remainder of the world does. The Indian producing areas lie mainly along the northern flank of the Deccan, from near Calcutta on the east to Baroda on the west. India ranks second in world manganese output, but a poor second to the U.S.S.R. The Gold Coast of west Africa ranks third. The U.S.S.R., India, and the Gold Coast together produce about 80 per cent of the world's manganese. Other countries of world significance in manganese output are the Union of South Africa and Brazil; these two plus the Big Three account for about 90 per cent of the world total.

Chromium

Chromium makes steel hard, tough, and highly resistant to heat and corrosion. Chrome steel is used for such purposes as high-speed tools, machine parts, acid-resistant containers, rust-resistant trimming, and armor plate.

Chromium is also used in certain iron-nickel and cobalt-tungsten alloys. As a nonalloy, it is used to line furnaces and to make certain chemicals. Important among the latter are dyes, pigments, and tanning extracts (hence, chrome leather).

Four countries produce about three-quarters of the world's chromium ore. They are the U.S.S.R., Southern Rhodesia, the Philippines, and the Union of South Africa. Other important producers are Turkey, Cuba, New Caledonia, and Yugoslavia (Fig. 286). These seven countries account for about 97 per cent of the world's chromium supply. The U.S.S.R. probably holds first rank, followed closely by Southern Rhodesia. The chief Russian deposits are in the Urals. Those of Southern Rhodesia are roughly central in that country. Philippine chromium ore comes from Luzon and that of the Union of South Africa from the eastern part of the Union. It should be noted that the United States has practically no chromium. The U.S.S.R. is the only major steel-manufacturing country which is self-sufficient in chromium, as well as the essential manganese.

Tungsten

The addition of tungsten to steel insures a metal which remains hard and strong even at high temperatures. Hence, tungsten steel is especially useful for high-speed cutting tools, saw blades, files, engine valves, and the linings of big guns. In addition, it is valuable for use in razor blades, knife blades, and armor plate. Some tungsten is also used in copper alloys and in alloys of cobalt and chromium.

China, including Korea, has long been the world's chief source of tungsten ores. Most of the ore comes from the southern portion of China Proper. The other truly major producer is Burma. Still other important producers are the Malay States, the United States, Bolivia, and Portugal (Fig. 286). Portugal is the only significant producer in all Europe. The United States production of tungsten ores is mainly in Colorado, Nevada, and California. Despite large tonnage mined, usually about 10 to 12 per cent of the world output, the United States imports additional supplies from abroad, chiefly from China and the Malay States.

Molybdenum

Molybdenum or "Molly steels" are strong in proportion to their weight and are highly resistant to shock. They also remain strong at relatively high temperatures. This characteristic enables them to serve, at least partly, as substitutes for chromium and tungsten steels. "Molly steels" have many uses, ranging from gears, tools, and pistons to magnets and oil-drilling equipment.

The United States, though short on manganese, chromium, and tungsten, leads the world in the mining of molybdenum ore. Approximately 90 per cent of the world supply comes from a famous deposit at Climax, Colorado. Mexico and Norway are the only other producing countries worthy of mention (Fig. 287).

Vanadium

Vanadium steels are very resistant to repeated shocks and flexings, particularly if vanadium is added to chrome steel. Such steels are highly useful for springs and axles in automobiles and railway equipment.

The bulk of the world supply of vanadium is mined as vanadium ore in Peru, the United States, Southwest Africa, and Northern Rhodesia (Fig. 287). United States production comes almost entirely from western Colorado.

286 *WORLD DISTRIBUTION of the major producing areas for manganese, chromium, and tungsten. Other important or potentially important areas are also included.*

287   *WORLD DISTRIBUTION of major producing areas for molybdenum, vanadium, and nickel. Other important or potentially important producing areas for molybdenum and nickel are also shown.*

Nickel

Nickel steels are highly resistant to heat and corrosion. Their uses range from cooking utensils, steam cabinets, and chemical apparatus to bullets and heavy machinery. Nickel is also mixed with copper to make Monel metal. Monel is used in the manufacture of equipment for restaurants, hospitals, and laundries.

Nickel occurs in several of its own ores, as well as in ores of copper, iron, gold, and platinum. Although this may seem to imply widespread occurrence of nickel production, the fact is that one limited area normally produces 80 to 90 per cent of the world nickel supply. This area is the Sudbury district of Canada, located in the eastern portion of Ontario not far north of Lake Huron and Georgian Bay (Fig. 287). Second place in world nickel output is held by New Cale-

donia. The U.S.S.R. should perhaps be mentioned as a nickel producer; production there is still very minor, but is increasing. The United States is almost completely deficient in nickel, but fortunately the Sudbury district is "next door" and supplies are readily obtainable in large amount.

Other Elements Used with Iron and Steel

Besides the ferroalloys mentioned above, there are several other metals used to greater or lesser degree in the steel industry: copper, lead, zinc, tin, and antimony. However, their most important uses are in connection with other than iron and steel manufacture. Hence, they are not normally considered as ferroalloys. Along with several others, they will be discussed under the general heading of nonferrous minerals.

CHAPTER OUTLINE

Iron ore and the ferroalloys

REVIEW QUESTIONS

1. Iron is one of the more abundant elements of the earth's crust. Why, then, are not iron ores widely distributed in each country or region of the world?

2. What is meant by "free" occurrence of a mineral? Illustrate.

3. Demonstrate that iron ore is essential to modern industry.

4. Name the Big Five nations in iron ore production. About what per cent of total world iron ore production is normally supplied by these nations combined?

5. Which nations own the fortunate combination of abundant coal and abundant iron ore?

6. Compare the geologic location and condition of the Minnesota and the Michigan iron ores. Discuss the effect of these differences on mining methods and costs.

7. Trace a shipment of iron ore from the Mesabi Range to Buffalo, New York. Include handling methods as well as ports, water routes, etc. Do the same for a shipment of western Pennsylvania coal to Milwaukee, Wisconsin.

8. Why is it that Birmingham, Alabama, can produce metallic iron (pig iron) cheaper than any other iron center in the United States?

9. What seem to you the basic factors which account for the marked leadership of the United States in world iron ore production?

10. Discuss France and Germany in terms of coking coal and iron ore.

11. Why does Sweden, with large, rich deposits of iron ore, export most of that ore to other countries? Also, why does most of the Swedish iron ore go out through the Norwegian port of Narvik?

12. What is meant by the term "ferroalloy" and what, specifically, are the chief ferroalloys?

13. Illustrate the imparting of special qualities to commercial steels by ferroalloys.

14. What is the "Achilles heel" of the United States steel industry? Explain.

15. Discuss the United States from the standpoint of self-sufficiency in coal, iron ore, and the ferroalloys.

SOME SUGGESTED REFERENCES

De Kruif, Paul, *Seven Iron Men,* Harcourt, Brace, 1929. A popular book dealing with the men who discovered and first developed the ores of the Lake Superior iron ranges.

Encyclopædia Britannica (1943 edition). See sections on Iron and Steel and on individual ferroalloys; see also equivalent sections in the *Britannica Book of the Year.*

Havighurst, Walter, *The Long Ships Passing,* Macmillan, 1942. An account of the explorers of and the development of the Great Lakes, and of the "long ships" which carry iron ore.

Jones, Clarence F., and Darkenwald, Gordon G., *Economic Geography,* Macmillan, 1941. A standard textbook in economic geography; organized on the basis of major occupations.

Leith, Charles K., *World Minerals and World Peace,* Brookings Institution, 1943. A consideration of the earth's mineral resources and their relation to international affairs.

Lovering, Thomas S., *Minerals in World Affairs,* Prentice-Hall, 1944. A book on the history, economics, geology, and geographical distribution of the important minerals.

Minerals Yearbook, U. S. Bureau of Mines. An annual report on mineral production and mineral industries of the United States.

288 *PORT RADIUM and the Eldorado Mine on the bleak shores of Canada's Great Bear Lake. The Eldorado Mine is a major source of pitchblende from which radium and uranium are secured. (National Film Board, Canada)*

CHAPTER 18

Some Significant Nonferrous Minerals

In addition to coal, petroleum, iron ore, and the ferroalloys, there are many other resources obtained from within the earth. Some of them are like coal and petroleum in that they are nonmetallic. Others are, in a sense, more closely related to iron ore and the ferroalloys in that they are metallic in nature. Nonmetallic minerals include salt, pottery clays, and building stone. Metallic minerals are exemplified by aluminum, copper, tin, and gold. All of them, metallic and nonmetallic alike, serve important purposes in those portions of the world which have become highly commercialized and industrialized. A few of them are also important in those sections of the earth which are still marked by primitive economies. Here one thinks almost immediately of such minerals as salt, clay, and stone.

SALT

Salt is essential to life. It is a "food mineral." Wild animals often travel long distances to natural salt licks or live close to them. Many primitive peoples do the same. Others choose to live near the sea or a briny lake where salt can be scraped up along the margins of shallow pools or lagoons. In addition to being a food, salt is a seasoner and preserver of food whether used in the dry form or in pickling solution.

Even our word "salary" is derived from salt. This goes back to the days when Roman soldiers were paid their wages in salt instead of money. The expression, still commonly used, "He is not worth his salt," refers to a person who is not worth the salary paid him. Salt is still a common medium of exchange. There are a good many places in the world where money is refused, but salt is eagerly accepted.

While we usually hear of salt as a food or in connection with foods, it is also a very important product in the chemical industries. Several chemical products, such as soda ash and caustic soda are made from it, and the manufacture of many others demands the use of large amounts of salt.

Most countries, either by mining or extraction from sea water, supply themselves with all the salt they need. For this reason, salt does not normally appear in international trade. This in no way detracts from the importance of salt, but merely indicates that it has wide geographical distribution and that man has no great difficulty in obtaining it.

Abroad, one hears of the salt mines of China's Szechwan Basin, the mines of Russia's Ukraine, and those of Germany and Poland. In the United States, most of the salt is produced in Michigan, New York, Ohio, Louisiana, and Kansas. The order given is that of rank in production. Some of the salt is obtained by mining, as the term mining is ordinarily understood, but most of it is "mined with a pump." Hot water is piped into underlying salt deposits and the resultant brine is pumped back to the surface to be evaporated and refined. Incidentally, some iodine often is left in, or added to, the refined salt as a preventative of simple goiter in humans. Most salt-producing districts look like oil fields because the derricks used in pumping operations closely resemble oil derricks (Fig. 289). Where salt is derived from sea water, the "workings" look much like small fields flooded with irrigation water (Fig. 290).

CLAYS, SANDS, GRAVELS, AND STONE

Like salt, these mineral resources are ordinarily taken for granted. Locally, they may be so common that even heavy utilization causes no comment. But whether they occur in local abundance or not, they are among the commercially significant minerals. The fact that a small clay deposit or larger deposits of sand and gravel, or a stone quarry may sell for thousands of dollars is a direct indication of commercial importance. As they are bulky and low in value per ton, such minerals can seldom bear the cost of long-distance ship-ment; they do not appear in foreign trade records. However, certain products made from them possess relatively high value and may be shipped long distances.

Clays

Beds of clay furnish raw materials for many kinds of products: ordinary brick, firebrick, tile, pottery, chinaware, and so on. It is pertinent to note that the annual value of *raw* clay produced in the United States alone is usually about $15,000,000 to $16,000,000.

Brick and pottery clays are widely distributed in the United States, but are mined, or dug, mainly in Ohio, Pennsylvania, West Virginia, and New Jersey. Ohio leads in both brick and pottery manufacture. In Europe, Germany is well known for chinaware and porcelains, the porcelains being produced chiefly for use in scientific laboratories. The chinaware of England, such as Spode and Wedgwood, is famous all over the world. Like the ware of Germany, it is exported to other countries, especially to the United States. Denmark, Czechoslovakia, and Austria have made their clays well known in the form of pottery, dishes, and laboratory vessels. China, ancient home of chinaware, and Japan make and export clay-derived products which are known for their artistic shapes and colorations.

289

SALT derricks in St. Landry Parish, Louisiana. Note their resemblance to oil derricks. (Veatch from U. S. Geological Survey)

290 SALT WORKS *along the edge of San Francisco Bay. Sea water is pumped into the salt ponds (background) where solar evaporation concentrates the brine and causes precipitation of the salt. After ponds are drained, the salt is "harvested" and taken to the refinery. (Leslie Salt Company, San Francisco)*

Sands and Gravels

It is probably anyone's guess as to how many million tons of sand and gravel are used in the world, or in the United States, each year. Certainly it is a tremendous tonnage. Most of it is used in the construction of roads, bridges, buildings, and airfields— private as well as public. Some of it is used directly as sand and gravel, as in certain types of roads, but much of it is used in cement and concrete, sand for exterior and interior plastering, and certain sands, the glass sands, for the manufacture of many varieties of glassware.

While sand and gravel are extensively distributed, they do not occur in sufficient amounts in many localities. Thus, despite their bulk and comparatively low value, they are often moved considerable distances either by trucks or by gravel cars on railroads. Sands and gravels are usually abundant along ancient and modern shorelines, in regions of continental glacial deposition, and in the arroyos and alluvial fans of dry areas. Fortunately, the portion of the United States where construction of all sorts is greatest has ready access to the sands and gravels contained in vast glacial deposits and in lake-shore and seashore materials.

Stone

As used here, *stone* refers to both crushed rock and rock which is used in block form. In many sections of the world, particularly

291   *QUARRYING operations at a Vermont granite quarry. (Rock of Ages Corp.)*

where sands and gravels are scarce, large tonnages of bedrock are drilled and blasted and then crushed for use in roads or concrete. Limestone is a good example of rock which is commonly mined and crushed; also, it is often pulverized completely and used in the manufacture of cement. Bedrock which is quarried and shaped is represented by some limestones, as the fossiliferous limestones of Indiana, by marble, by granite, and by slate. These stones are used mainly in building con

struction either as actual building blocks or as ornamental trimming and flooring. Some slate is used in the form of roofing shingles, as well as for blackboards.

The world has literally thousands of stone quarries, ancient and modern. They are scattered from China and Egypt to the New World. Among them may be mentioned the very famous marble quarries at Carrara, Italy, the "black marble" quarries near Knoxville, Tennessee, the granite quarries at Barre, Ver mont (Fig. 291), and also the slate quarries in eastern Pennsylvania.

SULPHUR

Sulphur was used anciently as a medicine and less anciently for old-style sulphur matches. Today, most of it is consumed by the chemical and papermaking industries. The chemical industries are particularly dependent upon sulphur. From it is made sulphuric acid, often referred to as the key ingredient of modern chemical enterprise. In addition, sulphur is used, in one form or another, in fertilizers, insecticides, explosives, vulcanized rubber, wood preservatives, and medicines.

For many years, and up to about 1912, the island of Sicily led the world in sulphur mining. Today, the United States produces approximately 75 to 80 per cent of the world supply, a supply which has increased at least fourfold since 1900. In most recent years, the United States alone has mined close to 3,000,000 tons of sulphur annually. Italy still holds second place, but now produces only about one-eighth as much as the United States. Other significant producers are Japan, Canada, and Norway. However, Canadian and Norwegian production is obtained as a by-product sulphur from smelters and chemical plants, rather than from natural sulphur deposits.

By far the greater portion of United States sulphur is obtained from thick deposits under part of the coastal plain of Texas and Louisiana. Like salt, the sulphur is mined with a pump. After the hot sulphur-charged water is brought back to the surface, it is led into huge bins where drying out and hardening provide mammoth sulphur cakes. These are easily broken up and loaded into railroad cars by power machinery (Fig. 292).

MINERAL FERTILIZERS

As this and other countries have used and abused their vital soil resources, there has been an ever-increasing demand for fertilizers. These may be of several kinds: some are ani-

292 *SULPHUR solution, coming by pipe from a nearby well, is discharged in vat or bin where it will harden to form a huge block. A huge, hardened block may be seen in the background, about at the level of the man's chest. (Monsanto)*

mal fertilizers, some are green fertilizers obtained by growing certain crops and then plowing them under, but many of them are mineral fertilizers. Some mineral fertilizers are obtained directly from the earth while others are by-products of smelting and chemical plants, or are made in special factories which draw upon the air for raw material. The chief mineral fertilizers are compounds of nitrogen, potassium, and phosphorus. For the market, these may be prepared separately, but more commonly, they are mixed. When mixed, calcium, another essential plant food, is usually included as part of the bulk.

Nitrates

The nitrate fertilizers are those containing nitrogen. Natural nitrates, as opposed to synthetic, are obtained almost entirely from a few sections in the Atacama Desert of northern Chile (Fig. 293). There the *caliche* is dug and scraped from the upper portions of several playas after which it is partially refined and shipped to Europe and the United States. Until about 1920, Chile had a virtual world monopoly of nitrates. These were useful not only for fertilizers, but for explosives, including munitions of war. Dire need for nitrates from closer sources and at lower prices encouraged the production of synthetic nitrates from the air and the recovery of nitrogen-containing materials from industrial plants. Today, synthetic and by-product nitrates control the world market. Chile, once supreme, produces only about 8 to 9 per cent of the world's annual supply. Much of the synthetic production, as in Germany and especially in Norway, is based on cheap and abundant hydroelectricity (Fig. 294). Synthetic production in the United States is based on coal.

Potash

Compounds of potash, containing potassium, are secured from factory wastes, seaweed, and mineral deposits. The chief mineral deposits of potash occur as buried beds in the upper portion of the earth's crust and in surface deposits and brines of desert salt lakes.

For many years, Germany has produced anywhere from 60 to 75 per cent of the world's

293

A TYPICAL nitrate "oficina" located on a small "island" in one of the playas of Chile's Atacama Desert. (J. L. Rich, in his The Face of South America *published by the American Geographical Society.)*

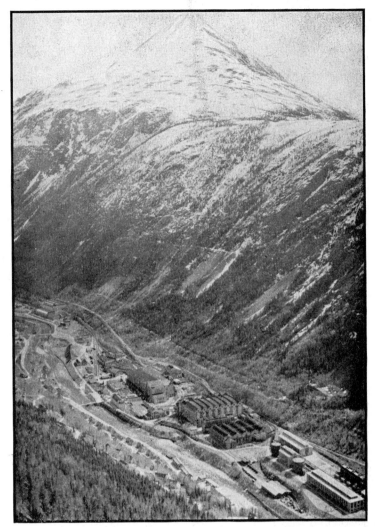

294

SYNTHETIC nitrate plant in a glaciated Norwegian valley. (Norwegian Official Photo)

mineral potash. It is mined chiefly in the Stassfurt district and in the Harz Mountains. France, obtaining her supply from mines in Alsace, holds second rank. French production accounts for about 15 per cent of the world output. Other important producers are the United States and the Soviet Union. Each produces about 10 per cent of the world total. Prior to World War I, the United States was dependent on Germany for potash. Today, the United States supplies about half its requirements, reaching that condition through an increase in mineral potash production plus the use of potash from industrial plants. Most mineral potash in the United States is obtained from the new production districts in the Carlsbad area of southeastern New Mexico (with 85 per cent of the total) and from the Searles Lake area on the northern margin of the Mohave Desert of California (Fig. 295).

Phosphates

Phosphorus-containing compounds are derived mainly from phosphatic limestones; thus two critical plant foods, phosphorus and cal-

295 *AN AIR VIEW of the "chemical" town of Trona located on the edge of Searles Lake (a desert "dry lake") in the northern part of the Mohave Desert. The edge of the "dry lake" appears at the left. From its deep, layered deposits are pumped the brines from which potash and other chemicals are extracted. (American Potash and Chemical Corp.)*

296

PHOSPHATE dredge in operation in Marion County, Florida. (Mansfield from U. S. Geological Survey) cium, are obtained from the same material. Lesser amounts are obtained from the slag of blast furnaces, particularly in the iron and steel manufacturing districts of Europe, where phosphoric iron ores are used more than in the United States.

The United States leads in phosphate mining. Most of the supply comes from the South, particularly Florida (Fig. 296) and Tennessee. Minor amounts are secured in Idaho, Montana, and Arkansas. Huge reserves are available in the Rocky Mountain states, from Utah to Montana (Fig. 297). Northwest Africa mines about the same amount as the United States, but production there is divided among French Morocco, Algeria, and Tunisia, with the latter country supplying the most. United States production is used at home, whereas the African production flows to western Europe. Other important producers are the U.S.S.R. and some of the Pacific islands, especially Nauru.

GOLD

Gold, more than any other mineral, has fired the imagination of man and sent him scurrying to the far reaches of the earth in attempts to find it. The lure of gold played a large role in the exploration of the continents and islands and sent many a vessel across unknown seas. It may be recalled that Spain was interested in the New World primarily for the gold (and silver) which its galleons might bring back to the homeland. Pizarro conquered Peru for Inca gold; Cortez subdued Mexico for Aztec gold; and Coronado explored much of what is now our Southwest in a vain attempt to find the imaginary Seven Golden Cities of Cibola. Much later, it was gold which caused the sudden and great interest in little-known California. Still later, gold brought Alaska into the world spotlight. Even today, gold is bringing per-

297 *DISTRIBUTION of the major phosphate deposits of the United States. Most of the mining is in the Southeast, but the great reserves are in the West.*

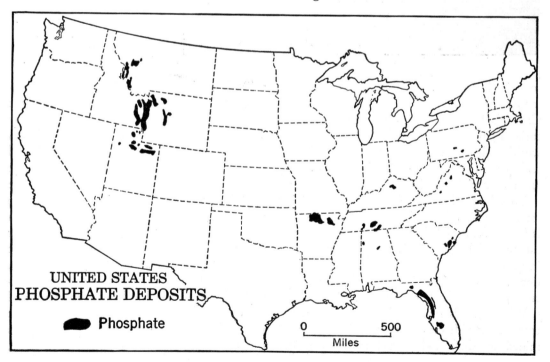

UNITED STATES
PHOSPHATE DEPOSITS

▰ Phosphate

0   500
Miles

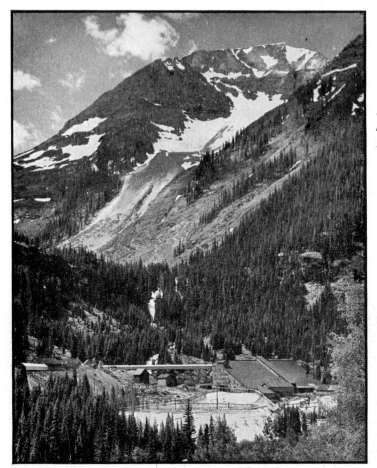

298

A GOLD mine of the shaft and tunnel type. Camp Bird Mine near Ouray, Colorado. (Corsini, Standard Oil Co. [N. J.])

sons in large enough numbers to establish modern towns in several isolated sections of Canada's far-flung territories. For more centuries than we know, gold has represented wealth, whether to nations or to individuals, and man and nation alike have striven to find and amass as much of it as possible.

Gold occurs both in the free state and in mixture with other minerals. When free, it is in the form of flakes, dust, or, sometimes, nuggets. Otherwise, it is mixed with quartz in veins of solid rock or is found in combination with ores of other metals, particularly ores of copper, lead, nickel, and silver.

When gold is found in quartz veins or in connection with ores of other minerals, it is mined by shaft and tunnel methods (Fig. 298). But when it is found in loose materials *placer mining* techniques are used. Placer mining may be carried on in a small way by panning. The pan is merely a shallow basin in which water and gravels are scooped and then rocked back and forth by hand until the water and gravels spill over the sides and the heavier gold remains in the bottom of the pan. Another method involves the use of a long trough with cleats on its bottom. Water and gold-bearing sand and gravel are sent down the trough and the gold collects against the upper side of the cleats. In large undertakings, huge hoses break loose the sand and gravel and wash them into the troughs. The most modern and large-scale method entails the use of mammoth dredges (Fig. 299), which suck up gold-bearing materials, remove the gold from them, and drop the waste material in great piles. While efficient and comparatively inexpensive, dredging turns whole countrysides into debris piles. When one views an area which has been dredged over, one wonders whether the gold was worth it.

World leadership in gold production has changed hands many times. Once it was Egypt with gold from fabulous Ethiopia; later it was Greece; still later Spain, and so on through many countries and their colonies. Soon after the discovery of gold in California, the United States became an important producer, but it remained second to Russia, the leader. Russia continued to lead until the discovery, near the turn of the present century,

of the South African gold fields. South Africa now holds first rank without question (Fig. 300). The richest fields are located in the Transvaal of the Union of South Africa, particularly in the district known as the Rand and centering on the city of Johannesburg. The Rand produces, depending on the year, from 35 to 50 per cent of the world's gold supply. The U.S.S.R. holds second place, and Canada and the United States compete for third. Other significant producers are Australia, Japan, Rhodesia, and Mexico.

Nearly all the gold mined in the United States comes from west of the Mississippi, especially from the Black Hills of South Dakota and from California, with lesser amounts from such states as Colorado, Arizona, Utah, and Nevada.

299

(Right) *GOLD dredge in operation in Yuba County, California, and (below) the debris-drowned land that is left behind the gold dredges. (Johnson and Stearns from U. S. Geological Survey)*

SILVER

Whether for jewelry, plating, or money, silver has been sought after nearly as much as gold. Much more of it, ounce for ounce, has been mined than gold, but its value has been consistently far less. Much of the world's silver is obtained from ores of other metals, particularly ores of copper, lead, and nickel. In fact, Mexico is the only country with any appreciable number of silver mines. Other countries have, chiefly, copper mines, lead mines, etc., where silver is a by-product.

Mexico's silver mines give it first place in world production (Fig. 300). Mexico can be counted on to produce about 35 per cent of the annual supply, while the United States, her closest rival, produces about 20 per cent. Canada normally mines about 8 per cent. Thus, the total North American production is nearly two-thirds of the world's annual out-

put. The remainder comes chiefly from Australia, Peru, and Spain. Nearly all of the United States supply comes from the West: Idaho, Utah, and Arizona rank first, second, and third, respectively. Colorado and Nevada are also important producers.

There is danger of overestimating the importance of both gold and silver. They are important, to be sure, but even in years of peak prices, their combined values (world totals) would purchase only one-third of the automobiles manufactured in the United States and would just about purchase the United States wheat crop.

DIAMONDS

Diamonds, like gold and silver, symbolize wealth. Although chiefly famous as jewels, including the crown jewels of many an

GOLD
△ Major producers

SILVER
◈ Major producers

DIAMONDS
◆ Major producers

Compressed Sinusoidal
equal-area projection

300   *WORLD DISTRIBUTION of the major producing areas for gold, silver, and diamonds.*

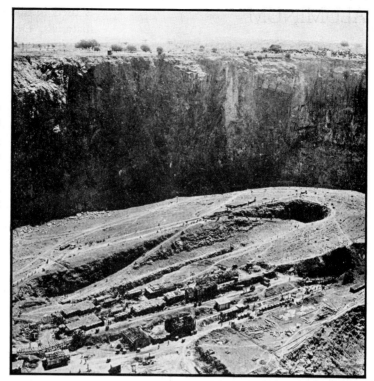

301

A DIAMOND mine near Pretoria in the Union of South Africa. From this mine came the famous white jewel known as the Cullinan Diamond. (Government Information Office, Union of South Africa)

ancient and modern ruler, their greatest usefulness is in connection with certain modern industrial activities. The diamond is the hardest of minerals. It is this quality which makes the diamond, and diamond dust, so useful in the manufacture of cutting and abrasive tools. Specifically, diamonds are used in the cutting points of well-boring and rock-drilling tools, etching tools, abrasive wheels, and glass cutters. In addition, fine wires, such as copper wires, are prepared by drawing them through very small holes in pieces of diamond.

Although known and prized for many centuries, diamonds did not become well known until special cutting processes which enhance their beauty and utility were invented. Successful commercial diamond cutting was not common until just before the time of Columbus. Furthermore, it was not until the discovery of the rich African fields, only half a century ago, that diamonds became at all numerous in world markets (Fig. 301). Present major producers, in order of importance,

are the Belgian Congo, the Gold Coast, the Union of South Africa, Sierra Leone, and Angola (Fig. 300). The Belgian Congo produces about half of the total world supply. Most of the cutting and marketing has been done in western Europe, at Antwerp and Amsterdam. Paris is another diamond center, as is Palestine. In the United States, New York City has been gaining steadily in both cutting and selling of diamonds. World War II brought a change which may be of continued significance. Soon after the beginning of hostilities, and just ahead of the German invasion, many Dutch and Belgian diamond cutters fled to Brazil and established businesses there. These undertakings have flourished and they are closely tied to the large United States market. Brazil does mine some diamonds, particularly of the industrial variety (black diamonds). Thus the new diamond-cutting industry there is not without at least some local supply of raw material. The dispersal of the industry appears likely to persist.

ALUMINUM

Aluminum is more abundant than iron in the rocks of the earth's crust. Yet as recently as a century ago, metallic aluminum was rare and costly. Even at the beginning of the present century, it was so scarce that the selling price was $2 per pound. Today, it is a common and inexpensive metal with many uses. The change occurred because modern techniques allow rapid and ready transformation of aluminum ore to alumina (aluminum oxide) and the transformation of alumina into metallic aluminum. When the industrial world found that metallic aluminum has many, rather than few, useful properties, the demand for more and more aluminum at lower prices rapidly increased.

Aluminum is light in weight, strong in proportion to weight, relatively noncorrosive, an excellent conductor of both heat and electricity, and capable of high polish. Little wonder that it has many uses and that production is about five times as great as it was twenty years ago. At present, its major uses, as exemplified in the United States, are:

	Per cent
Transportation equipment	40
Foundry and metal working	23
Machinery and electrical equipment	9
Cooking utensils	6
Electrical conductors	5
Building material	5
Chemical industries	5
Metallurgy	4
Food and beverage equipment	2
Miscellaneous	1

Most significant has been the great increase in the use of aluminum in the manufacture of aircraft, streamlined trains, and long-distance electrical transmission lines. Much aluminum is used in alloy form with other metals and materials. Duralumin or dural is an alloy of aluminum and copper, a metal much stronger than aluminum or copper alone. Powdered aluminum and iron oxide, when mixed, provide incendiary bombs. Carborundum, well known abrasive, is aluminum carbide.

Despite its common occurrence as an element in earth materials, large deposits of commercial aluminum ore are rare (Fig. 302). Practically all aluminum is obtained from one ore, known as *bauxite*. The ore takes its name from Les Baux, a town in southeastern France. France, for many years, mined more bauxite than any other nation. However, during World War II, when European production was in the hands of the German invaders, production was greatly increased in the Guianas, particularly in British Guiana. At that time, Guianan output was nearly double that of the normal French production. Today, French production is far behind that of the Guianas and the United States, but well ahead of such other important producers as the Soviet Union, Hungary, Italy, Yugoslavia, and Indonesia. In the United States, bauxite is mined almost entirely in Saline County, Arkansas. The deposit there is now nearly depleted and no major deposits are available elsewhere in the country. Even more than in the past, the United States must look abroad for its bauxite supply.

After bauxite is dug from the earth, chiefly by large power shovels, it is crushed, washed, and screened. Most of the bauxite is then shipped to other lands to be smelted into alumina and refined into metallic aluminum. For this reason, the chief producers of bauxite are not the major producers of aluminum metal. Most of the smelters and refineries are located in Germany, the United States, and Canada. It is these countries which have led in the manufacture of metallic aluminum. The single great smelting plant in the United States is at East St. Louis, Illinois. There bauxite from Arkansas and the Guianas is changed into alumina. The alumina then

302 WORLD DISTRIBUTION of the major producing areas for bauxite, copper, and tin.

303 ONE OF THE huge plants, at Alcoa, Tennessee, which transforms alumina (aluminum oxide) into metallic aluminum. (Aluminum Company of America)

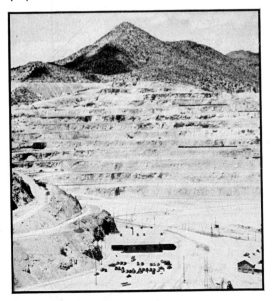

304   *OPEN-PIT copper mine at Morenci, Arizona. (Copper and Brass Research Association)*

travels to places of cheap and abundant hydroelectric power where it is refined into metal, such as Alcoa, Tennessee (Fig. 303); Badin, North Carolina; and Niagara Falls and Massena, New York. Canada's production of aluminum is based on abundant hydroelectricity provided by large plants located along north-bank tributaries of the St. Lawrence at points where water-borne bauxite from the Guianas reaches them cheaply.

MAGNESIUM

Within recent years, particularly since 1939, magnesium has become very important. It is a sort of "twin brother" to aluminum, both in properties and uses. Like aluminum, it occurs in many minerals, yet has few ores. Similarly, it must be elaborately processed in order to transform it into a metal.

Because magnesium is lighter than aluminum, but just as strong, it is used primarily in aircraft engines and plane parts. Today, a single large plane contains as much magnesium as was produced in an entire year some forty years ago. Comparatively small amounts of magnesium are still obtained from the ore known as magnesite, but most of it now comes from buried salty or briny deposits and, strangely enough, from sea water. The United States is the unquestioned leader in world production; the bulk of the supply comes from southern Michigan and coastal Texas. The latter utilizes a supply of sea water and large amounts of electricity to transform the magnesium in the water into metal.

The fact that most of the magnesium produced during World War II was used in the manufacture of war aircraft, incendiary bombs, and tracer bullets led to a sharp decline in output with the cessation of hostilities. During the war, a huge plant, using magnesium ore from western Nevada, was constructed and operated near Boulder Dam and the city of Las Vegas, in southern Nevada. This plant, reputedly the world's largest, ceased to operate even before the end of the war.

As a strong "light metal" in an age demanding less weight and more and more speed, magnesium would seem to have a promising future.

COPPER

Unlike aluminum and magnesium, copper has been known and used for several thousand years. With the possible exception of gold, copper was the first of the metals to be used by man. Certainly it was used in Egypt as early as 5000 B.C. and it entered importantly into the early trade of the Mediterranean, Asia Minor, and northeastern Africa. Bronze, an alloy of copper and tin, was probably known by 2000 B.C. In North America, copper was used to some extent by the Indians of the Lake Superior region. Also, it was traded by them in small amounts to Indian groups farther south.

Native or free copper occurs as chunks of pure copper which are practically indistinguishable from the refined metal. It is found mainly in the Keweenaw Peninsula of northern Michigan. Because of its location near the shores of Lake Superior, copper of this sort is often called Lake copper. The metal is found occasionally at the surface, but most of it has to be mined expensively by means of deep shafts. One shaft is more than a mile in depth. It was the surface occurrence which enabled the Indians to discover it and, later, to make use of it. They learned that it was soft enough to be hammered into various shapes for use as axheads, arrowheads, spear points, bowls, and ornaments.

Nonfree copper occurs in a wide variety of ores. The ores occur either as veins, as in the famous Butte district of Montana, or widely scattered among other rocks, as in the copper districts of Utah, Arizona, and Nevada. Most of the ores of the western United States contain only a small percentage of copper per ton, but, except for the rich veins at Butte, they can be mined by the cheap open-pit method (Fig. 304). Open-pit production of western ores has taken the leadership away from Michigan's Keweenaw Peninsula.

While processes vary somewhat, there is much that has to be done to copper ore before it is available as pure, metallic copper. Western ores, for example, have to be crushed, concentrated, smelted, and refined. Most of them are crushed, concentrated, and smelted near the mines. The copper which comes from the smelters, called "blister," is about 98 per cent pure. The blister, smaller in bulk and much higher in value than the original ores, travels long distances to refineries (Fig. 305). Thus, copper from Arizona, Utah, Montana, Nevada, and Michigan, to mention the leading copper-producing states in order, is refined chiefly at places along the Atlantic seaboard, particularly in the New York-Baltimore area. These same places are

305 INTERIOR of a New Jersey copper refinery, showing anodes being lowered into the cells used in the electrolytic refining process. (Copper and Brass Research Association)

importing centers for copper from foreign sources. Exceptions to the Atlantic seaboard location of refineries are to be found at Great Falls, Montana, and Hubbell, Michigan. No matter where the refineries are located, they demand large amounts of electricity because the refining process is an electrolytic one.

The United States leads the world in copper production (Fig. 302). Chile normally ranks second, followed in order by Rhodesia, Canada, Belgian Congo, and the U.S.S.R. The rank is practically the same whether one is thinking of tons of copper mined or tons of copper coming from smelters. In refining, the United States is far ahead of any other nation; it is the only one of the major copper ore producers which refines more copper than it mines. This is made possible by imports, chiefly from Chile. The bulk of the African copper is refined in western Europe.

The world's metallic copper is used in scores of ways. Pound for pound, most of it is used in the electrical industries (for generators, motors, switchboards, etc.) and in telephone, telegraph, and power lines. The Bell Telephone System has in use at one time enough copper wire to reach almost from the earth to the sun! Other uses include wire cloth and screen, rods, ordinary electric wire, sheathing, munitions, cooking utensils, and alloys. It will be recalled that bronze is an alloy of copper and tin. Brass is an alloy of copper and zinc. Duralumin, mentioned before, is an alloy of copper and aluminum. In wartime, copper production booms because of heavy demands for ships' wiring and parts, for airplane parts, and for shell cases. Peace normally brings a marked drop in production, but even then, the uses of copper are so many and varied as to provide a large market.

TIN

Tin, like copper, is a metal of both ancient and modern use. It was used in the making of bronze nearly 4,000 years ago. Like gold, tin was one of the reasons why man "went places." Phoenician traders, perhaps as early as 1200 B.C., journeyed in their small Mediterranean craft all the way from Asia Minor to the tin mines of Cornwall in Britain. Cornwall tin became an important item in the bronze trade of the Mediterranean world.

Tin is relatively easy to melt, it sticks readily to other metals, it is resistant to vegetable and fruit acids, and it is nonpoisonous to man and animals. Thus one can easily understand why nearly half of all the tin produced in the modern world is utilized in the manufacture of tin plate. Most of this, in turn, is used for tin cans. Strangely enough, tin cans are mainly steel cans. They consist of thin sheets of relatively soft steel with only a thin coating or plating of tin. This becomes apparent when tin cans are used and discarded: the rusting which ensues is evidence of the deterioration of steel, for tin does not rust. Another definitely major use is in the manufacture of solders. In addition, tin is used in the manufacture of bronze, tin tubing, foil, printing type, and terneplate. The last is an alloy of tin and lead; while it cannot be used for food containers, for fear of lead poisoning, it is very useful in the form of containers for oil and gasoline, as well as for roofing material.

Commercial deposits of tin-bearing materials normally occur in loose, easily mined form (Fig. 306). By means of power shovels or huge dredges, these materials are picked or sucked up, washed, and concentrated. Concentrates are moved to smelters, most of which are near the "tin pits," and the product then travels long distances to refineries which produce metallic tin. In some tin-mining districts, those of lesser importance, tin ore occurs in a hard-rock form and must be mined by more expensive methods. Ores of this sort are merely concentrated and shipped without smelting.

For many years the Federated Malay States have led in the mining of tin ore (Fig. 302). In the past twenty years, they have produced from 30 to 37 per cent of the world supply. Production there was interrupted during World War II when the Japanese invaders destroyed or severely damaged most of the mining equipment. However, when the Japanese were driven out, the damage was repaired and production was resumed. The next most important producer of tin ore is Indonesia which mines close to 20 per cent. Most of this comes from Banka, a small island located just east of the southern part of Sumatra. Malay States ore is smelted at Singapore and then sent to Britain for refining; Banka ore is smelted locally and shipped to refineries in the Netherlands. The only other major producing area for tin ore is on the eastern margin of the Bolivian Plateau. This area normally produces from 12 to 24 per cent of the world output. Bolivian ores are both smelted and refined in Britain. Lesser producers are Thailand, Burma, Nigeria, Belgian Congo, and China. No one of them produces as much as 10 per cent of the tin ore supply.

306

TIN MINE in Federated Malay States. (British Information Services)

It is important to note that the United States, major consumer of metallic tin, has no tin ores. Its supplies come primarily from the refineries of Britain and the Netherlands.

LEAD AND ZINC

Lead and zinc are commonly mentioned together because they often occur in the same mining districts. For example, the tristate district, including portions of Oklahoma, Kansas, and Missouri, is the world's leading production area for both lead and zinc ores (Fig. 307).

Among the nations, the United States is first in lead mining. Its production is usually from 20 to 30 per cent of the world total, depending on the year. The afore-mentioned tristate district, especially southeastern Missouri, leads. On a strictly state basis, Idaho and Utah rank second and third, followed by Oklahoma, Montana, Kansas, and Colorado.

Abroad, major producers are Australia, Canada, and Mexico, with lesser productions in Germany, Yugoslavia, Burma, and Spain. Spain has some of the oldest lead mines of the world. They have been in operation for more than 2,000 years.

The United States also leads in the mining of zinc (Fig. 307). It normally mines about 30 to 40 per cent of the world supply. Most of it is obtained in the tristate district, and Oklahoma is the chief producing state. New Jersey holds second rank, followed by Kansas and Tennessee and several western states. Australia, Germany, Canada, and Mexico are important foreign producers.

Most of the lead is used for storage batteries, coverings for electric cables, paints, and leaded gasolines. Other important uses include ammunition, foil, solder, printing type, and pipe. Lead's low melting point, resistance to battery acid and other corrosives, and the ease with which it can be shaped or worked, account for the major part of its usefulness.

Zinc is used mainly in the manufacture of

galvanized iron and steel. The major characteristic that accounts for this chief use is its resistance to oxidation or rusting. Thus, a steel pail which becomes a galvanized pail by coating it with zinc is rustproof, as are galvanized screens, wires, and pipes. Mixed with copper, zinc becomes brass, an alloy with many familiar uses. Zinc is also used in paints, fruit jar covers, photoengraving sheets, and medicines.

ANTIMONY

Usually one hears little about antimony. Yet, it is one of the important industrial nonferroalloy minerals. In recent years, the annual tonnage of antimony has greatly exceeded that of some of the well-known ferroalloys such as vanadium and tungsten. Antimony is often mentioned in connection with lead because some of it occurs in association with lead ores and because metallic antimony is used mainly in combination with metallic lead. In fact, its chief use is in the manufacture of what is known as "hard lead." Alloyed with tin and lead, antimony provides pewter and metal for bearings. Another use is in the making of chemical smoke screens.

The outstanding area in the mining of antimony ore is in the central section of the South China hill country (Fig. 307). This area usually produces about one-half of the world supply. Parts of Mexico and the high plateau of Bolivia also mine important amounts. Lesser amounts are mined in several countries, chiefly Germany, Algeria, Peru, and Australia. War and internal strife have greatly interfered with Chinese production so that, temporarily at least, Mexico and Bolivia are more important than South China.

LEAD AND ZINC
● Major producers (lead only)
◉ Major producers (zinc only)
○ Major producers (lead and zinc)

ANTIMONY
▲ Major producers

MERCURY
■ Major producers

307   *WORLD DISTRIBUTION of the major producing areas for lead and zinc, antimony, and mercury.*

MERCURY

Mercury is "the metal which is a liquid"; at least, it is the only metal which is in liquid form at ordinary temperatures. Commonly called quicksilver, it is familiarly seen in the mercury thermometer. Because it occasionally occurs in the free state, in miniature pockets within its ore, and because it can be easily "cooked out" of its ore rock, it was known early in the Mediterranean world. It was chiefly a curiosity because it eluded the fingers when one attempted to pick it up and because it readily coated objects made of other metals, such as gold rings or copper coins. In modern times, it is used in a wide variety of scientific instruments, such as thermometers and barometers, and in paints, medicines, electrical control devices, and special types of lights.

The world's mercury supply is obtained mainly in Spain and Italy (Fig. 307). Those two countries ordinarily produce from 60 to 70 per cent of the total. The only other large producer is the United States. It mines anywhere from 12 to 17 per cent of the world output, depending on the year. Mexico, the U.S.S.R., Canada, and China should also be mentioned in this connection, but no one of them mines as much as 8 per cent of the world's annual production. The oldest and most famous mines are those of Spain. They are located near the southern edge of the Iberian Plateau where an abrupt drop-off forms the Sierra Morena. Italy's mercury mines are in its northeastern mountains. In the United States, mercury is secured from several western states, but California produces about as much as all others combined.

URANIUM

No discussion of important minerals today would be complete if uranium were omitted from it. The world's attention was suddenly focused on uranium when an atomic bomb was dropped on the Japanese city of Hiroshima in August, 1945. The bomb's terrific explosive force was derived from the energy contained in uranium atoms. That energy may some day supplement coal and petroleum for power and heating purposes, or it may, in the form of bombs, destroy man himself.

The greater bulk of the world's limited uranium supply is obtained from an ore known as pitchblende. Pitchblende is also the source material for radium. Minor amounts of uranium also are extracted from another ore called carnotite. When transformed into a metal, uranium resembles metallic nickel in both color and luster; otherwise it is a black powder. The latter is used as a coloring for certain kinds of porcelain. The major deposits of uranium ore occur along the shores of Canada's Great Bear Lake (Fig. 288) and in the southern part of the Belgian Congo in the Katanga area, long famous for its radium and copper ores. Minor deposits are located in the western United States (western Colorado and eastern Utah) and in the portion of the Soviet Union known as Russian Turkestan. If there are other significant deposits, they are either undiscovered or shrouded in the secrecy which attends uranium, atomic energy, and atomic bombs. If the use of atomic energy is placed under international control, to serve rather than to destroy man, the world will know eventually the full story of uranium, including the geographical distribution of known reserves.

The present chapter concludes the systematic discussion of the natural or physical elements of geography. Such discussion has not omitted mention of the cultural elements or the pointing up of the physical conditions in terms of human needs, abilities, and activities; nevertheless, it remains for succeeding chapters to give definite, specific attention to the human or cultural elements of geography. The chapter which follows this is an introduction to the human scene—an introduction to the varied and changing world of man.

CHAPTER OUTLINE

Some significant nonferrous minerals

REVIEW QUESTIONS

1. Annual world production of salt is about 90 billion pounds and that of the United States is about 34 billion pounds. Can you account for such tremendous production? Explain the proportionately great United States production.

2. Why is there practically no international trade in salt?

3. What large sections of the United States possess abundant sands and gravels? Why?

4. Explain the term "by-product sulphur."

5. Discuss "mining with a pump" in reference to salt and sulphur.

6. Is the reference to sulphur as the key ingredient of modern chemical enterprise justified? Explain.

7. Discuss sources of the mineral fertilizers used in the United States.

8. Account for the long-time importance of gold. Where are the chief gold-producing areas of the world today?

9. Why is there "danger of overestimating the importance of both gold and silver"?

10. Discuss the importance of industrial diamonds.

11. What are the properties of aluminum which account for its great demand? Nearly two-thirds of the aluminum produced in the United States is used for two general purposes. What are they? How does the United States stand in reference to ownership of major bauxite deposits?

12. Trace a shipment of copper, and what happens to it, from a "pit" in Arizona until it is placed on the eastern market as metallic copper. Explain the fact that the United States refines more copper than it mines.

13. Account for the commercial importance of tin. Discuss tin demand and sources of supply for the United States.

14. Why has the demand for lead increased so greatly within the past century and especially within the past 50 years?

15. Obtain the most recent information available on source areas, production, use, and control of uranium.

SOME SUGGESTED REFERENCES

Bengtson, Nels A., and Van Royen, William, *Fundamentals of Economic Geography*, Prentice-Hall, 1950. A new edition of a standard textbook in economic geography; contains much material on geography as a whole; see especially Chapters 19 and 26 which deal with such items as salt, fertilizers, nonferrous minerals, etc.

DeMille, John B., *Strategic Minerals: A Summary of the Uses, World Output, Stockpiles, Procurement*, McGraw-Hill, 1947. A useful reference on critical minerals in a world ostensibly at peace, but in a "cold war."

Glover, John G., and Cornell, William B., *The Development of American Industries*, Prentice-Hall, 1946. A book on the history and present economic significance of our basic industries; see Chapters 18-24 concerning copper, lead, etc.

Jones, Clarence F., and Darkenwald, Gordon G., *Economic Geography*, Macmillan, 1941. A standard text in introductory economic geography; see especially Chapters 21-24 inclusive.

Lovering, Thomas S., *Minerals in World Affairs*, Prentice-Hall, 1944. A book on the history, economics, geology, and geographical distribution of important minerals; see Part IV, the Nonferrous Industrial Metals.

PART THREE

Elements of the Cultural Setting

308 *LOOKING downstream along the Vézère River near St. Léon, France. Note in the background the even skyline of the plateau into which the valley has cut. (H. M. Kendall)*

CHAPTER 19

Introduction to the Cultural Elements

Understanding the elements of the physical setting has been the focus of attention so far. Equally important to the attainment of the objectives stated in Chapter 1 is a consideration of man and his works as they are distributed over the earth and related to it. The human habitat in its many varieties is the result of the *interrelation* of physical and cultural elements; it is *not* the result of either alone.

CULTURAL ELEMENTS

The *cultural elements* of the human habitat include man himself and the features which result from his presence and activity (Table 1, p. 4). Collectively, man and his activities and creations produce what is known as the *cultural setting*, just as the physical elements collectively create the physical setting (see Chap. 4).

Various combinations of the physical elements present different possibilities of use to man. Because man is present in differing numbers, because ways of doing things vary from one human group to another and from one time to another, or because one group of human beings discovers possibilities which another overlooks, cultural settings vary as much as do physical settings. Thus, to the physical complexes which are presented to

man, there are added many which man himself creates, either by addition, removal, or both.

Man

From the geographical point of view, the basic questions about man concern numbers; distribution, or arrangement, including movement, throughout the physical habitat; and density or number per unit area. Some parts of the face of the earth are entirely devoid of human inhabitants; other parts are occupied by large numbers of people living in close proximity with one another. In the first instance, the physical setting is altered not at all. In the second instance, alteration may be so great as almost completely to change the character of the physical setting. Though two portions of the habitat may have been very nearly alike before man entered the scene, they may be quite unlike as a result of his activity. The facts of number, distribution, and density of man are considered in the next chapter.

Cultures and the Works of Man

The manner in which human beings live and make a living in an area is not the same for all peoples. Even given essentially the same physical setting, two different groups may create quite contrasted scenes. For example, the character of the rice-growing areas of southeastern China is a far cry from that of the rice-growing areas in the southeastern United States. Differences exist largely because the traditions, or the learned ways of behaving, of one group of human beings differ from those of another. So also do the material manifestations—the houses, the roads, the fields, the equipment, and the like—of one group differ from those of another. The sum of the traditions for any one distinctive human group and of the material manifestations of those traditions is spoken of as that group's *culture.*

There is not one single way of living in a given physical setting, but rather there are as many ways as there are cultures. Similar physical settings may be occupied by peoples who have basically similar ways of making a living, but who otherwise have a notably different culture. For example, there are many similarities between the physical settings of southeastern China and southeastern United States; agriculture is the major way of making a living for the peoples of both areas; but the other features of the culture of the inhabitants of southeastern China create ways of living which are alien to those in the southeastern United States.

The character of any specific portion of the earth is conditioned in part, then, by the culture of the group which inhabits it. In addition, much of the individuality of any area derives from the fact that it has been occupied through a period of time. Through time, the culture of any one group evolves new forms and passes through several stages. Or, several groups with different cultures may occupy the land successively. Often, this succession results in features of the cultural setting, like the location of settlements or the pattern of roads and fields, which may persist long after an economic stage has been passed or after one culture group has been replaced by another. To understand the present situation in an area, the *sequent occupance* must often be examined.

SETTLEMENT. Perhaps the most common indicator of man's presence and activity in an area is his dwelling and the other buildings which go along with it. Individually, the house gives a clue to the sort of living which man carries on and thus suggests other forms which he has created. Collectively, houses provide conspicuous forms which are man-made and which contrast with the nature-made features of the physical setting. The characteristics of *settlement,* as the arrangement of human groups over the face of the earth may be called, include not only the people, but also the details of their relationship to the habitat. Some of the outstanding features of settlement are treated in Chapters 21 and 22.

ECONOMIES. Settlement is at least partly adapted to the physical setting, but it also reflects the main activities by which human groups make a living, their *economies.* The largest and most complex groupings evidence the economy which we call *manufacturing,* wherein most of the individuals are not directly concerned with securing a livelihood through use of the land itself, but rather through the transformation of all sorts of raw materials. Somewhat less complex is the economy which we call *agriculture,* wherein man uses land for direct production of plants and animals and materials produced by them. There is also the economy, commonly still less complex than agriculture, which depends solely upon animals, or *pastoralism.* And, finally, simplest of all is the *hunting-fishing-collecting* economy, wherein man hunts other animals, fishes in streams and lakes, or gathers plant products, thus gaining a living directly from the physical resources of the local area which he occupies. These, then, are the four chief economies: manufacturing, agriculture, pastoralism, and hunting-fishing-collecting.

Two other ways of living must be added to those already listed. Mainly as a result of the increasing importance of manufacturing, there has been an extension of hunting-fishing-collecting from its original form as a simple way of existence for a single group to a way of accumulating surpluses of raw materials. Mining, forestry, and large-scale hunting and fishing have come to be vital to the modern world. The pursuit of these activities may be thought of as a fifth economy, *exploitation*.

Finally man has come to move more freely over the earth's surface. He has acquired knowledge which allows him to free himself from dependence upon one small segment of the human habitat. In consequence, all parts of the human habitat are being drawn closer and closer together in their effects upon one another. The function of world linkage has become so significant as to create one more economy, *commerce*.

Economy and other cultural elements are discussed in their broad outlines, particularly as they affect settlement, in Chapter 22. Following the generalized treatment, each of the economies is described in detail through succeeding chapters. As a conclusion, the pattern of transportation, which is both a yardstick of activity and a net meshing the parts of the whole human habitat together, is treated in Chapter 28.

Just as in the study of the physical features and their combinations in physical complexes (Chapter 4), the understanding of the cultural features and of the part they play in the whole habitat is furthered by consideration of a specific example. It should be noted that reference is first made to the character of the physical setting, for this is the matrix in which the cultural features are embedded. The geography of an area includes both; one alone is not the complete story. Only when the physical background is presented does the geographic significance of the cultural elements become fully appreciable. The following sketch suggests some aspects of the variety which is induced into the different parts of even a small segment of the habitat through man's activities.

THE VEZERE VALLEY: A TYPE STUDY

Physical Setting

The Vézère River is one of several right-bank tributaries of the Dordogne River in the southwest part of central France (Fig. 308). Like many of the other tributaries, this one has cut its way westward from the upland area, known as the Massif Central, to the extensive lowland of southwestern France. Its course leads across a low limestone plateau which fringes the western side of the Massif Central. A portion of the valley in the course across the limestone plateau, a section in the vicinity of the villages of Sergeac, St. Léon-sur Vézère, and Le Moustiers, is here chosen to illustrate characteristics of the cultural setting and of the changes in those characteristics through time (Fig. 309).

In this portion of its course, the Vézère is less than a hundred feet wide, and it follows a winding course over the wide floor of an entrenched valley (Fig. 310). On the outsides of the bends, steep slopes reach directly from the river to the plateau level about one hundred feet above. On the insides of the bends, there are relatively large, scroll-shaped valley flats extending gradually away from the stream to less abrupt valleysides. The course of the stream is blocked in places by shallow rapids because the present river has cut regularly below the level of the flats. There are few tributaries and, in consequence, the valleysides stretch unbroken, whether they are at the river's edge or as much as half a mile back from the river (Fig. 308).

Some of the detail is suggested by a cross section of the valley (Fig. 311). Starting on the general level of the plateau, on the outside of one of the bends in the river, the surface declines gently toward the brink of the valley. The gentle slope gives way to a cliff from twenty-five to forty-five feet in height. At its base, a more gradual slope is again produced by an unassorted accumulation of weathered rock materials, or *colluvial base,* and this leads directly down almost to the stream's edge. In some places, the base of the cliff is eroded so as to form an overhang of as much as twenty-five feet; in other places, the overhang is less and is masked by the accumulation of rock debris.

Across the stream, there is a low steep bank from the top of which the surface extends nearly level away from the river. This is the valley flat; in places, it is as wide as one-half mile, but in other places it is much narrower. At the outer edge of the flat, the valleyside is reached, this time much more gently sloped and with no bedrock exposed.

This same profile is repeated wherever one crosses the valley except that the steep and the gentle sides alternate. Farther downstream, the valley is more deeply entrenched so that the cliffs are more prominent. Farther upstream, the valley is shallower and the cliffs are not so high.

Soil covering is closely related to the different types of surface. On the upland to either side of the valley, it is thin and stony, with irregular fragments of partially decomposed limestone scattered through it. On the valley flats, alluvial material, fine grained in general, is deeply spread; only on the edges of the flats at the valleysides are there any considerable areas of gravel. On the valleysides, rock debris and the products of its consequent weathering are mixed with alluvium so that areas of easily worked materials are spottily distributed.

Much of the upland and much of the valleysides remain forested or have been reforested (Fig. 310). But the valley floor appears to have had an original cover chiefly of grass. The forest that remains is dominantly of chestnut and oak, though there are many poplars in the valley bottom and the stream is lined in places with willows. Some parts of the upland appear too dry for forest and the

cover in these places consists of low bushes intermixed with grasses.

The dryness of the upland is emphasized by the absence of much surface water. This results primarily from the nature of the rock material of which the plateau is made (see p. 246). The whole area is open to the west and is close enough to a windward ocean to have a Mid-latitude Marine (Cfb) climate so that the dryness is not climatic. Precipitation averages approximately thirty-five inches per year. Ground water is plentiful, especially in the valley, where springs abound along the cliffed sides. Rarely are the valley flats too dry to support plant growth, even during prolonged droughts. When melting snows of the Massif Central augment the waters of the Vézère, the valley flats are often inundated. Flooding provides an additional source of soil moisture.

There are no mineral resources in or near this section of the valley. Thus it is upon the climate, land surface, vegetation, and soil that the living of the inhabitants must be based.

Cultural Setting

Human beings have lived in this area for thousands of years. They have occupied it in different ways and their settlements have used different parts of it as the cultures have changed.

OCCUPANCE BY PREHISTORIC MAN. In the Vézère Valley, the discovery of prehistoric artifacts has led to a knowledge of the way in which early man lived and of the kind of places which he used for dwellings. It is therefore possible to reconstruct something of the cultural setting of this long-past period.

For his dwellings, prehistoric man chose two kinds of sites. He lived either in solution caves in the limestone of the plateau or in rock shelters. Both of these types of site are found on the steep valleysides, but not on the gentler slopes. The rock shelters were really places where the erosive processes had created

309 *PART of southwestern France (and nearby Spain), showing major surface regions. Note location of the Vézère River, St. Léon, Sergeac, and Le Moustiers.*

a sufficient overhang at the base of the cliffs to offer some protection from the weather.

Though the overhang is now masked in many places by the accumulation of rock debris, it is probable that it was open at the time prehistoric man used it, for he is not known to have had any implement with

which to excavate large amounts of earth. What was more important was the height of the rock shelter or cave opening above usual floodwater level. From either type of site, the land drops steeply to the river's edge.

Relatively little is known about prehistoric man's way of living. What is known has been gleaned from such remnants of his culture as have withstood the ravages of time. Stone implements which have been found by excavating cave floors or earth fill adjacent to the rock shelters are those of the hunter or fisher. Cave roofs and walls are decorated with drawings of a wide variety of fish and animals. Among the animals are bison, horses, and deer. Mixed in with the implements are bone fragments showing teeth marks; meat was an important element in the diet. That man of this period knew fire is attested by the remnants of charred bone. But there is nothing to indicate whether or not agriculture was practiced. The lack of pictorial representation of plant life on the cave walls, in contrast to the plentiful representation of animal life, implies the lack of importance of agriculture.

It is suggested, then, that prehistoric man lived by the hunting-fishing-collecting economy. He chose his dwelling site for protection, but also for nearness to the streams and to the upland forests. He had no interest in the relatively flat lands, the easily cultivated lands of the valley floor.

PRESENT-DAY OCCUPANCE. In contrast to the concentration on the steeper valleysides by prehistoric man, the present-day inhabitants seek out the valley floor and the remnants of the upland surface on either side of the valley (Fig. 310). The roads follow the outer edge of the valley flats or the edge of the upland surface, avoiding steep slopes wherever possible. Houses, hamlets, and villages are similarly restricted to the flatter lands. The gentler valley slopes are partly in cultivation, but the steep slopes are little used.

Both on the relatively sparsely populated upland and in the more densely peopled valley floor, there is a tendency toward clustered arrangement of dwellings. Upland hamlets occupy sites where the upland surface breaks to the gentler valleysides. Valley hamlets and villages are on portions of the flats which, because they are higher, are less subject to flood, or where, because of poor soil, cultivation is difficult or unprofitable. In the section of the

valley under consideration, three kinds of sites are utilized (Fig. 310). Sergeac is near the downstream end of its flat where the flat gives way to a gently rising valleyside. St. Léon is on the outer edge of its flat opposite a spur against which the river is flowing; this position gives control over the best fording place in this part of the course of the Vézère. Le Moustiers is on the lower part of a steep valleyside and the adjacent flat where a tributary valley joins that of the Vézère.

Each of these villages consists of a part of the main road along the valley where houses are grouped closely together. Rows of two-story houses line each side of the road. In some of them, a room on the first floor is set aside as a store. Here and there, a narrow opening between houses gives access to the section back from the street. Back of each house, there is a small garden. And beyond that, another irregular row of houses is to be found.

The older houses are made of limestone blocks partly covered with plaster. Roofs are made of thin, flat, overlapping slabs of limestone. Some of the houses are whitewashed, but most of them are the dun shade of the original plaster covering. Newer houses use frame construction with slate or tile roofs. The few isolated houses in the valley are built the same; each one has its barn of similar construction.

The people of this area are farmers first and foremost. The gardens adjacent to the houses supply kitchen needs, but in addition each family cultivates fields on the valley flats or on the lower valleysides. In fields much less than an acre in size, wheat and maize are the main grain crops. Together, they are of equal importance with potatoes and other vegetables. Apple, pear, peach, and plum trees dot the farmland, but no land is specifically given over to orchard alone. Vineyards, which formerly covered nearly all of the south-facing valley slopes, are now unimportant for the phylloxera, a kind of plant lice, has destroyed the vines. In some places,

| Upland Remnants | Slope Lands | Valley Bottoms | Wooded Land |

0   ½   1
Mile

310   *A PORTION of the Vézère valley, showing surface divisions, wooded land, and houses and barns. Letters indicate villages:* (A) *St. Léon,* (B) *Sergeac, and* (C) *Le Moustiers.*

truffle-bearing oaks have replaced the vines, but most of the upper slopes are uncultivated. Wheat is the main grain crop of the uplands; most of the small remainder of cultivated land there is used for vegetables.

Plow cultivation is not common. The ordinary implements are the mattock, the spade, and the hoe. Largely because of this, crops are intermixed, with no clear-cut division into fields of one crop only (Fig. 312). Each field consists of a patchwork of a few rows of maize, a fifteen- to twenty-foot strip of wheat, and several rows of vegetables of different kinds.

| Limestone Plateau | Colluvial Base | River Deposits |

0   50
Feet

311   *A CHARACTERISTIC cross section of the Vézère valley. Vertical and horizontal scales are the same.*

312 *THE PATCHWORK of small fields in the Vézère valley, viewed from a point near the top of the steep valley side, looking across the valley. The river flows too close to the base of the steep slope to be visible in this picture. (H. M. Kendall)*

Thus the cultivation is intensive rather than extensive.

The raising of hogs accompanies the garden agriculture in the valleys and sheep grazing accompanies it on the upland. There are some cattle primarily for the supplying of dairy products. Each household has its small poultry flock in which geese predominate. The hogs and geese are essential to the production of the one commercial agricultural product of the area. Hogs are used to locate truffles, subterranean fungus growths on the roots of certain oak trees; geese are fattened on maize so that their livers become fatty and large. The livers and the truffles are combined to make the commercial delicacy, *foie gras truffé*.

Except for this one item of commerce, production is directed toward the supplying of local demand. The area is one of plenty so far as food, shelter, and clothing are concerned, but "extras" or luxuries of life, common in the industrial or urban portions of the Western world, are lacking. Poor articulation with the transportation pattern of the rest of France emphasizes this isolation.

Thus an agricultural people live and create ways and means of living that contrast sharply with those produced by an earlier group. The flatter lands and their use principally to provide plant products are the objects of modern attention. Collectively, the cultural features of the habitat at the present time differ vastly from those in prehistoric times even though the facts of the physical setting have been little altered. It is to the cultural elements that attention is turned in the succeeding chapters.

··

CHAPTER OUTLINE

Introduction to the cultural elements

REVIEW QUESTIONS

1. Select two areas of comparable size which have essentially the same physical setting. Demonstrate that the two areas selected may appear to be quite unlike "because ways of 'doings things' vary from one human group to another and from one time to another."
2. Suggest some of the more prominent cultural features of the people of the United States.
3. Illustrate the meaning of sequent occupance by reference to the area which you know best.
4. Give examples of each of the economies drawn, if possible, from your own experience or general knowledge.
5. In your own words, describe the physical setting of the Vézère Valley. In what ways does the physical setting of the Vézère Valley differ from that of the Lake St. John Lowland (Chap. 4)?
6. Just how is man's present-day activity in the Vézère Valley adjusted to the physical facts of the area? How were the physical features significant in the past?
7. Discuss the physical setting and the human occupance of an area which you know well. Do this in a manner similar to the discussion of the Vézère Valley in the text.

313   *EXTREMES of man's attachment to the land.* (Above) *A street in a village in the Szechwan Basin of China;* (below) *Fifth Avenue, New York.* (*Above, American Museum of Natural History; below, Sozio from Gendreau*)

CHAPTER 20

World Population

··

The first—and by a large margin the foremost—of the cultural elements of geography is man himself. How many people are there in the world? How are they distributed over the face of the earth? How closely are they crowded together, or how widely are they separated from one another? These are questions the answers to which provide much of the basis for understanding (1) the changes which man has wrought in the physical environment and (2) the limitations which the physical environment has placed upon man.

The whole of human history has been concerned with learning how to live in the variety of physical environments encountered over the face of the earth and how to live with the constantly increasing numbers of human beings and their works. Man's first efforts, like those of any other animal, sought primarily to secure food and protection directly from the physical environment. Slowly in the beginning, but with ever increasing tempo, man came to alter what he found or to discover new ways of using what he found to make his existence easier. He learned to tame animals and plants in order to provide himself a more dependable food supply. He learned to use animal and plant products for clothing to protect himself against heat, cold, and moisture. He learned to build houses rather than to seek caves and trees for shelter. And, as he learned how to use the physical setting better, his numbers increased.

Eventually, a stage was reached at which it was easier for some individuals or groups to move to new areas rather than to try, with their existing culture, to increase the facilities for living together. Repeated through centuries, this pressure toward migration brought about a spread of human beings over most parts of the earth's surface. All sorts of physical environments were encountered, but relatively few of them offered entirely satisfactory habitats. Some proved quite uninhabitable until cultural evolution made possible new ways of living; some remain still unable to support more than a temporary population.

The most favorable areas, considering the stage of man's cultural development, became the nuclei toward which all mankind was drawn. They form the great centers of population today—clear-cut, densely populated regions as opposed to vast sparsely settled or uninhabited areas. Uneven spread of human beings over the world is a geographic reality the details of which may be sought in the facts of population numbers, distribution, and density.

POPULATION NUMBERS

Present World Population

The exact number of human beings in the world is not known, but reasonable estimates are available. The total figure at any one time

Table 20 APPROXIMATE WORLD POPULATION (CIRCA 1949)[1]

CONTINENT	TOTAL POPULATION	PERCENTAGE OF WORLD POPULATION
Asia (including East Indies and Philippine Islands)	1,334,000,000	57.0
Europe	487,000,000	20.8
North and Middle America	215,000,000	9.2
Africa	187,000,000	8.0
South America	106,000,000	4.5
Australia and Oceania	12,000,000	0.5
Antarctica	0	0.0
TOTAL	2,341,000,000	100.0

[1] Population figures generalized from "Areas and Populations of the Countries of the World," *1950 Britannica Book of the Year,* Encyclopaedia Britannica, 1950. Reproduced by permission of the publisher.

cannot be known for several reasons. Among these, two may be suggested: first, there is constant loss through death and constant addition through birth, but both of these changes proceed at rates which are variable in time and from place to place; second, the methods of demographic accounting (census taking, vital record keeping, etc.) are neither uniform nor completely reliable throughout the whole world. Even were these methods to be made uniform and completely reliable, there would be little value in knowing precisely how many people there were in the whole world at any one instant of time. The total is so large that a few millions may be neglected without altering the general view of man in his habitat.

Sound estimates indicate that there were approximately 2,300,000,000 human beings spread very unevenly over the whole world by 1949 (Table 20). Asia was the home of by far the largest number, roughly 57 per cent of the total. Into little Europe were crowded just over one-fifth of all the people in the world. At the opposite extreme, Antarctica had no permanent population and Australia, nearly as large as Europe, supported less than one-third of one per cent of the world total.

In terms of political units, nearly half the world's population lived in four countries: China, the Dominion of India, the Union of Socialist Soviet Republics, and the United States of America. China alone, with 464,-000,000, accounted for one-fifth and India, with 342,000,000, nearly one-sixth. Though the U.S.S.R. and the United States followed next in order of total number, they were far below China and India. The U.S.S.R. had a population of 193,000,000 and the United States, of 150,000,000. These four political units were the giant countries in terms of population numbers. Though the actual figures are changing constantly, the relative position of the countries, both as compared with each other and with other countries, has not changed materially. The U.S.S.R. has added territory and hence the population is now probably in excess of 200,000,000. Increase through natural causes has raised the population of the United States to about the 150,-000,000 mark (see Appendix C).

Population Growth

Throughout human history, world population has continued to grow. The rate of growth was slow at first, but it has increased rapidly during the past few centuries. With the very simple hunting-fishing-collecting economy practiced by early man, any given area could support few individuals. As agriculture and the domestication of animals were invented, the ability of certain areas to support larger groups became evident. In addition, these cultural inventions made possible permanent habitation of new areas. Further inventions and the improvement of those already existing brought with them increases of population. Yet, though certain small areas came to have very large populations, most of the world remained empty or sparsely occupied until the stage of cultural evolution known as the Industrial Age was reached.

The Industrial Age had its beginning in northwestern Europe, and it was there that rapid population increase first occurred. The effects of industrialism were rapidly diffused throughout large sections of the world. Movement of large groups of people from one part of the world to another, such as the large-scale colonization of the Americas by Europeans, became feasible for the first time. Advances in medical science changed the balance between births and deaths. Technological advances made possible the use of different kinds of physical environment and allowed the accumulation of surpluses. What was lacking in one place could be secured from another as facilities for movement over the earth were developed. Dependence upon any one small area for the support of a given group of people was greatly modified or, in some instances, altogether eliminated. In a sense, nearly the whole earth came to be the habitat of the peoples provided with adequate means of transportation.

Some notion of the increase in actual numbers may be gained from Table 21. No reasonable estimates can be made of world population for periods before 1650 even though such estimates may be available for specific small areas. Actually, of course, the figures since that date are themselves not precise, but they are sufficiently accurate to give some concept of the tremendous spurt in population growth which has accompanied the spread of industrialism over the world. Not only has the total increased steadily, it has increased at a faster and faster rate.

Table 21 ESTIMATED TOTAL WORLD POPULATION AND POPULATION INCREASES BY PERIODS (AFTER ESTIMATES IN *World Population* BY CARR-SAUNDERS)

YEAR	ESTIMATED WORLD POPULATION	INCREASE PER FIFTY-YEAR PERIOD
1650	545,000,000	. . . .
1700	. . . .	. . . .
1750	728,000,000	(91,500,000)[1]
1800	906,000,000	178,000,000
1850	1,171,000,000	265,000,000
1900	1,608,000,000	437,000,000
1940	2,200,000,000	(592,000,000)[2]

[1] Average of fifty-year periods for century
[2] Forty- rather than fifty-year period

While world population shows few signs of having reached a peak number, its growth is not uniform in all regions and among all groups of people. Basically, the numbers of people in any area depend on the balance between birth and death rates. The changes resulting from industrialism have combined to reduce mortality rates through improving the conditions of life. There has likewise been a decline in birth rate, though this lags behind the lowering of the mortality rate. The end result is that, with the impact of industrialism, there is at first a remarkable increase in population, which is followed in time by a slowing of the rate of increase so that total numbers grow either very slowly or remain more or less constant. Actual decline of total numbers may eventually occur.

It was previously noted that large increases occurred first in northwestern Europe. The one hundred million people of Europe in the middle of the seventeenth century had become five times that number by 1940. The increase began in the late seventeenth century and attained its greatest rate in the late nineteenth and early twentieth centuries. It is now slowing; estimates indicate a maximum will be reached throughout western and central Europe about 1960. Only in the European portion of the U.S.S.R. and in the countries of southeastern Europe is there likelihood of rapid increase.

Throughout the rest of the world, the areas to which the features of the Industrial Age were transmitted earliest have shown a tendency toward stabilization, and even decline, in population numbers. This is notably true in the northeastern United States. On the other hand, the large populations of Asia, Africa, and South America evidently have just reached the stage in which western Europe found itself when its population increase was greatest. In Asia, Africa, and South America generally, death rates are declining, but birth rates remain high.

POPULATION DISTRIBUTION

The distribution of population over the earth is extremely uneven. Antarctica and a few isolated islands scattered through the world's oceans are entirely free of permanent human habitation. At the opposite extreme, in areas like Java, many millions of people live in close proximity to one another. This very unevenness creates one of the most significant cultural patterns: the pattern of population. One of the better ways to show the pattern of population distribution over the world is by the use of a *dot map*.

Dot Maps

When numerical data are available for any given area and when it is desired to show the arrangement of the data on a map so that the pattern will be easily visible, the dot map is a most useful device. Each dot that appears on the map represents a certain number of units, such as 500 people or 10,000 acres of land in a specific crop. Dots are placed on a base map so that each one represents the center of the area in which the specified number of units is found. Obviously, dots are closest together where the units are most numerous in actuality and farthest apart where the units are least numerous in actuality. In some areas, dots may merge while in others they may be widely separated or lacking entirely. The relative closeness creates variation in shading on the map and by that means conveys the notion of pattern distribution. Fig. 314 is a dot map of world population.

On the scale on which Fig. 314 is constructed, the main purpose is to show where there are large numbers of people and where there are few. One cannot use the map for detailed comparison between small areas, principally because of the difficulty of making an actual count of the number of dots in

3I4 *A DOT map of world population.*

one area as compared with another. Where there are large numbers of people, the dots form a solid shading; at the other extreme, a single dot often serves for hundreds of square miles. Nevertheless, this map does make easily visible the nuclear areas about which the world's population is oriented.

Main Features of World Population Distribution

Four parts of the world stand out as centers of large population clusters (Fig. 3I4): eastern Asia, southern Asia, western Europe, and northeastern North America. In all four, many of the dots are so close together as to be indistinguishable as separate dots. From these centers, the dots thin out to become widely scattered or absent altogether.

In great contrast to the main four, many areas are nearly or completely empty of dots. This is true of Antarctica, the greater part of Australia, the central and northern portions of Asia, the northern fringe of Europe, the Saharan portion of Africa, the northern portion of North America, and the interior of South America. The cold lands of the world, the great deserts, and the tropical heart of South America are conspicuously empty.

Between the areas of great concentration and of great emptiness, population spreads thinly over the land, creating fringe zones of moderate numbers. Here and there, as in the Nile Valley or on the island of Java, large numbers of people occupy relatively small and isolated areas which give way without transition to practically empty lands.

In general, the pattern shown on Fig. 3I4 cannot be expected to undergo radical changes in the future. Many of the forces which determine the distribution of population are fixed. For example, in northern China, there is a great extent of plain limited to the north, west, and south by more rugged lands and to the east by the sea (Plate IV). Across this surface flows a great river in a course which has shifted frequently. The climate of the area is Semiarid (BS) and Humid continental climate with long summers (Dwa), thus placing it on the margin of the region of normal humid agriculture (Plate V). As yet, human beings cannot alter the climate. Though many efforts have been made, control over the shifting course of the river has not yet become adequate. The character of the land as a plain cannot be changed. Hence, the physical base upon which the people depend is essentially a constant. True, the people themselves can alter their method of living. Instead of remaining farmers, they may become industrialists. Communication lines may be amplified so that the area will be less dependent upon its own resources, may become less of a subsistence area. Nevertheless, these changes will not occur rapidly and they will not destroy the existence of a nucleus in the world population pattern. The details of arrangement within this area may change and its outlines may expand or contract, but there appears to be no force which will eradicate it throughout the life of many generations.

Continental Patterns of Population Distribution

ASIA. A glance at the dot map of world population distribution (Fig. 314) reveals two great areas of concentration in Asia: the eastern fringes of the continent and India. Yet, within each of these general areas variations of intensity are observable.

The eastern Asiatic zone begins with the three southern islands of the Japanese group. From that location, the belt of large numbers of people follows across to the inner or western coastal zone of Korea and on through southern Manchuria. It is practically continuous into China, but within China several centers of large population stand out. The North China Plain, the basins along the Yangtze River, the lower valley of the Si

River, and the coastal region between the mouths of the Yangtze and Si are all areas supporting tremendous numbers of human beings. Parts of two large islands off the Chinese coast belong also to this great population concentration: western Formosa and northern Hainan.

At the southern frontier of China, the great concentration of population ends. From there to India, only small clusters, separated from one another by stretches of nearly empty land, can be noted. On the islands southeast of the mainland, population is likewise scattered except in Java, southwestern Celebes, and the central western Philippines.

Again on the mainland, the great populations of India stand out with a sharpness equal to those in eastern Asia. The zone of large numbers follows the Ganges River from its delta well westward to the headstreams of the Indus River. Likewise, the east coast of the Indian Peninsula throughout its whole length and the west coast northward to just beyond Bombay are peopled by large numbers. Southwestern Ceylon may be considered a further extension of the Indian coastal regions.

Except for the areas mentioned, the great expanse of the Asiatic continent is comparatively empty of human beings. A delicate trace of peopling appears north of the Aral Sea and extends eastward along the Chinese frontier. Small and poorly defined clusters are attached to the upper portions of the rivers emptying into the Aral Sea. A very thin scattering marks the western and northern Chinese boundaries and the margins of Afghanistan.

One clear relationship is evident in both the eastern and southern regions of concentration: the great populations live on the plains areas (compare Fig. 314 and Plate IV). Most of the peoples of Asia are rural and their livelihood depends upon intensive cultivation of flat and well-watered or irrigable alluvial lands. In many places, the break from intensively occupied land to unoccupied land is line-sharp; often it is so clear that a map of population distribution might equally well be a map of plains (Fig. 113).

Large concentrations in Asia are, as a rule, not the expression of large cities with their attendant masses of population both within the city itself and in its suburbs; they are rather the result of an even spread of agricultural villages over the land. Even in the spottily occupied lands of the southeast, attachment to the alluvial plains is marked. In Burma, the delta and the middle valley of the Irrawaddy River are the foci; in Thailand, the lower valley of the Menam River stands out; and, in Indochina, the delta of the Mekong River and the small coastal plains along the South China Sea form the centers of concentration. Again, in Java, the large populations live on the plains, but on that island there are also volcanic soils of exceptional fertility which play an important part in detailed population distribution.

The narrow wedge of population in Asiatic Russia is of quite different nature. It corresponds closely to the eastward extension of the great Black Soil (chernozem) Belt which starts in southern European Russia (Plate IX). An added factor making for concentration of people is the presence of the Trans-Siberian Railway linking a chain of growing urban centers and offering transportation facilities to urban and rural dwellers alike.

The empty and nearly empty spaces in Asia (Fig. 314) remain so largely because they are physically ill suited to agriculture. In the north, the lands are too cold; there also many of the plains areas, as the lower Ob Valley, are too poorly drained. Central Asia is too mountainous, too dry, or, because of elevation, too cold. Southwestern Asia is too dry; and southeastern Asia, too rugged. Into all of these regions, the great masses of Asia's peoples have not spread. Despite changes in technology, it is doubtful if these vacuums of Asia will ever be settled by the tremendous numbers of people, ever increasing, which clog the lowlands of the continent's eastern and southern fringes.

EUROPE. The most striking feature of the distribution of population in Europe (Fig. 314) is the concentration which appears about the southern end of the North Sea. In the British Isles, London forms the main center. Outward from it, an essentially even spread over the English Lowland continues northward along the east coast into central Scotland and westward to the Welsh Uplands. On the European mainland, a heavily populated coastal zone extends from the mouth of the Seine River in France to the mouth of the Elbe in Germany. From this coastal strip, the zone of greatest numbers reaches inland, sending one arm southeastward along the southern margin of the Plain of North Europe into the Ukraine (compare Fig. 314 and Plate IV) and another southward along the Rhine River into Switzerland.

In addition there are a number of separate population centers. One of the largest focuses on Moscow. Another is the solidly filled lowland of the Po River in northern Italy. The western coast of Italy in the vicinity of Naples and of Genoa form added nuclei as do Barcelona in Spain and Oporto in Portugal. Similarly, coastal Sicily is densely peopled.

Population spreads relatively evenly over most of the rest of the continent, thinning out to nearly empty land north of the sixtieth parallel, roughly north of the latitude of Stockholm, and near the Caspian Sea. In Europe there is not the sharp transition between heavily populated areas and empty areas that there is in Asia. Furthermore, in the areas where the dots are thinly scattered (Fig. 314), there appear clear-cut nuclei which give the pattern a spotted look, as in the European portion of the U.S.S.R. This results principally from the fact that Europe is much more highly industrialized than is Asia. Cities, often quite widely separated, form points of attachment for larger numbers of people, while agricultural population is much more thinly spread over the land between the cities.

There is a certain correspondence between

the areas with large numbers of people and the areas of plains (compare Fig. 314 and Plate IV), but the relationship is not so clearly illustrated in Europe as it is in Asia. To be sure, one can make out the pattern of the most rugged mountain ranges, as for example the Alps, the Carpathians, and the Apennines. Yet, the hilly zone stretching from eastern France to southern Poland is in many places peopled by as large numbers as the Plain of North Europe and by even larger numbers than much of the plainsland of Russia. Evidently other factors than surface play important roles in the distribution of population over Europe.

Since the population is more completely industrialized than in Asia, it is more closely tied to the basic sources of industrial power —coal, especially—and to routeways which make possible the easy movement of people and goods. Many of Europe's population nuclei are the coal fields which dot that continent (Fig. 269), as for example, the Ruhr field of west Germany or the Midlands area of Great Britain. Likewise, the main lines of transportation which, like the Rhine River, give easy access to the continental interior from the fringing seas, form axes of settlement. This is not to say that the plains are avoided; rather, the other types of surface are used by large numbers of people to whom flatness of land and alluvial soils are not of major concern.

Climate, too, plays a significant part in ordering the distribution of population. The cold northern edge of the continent with Subarctic (Dfc) and Tundra (ET) climates is virtually empty of people as is also the area of Arid (BW) climate adjacent to the Caspian Sea. Much of the interior of the Iberian Peninsula is empty too because of adverse climatic conditions—adverse to agriculture.

Over the whole continent, the relationship of the distribution of people to the land is much more complex than it is in Asia. No one element in the physical setting can alone be held responsible. The complex culture of the West is better able to contend with adverse features of the physical setting; the ability of the land to support population under that culture is far different from the ability of the land to support population under Oriental culture.

NORTH AMERICA. The third main area of population concentration lies in eastern North America. Consideration of the population dot map (Fig. 314) makes it evident that this concentration is less clear-cut than that of either Asia or Europe. The greatest numbers of people live within the triangle, the points of which are Boston, Washington, and Chicago. Outward from this core triangle, dots spread relatively closely and evenly southward to the Gulf coast. Westward, close spacing comes to an end almost along the one hundredth meridian (western Kansas). Beyond that line, there are a few small clusters, but only three of them, all lying close to the Pacific coast in the Puget Sound-Willamette Valley lowland, the San Francisco embayment, and the Los Angeles area, represent considerable numbers of people.

The tendency toward a spotted, or nucleated, pattern is even more noticeable than in Europe, primarily because of the even greater urbanization of North America. The foci are cities rather than intensively used agricultural lands. The great river plain of the Mississippi, while not empty, is settled by far fewer human beings than the river plain of the Yangtze in China (Fig. 314). Yet, the relatively low density of rural areas is not a reflection of the lack of significance of agriculture; it results rather from differing methods of land use and also from differences in the length of time the land has been occupied by agricultural people. In China, in fact in all areas occupied by Oriental peoples, human muscle supplies the power upon which agricultural production depends; in the United States, perhaps more than in any other area of Western culture, machines provide the power in agriculture as in all other phases of economic activity. Fewer people are engaged in direct agricultural labor and hence any specific area of agricultural land is peopled by smaller numbers.

Strikingly empty are the North American lands of Subarctic (Dfc) and Tundra (ET) climate (compare Fig. 314 and Plate V). The sharp break between nearly empty and moderately full lands in the interior of the United States lies close to the location of the boundary between the Semiarid (BS) climates and the humid ones. The mountain, hill, and plateau regions of the West likewise stand out as "empty" lands. The reasons for the distribution pattern in North America are complex, perhaps even more complex than in Europe, but, nevertheless, evidences of the significance of the physical setting are unmistakable.

OTHER CONTINENTS. Among the other continents, Africa supports the largest number of people. Particularly striking are the large numbers in the lower valley of the Nile River (Fig. 314). There, on a well-watered river plain set in a slotlike trench cutting across barren desert, millions of agricultural people make their home. This ribbon of heavily peopled land is comparable on a small scale with the great river plains of Asia, but is quite unlike any other area of large numbers on the African continent.

Such other well-populated areas as there are in Africa are widely scattered and discontinuous. In the northwest, the Atlas lands form one notable zone. Here, plains are limited in area and isolated from one another, forcing settlement of hilly and mountainous terrain. Along its southern margin, this belt is limited by Arid (BW) climate.

A faint sprinkling of dots over the great western bulge of the continent shows three main nuclei of population, all of them in Nigeria. In the north is Kano, the ancient city which is a southern gateway to trans-Saharan routes. The other two nuclei are in southern Nigeria on either side of the lower course of the Niger.

Two other foci are to be seen in central eastern Africa; one on the highlands of Ruanda-Urundi at the northern end of Lake Tanganyika, and the other in Uganda northeast of Lake Victoria. The final African center lies on the South African Plateau near Johannesburg. The location of these three centers is not determined by the presence of plains. The centers in Ruanda-Urundi and in Uganda are clusters of native peoples carrying on an agricultural economy. Their concentration is in part due to purely political action. The land has been restricted by the governing European powers to native ownership and occupancy, in a delayed attempt to correct earlier seizure of native lands. The Johannesburg nucleus is primarily an indication of the mineral wealth of the nearby Rand.

The population of South America (Fig. 314) is clearly arranged in clusters about the fringes of the continent. Furthermore, each cluster is isolated from the one nearest it by empty or nearly empty land. In the Pacific coastal regions, the main clusters are almost all away from the sea. Within the low latitudes, they occupy the comparatively cool highland basins; beyond the Tropic, in central Chile, they occupy the longitudinal valley between the coast range and the sea (Plate IV). In eastern South America, there is closer attachment to the sea; only in southeastern Brazil, near São Paulo and inland from Rio de Janeiro, are uplands the site of settlement. The huge empty interior of South America is tropical forest and grassland never occupied by any large number of native peoples and quite undesirable for colonization by people of European origin. South of the fortieth parallel or about the latitude of Bahía Blanca in Argentina, dryness, coldness, and ruggedness are the qualities which preclude intensive settlement.

Australia is the most nearly empty of all the continents on which a permanent population exists. Four nuclear cities (Brisbane, Sydney, Melbourne, and Adelaide) can be noted along the southeastern coastal stretch (Fig. 314), but there are no "filled-up" areas.

Only a few dots indicate the presence of the scanty population of the rest of the continent.

POPULATION DENSITY

The dot map of population distribution (Fig. 314) portrays the spread of people over the earth and gives some notion of the relative numbers living in one area as opposed to another. Yet, in the more crowded regions it gives little idea of *the number of persons per unit of area*. It does not answer the question, how do the main centers of eastern Asia compare with those of Europe in terms of close packing? In other words, it gives no quantitative knowledge of intensity of population. One of the devices which amplifies the understanding derived from the dot map is the map of population density.

Meaning of Population Density

ARITHMETIC DENSITY. The most common expression of population density is a statement of the number of people living in a unit area, ordinarily the number of persons per square mile of land. This is known as *arithmetic density*, or *man-land ratio*. When one says population density, it is arithmetic density that is meant unless another type of density is specifically mentioned. Arithmetic density is usually expressed by a figure which is obtained by dividing the number of people in a given territory by the number of square miles included within the territory. For example, there are approximately 11,750 square miles of land in Belgium; the population, in 1949, was approximately 8,600,000. We may say then that the arithmetic population density of Belgium was 731 per square mile. This figure of density includes all types of land within the unit and makes no distinction be-

tween isolated small population groups or individuals on the one hand and concentrated large groupings on the other. It can therefore give only a broad suggestion of the real intensity of population. This is particularly true when the base units of land are relatively large; the smaller the land unit used, the more nearly accurate is the impression derived.

Despite this handicap, the idea of arithmetic density may be used to good advantage to amplify the idea of population pattern. As has been stated, the world population is approximately 2,300,000,000 and the world's total land area is about 58,000,000 square miles. The average density for the world is, then, 40 per square mile. Yet, it is perfectly obvious from our study of the dot map of world population distribution (Fig. 314) that the arrangement over the earth is far from uniform. Actually, densities range from zero persons per square mile in Antarctica to over 100,000 per square mile in some of the world's larger cities. If, however, the land surface of the earth is considered in small enough units and the density for each of the small units is plotted on a map, there emerges a revealing pattern of population densities.

OTHER TYPES OF DENSITY. The idea of population density may be treated in many ways other than the simple statement of man-land ratio. In detailed studies of small areas, these other measures of density are usually of greater significance than the commonly used arithmetic density. In the attempt to understand the problems of underpopulation or overpopulation, of the ability of the land to support population, or of land use, it is frequently desirable to know how many people there are in any given area per unit of arable land (land fit for cultivation). The figure expressing this relationship is known as the *physiological density*. Similarly, another frequently used figure is that of *agricultural density*, or the number of agriculturally occupied people per unit of arable land. *Rural density* is the number of people carrying on rural activities and living in rural settlements within a unit area; *urban density* represents the number of people carrying on urban activities and living in urban centers within a unit area. The major difficulty involved in the use of any of these types of density for world comparisons is the inadequacy of data. While there are sufficiently accurate figures available for area and for population by relatively small units, at least for the parts of the world where the greater numbers of the world's people live, there is far from adequate information on arable land and on the economic activity of individuals. It is therefore more desirable to use arithmetical density for world comparisons, but it is absolutely essential to remember the shortcomings of the results.

Density Maps

Maps of population density are frequently used instead of dot maps to indicate the distribution of people over the land. Actually, a greater contribution is made when they are used in conjunction with dot maps. Since the dots on most dot maps are placed approximately where the population actually lives, the detailed pattern of distribution which results is a relatively true one. At the same time, there is nothing about a dot map that expresses quantitatively the number of people per unit of land. On the other hand, the density map does show how many people live on a given unit of land, but does not show just where within the unit these people live. Together, the maps show both the "where" and the "how closely packed."

World Population Densities

The world map of densities (Plate VI) re-emphasizes the broad pattern expressed by the dot map of population distribution (Fig. 314), but does so in quantitative terms. By a comparison of the two maps just referred to, this point can be illustrated. One of the areas where large numbers of people are concentrated is the North China Plain. On the dot map, it is clear that the number is large and that the area occupied has a distinct shape; on the density map, the shape of the intensively occupied area is less exact, but one can see that, while the density is over 250 per square mile for the whole region, there is one strip along the inner edge of the plain where the density rises to over 500 per square mile.

Very high densities in dominantly rural areas are characteristic of the Asiatic population concentrations. There, intensive use of the relatively small amounts of level alluvial land supports almost unbelievable densities. Rural density exceeds 1,280 per square mile, more than two per acre, on many of the small plains of the Japanese islands. In the Canton area of South China, average densities over 4,000 per square mile are reported. (Fig. 315).

Similarly, great densities are to be found in the dominantly rural valley of the lower Nile.

In other areas, high densities result mainly from the spatial frequency of large cities, as, for example, in the Rhine-Ruhr area of Germany or the London and Lancashire districts of England. Some of the large cities of the world have extraordinary densities where, for example, the crowding has become so great as to force a vertical layering of population in closely packed apartment districts. And all of the cities of the Western world have huge temporary densities at least during the busy, daytime hours. In centers like New York, with its great office buildings and stores, its skyscrapers so characteristically American, the daytime population density may temporarily exceed a million per square mile.

AREAS OF ESPECIALLY HIGH DENSITY. Outstanding in the eastern Asiatic area of dense population are the areas with densities over 500 per square mile (Plate VI). In the Japanese islands, the plain upon which Tokyo stands is the northeastern end of such an area. A zone extends southwestward to include all of the small plains which border the Inland Sea between the islands of Honshu, Kyushu, and Shikoku. In China, as has been noted, the inner central portion of the North China Plain has densities well over 500 as do also a small portion of the Szechwan Basin of the upper Yangtze, the lower portion of the Yangtze Plain and the river's delta, the small plains which fringe the southeast coast, and the Canton region in the delta of the Si. The southern portion of Formosa and some parts of Java are likewise extremely densely peopled. In India, the lower and middle valley of the Ganges River and small portions of both the southeastern and southwestern coastal lowlands support well over 500 persons per square mile.

The European nucleus shows fewer and less extensive sections of very high density, while those of North America are still more limited. In the British Isles, the Central Lowland of Scotland, the Newcastle, Lancashire, Cardiff, and London areas reach slightly above the figure of 500. On the mainland of Europe, the Flanders Plain, the Rhine Delta, the middle Rhine-Ruhr area, and the Dresden section of Germany are the only sizable regions which reach the 500 figure. In North America, only the coastal zone between Boston and Philadelphia attains such density.

The only other area of very high density is the valley of the Nile River in its Egyptian portion. There, the degree to which people are crowded together becomes all the more noticeable because of the nearly empty lands to either side of the valley.

AREAS OF ESPECIALLY LOW DENSITY. At the opposite extreme in the density scale lies Antarctica with a density, so far as permanent population is concerned, of zero per square mile. The same applies to inner Greenland. Much larger areas show densities below two per square mile. The great belt of land with Arid (BW) climate reaching from the Atlantic coast of northern Africa through Arabia and northeastward into western Manchuria is, for the most part, very scantily populated. From northern China, this thinly peopled zone spreads further northward to include all

of northern and eastern Siberia and westward over the Arctic fringe of Europe. Throughout this whole zone, climate is an effective deterrent to the support of great population densities. Likewise, isolation or difficulty of access, an expression of the location factor, plays its part in keeping the density low.

The same influences are likewise significant in producing the areas of low density through many other parts of the world. In southwest Africa and over the larger part of Australia, Arid (BW) climate prevails; and population densities are very low. In the Patagonian portion of South America and in the Great Basin and Rio Grande areas of North America, similar conditions prevail. Subarctic (Dfc) and Tundra (ET) climates coupled with isolation produce the thinly peopled expanse of Alaska, Canada, and Labrador. The presence of rugged high mountains suggests the dominant reason for low densities in many parts of Alaska, western Canada, and the central western United States as it does also for some of the Andean sections of southern South America.

Other prominent areas with a density less than two per square mile are to be found in the northern interior of South America and in western and northern New Guinea. Here again, difficulty of access and climate are the main reasons.

Limitations on Population Density

From the preceding brief examination of the areas of extreme population density, it is evident that the limitations imposed on density are not derived from the elements of the physical setting alone. The quality of the physical base is, to be sure, a significant *part* of the story, but it is *not the whole* story. Density really depends primarily upon how people make a living, that is, upon occupations; occupations are strongly dependent in turn upon the nature of the physical setting. Yet, actu-

315　*SOMETHING of the feeling of high population density in parts of China is conveyed by this photograph of the market in Pishan, Szechwan. (CNS Photos from Paul Guillumette, Inc.)*

ally, it is nowhere too hot, too cold, too dry, or too wet for man to live; rather, it is everywhere basically a question of whether man knows how to and can *make a living* in an area or not.

Consider western and northern New Guinea. A review of the climate, landforms, native vegetation, and soils (Plates IV, V, VII, and IX) is sufficient to convince anyone that the physical setting is not radically different from that of the Ganges Delta. Yet, New Guinea supports fewer than two persons per square mile while the Ganges Delta supports over 500. Again, many parts of the Amazon Basin are similar to southern Nigeria physically; yet, southern Nigeria is inhabited by from 50 to 100 persons per square mile while little of the Amazon Basin can show a density as high as 25 per square mile. The lower valley of the Yangtze in China has densities far over 500 per square mile; density in the lower Mississippi River Valley in the United States, a broadly similar physical area, drops below 25 per square mile.

Sufficient examples have been given to show that elements other than physical must be effective limitations on population density. If the physical base does not provide the answer alone, then we must turn to the cultural scene. How do the ways of living and of making a living of the inhabitants of New Guinea differ from those of the people of the Ganges Delta? Are the people who live in southern Nigeria the same in their way of life as those who inhabit the Amazon Basin? Do the people of central China use the land in the same manner as those who occupy the lower Mississippi Valley?

When we examine these questions we must seek the relevant social, economic, and political facts. Such facts are often more significant in the explanation of the irregular scattering of population over the world and of the varying population intensities than are the features of the physical setting. The relevancy and significance of social, economic, and political facts are pointed up by the facts of settlement, which are discussed in the next chapter.

••

CHAPTER OUTLINE

World population

Population numbers
  Present world population
  Population growth
Population distribution
  Dot maps
  Main features of world population distribution
  Continental patterns of population distribution
    Asia
    Europe
    North America
    Other continents
Population density
  Meaning of population density
    Arithmetic density
    Other types of density
  Density maps
  World population densities
    Areas of especially high density
    Areas of especially low density
  Limitations on population density

REVIEW QUESTIONS

1. Has there been any change, throughout the period of human history, in "the limitations which the physical environment has placed upon man"? Explain.
2. Why have certain physical environments proved uninhabitable while others have been eminently satisfactory human habitats?
3. Is there any close relationship between the area of a country and the size of that country's population? Is there any close relationship between the physical nature of the country and the size of its population?
4. Outline the broad features of world population growth.
5. Suggest reasons for the difference between the rate of growth of population in northwestern Europe and that in southeastern Europe.
6. Why is the rate of population growth not uniform over the whole world?
7. Describe the main features of world popula-

tion distribution. Offer some reasons for the "blank spots" on the world population map.

8. What are the outstanding features of population distribution in Asia? What relationships between population distribution and physical features of the land are outstandingly evident?

9. Why does the population pattern of Europe have "a spotted look" while that of Asia does not?

10. Be able to describe the essential features of population distribution on each of the continents. Relate these features to facts of the physical setting.

11. Why is arithmetic density of population so common a basis for the construction of world population maps?

12. For what purpose would a world map of agricultural population density be especially useful? Why?

13. Is there any reason to believe that population density is causally related to the character of the physical setting? Discuss.

14. What consideration is basic to the study of limitations of population density, from a geographic point of view?

15. Give some examples of social, economic, and political facts which must be considered in any well-founded attempt to understand population distribution over the world.

SOME SUGGESTED REFERENCES

Bowman, Isaiah, ed., *Limits of Land Settlement: A Report on Present-day Possibilities,* Council of Foreign Relations, 1937. A work of the symposium type by ten specialists; concerned with settlement possibilities and population capacity in the world's frontier areas; a point of departure for the geographic study of current population problems.

Carr-Saunders, A. M., *World Population,* Clarendon Press, 1936. A standard reference in the study of population; largely sociological, but geographical in part.

Davis, Kingsley, ed., "World Population in Transition," *Annals of the American Academy of Political and Social Science,* Vol. 237, January 1945. A collection of articles by leading students of population problems; treats of a wide variety of topics such as population distribution, population growth, overpopulation, etc.; concisely and clearly written; primarily informative.

Moore, Wilbert E., *Economic Demography of Eastern and Southern Europe,* Series of League of Nations Publications, II. Economic and Financial, 1945. II.A.9. A detailed study by the Office of Population Research, Princeton University; concerns present and estimated future population.

Notestein, Frank W., *et al., The Future Population of Europe and the Soviet Union: Population Projections 1940-1970.* Series of League of Nations Publications, II. Economic and Financial, 1944. II.A.2. Similar to the preceding reference; deals with a larger area; somewhat less detailed than the preceding reference.

Thompson, Warren S., *Population Problems,* McGraw-Hill, 1942. A thoroughgoing treatment of population problems from many points of view; a standard text for population study.

316 *SETTLEMENTS of nomadic peoples are simple, temporary, and easily moved features on the land, like this dwelling and stone corral in the Gobi of Mongolia. (American Museum of Natural History)*

CHAPTER 21

Settlement Types and Contrasts

. . . .

The relation of the people to the land is not expressed adequately by descriptive statements of numbers, distribution, and density of population. These facts tell little of just how the people of one area are grouped as compared with those of another area. Only a knowledge of population *arrangement* provides specific information on the man-land relationship, for it provides a clue to the differences in mode of life from one part of the human habitat to another.

For example, one speaks of the great numbers of people who live on the North China Plain as contrasted, say, with the few who live in inner Asia. Numbers and general distribution are recognized immediately. One can add a statement about the density in each area. But, beyond that, there is no indication of what the relation of the people of either area is to the land, or just how they are arranged within each area. Is the population of inner Asia *sedentary*, fixed in certain locations, or is it *mobile*, shifting from one location to another? Do the inhabitants of the North China Plain live in clusters of houses or on isolated farmsteads? Are the population groupings in either place large or small? Do the people derive their living directly from the land? Or are they interested only in the transformation of raw materials and only indirectly concerned with the production of food, shelter, and clothing? In short, are they

rural or urban folk? These are more detailed considerations than those of number, general distribution, and density. They are the facts of *settlement*, of the arrangement of population on the land.

MAJOR CONTRASTS IN SETTLEMENT

Mobile versus Sedentary Population

In some parts of the world, human beings, in making their living, move from one place to another without fixed abode. These people are *nomads*, like many of the tribal groups of inner Asia, for example. Their whole living depends upon herds of animals such as sheep and goats. Most commonly, nomads inhabit desert margins where rainfall is irregular in occurrence and uncertain in amount. The animals must have pasturage and this means a constant search for areas of plentiful grass. Nomads must be ready to move when word of rainfall in any accessible area reaches them, for rainfall means new pasture. Though nomads live in groups, their dwellings are purely temporary and are easily moved from one location to another (Fig. 316).

Similar to the nomads of the desert margins are those of the Arctic tundra as, for example, the Lapps of northern Scandinavia. These small groups depend for their whole existence upon the reindeer; their arrangement upon the land is a shifting one between the summer pasturage in the tundra and winter shelter within the margins of the northern coniferous forest, or taiga.

In other areas, as in some of the tropical forests, some tribal groups depend entirely upon what they can secure from hunting and fishing, or by collecting the edible plant products of the forest. For a period, they attach themselves to specific locations, building crude dwellings as centers of activity (Fig. 317), but the time comes quickly when the local sources of supply are exhausted. Then, the group must move to a new area. The population is a mobile one, although perhaps not as mobile as the nomadic groups that depend upon animal pasturage.

The Eskimos of the Arctic fringelands are another example of a mobile population, shifting their place of attachment to the land with the demands of their fishing-hunting-collecting way of making a living. They are less mobile than the forest tribes or the nomads, for certain locations are known by them to offer better bases for hunting, fishing, and collecting than others, and to these bases they frequently return. Yet, the imprint they make upon the land is slight.

Unlike mobile populations, most of the world's people are tied to specific places on the surface of the earth. This *sedentary* or fixed population provides relatively long-lasting patterns and forms. These can be observed and compared and they form essential elements in a thorough understanding of the cultural phase of the human habitat.

Disseminated versus Agglomerated Population

Among sedentary populations, the character of settlement varies widely. At one extreme is the isolated dwelling which houses a single individual or family (Fig. 318). At the opposite extreme, dwellings may be so closely massed as to leave no part of the local surface uncovered, or at least only a small plot surrounding or next to each of the individual dwellings. In some of the world's large cities, population closeness is measured not in terms of the area occupied, but actually in terms of vertical as well as horizontal arrangement. Apartments crowd one small group on top of another. People are literally "piled up."

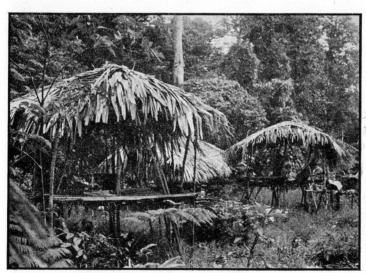

317

A DESERTED native encampment on the floodplain of the Idenburg River in northwestern New Guinea. Crude settlements of this sort form temporary centers for the small, mobile populations of the tropical forests. (Archbold Expeditions of the American Museum of Natural History)

318 ISOLATED *farmstead in the wheatlands near Dimmitt, Texas. (Lee, Standard Oil Co. [N. J.])*

When individual dwellings are scattered over the land, the population pattern is said to be *disseminated*. When dwellings are packed close together, the settlement pattern is spoken of as *agglomerated*. As the derivation of the word implies, disseminated population is population "scattered abroad," population which is strewn like seed over the land. Similarly, agglomerated population is population "collected into a mass."

It must be clearly stated that the two terms, disseminated and agglomerated, are used relatively. Study on a world scale precludes considering each individual human being. It is necessary to use a coarser base. And that base can reasonably be the dwelling. On such a scale, complete dissemination is understood to mean a scattering of single dwellings, with their associated buildings, over a given area, so arranged that there is no suggestion of grouping or clustering. Complete agglomeration, on the other hand, implies close massing of dwellings and other buildings with no isolated dwellings between clusters.

Dissemination may characterize population arrangement in either sparsely or densely settled lands. No minimum or maximum distance between buildings can be stated to serve as the line between dissemination and agglomeration. It is simply the scattered or the clustered nature of the pattern which the descriptive term indicates. Possible, too, is the mixed or combination pattern in which agglomerations are spotted throughout a general background of disseminated settlement.

Man is, after all, a gregarious animal; he tends to live in groups rather than alone. There is ample evidence to show that man existed first as a tribal animal wandering about in search of food. When agriculture was invented, the tribal groups settled down. Thus early sedentary population assumed an agglomerated pattern. In many parts of the world, this agglomerated pattern has persisted right down to the present. Dissemination came relatively late in the human time scale. Though it characterizes relatively few parts of the world, those parts are extensive.

Rural versus Urban Population

Just as in the use of disseminated and agglomerated for the description of settlement pattern, the distinction between rural and urban is a relative one. There is no immediately evident sharp line which divides rural folk from urban. A *rural* population means one predominantly engaged in primary production of the basic necessities of life directly from the land itself. An *urban* population means one which has no direct interest in the production of the materials of food, shelter, or clothing from the land itself. Urban folk are engaged in transporting, manufacturing, buying, and selling the materials for their food, shelter, and clothing, or for their general comfort; or in educating the people, or in managing the affairs of state, or in merely "living in town."

Obviously, rural population may be arranged in a disseminated pattern more commonly than can urban population. Yet, rural folk need not necessarily be scattered over the land. In fact, agglomerated rural population is more common and more numerous, for the world as a whole, than is disseminated. Urban population is almost entirely agglomerated. It is estimated that fully three-quarters of the world's population lives in agglomerations of one type or another.

Despite the huge size of many centers like London, New York, or Paris, the actual total of urban population is far less than the total of rural population. Urban settlement characterizes the Western world, specifically Europe and the areas colonized by peoples of European origin. On the other hand, the rural agglomeration is most distinctly Oriental.

RURAL SETTLEMENT

Even today, in this Machine Age, dependence upon primary production from the land is fundamental to our whole existence.

Direct use of the land is the way of living for the vast majority of human beings; in other words, most populations are rural. Their arrangement on the land is the matrix in which urban populations are set.

Agglomerated Rural Population

A rural agglomeration is a relatively closely built cluster of buildings surrounded by fields, pastures, or woodland areas. Dwellings constitute much of the whole cluster, but there are also storage sheds for farm produce and for implements and barns for housing animals. Possibly also, there is a church, a school, and a town hall. Practically the entire population is concerned with cultivating the surrounding land or in raising animals—in living directly from the land. To augment their living, some of the inhabitants may engage in selling some commodity. For example, someone in the settlement may offer food for sale and possibly add to that a small supply of tools or machinery. Professional people, like doctors, ministers, and teachers, may live in the agglomeration. But primarily, the life of the settlement is tied to the land and, except as the settlement may contribute its agricultural surpluses to the outside world, it is essentially self-contained. The settlement is first and foremost the dwelling place of an agricultural society.

Rural agglomerations are usually described as *hamlets* or *villages*. There is no clearly defined difference between the two except in size; hamlet is used to describe a very small rural settlement of, say, five or six, or even fewer, dwellings and their associated buildings whereas village implies a greater number. Generally, too, village implies a greater number of people who are not directly concerned with farming, and it suggests the presence in the settlement of buildings set aside as stores.

The appearance and structure of the hamlet or village varies widely from one part of the world to another. There is no universal characteristic except that of function; always, the agglomeration forms the dwelling place for a group engaged in direct use of the land. Beyond that, the number, size, appearance, and arrangement of buildings corresponds to the traditions and habits of the particular group of people and to the nature of the land from which they derive their living.

For example, the village of many parts of southern Japan consists of a close-packed cluster of bamboo and thatch dwellings and sheds, so tightly pressed together as to allow only narrow passageways between adjacent buildings. The whole settlement occupies a bit of ground only slightly above the level of the surrounding irrigated rice fields. Seldom are there roads leading to and from the village. Narrow pathways following along the tops of the low dikes which separate the rice fields are the only connecting lines from one village to the next. Commonly, the village is encircled by a brushy hedge which stands out prominently because of the absence of trees and bushes elsewhere.

Inhabitants go out from the village early in the day to work their fields, returning again at night. One farmer's land is seldom in one continuous piece, but rather it is in several fragments in scattered locations about the settlement. The whole life of the inhabitants, often members of only one or two large family groups, is a daily pulsing out onto the land and back into the village. Both the scattered nature of the landholdings and the intensity of the agriculture demand constant attention. The village is the focal point from which a small portion of the human habitat is made to perform its function.

The hamlets or villages in many parts of Europe are in considerable contrast to those of the Orient. In southern France, for example, villages like St. Léon, referred to previously, or Flamerens (Fig. 319) are common. Flamerens crowns the top of a low hill with fields spreading down the slopes and away from the settlement. The village is roughly rectangular in shape with a château at one end and a church at the other. Forming the sides of the rectangle are the houses of the rural inhabitants built one against the other. There is thus enclosed a *place* or square with exits on either side of the church and château. Immediately back of the houses on the hill slopes are small kitchen gardens. Farther down the slopes are larger fields and, beyond them, pastures and bits of woodland.

There is the same daily movement out from the village to the fields and back, but it does not have the regularity of that of the Oriental village. Agriculture is less intensive and demands less constant attention in France than

319 *THE VILLAGE of Flamerens in the Aquitaine Basin of southwestern France.* (*H. M. Kendall*)

in the Orient. In addition, the village is not so completely a family settlement. Finally, the European village is tied in by roads to the transportation net of the larger area; the village in Europe is not so self-contained as is that of the Orient.

In certain other parts of Europe, as in Hungary, rural agglomerations of several thousands of people are not uncommon features. These huge villages cover considerable areas of land with each dwelling and its associated buildings set on a small plot of land. But the farm buildings are definitely clustered, arranged along streets to form collected settlements set in open cultivated or pastured land.

In the eastern seaboard regions of the United States, as in New England or the South, agglomerated rural settlement was the early mode. In colonial New England, farmhouses were built close together, usually fronting on a *common*. The common was originally a pasture area near the farmhouses owned and used collectively by all the inhabitants of the village. Where it still remains today, it has become the village park. In the South, early establishment of plantations with their needs for large labor forces and the consequent importation of slaves developed another kind of rural agglomeration in the compact slave quarters.

These few examples suggest that there is great variety in the detail of rural agglomerated settlement. The unifying characteristic is the tie of the population to the land.

Disseminated Rural Population

At the opposite extreme from the hamlet or village is the isolated farmstead (Fig. 318). The farm dwelling with its adjacent barns and sheds forms the population unit. Fields, pastures, and other land, from all of which the family draws its living, stretch out from the central unit unbroken by other buildings. The distance between farmsteads may be slight, say one-quarter of a mile, or great, as much as several miles. There is none of the compactness of the agglomeration; nor is there the daily flow of large numbers of people to surrounding fields. Land used intensively usually lies close to the farmstead itself. Extensively cultivated lands, pastures, and wooded areas are commonly farther away. Each farm serves as a unit in itself, not as a fragment of a larger integrated hamlet or village.

World Distribution of Rural Settlement

The farm village characterizes the greater part of the Orient. Except for a few relatively small areas like Hokkaido, the northern island of the Japanese group, isolated farmsteads are rare. Throughout the southern islands of Japan, the densely peopled plains of China, the Indies, Malaya, and India, close-set compact hamlets and villages are sprinkled thickly through the intensively cultivated flatter lands.

On through the Near East, as in the lowland of the Tigris and Euphrates rivers, and into Africa, as in the valley of the Nile. the rural agglomeration persists almost exclusively. In the larger part of Africa which is occupied by native peoples, like the Guinea lands, the Congo Basin, or parts of the East African Plateau, the agglomerated pattern of rural settlement is repeated.

The hamlet or village is the characteristic settlement unit through most of southern and eastern Europe. Even into the western part of that continent, it continues as a prominent form, but with the disseminated pattern becoming more and more prominent as one proceeds northwestward. Yet, even in northwestern Europe, a thin scattering of rural population fails to mask the basic agglomerated pattern.

Through South and Middle America into Mexico, agglomeration is the rule, but in

North America, and especially in the United States, it is virtually absent. As has been indicated, early settlement, like that in New England, was of the agglomerated sort. This has been replaced, however, by dissemination. In the United States, the farm village remains only as a relict form, or its essentially rural character has been replaced by one that is urban. In a few places, as in some of the Mormon settlements of Utah, the hamlet or village remains the unit, but through the greater part of the United States dissemination is the rule.

It is in lands quite recently settled by peoples of northwestern European origin, or under their influence, that the disseminated pattern is most characteristic. In addition to the United States, Canada is an area of scattered rather than clustered rural population. So also are the greater part of Australia, New Zealand, the areas of European colonization in South and East Africa, and some parts of South America. The "habit" of agglomeration has been lost in these areas.

The Orient is perhaps the extreme of agglomeration; the United States, of dissemination of rural population.

URBAN SETTLEMENT

The basic clue to the difference between a rural agglomeration and an urban agglomeration is the function or functions which the agglomeration performs. What is the purpose of the settlement? We have seen that the hamlet or village is essentially a cluster of dwellings and associated buildings which houses people most of whom are engaged in the direct use of the land. There is no great difference between one section of a rural agglomeration and another; the form and structure, or *morphology*, of a rural settlement is relatively simple. In an urban center, most of the people are engaged in other activities than the direct use of land. The settlement includes the dwellings of these people, but it also includes buildings of quite different aspect where the various economic activities are carried on. There is a marked difference between one section of an urban agglomeration and another. For example, an urban center existing on a coast and serving as a port has a definite dock and warehouse district quite distinct from, say, the residence district. The morphology of an urban settlement is more complex than that of a hamlet or village. Since it is from function that this essential difference between rural and urban agglomerations derives, it is to the study of urban functions that one must turn for the first clue to the characer of urban settlement.

Urban Functions

Urban functions are of six major kinds. In the United States, the one that comes first to mind is, ordinarily, the making or altering of goods the better to suit them to human use. More often than not, it is done on a large scale as *manufacturing*. It may, however, be carried on on a relatively small scale as a *craft*.

Next most common is the function of the exchange of goods, or *commerce*. There are really three facets to this function. One of these is *collection*, or the bringing together of large amounts of goods for expediency in handling. For example, mining provides raw materials for manufacturing, but often ores or concentrates must be brought together from many small sources so as to be available in large enough amounts. So also must the products of the forests and seas be accumulated. Storage of large amounts of agricultural and manufactured goods to facilitate later exchange likewise requires the performance of the function of collection. In the exchange process, the *distribution* function must also be performed as, for example, when materials are brought into a port in large bulk and then sent out in smaller lots. Exporting

320 *SITUATION features of two present-day metropolises:* (A) *New York,* (B) *Paris.*

centers and supply centers carry on the same type of activity. Commerce may also involve *transfer,* as in the instance of change of method of transportation. Where river transport has to give way to overland transport, or vice versa, transfer is essential to the performance of the commercial function.

There are four other functions which are known as urban. *Administration,* as in government, is a necessary function of organized social life which must be carried on at some center of population. Similarly, the function of *defense,* as illustrated in fortress towns or naval bases, is necessary and can be performed only in agglomerated settlements. Universities, religious centers, and art centers perform a *cultural* function. It should be noted that

cultural is here used in a very restricted sense. Lastly, health and tourist centers perform the function of *recreation.*

The urban functions, then, are manufacturing, commerce, administration, defense, culture, and recreation. They stand contrasted to rural functions. When the population of any agglomeration, regardless of actual numbers, is primarily engaged in cultivating the land or in raising animals, the agglomeration is described as rural; when the population is in greater part engaged in one or more of the urban functions, the agglomeration is described as urban.

Situation and Site

SITUATION. To understand any agglomeration, it is necessary to appreciate its relation to the area in which it is located, its regional position or *situation.* This does not mean the precise location, which is indicated by latitude and longitude, but rather the relationship of the agglomeration to the region which it serves. For example, New York City is located on the coast of northeastern United States where an embayed river mouth offers possibilities for the development of a protected harbor and where a relatively open valley system (that of the Hudson-Mohawk) affords relatively easy access to the interior of the United States (Fig. 320A). To illustrate further the idea of situation, it may be said that Paris lies near the center of the Paris Basin where tributary streams converge upon the Seine River to form a focus of routes (Fig. 320B). In this statement, the expression Paris Basin is understood to imply a plains area of northern France encompassed on the north, east, and south by nearly continuous belts of upland. The breaks in the upland rim, like the Gate of Poitou to the southwest and the Col de Saverne to the east, form natural land routes which center, as do the streams, upon the Paris location.

SITE. In contrast to the concept of situation,

the detailed position of the agglomeration on the land is spoken of as the *site*. The site may be a hilltop, a peninsula, an island, or any other such specific bit of the surface.

The original site of New York City was the downstream end of a relatively high island near the seaward end of the estuary of the Hudson River. The present site includes not only the whole of this same island, but the entire surface of other nearby small islands, the adjacent end of Long Island, and the nearby shores of the mainland (Fig. 321A). The original site of Paris was an island in the Seine River a short distance downstream from the junction of the Seine and the Marne, where relatively high land approached close to the river's edge on both banks (Fig. 321B). The present site includes not only the original island, but the flood plain and valley slopes on both sides of the Seine upstream to just beyond the Marne junction and downstream for a distance of several miles.

Both situation and site change with the passage of time. Increase in population in any agglomeration brings with it expansion over a larger area, as has been suggested in the examples of New York and Paris. Loss of population may cause contraction of the site.

So far as situation is concerned, change is perhaps less obvious, but it is nevertheless real. For example, modern highways may by-pass an old agricultural market town. The flow of goods is thereby diverted and the market loses its significance as a regional commercial center; its situation is changed. Or, the productivity of an area may be altered by a shift from agriculture to manufacturing; new urban centers might arise to replace or compete with an older service center. The situation of the older agglomeration might thereby be radically changed.

Morphology

SIZE. Urban agglomerations cannot be reliably distinguished from rural agglomer-

321 *SITE features of two present-day metropolises:* (A) *New York,* (B) *Paris.*

ations in terms of mere size. An agglomeration may consist of a relatively small cluster of dwellings housing few people and covering only a few acres of land, or it may have inhabitants numbering in the millions and be so extensive as to cover hundreds of square miles. But neither the number of people nor the areal extent are sure measures of the function or the importance of the agglomeration. To be sure, rural agglomerations are usually smaller than urban ones. Likewise, large centers are usually of more importance than small ones. Yet, the small collection of buildings and the few people who live in them at a grain-collecting center in the wheatlands of the Great Plains of the United States may have a regional significance far beyond that, say, of twice as large a settlement in the more heavily populated Northeast.

Size is often used arbitrarily, for convenience, as in the United States censuses in the past, to distinguish between rural and urban agglomerations. But such arbitrary distinction may lead to misunderstanding of the significance or even of the nature of the settlements of any area. Only broadly, and then only as a contributing element to the whole problem, may emphasis be placed on size alone.

INTERNAL PATTERNS. The skeleton of any agglomeration is the pattern or scheme of its streets, which may be arranged either according to some geometrical plan or completely without regularity. Often the features of site conspire to favor certain lines of movement between buildings over others, and thus to determine the over-all configuration. Again, site may impose no control, so that the pattern develops entirely in accord with the desires or whims of the inhabitants.

In urban agglomerations that are old and had their origins in simple groupings of rural people, the patterns of streets may be quite irregular. The exact alignment of early houses and other buildings was not a matter of importance to the inhabitants. As the settlement grew large enough so that actual, formal streets were laid out, they had to follow as best they could the irregular lines between buildings. Much of the pattern of streets of lower New York (Fig. 322A) or that of the heart of Paris (Fig. 322B) like Topsy, "just grew."

Sometimes, pattern has been determined, directly or indirectly, by government decree. The urban settlements of Spanish America were laid out with a central plaza and streets parallel to its sides. Thus came a pattern of rectangular nature, with streets crossing one another at right angles. In the central and western United States, the rectangular land survey brought original focus upon roads crossing one another at right angles. Generally in crossroads agglomerations, additional streets developed logically along lines parallel to the roads forming the crossroads and thus at right angles to one another.

Increasing importance and size of an agglomeration create the need for speed and ease of access to its center from the periphery. Thus came the development of the radial pattern whereby streets lead from points on the periphery directly to a common center, much as the spokes of a wheel lead from the rim to the hub. Cross streets then tend to assume a weblike arrangement. The skeleton of streets of Washington, D. C. (Fig. 322C) is a complex combination of radial and rectangular patterns. So is the skeleton of Indianapolis (Fig. 322D), but more simple.

Beyond these three basic patterns, irregular, rectangular, and radial, there are many others which have grown out of the vagaries of private individuals or of real estate development. These are irregular in a sense, but they are usually symmetrically so. Circular drives, curving and recurving lines, figure eights, and dead-end courts leading in from each of four sides of a large rectangular block are some of the familiar forms to be encountered in present-day growing urban agglomerations.

All of the patterns may occur in combination as well as individually, especially in larger urban areas. As one proceeds uptown, the irregular pattern of lower New York (Fig. 322A) becomes a well-crystallized, rectangular pattern, with only one notable exception,

322 *PATTERNS of principal streets in parts of four urban agglomerations.* (A) *lower New York,* (B) *central Paris,* (C) *central Washington,* (D) *central Indianapolis.*

Broadway. The repeating radial patterns of Washington, D. C., are imposed upon a rectangular base (Fig. 322C). The radial pattern about the Place de l'Etoile in Paris links tenuously to the irregular framework farther into the old city, to the circular boulevards which belt the city, and to the great cross avenues of modern construction which tear right across the old irregular pattern (Fig. 322B). Similarly, where peculiarities of site restrict full development of any one pattern, local modifications are introduced. For example, the city of Syracuse, New York, has a street pattern basically rectangular, but much of the city's site is characterized by drumlins. The steepness of slope of certain of the drumlins interferes with an unrestricted rectangular pattern (Fig. 323).

Whatever single pattern or combination of patterns exists, the character of the agglomeration is deeply affected. The alignment of houses and other buildings is crystallized by the position of the streets and thus the agglomeration acquires a fixed quality. Additions to it or detractions from it, both measures of growth, must in some way be articulated with the existing pattern. Despite changes of detail, the agglomeration as a whole retains a distinctive appearance, determined at bottom by its pattern of streets.

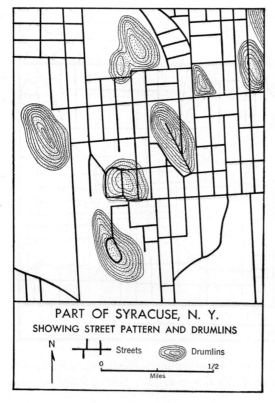

PART OF SYRACUSE, N. Y.
SHOWING STREET PATTERN AND DRUMLINS

N   Streets   Drumlins

0   1/2
Miles

323   *PROMINENT landforms may be responsible for irregularities in street pattern, as in the southeastern part of Syracuse, New York. There, steepness of slope on some of the drumlins which are part of the site has necessitated departures from true rectangularity.*

PROFILE OR CROSS SECTION. Something of the nature of any agglomeration is told by its *profile*, or sky line. In small rural settlements, the buildings are often widely spaced. Individual houses rise above low sheds and huge barns may overshadow all. Rising near the center of the settlement may be the thin spire of a church. Yet, the whole profile of a small rural settlement is irregular and jagged. Trees often raise their rounded crowns to soften the sharpness of angular roof lines. Large urban agglomerations, especially in the United States, present quite a different profile. The outer edges may look like the profiles of rural settlements. As the center is approached, the buildings rise more massively and higher, giving almost the impression of the cross section of a pyramid. The lines are straight or symmetrically rounded, man-made forms rather than natural ones (Fig. 324).

In other parts of the world, this "piling up at the center" is less characteristic than in the United States. In Japan, for example, an urban agglomeration has a profile which, because of the absence of tall buildings, is almost indistinguishable from that of a rural settlement. Only by great length does it suggest large size and reveal urban nature.

FUNCTIONAL AREAS. Urban agglomerations perform various functions for the groups living in them and for the area which surrounds them. While these functions may occur singly or in combination, each one involves certain types of buildings; for example, the appearance of a retail store like a grocery store, carrying on the commercial function, contrasts sharply with the appearance of a factory, which carries on the function of manufacturing. Similarly, a zone of retail stores within an agglomeration creates a scene quite different from the scene created by a grouping of factories. A residential zone is easily distinguished from, say, the campus of a college.

Each function presents a distinctive form, which tends to be localized within the agglomeration. An area which performs a special function is known as a *functional area*.

324 PROFILE of lower Manhattan as seen from the Staten Island ferry. (Collier, Standard Oil Co. [N. J.])

Taken together, functional areas form a discernible pattern. They provide the remaining element of the morphology of agglomeration.

It is common, in American settlements at least, to refer to the downtown section. Usually, this means the section of the settlement which is given over to stores, public buildings, and the like. It is usually a part of the settlement definitely removed from individual residences, although large apartment buildings are often located in the downtown section. Similarly, there is generally a factory section. On the part of Americans, the concept of functional areas is thus tacitly recognized.

Within older settled parts of the Western world, distinctions between the specialized areas of any agglomeration are less clearly marked than in newer settlements. The history of the growth of any agglomeration often reveals why the various functions are performed in scattered rather than in collected zones. In European settlements, for example,

residence often is maintained close to or in the same building with retail stores. The function of commerce may thus be so scattered as to leave no impression of a "downtown" section. In Oriental settlements, the same building may house a craft workshop, serve as the residence of the craft workers, and, at the same time, house persons engaged in intensive agriculture on a small plot of land nearby.

The arrangement of the functional areas results from the interplay of a wide variety of forces. At an early stage, the intersection of two highways, which may have given rise to the settlement in the first place, may be an attractive site for a store. Here people from the vicinity come to purchase needed supplies or to dispose of surplus agricultural items. In time, a second store might be established because there is good commercial opportunity. A third and many others may follow. An inn may be built near the crossroads. Gradually, there appears a nucleus within which all the buildings are used for commerce; they are occupied during the day by the people engaged in the performance of that function, but they do not live there. A distinct functional area develops, a *commercial core* in this instance (Fig. 325A).

Sometimes, factories are attracted to a commercial core by the presence of a large number of people, families of those active in commerce, which provides an available large labor supply. Wealth accumulated in commercial activity might be available for investment in industry.

Sometimes, however, factories have to be built on the outskirts of a settlement. If past growth of the commercial core has made land values too high, and the presence of residences about the commercial core makes adjacent land unavailable, factories are forced to the outskirts. Gradually, under such conditions, there might grow up an industrial belt encircling the commercial and residential centers (Fig. 325B).

The growth of any agglomeration brings with it continual, far-reaching adjustments of its functional areas. If a settlement has developed a commercial core surrounded by residences and that, in turn, is encompassed by an industrial ring, further growth in population requires expansion of the residence area. Often the only possibility lies in jumping beyond the industrial ring; soon new residence areas appear on the fringe, sometimes close to the factories for the workers, and sometimes well away from the factory belt for those who can afford to choose their own site. Here and there, small agglomerations may develop physically entirely separate from the original nucleus, but economically, still part of it.

As newer residence areas spring up, there is usually a decline of the old residence belt near the center of the settlement. This decline is accompanied by outward spread of the commercial core and inward growth of the industrial belt. Old residences of the settlement's youth become rooming houses,

gradually deteriorating and eventually being removed to make way for expansion of the other functional areas. To such zones on the fringes of the commercial core, the name *blighted area* or *slums* is frequently given in American cities.

With continued spread, distances within the agglomeration, especially between the residence districts and the commercial core, become so great that new scattered nuclei of commerce begin to appear irregularly in the outer residence districts. These are the occasional "corner stores," the "neighborhood shopping centers," so characteristic of growing American cities.

Further still, modern transportation has made it possible for urban folk to have their dwellings at considerable distances from their work. Intangibles, like the desire for space, and tangibles, like tax rates, have both contributed to the migration of urban people away from the urban nucleus. Where this movement has actually occurred, a zone of interpenetration of urban and rural settlement, the *rural-urban fringe,* has come into being.

Similarly, as the agglomeration spreads, details of site such as steepness of slope or the presence of a lake shore or a river may limit the growth of one or another of its functional areas. Congestion of traffic may necessitate cutting new streets or widening old ones. This in turn may bring about the rearrangement of functional areas, thus altering the whole character of the urban unit. Both physical and cultural elements combine to create the individuality of any urban agglomeration. Thus cities grow and change.

Types of Urban Agglomerations

As specified earlier, an urban agglomeration is one in which the greater part of the population is engaged in the performance of one or more of the urban functions. Geographically, the whole agglomeration is considered as the unit. Often, a continuously built-up area forming one agglomeration includes several political units. As a geographical unit of settlement, New York City, for example, spreads not only beyond the political city limits, but even across state boundaries. It is, nevertheless, all one urban agglomeration. No one can tell from the appearance of the agglomeration where one crosses a "city line." Similarly, there is no break in the geographical continuity of urban settlement in passing from the political unit of Chicago into Evanston.

Considered in this way, there are three types of urban units: town, city, and metropolis. Distinctions among these three are made first on the basis of the number of functions which each performs and secondly on the basis of morphology.

TOWN. When one of the urban functions dominates the life of the agglomeration, that agglomeration is known as a *town*. To be sure, in most American market towns, there are town halls or public buildings which indicate that government is carried on. There are schools and churches, visible evidences of the cultural function. Perhaps there is a printing shop where a newspaper is printed. And there may be a golf course, or a park with tennis courts, or a swimming pool. Yet, the main function of the center is as a market for farm produce; its place in the region depends on commerce.

CITY. When an urban area acquires a second important function, it becomes a *city*. The acquisition of one or more additional functions materially complicates the pattern of functional areas. There is no longer simply a downtown section and the residential area; there are at least three clearly marked elements. In the example on this page in which

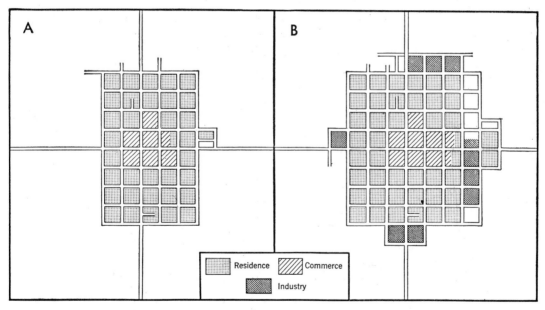

325 ARRANGEMENT *of functional areas in hypothetical urban settlements, assuming a rectangular street plan: (A) a town with commercial core surrounded by residences; (B) a small city with commercial core, residence zone, and incipient industrial belt. In (A) note the concentration of commercial function near the intersection of through roads. In (B) note the fringe location of industry and the close approach of the commercial core to the industrial belt along a through route.*

a market center added a manufacturing zone, there would be three functional areas: the commercial core, the manufacturing zone, and the residential area.

Commonly, a successful market town in America adds the function of manufacturing. In this growth, the manufacturing plants are not like the newspaper of a town; rather, they exist in their own right, serving a market well beyond the immediate confines of the settlement in which they are located.

Again, a market town may grow to such prominence that it is selected as the administrative center for a relatively large area. It carries on governmental functions as a county seat or as a state capital.

Usually, city populations are larger than town populations. Yet, this is not imperative. The essential distinction lies in the greater structural complexity of the city. As a city adds to its functions, it tends to spread over a greater and greater area. On its outskirts, it begins to develop miniature reproductions of its own central section; thus, *suburban communities* come into being. Or a city, like Los Angeles, may spread to engulf other cities and towns and thus further add to its complexity.

METROPOLIS. The spread of the urban way of life, coupled with population increases of tremendous size, has created many huge urban areas throughout the world (Table 22). London, New York, and Paris are examples. Increase in size has been attended by constantly increasing complexity. Not only has each agglomeration passed the stage at which its patterns were easily comprehended and its individuality as an urban unit recognized; each has expanded so as to become a large region in its own right. Yet each performs urban functions for a greater and greater surrounding tributary area. Eventually, the tributary area has grown to include a large part of, or even the whole of, the human habitat. Such a center carries no longer merely a local or national significance, but rather world import; it may properly be called a *metropolis*.

No specific figure of size can be used to define a metropolis. In general, that name is not applied to urban units with a population of under one million, but not all settlements of over one million may be accounted metropolises. Metropolis implies the presence of *satellite cities,* cities in their own right which have been tied into, or engulfed by the spread of, one huge urban nucleus. Really an undefinable atmosphere of world significance, coupled with large size and great morphological complexity, justifies the use of the term metropolis. When the agglomeration is clearly a part of the region in which it exists, when it performs urban functions dominantly for that region alone, it is not classed as a metropolis no matter how large the number of its inhabitants or what the extent of built-up area.

There are in the Orient several urban agglomerations of over one million inhabitants, complex in structure and performing many of the urban functions, and yet primarily of local significance. These are huge cities, but not metropolises. Nagoya in Japan is such a city; in contrast, say, with Tokyo, Nagoya is of little note outside Japan. Similarly, Madrid has few of the metropolitan characteristics of Barcelona in Spain, and Turin has little of the international air of Rome.

Though the term metropolis is not a rigid one, an approach to exactness may be made by study of the area economically tributary to an urban unit, that unit's *trade area.* It is easiest, of course, to delimit the trade areas of towns. Those of cities and metropolises are harder to discern. In studying a market town, for instance, one can plot easily the farm area it serves. At some distance from the town, the flow of goods and people is away from rather than toward the town, marking the commercial divides between one center's trade area and another's. By joining together the divides on all sides of a settlement, its trade area may be outlined. As an illustration, the trade areas of a section of southern France are shown in Fig. 326.

Trade areas of towns may overlap slightly.

Table 22 URBAN CENTERS OF MORE THAN A MILLION INHABITANTS
(CIRCA 1940)

(Figures are for the total urban agglomerations, not for political units.)

NORTH AMERICA		EUROPE	
New York	11,690,000	London	8,700,000
Chicago	4,499,000	Paris	4,963,000
Los Angeles	2,905,000	Berlin	4,670,000
Philadelphia	2,899,000	Moscow	4,137,000
Boston	2,350,000	Leningrad	3,191,000
Detroit	2,296,000	Vienna	1,930,000
Pittsburgh	1,994,000	Manchester	1,750,000
Mexico City	1,757,000	Hamburg	1,682,000
San Francisco	1,428,000	Budapest	1,585,000
St. Louis	1,368,000	Brussels	1,300,000
Cleveland	1,215,000	Liverpool	1,290,000
Montreal	1,140,000	Warsaw	1,289,000
Baltimore	1,047,000	Rome	1,280,000
		Milan	1,264,000
ASIA		Barcelona	1,250,000
Tokyo	7,865,000	Madrid	1,171,000
Shanghai	3,499,000	Glasgow	1,132,000
Osaka	3,252,000	Naples	1,130,000
Calcutta	2,488,000	Birmingham	1,030,000
Pekin	1,568,000		
Tientsin	1,514,000	SOUTH AMERICA	
Bombay	1,490,000	Buenos Aires	3,175,000
Hankow	1,400,000	Rio de Janeiro	1,564,000
Nagoya	1,328,000	São Paulo	1,500,000
Kyoto	1,090,000		
Hongkong	1,072,000	AUSTRALIA	
Canton	1,043,000	Sydney	1,398,000
Nanking	1,019,000	Melbourne	1,193,000

AFRICA	
Cairo	1,312,000

From Preston E. James (with the collaboration of Hibberd V. B. Kline, Jr.), *A Geography of Man,* Ginn, 1949, p. 446. Reproduced with the permission of the publisher.

326 *TRADE AREAS of a section of southern France in which periodic fairs are still important economically. Note that the trade area of the fairs at Auch, the largest urban center in the Department of Gers, includes much of the trade areas of the fairs in secondary centers.*

In addition, those of towns combine to form those of cities. There is, thus, greater overlap in the instance of city trade areas than in those of towns. Pyramiding in this fashion, areas tributary to urban centers tend to become more extensive as the size and complexity of the centers increases. When it is apparent that the greater part of a continent and even areas across oceans on other continents lie directly within the trade area of any huge city, then that city may properly be classed as a metropolis.

Distribution of Cities

The urban form of settlement is relatively closely limited in its distribution over the world. The large city is seldom to be found in areas of low population density (compare Plates I, VI, and Table 22). In detail, there are exceptions to this generalization. For example, Madrid, with its population of over a million, stands conspicuously in the thinly peopled expanse of the Spanish Plateau, and Rome rises abruptly out of almost empty surrounding lands. Yet, from a world view, the thinly peopled areas are nearly devoid of cities.

With only a few exceptions, cities are not found in the great lowlands of the low latitudes. Bombay, Calcutta, Singapore, Batavia, Canton, and Manila in the Asiatic sphere and Rio de Janeiro in South America stand as the major exceptions. In the low latitudes, despite the scarcity of cities, there are some of the world's greatest population densities. Thus, it can be seen that urbanization is not a necessary corollary of high population density.

Examination of the distribution of cities reveals no strict tie to climate. Though mountains usually preclude the growth of large cities, landforms are seldom major determinants in city distribution. Nor can the character of the native vegetation be demonstrated to be the outstanding control; nor can soil. Of all the physical elements of the habitat, mineral resources appear to have the greatest attractive force. Yet, for example, while cities do exist on coal fields, not all coal fields have cities on them. One is forced to conclude that world distribution of cities is not accountable for in terms of the physical setting alone, or even primarily.

What does become evident about the world distribution of cities (Plate I) is that they are most numerous in the middle latitudes and that, in Europe and America, they are the dominant features within these latitudes. Considering the history of urban forms, one comes to realize that urbanization has become more and more an earmark of what we call Western civilization. As the culture of the West spread over the various continents, urban settlement spread with it. Instead of developing slowly from rural settlements as did the cities of early history in the lands adjacent to and on the shores of the Mediterranean Sea and the later ones of northwestern Europe, urban forms were often created anew as the lands of

the world were brought within the European sphere.

The world distribution of cities, then, reflects the spread of a culture, the Western or European, more sharply than it does any other element of the human habitat. Where that culture has been brought by actual colonization, as in the United States or Australia, urban forms are even more prominent than in the region of their origin. Where Western culture has come only as a control in the form of government or commercial activity, as in India or China, urban forms have likewise appeared, but they rest as unassimilated forms on a plain of rural settlement types. It is as a measure of the spread of the culture of the West that the distribution of cities may best be understood.

....

CHAPTER OUTLINE

Settlement types and contrasts

REVIEW QUESTIONS

1. Suggest additional examples, from your own experience if possible, to illustrate how a knowledge of population pattern provides specific information about the man-land relationship in various parts of the world.

2. What are the major contrasts in settlement? Give specific examples of areas in which each of the major settlement types is found.

3. In what ways do the forms created in the landscape by a mobile population differ from those created by a sedentary population?

4. Is there any precise means of distinguishing definitively between a disseminated and an agglomerated population? Discuss.

5. Offer a reasoned explanatory argument in support of the statement that, "Urban settlement characterizes the Western World. . ."

6. Why is some consideration of rural settlement necessary in geographic study of the world, even in this Machine Age?

7. What is the difference between a hamlet and a village? Is the difference clear cut?

8. Can agglomerated rural settlement be associated with specific parts of the world? How can the association be explained?

9. Suggest some of the geographic reasons for disseminated rural settlement in Iowa, for example; in the Great Plains of the United States; in Southern Rhodesia.

10. What are the urban functions? How do these functions produce differences in the appearance of urban agglomerations as contrasted with rural agglomerations?

11. From your own observation, give examples of urban agglomerations which perform different urban functions.

12. Differentiate between situation and site. Give specific illustrations.

13. Enumerate the elements which, collectively, constitute the morphology of a population agglomeration. Which one is most significant in determining whether the agglomeration is rural or urban?

14. Describe, geographically, the population agglomeration with which you are best acquainted. Is it a hamlet, village, town, city, or metropolis? Support your statement as completely as possible.

15. List several examples of towns, cities, and metropolises. Be prepared to tell why you classify each one as you do.

16. What is the significance of a trade area for any urban agglomeration?

17. Why are there so few large urban centers in the tropics?

18. Is it possible to explain the distribution of cities in terms of the physical elements of the landscape? Give examples to illustrate the reasons for your answer.

19. How does urban settlement in the interior of the United States, for example, differ from that in northwestern Europe?

20. Discuss the relationship between the distribution of Western culture and the distribution of cities.

SOME SUGGESTED REFERENCES

Aurousseau, M., Three articles by this author, despite their age, are essentially an excellent point of departure for further study. They are: "The Arrangement of Rural Populations," *Geographical Review*, Vol. X, 1920: 223-240; "The Distribution of Population: A Constructive Problem," *Geographical Review*, Vol. XI, 1921: 563-592; and "Recent Contributions to Urban Geography: A Review," *Geographical Review*, Vol. XIV, 1924: 444-455.

Dickinson, Robert E., *City Region and Regionalism: A Geographical Contribution to Human Ecology*, Keegan Paul, Trench, Trubner & Co., Ltd., 1947. A detailed and critical development of "the concept of the nucleated settlement . . . as a focus of human activity and organization" for its tributary area; advanced and technical.

James, Preston E. (with the collaboration of Hibberd V. B. Kline, Jr.), *A Geography of Man*, Ginn, 1949. An excellent study of major world regions; thorough treatment of settlement.

Mumford, Lewis, *The Culture of Cities*, Harcourt, Brace, 1938. A brilliant treatment of the role of cities in modern civilization; traces the growth of cities from the medieval period to the twentieth century and analyzes the economic, political, and social functions and problems of modern urban areas; for the nonprofessional reader.

Taylor, T. Griffith, *Urban Geography*, E. P. Dutton & Co., 1949. A recent textbook concerned with site, evolution, pattern, and classification of urban agglomerations.

327 RURAL settlements and intensively cultivated fields occupy the plains of Japan while most adjacent hill lands are avoided. View over the Niigata plain near the town of Nakajo, Honshu, Japan. (Comstock Small)

CHAPTER 22

Determinants of Settlement Pattern

Any given settlement pattern is the result of the interplay of many elements, both cultural and physical. This is true whether the population is sedentary or mobile, disseminated or agglomerated, rural or urban. It is not a matter of whether the physical or the cultural elements are the more important, but a matter of particular combinations of physical and cultural conditions resulting in specific settlement patterns. The examples which follow serve to illustrate two actual combinations and the resultant patterns.

On many of the small plains of Japan, settlement consists of small rural agglomerations which dot the flat land and almost completely avoid adjacent hill lands (Fig. 327). It will be recalled that the culture of the Orient includes the habit of living in hamlets or villages. Furthermore, the great part of the population of Japan derives its living through an intensive, irrigated agriculture in which human muscles provide the power. Large numbers of people live on relatively small areas of land and their living depends upon the choice of a crop which yields large amounts per unit of area cultivated. For the Japanese people, this crop is rice. Rice demands relatively high temperatures and a large supply of moisture. It produces best where it can be grown with irrigation adding water beyond the amount derived from rainfall and applied as needed. Irrigation can be practiced most easily on plains; the more

steeply sloping hill land and mountainland is less desirable if not downright undesirable. In Japan, most of the land is hilly or mountainous, with only 15 or 16 per cent of the total area having a gentle slope. Thus, small bits of plain are especially attractive. Population crowds onto them and gathers in clusters. The spacing of the clusters is in part related to the land which can be effectively cultivated by the people of each village. Yet, on any plain there may be small areas of poor soil, or sections which cannot be reached by irrigation waters. These poorer spots, too, are in part determinants of village spacing. Thus, both the heritage of the people and the nature of the physical complex in which they live contribute to the creation of a distinct settlement pattern.

A second example may be taken from the Corn Belt of the United States. The group which settled this area had lost the village habit; their culture included the trait of disseminated rural settlement (Fig. 328). Land was plentiful. Furthermore, the federal government's land policy, including the rectangular survey and the granting of large acreages to each farmer, regularized the pattern of property lines and of roads. The survey marked off the land into squares one mile on a side. Along each side a strip was left to be developed as a road. Each farmer was allowed to acquire one-quarter of a square mile of land. Individual farmsteads were thus separated from one another, furthering the tendency toward complete dissemination. A relatively wide scattering of urban agglomerations, market towns, was tied inevitably to the regularized road pattern.

The extensive plains of the interior of the United States impose few limitations on the actual location of any farmstead. Marked local climatic variations are absent. With the mechanized agriculture of the present and with the existence of adequate means of transportation and exchange, dissemination is more effective than agglomeration in allowing the fullest use of the habitat by the inhabitants. The landscapes of this area have origins in facts as diverse as these and in others too numerous to include in this brief statement. Thus again, elements of both the cultural and the physical setting contribute to the determination of the settlement pattern.

RELATION OF SETTLEMENT TO OTHER CULTURAL ELEMENTS

The elements of the cultural environment are of major significance in determining settlement pattern. What people do for a living, and all the paraphernalia that go along with living, are responsible for differences from place to place just as are climate, landforms, native vegetation and animal life, soils, sources of water, and mineral resources. For example, as has been stated previously, for a people who have no knowledge of well drilling or of irrigated agriculture, deserts offer few, if any, settlement possibilities; people of this sort would find no points of attachment, no way of living which would utilize such positive

328 *AERIAL view of the Corn Belt, Clayton County, Iowa. Scattered farmsteads and a checkerboard pattern of fields characterize the landscape. (Parma from Black Star)*

advantages as might exist in one part of the desert as opposed to another. On the other hand, a group that understood how to drill wells that would tap underground sources of water could live quite satisfactorily wherever the desert had ample underground water. Settlement by such a group would tend to concentrate near water sources and to be of the agglomerated type. The long-established oases of the Sahara or Arabia (Fig. 329) and the more recently developed Salt River Valley of Arizona offer eloquent evidence.

An important part of any culture is the *economy*, or the way of making a living. If we are to understand differences in settlement over the face of the earth, we must consider the broad classes of economy. Each class represents a kind of solution to the problem of mastery of the human habitat.

There is an almost infinite variety in the practice of any one economy by different peoples; in addition, variety is introduced into any economy with the passage of time. Consider, for example, agriculture. Agricultural practices differ noticeably from one group to another even though the physical settings occupied by any two groups may be quite similar. Likewise, there is change in the agricultural methods of any one human group through time. Both of these facts undoubtedly affect settlement pattern. The wheat agriculture of the Great Plains of the United States is materially different from that of the Russian Steppes, to suggest only one example of difference between human groups. The grain agriculture of southern New England in the mid-nineteenth century has been supplanted by dairying in the present, to suggest the changes within the same cultural group with time.

While variations of the magnitude just cited are important matters in detailed study, they cannot reasonably be fitted into a survey on a world scale. It is rather to the broad classes of economy that attention is here directed.

Economies

HUNTING-FISHING-COLLECTING. The simplest of all economies is the *hunting-fishing-collect-*

329   *OASIS of Khafs Daghrah in the Nejd, Saudi Arabia. (Corsini, Standard Oil Co. [N. J.])*

330 *PASTORALISM demands mobility, especially where pasture is scanty. A herd of goats in Big Bend National Park, Texas. (Glenn Burgess, Alpine, Texas)*

ing economy. In this type of economy, the populace is absorbed in securing food, shelter, and clothing from the area in which it lives. This economy adjusts to the character of the physical setting with little attempt to change that setting. It is obvious that such an economy places strict limits upon the size of the human group which is supported in any given area. At best, the occupying of an area is temporary. Mobility is essential; the human group has no fixed place of abode. While there may be temporary marks on the landscape, those marks are sooner or later obliterated.

The hunting-fishing-collecting economy dominates in only a few areas of the world today. And these areas are on the fringes of the heavily peopled parts of the human habitat. In the East Indies and on the poleward margins of the Americas and Eurasia, small groups still live primitively, by hunting, fishing, or collecting, or by the combination of all three. A few small groups in the Amazon and African forests and the Bushmen of the Kalahari still follow this primitive way of living.

PASTORALISM. With the domestication of animals came a way of making a living which differed from the hunting-fishing-collecting economy—*pastoralism*. Man's problem became one of watching over animals, of seeing that there was food and water for them, and of protecting them from wild animals (Fig. 330). Pastoralism offered support for larger human groups, but it still demanded mobility. Thus it acted as a determinant of a particular kind of settlement pattern.

AGRICULTURE. Still another economy, *agriculture*, developed when man domesticated plants. And here for the first time came the possibility of permanent attachment to the land. When sedentary, as opposed to migratory, agriculture developed, man truly "settled down." It was no longer necessary for him to hunt for food or continually to move in search of pasturage for animals. Agriculture enabled man to select a place of habitation and to live either in groups or in isolation. The agricultural economy permitted either a disseminated or an agglomerated settlement pattern.

MANUFACTURING. Finally, man developed *manufacturing*, the most complex of his economies. It requires not only direct production from the earth, but alteration or combination of agricultural and mineral products. And this economy produced spectacular effects upon the arrangement of population over the land. It demanded living in groups usually fixed in certain small parts of the earth. Here the physical setting has a prominent place, for the availability of source materials is equally significant with the availability of man power.

EXPLOITATION. As adjuncts to manufacturing economy, two other economies have arisen. The need for accumulation of materials brought into being an amplification of the simple hunting-fishing-collecting economy. The increased use of metals in manufacturing necessitated the securing of materials directly from the earth's crust by mining. The forests were tapped to supply wood and other plant materials by modern forest operations like lumbering or gathering of fruits, gums, saps, and the like. The sea provided still further raw materials. All of these ways of making a living, in so far as they are carried on without thought of replacement of the resource, may be spoken of as *exploitation*.

COMMERCE. Manufacturing implies division of labor and exchange of products. When the individuals involved are not concerned either with direct production or with the making or altering of products for human use, but are instead concerned with bringing together raw materials or in transporting and distributing manufactured products, they are engaged in *commerce*.

Both exploitation and commerce are limiting elements in settlement pattern. Mining involves the concentration of human beings where there are ore deposits and thus tends to produce agglomerated settlements. Exploitation of the forest may require either large numbers concentrated at one site or very small groups scattered through the forest. It thus produces both agglomerated and disseminated settlement patterns. Use of the sea requires and implies ports on the sea's edge. And commerce demands ties to certain sites at route ends and crossings.

Other Cultural Factors

In addition to the broad economies which are listed above, one must take into account the cultural heritage of the individual group if one is to understand the settlement pattern of any area. Different segments of the human race have acquired, throughout their histories, certain ways of doing things, certain attitudes, certain ways of thinking. All of these cultural ways are made observable in the forms of individual buildings, settlements, fields, modes of transport, and other cultural impedimenta. No two groups develop the same culture; each has its own way of fitting into the physical setting and of making use of the elements of that setting. Several cultural habits have already been cited. For example, the dispersal of American agricultural settlement in individual farmsteads differs notably from the tendency toward agglomerated settlement in southern France. The flat-roofed dwellings of the Saharan oases stand in marked contrast to the steep-pitched roofs of northwestern Europe. These are only symbols of difference of habit, differences of tradition, all of which, accumulated through time, distinguish one culture from another.

Many of the features of settlement are brought about simply because people of one culture are more or less able to make use of a given physical setting than people of another culture. When contacts between human groups were few and difficult to make, distinctive features were numerous and could be easily observed. Now, the differences are less sharp for there are few human groups so isolated that their traditional way of living is not increasingly subject to outside influences.

Consider the change which has come in the life of the Eskimo. Prior to contact with European peoples, the Eskimo was a primitive hunter and fisher. His very life depended upon his skill in securing the necessities for survival by seeking out the animal life over long distances and with crude implements. When Europeans came, the Eskimo was provided with firearms which made hunting easier for a time, until the kill exceeded the rate of reproduction. This meant first of all a change from essentially mobile to sedentary settlement. Where formerly a family group, or perhaps two or three such groups, might select dwelling sites at one place, remaining so long as the supply of food within hunting distance was sufficient, there came to be larger settlements near the points where contact with the Europeans could most easily be made. The balance between the ability of the land and sea to support and the way of living of the group was destroyed. It became impossible for the Eskimo to exist in his former habitat; he became a charge of the European peoples since he had adopted some features of their culture.

While each group has developed its own cultural hue and there are therefore a great number of culture groups in the world, two great cultures stand out clearly in the world today—the culture of western Europe and the Americas, known collectively as *Western* culture or civilization, and the culture of eastern and southern Asia, known as *Oriental*. Western culture is distinguished basically by its dependence upon the use of machines powered by chemical and electrical energy; Oriental culture, by the use of human power.

Largely through its use of machine power, Western culture has spread from its original European base throughout most of the world. First, it moved by colonization to the Americas and then through trade to Africa and the East. Advantages both in numbers of people and in equipment made possible an early disruption of the culture groups which the Europeans found in North America and a somewhat slower one in South America. The effects on native cultures in Africa occurred less rapidly and were less complete largely because there was less attempt at actual colonization; the possibilities of trade were of prime importance and the effects of contact were largely observable only in the slow disintegration of the African ways of living rather than in a wholesale destruction of them.

Last of all, and well after industrialization had become the keynote of Western culture, the active spread to the centers of Oriental culture took place. Here also, Western influences have altered and continue to alter the native culture. Yet, here there is a profound difference from what has happened elsewhere. In the Orient, the numbers of people are far greater than in any other area to which Western ways have been transferred. The West was superimposed on an already complex culture. Orientals began to take enough prominent parts of what the Westerner offered to give a semblance of complete absorption. Witness the industrialization of Japan from the late 1860's to the 1940's.

Slowly the industrial or machine way of life spread to other Oriental culture areas, to India, China, and even to parts of the East Indies. But Western ways have been imposed upon a base and not substituted for it. Western culture in the Orient is like a layer of paint upon a wooden house. Though eastern and southern Asia have felt the contact of the West, the underlying Oriental culture still remains.

Through the past three decades, cultural change has been particularly apparent within the U.S.S.R. It cannot yet be stated whether the change has brought about a real amalgam of Western and Oriental cultures or is simply a phase in the evolution of Western culture. On the surface, like a veneer, Western cultural forms, represented chiefly by dependence upon use of machines, are certainly evident. Beneath the surface, the use of human power still prevails. Yet, one distinguishing characteristic labels the Soviet development as somewhat different from both the standard Western and Oriental cultures. That one distinguishing characteristic is the complete subjugation of private ownership and the substitution for it of state ownership. The individual human being is, for the Soviet group, no longer the unit; rather, the whole population operates collectively for the state.

Whether the development within the U.S.S.R. is viewed as an amalgam of the two dominant world cultures or as an evolutionary phase of one of them, the way of life which it represents has spread rapidly from former European Russia over a significantly large portion of the Eurasian land mass. On the west, it comes into direct contact with typical Western culture, has actually superseded it in part of the contact zone; on the east, it is spreading actively through a large segment of Oriental culture, apparently more thoroughly than typical Western culture did before it. There is certainly indication that a third culture, the *Soviet* culture, may be attaining the world significance of both Western and Oriental cultures.

Because its ideology is directly concerned with the place of the individual in the scheme of the state, Soviet culture must inevitably have effects upon the way in which the individual makes a living and, through this, upon settlement. And these effects may be found to differ greatly from those of Western and Oriental cultures. At the present, however, it is not clear exactly what the differences are.

In the more isolated parts of the world like the interior forests of the Amazon Basin or the nearly unknown interiors of Borneo and New Guinea, for example, native cultures still bear little of the imprint of the two dominant world cultures. But native cultures play less and less significant roles throughout the world. Their effect in shaping settlement patterns is confined to small areas and to small populations. They exist really as curious fragments from the past.

The economy of a people and the accompanying cultural heritage have the greatest potency in lending individual character to settlement in any one area. A physical setting may impose limits more or less broad upon utilization by human beings; but, for every economy, there are as many settlement possibilities as there are culture groups. Realizing this, one can recognize that the study of the cultural elements must not be a detailed catalogue; rather, it must be an analysis of those features which are areally and humanly of major significance.

RELATION OF SETTLEMENT TO PHYSICAL ELEMENTS

The physical elements of the human habitat operate less directly as determinants of settlement pattern than do the cultural elements. A physical fact gives an area a character which offers certain possibilities to a human group; it is normally passive, not active. Within any specific area, the settlement habit of a group may have to be modified to fit the local conditions to greater or lesser advantage. It is in this sort of relationship that the physical elements may be considered determinants of settlement pattern; they set the limits within which the culture operates.

Climate

Climate imposes certain broad, indirect limitations upon settlement. Where the climate limits the available amount of moisture, both for plants and for man's direct uses, human activity is concentrated near the places where the largest amount of moisture can be assured—near a spring, along a stream, or where wells make ground or artesian water accessible. The size of settlements is limited by the amount of water available. The scattered oases of the western Sahara, separated from one another by completely unoccupied desert, attest this close relationship to water.

Similarly, the temperature may have an effect upon the pattern of settlement. But it is locally rather than generally that temperature makes itself felt. Within mountain areas, for example, one valleyside may be much sunnier than the other and hence much warmer. It is that side that is chosen for settlement rather than the shadier side. Warmth is not the only consideration; on the shadier slope, lower evaporation often leads to excessive wetness, which in turn may produce landslides or avalanches in mountain country.

Two tributary valleys to the upper Rhone bring out the importance of sunshine. The Lötschental, or valley of the Lötsch River (Fig. 141) opens a moderately wide corridor parallel to and a little north of the Rhone, but turns abruptly southward to join the Rhone a short distance downstream from the town of Brig (Fig. 331). The middle and upper course of the Lötschental lies along a northeast-southwest line. Its northern side is thus far sunnier than its southern side; hence, practically all of the settlement in the valley is on this northern side. A little farther westward, downstream, the Rhone is joined by a tributary flowing from the south. The valley of this tributary, the Val d'Anniviers, lies

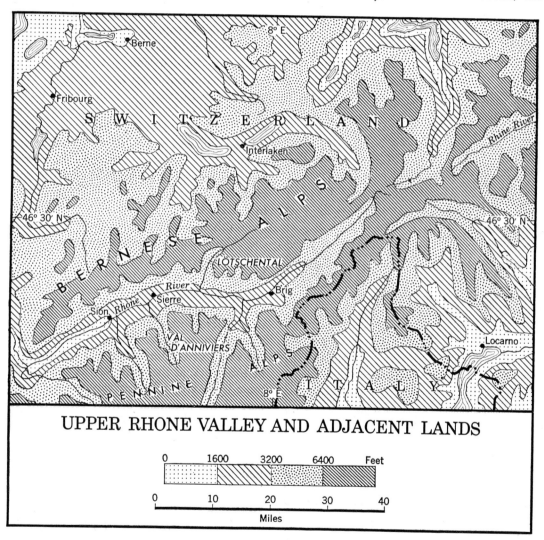

UPPER RHONE VALLEY AND ADJACENT LANDS

0   1600   3200   6400   Feet

0   10   20   30   40
Miles

331   *THE LÖTSCHENTAL and the Val d'Anniviers are tributary valleys to the Upper Rhone valley in Switzerland.*

along a north-south line. Consequently, both sides of the valley are equally sunny and settlements are found on either flank. Thus climate induces detailed modification in pattern of settlement.

THE BRENNER PASS ROUTE

332 *THE BRENNER Pass route across the Alps from Italy to Austria is an axis to which settlements within the mountain belt are attached.*

Landforms

Perhaps nowhere is the relation of settlement pattern to landforms so clearly observable as within mountain areas. There, steepness of slope and altitude set well-defined limits. It is the valleys that cut back into the mountain mass or the basins which lie nearly hemmed in by steep, high slopes that form the zones for settlement. For the valleys are the passages over barrier ranges, lines along which both goods and people may flow in linking together the lands on either side of the mountains. And it is within the valleys or in the basins that flat land is present.

Both commercial and strategic forces favor agglomerated settlement at the ends of mountain routes and, in many instances, along them, while the mountain surfaces to either side offer little encouragement to settlement of any sort. The famous Brenner Pass route across the Alps from Italy to Austria provides an example. The Italian city of Verona in the Po Lowland (Fig. 332) is fixed near the southern outlet of the Adige Valley from the Alpine mass. Upward along the Adige and its tributaries a relatively easy gradient leads to the main crestline of the Alps. Along the route, villages and towns, like Bolzano and Bressanone, mark the junctions of tributary valleys with that of the Adige. The descent to the valley of the Inn is easy. And in the valley of the Inn stands the Austrian city of Innsbruck at the outlet of the route. This route is the only relatively easy one across this part of the mountain barrier; settlement focuses upon the route outlets and is dotted like a loose string of beads between them.

Where agriculture is the mode of life in a mountain area, availability of relatively flat land becomes an important element in determining settlement pattern. Witness to this fact is the arrangement in Japan, already described.

In lands of less marked relief, the relation of settlement to landforms is less direct. In

333 *THE HILLTOP village of Lectoure in southwestern France.* (*H. M. Kendall*)

the past, hilltop sites were frequently chosen for easy defense. Many agricultural villages of southern France, like Lectoure (Fig. 333) and like Flamerens previously mentioned, were placed on hilltops for defense reasons. And even many of the cities of Europe, like Salzburg, were originally hilltop attachments to "strong points" (Fig. 334). The nucleus of Salzburg was a fortress crowning a prominent and cliff-ringed hill rising where the corridor valley of the Salzach River breaks out through the northern face of the Austrian Alps. Extensive spread from this nucleus followed disappearance of the original need for defense.

Adjustment to landforms is almost impossible to understand in detail without reference to the culture of the group involved. A prominent example is the difference in settlement patterns on the Mississippi Delta and on the Yangtze Delta in China. Part of the difference lies in the fact that agglomerated rural settlement is a characteristic feature of Oriental culture, but not of Western culture as exemplified in present-day United States.

Another part, however, derives from the fact that Western farmers have not generally chosen to cultivate river flood plains. Considering the type of agriculture which he practices, river flood plains offer the Western farmer hazards rather than advantages. But, to the rice-growing agriculturists of the Orient, a flood plain offers the most desirable of sites.

In all discussions of settlement pattern, it must be remembered that no single physical element operates alone. Landforms, like all other elements, exert only a partial influence. It is in this light that the preceding suggestions have been made; it is in the same light that the other elements should be examined.

Other Elements of the Physical Setting

NATIVE VEGETATION. Just as the settlement pattern is related to climate and landforms, so is it related to native vegetation, native animal life, soils, sources of water, and mineral resources. Of all of these elements probably water sources and mineral resources have the most direct effects, but the others cannot be wholly neglected.

Until the invention of the steel plow, grasslands proved unlikely lands for agricultural settlement. The sod cover was generally too difficult to remove for easy working of the soil. Furthermore, since most grasslands occur on the margins of humid climatic areas where moisture for crops is unreliable, there was no certainty that agriculture would be likely to succeed even if the soil could be worked. In other places, notably within forested lands, grass cover may indicate excessive water and thus pose the problem of drainage. Or, grass openings in forested areas may indicate excessive soil drainage and thereby pose the problem of irrigation. To any of these conditions, adjustment by the human group is reflected in the details of settlement pattern.

NATIVE ANIMAL LIFE. In some parts of the world, native animal life influences settlement importantly. For example, on the fringes of the central African forests, settlement is spotty *in part* because of the need for protection from the destruction wrought by elephant herds or the occasional forays of carniverous animals. Such settlement as there is in these lands is of the agglomerated type. This fact is basically a trait of the native culture, but the trait itself is related to the presence of a numerous native animal population. A single human being or a small family group is vulnerable to the animals, but a large tribal group can organize hunts directed against the marauders and gradually can drive out the animal population.

Insect pests may be even more troublesome than larger animals. Rather than affecting the detailed settlement pattern, though, they affect the total population pattern by making certain areas uninhabitable. Depopulation of some parts of tropical Africa is directly related to the prevalence of the tsetse fly, carrier of sleeping sickness. Only recently has a possibly effective control of this pest been announced.

SOILS. Soils likewise have a manifest influence on settlement, as has already been indicated. In densely peopled lands where agriculture is basic, every last bit of productive soil must bear its utmost load. It cannot be used therefore for housing; houses must stay off good soil. In a sense, soil is therefore a determinant of settlement pattern.

The effect of soil is more truly applicable on a local scale rather than on a world-wide one. In the Vézère Valley, settlement is of the agglomerated type and is in part directly related to soil; that is, the hamlets within the valley tend to be located on lands which are least suited to cultivation. In an area of much more productive soils, like the Iowa lands, settlement of the dispersed type shows little, if any, relation to detailed soil differences.

WATER AND MINERAL RESOURCES. Water and mineral resources exert far more influence than native vegetation, native animal life, and soils. If water is available generally, then settlement *can* be dispersed; if water is available only at certain widely scattered places, then the pressure is toward agglomerations.

Through human efforts, the character of the water supply may, of course, be altered. Lands that formerly were occupied only at or near infrequent springs may be made habitable for a dispersed agricultural population by irrigation works, as in our own West. Modern irrigation practices in the Nile Valley have allowed settlement and use of the land farther away from the river than did the early irrigation methods. In addition, modern methods have made dispersed settlement possible. Construction of huge water transportation and storage facilities have made infinitely more easy the expansion of large cities, like New York or Los Angeles (Fig. 204).

Almost of equal significance is the presence of too much water. Life and settlement in the Low Countries, for example, has always been largely dominated by its presence. Here, the sea made certain sites good for defense, sites where a small and relatively weak group could maintain itself against the thrust of larger and more powerful peoples. Venice furnishes another example where water used for defense was a determinant of settlement pattern.

Bodies of water, as routeways and as sources of food, affect settlement pattern. Attachment to the sea, with shore line settlement, existed in the earliest times in the pattern of the Aegean area as it did later in the United

States, and as it still does in many parts of South America. An axis of dense population exists in Europe along the lower and middle reaches of the Rhine River and its affluents. Within this belt, the rivers as routeways were originally the chief determinants of pattern details.

Mineral resources here and there over the world affect the location and character of the settlement pattern. If a mineral is of sufficient value, all other factors fade into insignificance —even the availability of water at the location. Before it was possible to secure nitrogen from the atmosphere, the Chilean nitrate fields (Fig. 293) furnished the only source. These fields are located in the completely barren desert of northern Chile, the Atacama.

Their very existence is indication of the lack of water, for the chemical nature of the nitrates is such that they can remain virtually at the surface only because of the intense dryness. Miners went into this area and established small agglomerations at each of the main sites; the land between remained utterly devoid of people. In order to maintain the mining communities, water had to be brought by pipe line from the Andes Mountains far to the east and all other supplies had to be shipped in.

Even in the more settled parts of the world, as for example in the east central part of Pennsylvania, mining tends to impose an agglomerated pattern of settlement. There, the presence of coal, a mineral basic to modern

334 *SALZBURG, Austria. The city spreads below the original location, a defense point where an eleventh-century fortress commanded the exit of the Salzach valley from the northern face of the Alps. (Ewing Galloway)*

life, and the coal-mining activities have created a pattern consisting of various-sized agglomerations, grouped about the pitheads and pressing upon one another over nearly the whole of the zone known to be underlain by coal. A dispersed settlement pattern could not provide the economically efficient utilization of the resource.

Thus from these few suggestions, it becomes obvious that each and all of the elements of the physical setting play some part in determining the way in which man arranges himself over the surface of the earth. In some places, it is one element which outshines all others; in other places, a different element may play the leading role. Nowhere do the elements operate singly. Rather, the sum total of the physical setting must be taken into account before the questions of "where" and "why" can be answered.

The relation of settlement to the physical elements, in turn, cannot be assessed without full reference to the cultural elements. Only in that way can true understanding be obtained. What appears at first to be an isolated fragment emerges in the end as an integrated tile in the mosaic of the present-day world.

••

CHAPTER OUTLINE

Determinants of settlement pattern

Relation of settlement to other cultural elements
  Economies
    Hunting-fishing-collecting
    Pastoralism
    Agriculture
    Manufacturing
    Exploitation
    Commerce
  Other cultural factors
Relation of settlement to physical elements
  Climate
  Landforms
  Other elements of the physical setting
    Native vegetation
    Native animal life

    Soils
    Water and mineral resources

REVIEW QUESTIONS

1. List several areas with which you are familiar. State what the settlement pattern of each is like. Suggest what facts would have to be considered in explaining differences between, or similarities in, the settlement patterns.

2. Why do areas of similar physical setting have different habitat values for human groups?

3. Why is mobility essential to a human group with a hunting-fishing-collecting economy?

4. In what parts of the world would pastoralism be expected to be the dominant economy? Why?

5. List as many phases of agricultural economy as you can. Give an example of an area in which each of these phases is dominant.

6. Explain just why it may be said that manufacturing is the most complex economy.

7. Why are exploitation and commerce spoken of as "adjuncts to manufacturing economy"?

8. It is often implied that there was no evolution of economies from hunting-fishing-collecting through pastoralism and agriculture to manufacturing for all human groups. Discuss the soundness or unsoundness of this implication. Give supporting examples.

9. What is the general importance of cultural heritage in settlement pattern?

10. Why is it that features of different cultures are less easily distinguishable in the present-day world than they were, say, in the Medieval Period? How is this fact of significance geographically?

11. List some of the outstanding differences between Oriental and Western cultures. Indicate how these differences are reflected in settlement pattern.

12. Suggest why Western culture has spread over a larger portion of the earth than has Oriental culture.

13. What is the basis for considering that a new culture may be developing within the U.S.S.R.?

14. Discuss the statement: "A physical fact gives an area a character which offers certain responsibilities to a human group; it is passive, not active."

15. Give an illustration, from your own experience, of the limitation imposed upon settlement by climate.

16. Demonstrate, by means of specific examples, the relationship between landforms and settlement pattern.

17. Name several well-known pass routes across mountains. Have these routes any effect upon settlement within or adjacent to the mountains they cross?

18. May there be any relationship between settlement pattern and native vegetation? Between settlement pattern and soil?

19. In what ways is water significant in explaining settlement pattern?

20. Can any single element, either cultural or physical, explain fully the settlement pattern of any area in the world? Discuss with specific illustrative examples.

SOME SUGGESTED REFERENCES

Bruhnes, Jean, *Human Geography,* Rand McNally, 1920. A translation of the French classic; one of the foundation works of present-day American study of the cultural elements of geography.

Hawley, Amos H., *Human Ecology: A Theory of Community Structure,* The Ronald Press Co., 1950. A modern sociological treatment of community structure; includes several chapters of significance in the study of settlement pattern.

Lowie, Robert Harry, *An Introduction to Cultural Anthropology,* new and enl. ed., Farrar & Rinehart, 1940. A standard work on human cultures.

MacCurdy, George Grant, *Human Origins,* Appleton, 1924, 2 vols. A scholarly account of the origin and development of man and of his prehistoric and early historic cultures; thoroughly documented.

Piddington, Ralph, *An Introduction to Social Anthropology,* Vol. I, Oliver and Boyd, 1950. The first part of a proposed two-volume textbook; description and analysis of primitive cultures; see especially Chapter 1 for a brief statement of the anthropological point of view.

Vidal de la Blache, Paul, *Principles of Human Geography,* Holt, 1926. An excellent translation and arrangement of unfinished book manuscript and notes of the famous French geographer, published posthumously; one of the most important attempts to suggest classification and definition of principles of human geography.

335 *STEEL, symbol of modern manufacturing, is seen here in a molten stream as it flows from an open-hearth furnace into a huge bucket, or ladle. Waste material (slag) is pouring from a trough in the ladle rim into slag pots, just before the ladle is moved to nearby molds where the steel is poured to become steel ingots. (U. S. Steel Corp.)*

CHAPTER 23

Manufacturing Regions

∙∙∙

Changes in the ways of life and ways of making a living for many of the world's inhabitants are indicated by the change in meaning of the word "manufacture" itself. Literally, the word means to make by hand. This is the old, original meaning. Today, it usually means to make, process, or fashion by the use of machines. Man has been manufacturing goods of one sort or another for several thousands of years, but only within the past two hundred has he learned to let machines do most of the work. The entire span of the Industrial Revolution, marking the significant change from human power and the home workshop to industrial power and the factory, is a matter of no more than the lifetimes of four or five persons. Such world-changing inventions as the steam engine, diesel engine, electric motor, airplane, blast furnace, assembly line, and the use of mineral fuels and water power to make them function, occurred, in a sense, only yesterday.

For those parts of the earth which have become highly industrialized, the old ways of life have changed with surprising rapidity: vast populations shifted from farms to urban centers; factories grew and encroached upon, or swallowed completely, many rural areas; persons by the millions were thrust closer to each other in teeming, smoky cities. Some nations, such as the United States, changed from the wilderness and the oxcart to huge cities and jet planes within less than one hundred and fifty years. The miracle is not that we face so many problems of adjustment and readjustment in the modern world, but that the problems are not more numerous and more serious than they are. Even many of the "faraway" places have been affected because some of the machines, literally "space-eaters," have so shrunk the world that today there are no two spots on earth which are more than fifty or sixty hours of flying time apart.

LOCALIZATION OF MANUFACTURING REGIONS

Many factors and conditions underlie the world distribution of major manufacturing regions. Chief among them are type of culture, availability of raw materials, availability of power, amount and type of labor, nature and spacing of transportation facilities, capital, and nature and size of markets.

TYPE OF CULTURE. Many peoples, even entire nations, have beliefs and follow ways of life that do not lead to industrialization. China is an example. Here the worship of the past, the long resistance to new ideas, and the emphasis on the family unit as opposed to national unity, are a few of the cultural factors which have prevented or hindered the growth of China as a truly important manufacturing nation. There are other peoples and nations in which the ideas and the manner of living are directly conducive to the origin and growth of manufacturing enterprises. In Great Britain, for example, opportunity for exercising initiative, the willingness to accept new ideas and new methods, and a rather pronounced national unity and political stability have fostered the growth of manufacturing.

RAW MATERIALS. The creation of a *major* manufacturing region normally must be based on the occurrence of certain raw materials and the possibility of securing others. Again, the situation is different from one section of the earth to another. For example, Denmark is so poor in key industrial raw materials that she has not, and probably cannot, become a leading manufacturing nation. On the other hand, Germany, with an abundance of high-grade coal, to mention only one key ingredient, became one of the outstanding industrial nations.

POWER. To make goods in the modern fashion demands more than the energy from human and animal muscles, for great amounts of readily controlled power are needed to make machines and to run them after they are built. So far, without attempting to guess what may eventually be done with atomic energy, solar power, or long-distance transmission of energy by radio, the world's industrial regions are mainly those with abundant coal. This is true despite the importance of power derived from water or from petroleum.

LABOR. Modern industry, despite all the work done by machines, requires abundant labor of several sorts, from highly skilled to semiskilled to unskilled. Any manufacturing region needs all three types of labor, which are hired at salaries or wages usually ranging from very low to very high. In general, a region which has all three types readily available at *comparatively* low costs has a distinct advantage over regions which possess only one or two types. England has had all three;

so have France and Germany. So has the United States, although it has at times suffered in international competition because each of its labor types has been higher priced than those of other parts of the world. Contrariwise, certain other areas or countries have had either insufficient labor supply or an insufficiency of skilled and semiskilled labor; Australia exemplifies the former, India the latter.

TRANSPORTATION. To manufacture goods requires the movement of raw materials of many kinds over long and short distances. Also, following manufacture, the goods must be distributed near and far to consuming areas. Without modern types of transportation and a sufficient fineness or detail of "transportation net," large-scale manufacturing is impossible. So close is the relationship that one may easily ascertain the *general world pattern* of major manufacturing regions by noting the portions of the earth in which transport lines, especially railroads, are numerous and are arranged in a network of fine mesh.

CAPITAL. It goes almost without saying that manufacturing requires large financial resources. To buy raw materials, provide power for machines, pay wages and salaries, install and maintain transport systems, develop and retain markets, not to mention payment of taxes and other obligations, demands tremendous sums of money. Regions or nations with abundant capital or with abundant credit (which amounts to the same thing) are in position to become industrially important—others are not. The United States and Spain stand in strong contrast here, as do Switzerland and Paraguay.

MARKETS. The world's most important industrial regions are those which have large and fairly stable markets within their own limits. Although not commonly recognized, it is a fact that each such region is its own best customer. The West-European Manufacturing Region consumes most of its own products; the Northeastern Manufacturing

Region of the United States does likewise. This in no way minimizes the importance of world trade in manufactured goods, because part of the flow, as in western Europe, crosses national boundaries. Also, the sale of manufactured goods in far-distant markets by nations which have dependable home markets plus major distant foreign markets is important. In general, the additional profit derived from distant foreign markets makes a great difference in the final "balance sheet." For example, the home market may "pay the bills," but no more, or very little more, while the distant markets, perhaps consuming only a small portion of the total production, may represent pure profit. To be sure, some countries within major manufacturing regions depend largely on distant foreign markets for the sale of the bulk of their manufactured products, but they are exceptional. Great Britain is the classic example, but even Britain sells much of its manufactures somewhere within the large manufacturing region of which it is a part.

THE BASIC FACTORS. The foregoing paragraphs suggest the complexities which have produced the modern world pattern of manufacturing regions. Reduced to simplicity, perhaps oversimplicity, one may say that manufacturing regions exist where there is the combination of sufficient technical knowledge, sufficient capital, and either large coal and iron ore deposits, or both. Certainly no *major* industrial regions exist where this combination is not present, and industrial regions which do exist without this combination are definitely not major. This in no way implies that the present pattern is necessarily permanent; in fact, the present pattern is itself the result of change. Cultures change, ideas spread, raw materials are exhausted in some areas and new sources are discovered in others, entirely new kinds of raw material come into use, populations grow or decline and with them go certain modifications of labor supply and of market—even capital "moves." The emergence of the industrial areas of the Soviet Union are good examples not only of change but of rapid change. Other examples are to be found in India and parts of South America.

MANUFACTURING REGIONS OF NORTH AMERICA

All of the world's major manufacturing regions are located in the Northern Hemisphere, mainly in northeastern United States, western Europe, and, to lesser extent, in Japan, eastern China, and India (Fig. 336). Within each major region there are many districts, or district groupings, marked by special concentrations of manufacturing. Outside of the major regions there are other, more or less scattered, districts located in several nations and in both hemispheres. The really "big" manufacturing regions are those in northeastern United States, northwestern Europe, and the U.S.S.R. As a consequence of many things, especially more abundant raw materials, better transportation, greater availability of capital, and less upset and devastation by war, the Northeastern Manufacturing Region of the United States has finally surpassed the West-European Manufacturing Region. The manufacturing regions of the U.S.S.R. are even now contesting the second place of the western Europe manufacturing region.

The Northeastern Manufacturing Region

LOCATION, EXTENT, GENERAL NATURE. From very small beginnings in southern New England, during Colonial days, the manufacturing districts of the United States have marched westward, growing in size and number decade

CHIEF MANUFACTURING
REGIONS AND DISTRICTS OF
THE WORLD

See separate maps for the United
States, Western Europe, British Isles,
and Eurasia.

Manufacturing Region and
Chief Districts

Chief Districts outside Manufacturing
Region

1   N. E. UNITED STATES AND
    S. E. CANADA
2   WEST-EUROPE
3   SOUTHERN JAPAN
4   EAST-CENTRAL CHINA
5   CENTRAL INDIA

Compressed Sinusoidal
equal-area projection

0   1000   2000   3000   4000   5000
STATUTE MILES

336   *AS YET the Southern Hemisphere has no truly major manufacturing regions. In
the Northern Hemisphere the Big Two of manufacturing regions are in eastern
North America and western Europe.*

by decade. And there has been, recently, a
spread into parts of southeastern Canada and
the South (Fig. 337). The Northeastern
Manufacturing Region is that portion of the
United States in which manufacturing districts are most numerous and most important.
Other districts, even though of considerable
local importance, are comparatively small and
widely separated. The region extends from
the Atlantic to eastern Nebraska and from
central Alabama to the southern Great Lakes
area and the St. Lawrence Valley. If placed
upon Europe, it would reach from western
England to the western edge of the Soviet
Union and from northern Italy to the southern section of Sweden. Within it are many
farming areas, mining sections, and a few
comparatively unused spots, but, primarily,
it is the earth's busiest factoryland.

Within the region are most of the coal
mines, most of the electric power plants, and

nearly half the petroleum-refining capacity
of the United States. Close by are major
source areas for petroleum, natural gas, iron
ore, and a wide variety of other essential raw
materials. The region contains nearly all of
the coke ovens, blast furnaces, and steel mills
of the United States. Within it are manufactured most of our automobiles, locomotives,
railroad cars, and ships, as well as most of
our tools, machinery, textiles, clothing, flour,
and books. With only a certain few exceptions, the familiar trade mark "Made in
U.S.A." could just as well be "Made in the
Northeastern Manufacturing Region." Just
as the region possesses great wealth in raw
materials, transport facilities, and machines,
it also has the highest population density and
largest total population of any part of North
America. People are present in sufficient numbers not only to make, run, and repair machines, but also to transport and to buy the

manufactured goods. Actually, the region is its own best customer.

Simply to call the region a major manufacturing region does not provide a reasonably complete understanding. Within it scores of different products are made and there are several districts with particular manufacturing specialties. All of them cannot be discussed here, but the more important ones deserve emphasis. Most fundamental in many ways are the districts which specialize in making iron and steel. The critical nature of iron and steel in our manufacturing economy has been apparent too often. Many times, lack of steel has forced the closing of automobile factories, agricultural machinery plants, railway equipment and repair shops, and other industries. While many things are needed to "feed" a manufacturing region and a modern industrial nation, steel is one of the most important.

IRON AND STEEL. The United States has led the world in iron and steel manufacturing for the past half century (Fig. 338). Nearly all of this iron and steel has been made in four districts (Fig. 339). The chief district is the world-famous collection of blast furnaces and steel mills located in western Pennsylvania, western New York, and eastern Ohio. Pittsburgh is its center, but that city is only one of scores of steel towns and steel cities in the district. Others include Johnstown in Pennsylvania, Buffalo in New York, and Cleveland in Ohio. For purposes of simplicity, the entire district may be referred to as the Pittsburgh-Lake Erie district. Normally it produces more than half of all the iron and steel of the United States and more than the total production of any other single nation. Production rests on bringing together Pennsylvania coking coal and Lake Superior iron ores more than on anything else (Figs. 268 and 278). Next in importance is the Chicago-Gary district, and, following that, the eastern

NORTHEASTERN MANUFACTURING REGION

Manufacturing Region and Chief Districts
Chief Districts outside Manufacturing Region

0   500
Statute Miles

337   *THE NORTHEASTERN Manufacturing Region of the United States, including a small portion of Canada, has become the world's leading manufacturing area.*

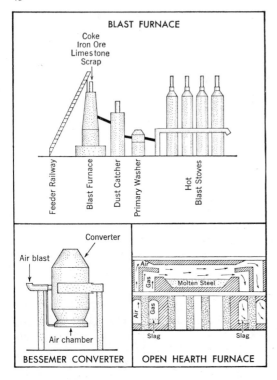

BLAST FURNACE

Coke
Iron Ore
Limestone
Scrap

Feeder Railway

Blast Furnace

Dust Catcher

Primary Washer

Hot
Blast Stoves

Converter

Air blast

Air chamber

BESSEMER CONVERTER

Air

Gas

Molten Steel

Air

Gas

Slag   Slag

OPEN HEARTH FURNACE

338 *IN THE blast furnace, iron is obtained from iron ore. In the openhearth furnace and the Bessemer converter, iron is made into steel.*

Pennsylvania district, which includes such famous steel centers as Bethlehem, Allentown, and Lehigh. To the south, in Maryland, is the huge iron and steel plant at Sparrows Point. The eastern Pennsylvania district and adjacent places receive much of their iron ore from foreign mines located particularly in Chile, Cuba, and Newfoundland. The long hauls across the ocean are less expensive than the short rail hauls needed to move the iron ore from the Great Lakes to the Atlantic seaboard. All the districts mentioned, from the southern end of Lake Michigan to the Atlantic shore area, consume tremendous amounts of scrap iron and scrap steel, as well as iron ore. Since all the districts are in the section of the United States where the largest amounts of iron and steel products are constantly being "junked," the scrap supply is huge.

The fourth ranking iron and steel district of the United States is the one in and around Birmingham, Alabama. As noted earlier (p. 390), the Birmingham district has the advantage of close juxtaposition of iron ore, coking coal, and limestone flux (Fig. 284). Its market area is less densely populated and less industrialized, but it has the South and much of the Southwest largely to itself. Moreover, its market is growing because the South is becoming increasingly industrialized year by year. The other iron and steel producers are widely scattered. Some are in northeastern New York State, in Massachusetts, and in Minnesota, and some, mainly single plants, are in Colorado, Utah, and California. The latter have limited market areas so far from the major iron and steel districts that local, comparatively small-scale production is feasible.

MACHINERY, TOOLS, TRANSPORTATION EQUIPMENT. The manufacture of these items is very closely allied with the iron and steel industry. In fact, these, plus iron and steel as such, have the highest value rating of any group of manufactured products. However, each of them, taken singly, is outranked by food and food products and by textiles and textile products. Machinery and machine tools range from harvesters and diesel engines to sewing machines and drill presses. Transportation equipment includes automobiles, busses, autotrucks and trailers, locomotives, railroad cars, airplanes, and ships. Again, as for steel, there is marked specialization by particular areas.

Textile machinery is manufactured mainly in southern New England and eastern Pennsylvania (Fig. 340). Electrical machinery is made mainly in the southern Great Lakes region and the coastal lowlands from Baltimore to Boston, including parts of New York State; Illinois, Ohio, Pennsylvania, and New Jersey stand out particularly (Fig. 340). Agricultural machinery and agricultural tools are made predominantly in the Corn Belt, with Illinois alone accounting for more than half the total (Fig. 340). The manufacture of foundry and machine-shop products is more widespread, occurring importantly in the large area from the Mississippi River to Boston and tending to concentrate in New York, Pennsylvania, Ohio, and Illinois (Fig. 340).

Most of the automobiles, trucks, etc., are produced in southern Michigan, northern Indiana, northeastern Illinois, southern Wisconsin, and northwestern Ohio (Fig. 340). Especially noted centers are Detroit, Flint, and Pontiac in Michigan, and South Bend in Indiana. Automobiles require so many kinds of materials and specially formed parts that many satellite industries have sprung up in the automobile centers or nearby. Even distant places contribute certain materials which make the completed automobile possible. The close connection between automobile manufacture and other industries is illustrated by the fact that within recent years the automotive industry has consumed about 20 per cent of all United States steel, about 18 per cent of the copper, about 30 per cent of the nickel, about 34 per cent of the lead, about 73 per cent of the plate glass, and about 80

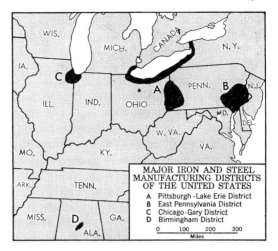

339 *SKETCH map showing positions of the major iron and steel districts of the United States. The district labeled* (A) *is the most important by far, followed, in order of production, by districts* (B), (C), *and* (D).

per cent of the rubber products. In addition, the industry uses a great deal of tin, zinc, aluminum, leather, upholstery cloth, wood,

340

THE PATTERN of leading manufactures in the United States (only major areas are shown). Note the relationship of each major area (in black) to the Northeastern Manufacturing Region (stippled).

paint, and lacquer—not to mention the heavy consumption of gasoline, lubricating oils, and greases by automobiles when they are put into operation. Thus, it is easy to appreciate the close relationship between, say, Detroit automobiles and Arizona copper, Pittsburgh steel, Ohio glass and rubber tires, and many other production districts and products.

More than half of the railway equipment, from boxcars and flatcars to locomotives and diesel streamliners, is made in Illinois, Indiana, and Pennsylvania (Fig. 340). Eastern Pennsylvania is particularly noted for locomotives; Illinois for Pullman cars and diners. Railway repair and maintenance shops occur mainly in the East, but are numerous as far west as the Mississippi.

Production of airplanes, airplane engines, and their many intricate parts and special instruments occurs in several places in the United States. The bulk of such production is in the northeastern manufacturing region and the remainder in the Far West (Fig. 341). For strategic reasons, militarily, it is desirable to concentrate the aircraft industry in the Middle West, not only where materials and personnel are available, but where the plants are far removed from coastal attack. The present spread of the industry is illustrated by major aircraft engine factories in Connecticut, New York, New Jersey, Pennsylvania, Ohio, Michigan, and Indiana. Completed commercial planes are turned out in large numbers in California (chiefly the Los Angeles area), Washington (Seattle area), Missouri (St. Louis area), Ohio, Pennsylvania, and Maryland. Military and naval plane production has much the same geographical spread. Like the automobile, the airplane demands many kinds of materials and the participation of many types of factories, both small and large.

Somewhat more than half the shipbuilding of the United States is carried on along the lower courses of the Delaware and Hudson rivers and the shores of Chesapeake Bay. There, launching facilities are excellent and the shipyards are not far removed from the vast amount of iron, steel, and machinery needed to build large modern vessels. New England, where our shipbuilding industry began, is handicapped by lack of local steel and other necessaries of large ships and now makes only small craft. The larger Gulf Coast ports, such as New Orleans and Houston, likewise produce mainly small craft, both of wood and steel. On the Pacific coast, at Bremerton and Seattle in Washington, and in the San Francisco and Los Angeles areas in California, many ships are built or repaired. West-coast shipbuilding suffers from a lack of large local steel and machinery supplies, although the huge timbers used for forms and launching ways are readily procurable.

The shipbuilding industry of the United States has a long history of "ups and downs." In time of war, the output has been tremendous; during peace, particularly during economic depressions, production has dropped to virtually nothing. The United States has a great shipbuilding capacity, but the high cost of labor and materials usually makes competition with the shipyards of western Europe uneconomical. This stands in sharp contrast to production in the United States of other transportation equipment, such as automobiles, railway trains, and aircraft.

FOOD PRODUCTS. The Northeastern Manufacturing Region produces and processes great quantities of food. Also, special containers, such as cans, jars, boxes, and bags, are made to hold the foods. The total business in food and food products holds first place, by value, among all our manufactures. Flour milling is done both within and on the edges of the region, much of it in or near the chief wheat belts (Fig. 363). Important flour centers are St. Paul, Minneapolis, Kansas City, and Buffalo. In meat packing, Chicago is the leading center, but there are scores of other centers located from St. Paul to Forth Worth and from Omaha to New York City (Fig. 342).

Canned and dried fruits are prepared throughout most of the Northeastern Manu-

341   *INSIDE a modern United States aircraft plant. (Douglas Aircraft Corp.)*

facturing Region and outside the region California holds a prominent place in this regard. Canned and dehydrated vegetables, likewise, are prepared in hundreds of places, particularly in the Corn Belt and from there east to the Atlantic. Most of the canning of fruits and vegetables is done in small plants located in rural areas, near the fields and orchards, rather than in large cities.

Cheese and butter are made chiefly along the northern edge of the Northeastern Manufacturing Region, next to and partly within the Hay and Dairy Belt. Wisconsin, Minnesota, and New York are especially noted for dairy products. Special breakfast foods are made in many places: Battle Creek in Michigan, and Buffalo and Niagara in New York State, stand out particularly.

A comparatively recent phase of food preparation and processing is that of quick-freezing. In addition to huge plants with a national marketing area, there are literally thousands of small plants which serve local communities. Also, there are many more thousands of "quick-freeze lockers" in farm homes and city homes. The opportunity to preserve fresh meats and to enjoy fresh fruits and vegetables in off-seasons is revolutionizing the eating habits of millions of persons. That a person living in Chicago may sit down to a meal including fresh, locally grown vegetables, while a January blizzard howls outside, is "something new under the sun." Two big facts stand out in this brief discussion of food manufacture: (1) it is an important part of "big business," and (2) the Northeastern

342 *U. S. GOVERNMENT inspectors examining carcasses on the hog chain in a Chicago meat-packing plant. (Armour and Co., Chicago)*

Manufacturing Region is more than a land of such products as steel, automobiles, machinery, and ships.

TEXTILES AND CLOTHING. Nearly all our cotton goods are made in the Northeastern Manufacturing Region; about two-thirds of them in Virginia, the Carolinas, Georgia, and Alabama, and most of the remainder in New England (Fig. 343). Production is heaviest in the Carolina and Georgia Piedmont. Textile production, more than anything else, accounts for the southward extension of the great manufacturing belt which otherwise is largely confined to the northeastern quarter of the United States. New England, for many years the leader in cotton goods, has become a very poor second. The Piedmont has definite advantages over New England in terms of

cheap coal and electric power, lower wages, lower taxes, and somewhat greater proximity to raw cotton from the leading cotton-growing states located in the western part of the Cotton Belt. A part of New England's production is based on imported Egyptian cotton; this cotton has a longer and silkier fiber than that cotton grown in the Cotton Belt and is used to make higher-grade, costlier goods.

The section of the United States from Maryland to southern Maine makes most of our woolen goods (Fig. 343). New England alone consumes slightly more than 10 per cent of the world's raw wool, including raw wool produced in the United States. New England's dominance in wool manufacture is further emphasized by the fact that Boston has become the major raw wool market of the United States. Many small woolen goods factories, including those which make woolen yarns and woolen knit goods, are to be found outside of New England, but their total production is not great.

While the bulk of the world's raw silk is produced in Japan and China, most of the silk cloth and finished silk goods are made in the United States. Production is highly localized in eastern Pennsylvania and adjacent New Jersey, with New York and southern New England accounting for the remainder (Fig. 343). Rayon is made chiefly in the southern Appalachian area and, to a lesser degree, in the districts which specialize in real silk. In both areas, the necessary wood pulp (mainly from southeastern Canada), cotton fibers, and chemicals are readily procurable. Only Japan has rivaled the United States in rayon production; just prior to World War II, Japanese production was only slightly less than ours; since then it has been considerably less, but it is slowly increasing again.

The designing, making, and selling of clothing is markedly concentrated in New York City and the New York metropolitan area (Fig. 343). Other centers are in the Middle West, especially Chicago and vicinity. In the Far West, Los Angeles has become increasingly important, particularly in the designing and making of outdoor and sports clothes.

OTHER MANUFACTURES. The description of manufacturing in the United States, especially in the major region, could be greatly extended. This is not surprising in a country which has attained world leadership in manufacturing enterprise. Beyond the major manufactures and manufacturing groups mentioned so far, there are many others which are only relatively less significant. Chemicals are produced and mainly consumed in the section from Illinois to western New England. They include some thirty basic materials, ranging from sulphuric and acetic acid to calcium carbide and zinc oxide, and draw upon a wide variety of raw materials such as wood, sulphur, coal, petroleum, salt, borax, soda, and even certain crops. Other activities include petroleum refining, ore smelting, and the fabrication of clays and stone; these were noted earlier, in the chapters on mineral resources. The printing of newspapers, magazines, and books is carried on in nearly all cities, but the chief ones are New York, Bos-

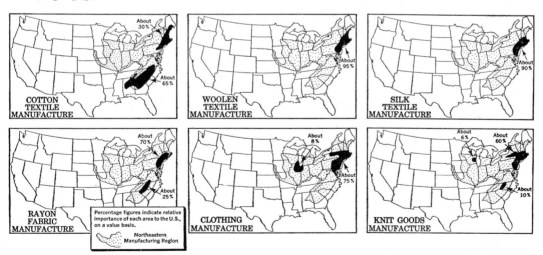

343 PATTERN of various textile and clothing manufactures in the United States (only major areas are shown). Note the relationship of each major area (in black) to the Northeastern Manufacturing Region (stippled).

ton, Philadelphia, Chicago, and St. Louis. Furniture manufacture, wooden and metal, is concentrated in the states of the southern Great Lakes region, including New York State. Rubber goods, which by bulk are mainly automobile tires, are made chiefly in Akron in Ohio, Detroit in Michigan, and Los Angeles in California. Cigarette factories are mainly in North Carolina, Virginia, and Kentucky.

THE CANADIAN SECTION. The Canadian portion of the northeastern manufacturing region occupies the Ontario Peninsula, from near Detroit to the beginning of the St. Lawrence River, and extends down the St. Lawrence Valley as far as Quebec City. While it is far less important than the United States portion, it manufactures a variety of products including wood pulp and newsprint, farming tools and farm machinery, motor vehicles, furniture, clothing, butter, cheese, and packed meats.

Lesser Manufacturing Areas

LOS ANGELES AREA. The combined industrial business of all the manufacturing districts which lie outside of the Northeastern Manufacturing Region amounts to roughly one-seventh of the United States total. The chief outlying district is located in the Los Angeles metropolitan area. World War II, particularly because of the demands of the Pacific theater of operations, caused a great upsurge of manufacturing in and near Los Angeles. This, added to the manufacturing already present, plus additional industries added since the war, has given the district first rank in the Far West. The district has so grown in population that many industries are needed to supply the local population alone. Manufactures are highly diversified, ranging from motion pictures and outdoor clothing to refined oils and assembled automobiles. A more complete listing includes papers, magazines, books, airplanes, tires,

hardware, furniture, household appliances, pottery, construction materials, and canned fruits and vegetables.

SAN FRANCISCO AREA. This includes not only the city of San Francisco, but the several other towns and cities which lie along or near the arms of San Francisco Bay. It also boomed because of World War II. Major industrial activities include petroleum refining, fruit and vegetable canning, meat packing, printing and publishing, fabrication of containers, baking, as well as refining of sugar, packaging and blending of coffee, and shipbuilding and ship repair.

PUGET SOUND-LOWER COLUMBIA RIVER AREA. In this district forests and fields are strongly reflected in the goods produced: finished lumber, wood pulp, wooden boxes, furniture, small wooden articles, and packed and canned fruits and vegetables. In addition, there are airplanes and ships. Here, too, World War II brought an industrial boom and a marked population influx. Since the war, shipbuilding has declined and the making of aircraft has had definite "ups and downs," but the comparatively large local market, plus the demand for products of forest, garden, and orchard elsewhere, have maintained a thriving business.

OTHER MANUFACTURING DISTRICTS. The remaining districts are small and of relatively less importance, no matter how significant they may be locally. They are scattered here and there between the industrial East and the districts of the Far West. Among them are the Salt Lake-Provo, Denver-Pueblo, Dallas-Houston, and New Orleans districts. Along part of the East Coast, but outside of the Northeastern Manufacturing Region, mention should be made of Savannah and Charleston as manufacturing centers.

These smaller manufacturing districts have come into prominence only in recent decades. All of them had their origin, continued their growth, and owe their present existence to some local advantage in one or more of the factors discussed earlier in this chapter.

MANUFACTURING REGIONS OF EURASIA

The manufacturing regions of Eurasia lie far apart (Fig. 336). Those in Asia occupy sections of the Far East and a few places in the interior of Siberia. Those of Europe are mainly in central western Europe and parts of the Russian Plain. Largest and most intricate of them all is the one in the west—the West-European Manufacturing Region.

West-European Manufacturing Region

LOCATION, EXTENT, GENERAL NATURE. The West-European Manufacturing Region stretches from the Pyrenees and northern Italy to southern Norway, Sweden, and Finland and from central Poland westward to include the British Isles (Fig. 344). In area this region is about the size of the Northeastern Manufacturing Region of the United States, and, until it was so greatly devastated by World War II, it was the world's leading manufacturing region. It is important to remember that modern manufacturing began in the westernmost part of this region, in England, and spread from there to the continent, as well as across the Atlantic to the United States and elsewhere.

Within the broad area of the West-European Manufacturing Region are intensively cultivated farmlands, important dairy districts, mining sections, cultivated forests, large commercial cities, and some relatively unutilized hill and mountain areas; but the region is marked throughout by both large and small concentrations of factories and factory districts. Nearly all of them lie on or near coal fields or iron ore deposits. The coals of England and Wales, and the Ruhr Valley of Germany, greatly aided by the Lorraine iron ores of France, have played major parts in the development of the region. The oldest, and

344

PATTERN of manufacturing in Europe. The chief manufacturing districts on the Continent are in Germany, France, Luxembourg, and Poland.

WEST-EUROPEAN MANUFACTURING REGION

RUHR DISTRICT

NO. FRANCE—BELGIUM—LUXEMBOURG DISTRICT

UPPER SILESIAN DISTRICT

West-European Manufacturing Region and Chief Districts

Chief Districts outside of Manufacturing Region

0   500

Statute Miles

still vitally important, manufacturing districts are in the British Isles, especially in England.

BRITISH ISLES. Most of Britain's industrial districts lie on the flanks of the Pennines (Fig. 345). At the southern end of the Pennines is the Birmingham district with its iron and steel plants and its tool, chemical, and railway equipment factories. On the western edge is the Lancashire district with its flour, pottery, and, above all, its cotton textile factories. To the east of the Pennines is the Yorkshire district, specializing in woolens, clothing, textile machinery, and cutlery. To the south of the Yorkshire district is that of Nottingham, with its manufactures of silk cloth, leather, cutlery, and hardware. To the north, near the Scottish Border, is the Newcastle district with its iron and steel. And, away from the Pennines, but not very far away, is the London district characterized by great diversity of manufactures. London's products include paper, printed materials, processed and packaged foods, leather, soap, chemicals, small wooden articles, and many kinds of clothing.

Outside of England are the comparatively smaller districts in Wales, Scotland, and Northern Ireland. Welsh manufacturing occurs mainly in the south, along the edge of the Bristol Channel, in the Cardiff district. Specialties are iron and steel, tin plate, and refined copper. Scotland's factories stretch across the Central Lowland from the Firth of Clyde to the Firth of Forth. The greater number are in the Glasgow district, famous for large ships, locomotives and other railway equipment, and several types of machinery. Here and there across the Central Lowland are cotton and woolen mills, jute mills, and establishments which make rope, cord, and thread. The Belfast district of Northern Ireland is a small one, but it is well known for fine linen cloth, fine lace, woolen cloth, and ships.

With the exception of the London and Belfast districts, there is a markedly close relationship between coal and iron fields and manufacturing districts; a map showing coal and iron ore distribution almost serves as a map of the manufacturing districts of Britain (Fig. 345). However, the fact that a few of the districts are not thus related must not be overemphasized: after all, London, although not "on coal," is only one hundred miles from Birmingham coal and only one hundred and twenty-five miles from Welsh coal—there is an excellent transportation system and there are no mountains or hills in between to raise haulage costs.

Manufactures are more vital to Britain than to any other major nation. Britain's area is so small and she has turned so largely to the machine for a living that most of her foodstuffs and raw materials must be purchased from other parts of the world. Thus there is a constant flow of products from her manufacturing districts, products which pay the costs of many types of imports from near and far. World War II strained the Britsh and their economy to the utmost. By war's end, many factories and factory towns had been ruined by bombs and fire; machinery was badly worn and much of it out of date; the people were very tired—and Britain was "broke." Peace merely brought a new kind of battle—a battle of "import, manufacture, and export." Britain knows well the meaning of "export or die."

RUHR DISTRICT. Of the many manufacturing areas on the Continent, the one which lies in the lower Rhine Basin of west central Germany has been the greatest. This area, for purposes of simplicity, may be called the Ruhr district, even though parts of it are, strictly speaking, outside the valley of the Ruhr River itself (Fig. 344). Fed by its own high-grade coal and by other materials such as Lorraine iron ore, this district has been the heavy-industry heart of Europe. Iron and steel are the key commodities and they lead to a wide variety of other products which range from steel rails and girders to machinery, locomotives, and armaments. Coal, plus other minerals such as potash, has provided raw materials for large chemical industries making dyes, caustic potash, synthetic rubber, and synthetic gasoline. The Ruhr district suffered heavy bomb damage during the latter part of World War II and additional damage when Allied troops fought their way into the area. Moreover, France, remembering all too well the importance of the Ruhr in Germany's war potential, has been loath to see this district restored to full production. One of the major problems of the postwar period has been what to do with the Ruhr. The coal is still there—the largest deposit of high-grade coal in all Europe; the workers are still there; the factories are largely rebuilt; it is hard to imagine this key industrial area of Europe being allowed to remain for long in a state of weak or partial production.

NORTH FRANCE-BELGIUM-LUXEMBOURG DISTRICT. Although sometimes considered as several separate districts, this one may be dealt with as a unit (Fig. 344). The portion of the district where France joins Belgium is noted for cotton textiles. The part next to Germany is famous for iron and steel (Lorraine) and woolen goods (Alsace). Luxembourg, which was "fought around" rather than fought over during World War II, has major iron, steel, and cloth manufactures. Belgium, partly fought over and still suffering from the years of German occupation, has largely rebuilt her zinc refining, iron and steel making, machinery and railway equipment manufacture, toolmaking, clothmaking, glass fabrication, and the cutting of precious stones. While she depends greatly on many other parts of the world for raw materials, she has plentiful high-grade coal and the Lorraine and Luxembourg iron ores are close by.

UPPER SILESIA. Considerably farther east is another major district located in the Silesian area, chiefly in the upper part of the Oder River Valley (Fig. 344). Prior to World War II most of the Upper Silesia district belonged to Germany. It is now entirely incorporated in Poland. The economy of this district rests upon local coal and iron ore which make possible a major iron and steel production.

345 EXCEPT for the London district, the chief manufacturing districts of the British Isles are located on or very near coal deposits. Compare this map with Fig. 269.

OTHER DISTRICTS. In addition to those already noted, the West-European Manufacturing Region contains several other districts. They are less significant, but only relatively so. Among them are Stockholm, Copenhagen, Berlin, Dresden, Munich, Prague, Amsterdam, Paris, Lyons, Marseilles, and Milan.

Manufacturing Regions of the Soviet Union

Since the Russian Revolution, near the end of World War I, the Soviet Union, built out of the wreckage of the old Russian Empire, has made rapid progress in manufacturing. Complete and ruthless control of business, as

well as all other phases of life, on the part of
the Soviet government has had one main objective—to make Soviet Russia strong at all
costs. Much to the world's surprise, the Soviet
Union was strong enough to contest bitterly
Germany's military occupation of a large part
of the Russian Plain during World War II
and, finally, to send the German forces in
headlong retreat. The bulk of Soviet manufacture is in the Russian Plain, particularly in
the section between Moscow and the Black
Sea. Warfare destroyed many of the key industrial areas. In addition, whole factories
were moved farther east, into the Urals and
Siberia, as the German armies advanced.
Most of the destroyed districts have been restored and the others, to the east, have been
maintained and enlarged.

RUSSIAN PLAIN DISTRICTS. The Moscow district (Fig. 346) produces about 15 per cent
of Soviet manufactures, including some iron
and steel, machinery, hardware, tools, textiles, flour, clothing, paper, and printed matter. However, the district is not as favorably
located in terms of high-grade coal and iron
ore deposits as are the districts farther south
and east.

The Donbas (lower Don River Basin) is
the chief manufacturing district of the Soviet
Union. It lies on the famous Donets Valley
coal fields and is just east of the rich iron ores
of the Krivoi Rog section which lies within
the great bend of the Dnieper River (Fig.
346). Heavy industry is the rule and typical
products are iron and steel, rails, locomotives,
railway cars, and tractors. Other products include chemicals, glass, cement, machinery,
tools, and armaments. There is a heavy flow
of coal to the Krivoi Rog iron ore; this enables
Krivoi Rog and other cities nearby to play a
major role in iron and steel production.

Several other, and lesser, manufacturing
districts of the Russian Plain extend from
Leningrad to Minsk and, much farther east
and south, to Stalingrad and Kuibyshev. Leningrad specializes in ships, electrical equipment, paper, furniture, cloth, and furs.

Minsk is noted for textiles, shoes, small machines, and paper. Stalingrad makes steel,
agricultural machinery, river boats, and refined petroleum products. Kuibyshev is a
noted petroleum-refining center.

URALS DISTRICT. Based on iron ore and manganese, and prodded by Soviet plans for eastward development, as well as by the German
invasion of western Russia during World War
II, the southern Urals have acquired a cluster
of comparatively new industrial centers (Fig.
346). They lack industrial coal, which must
come to them by long rail haul from the Donbas and from the Karaganda and Kuznetsk
fields far to the east. In fact, scarcity of good
coal is so much of a problem that it is doubtful if the southern Urals district would have
become a significant iron and steel producer
in a nation with a free economy. As it is,
the Soviet government has decided that iron
and steel shall be made there, regardless of
what may be called the "economics of the
situation." However, part of the south Urals
iron ore does move to other sections.

KUZNETSK DISTRICT. This manufacturing
area lies more than a thousand miles east of
the southern Urals (Fig. 346). The chief center is Stalinsk, and iron and steel are the
major products. Local coal is abundant and
of high grade; local iron ores are supple-
mented by iron ores from the Urals and some
Kuznetsk coal travels to the Ural ore districts.
Although the Kuznetsk district is south of the
Trans-Siberian Railway, new lines connect the
district with the main east-west rail artery.

OTHER EASTERN DISTRICTS. The Soviet plan
to develop all territories as much as possible
is partly reflected in small manufacturing districts that lie much farther into Siberia than
the Kuznetsk. These districts are located here
and there all the way to Vladivostok, on the
shore of the Sea of Japan (Fig. 346). One is
at Krasnoyarsk, at the junction of the Trans-
Siberian Railway with the upper Yenisei
River; two are located in the southern Lake
Baikal region; another, Khabarovsk, is at the
junction of the Amur River and the Trans-

EURASIAN MANUFACTURING
REGIONS
AND
CHIEF DISTRICTS

Manufacturing Region
and Chief Districts

Chief Districts outside
Manufacturing Region

I—WEST EUROPE   III—EAST-CENTRAL CHINA
II—SOUTHERN JAPAN   IV—CENTRAL INDIA

1—Moscow District   5—Krasnoyarsk District   9—Honshu-Kyushu Districts
2—Donbas District   6—S. Baikal Districts   10—Calcutta District
3—Ural Districts   7—Fushun-Anshan District 11—Bombay District
4—Kuznetsk District 8—Yangtze Valley Districts

Statute Miles

346 *EURASIA'S four chief manufacturing regions consist of an old, long established region in the west and three comparatively young ones far to the east. In the Soviet Union, large numbers of important manufacturing districts make up what may soon be recognized as a new region—the Russian Plain-South Siberia Region.*

Siberian Railway; and on the coast is the Vladivostok district. Thus, the manufacturing areas of the Soviet Union now stretch, in numbers decreasing eastward, from Poland to the Pacific.

Manufacturing Regions of Japan

From 1905 to 1945, at the close of World War II, Japan made truly astonishing progress as a commercial and manufacturing nation. Stimulated by her victory over Russia in 1905 and by the ideas and machines of the Western World, Japan changed from a feudal, agricultural nation to a highly organized industrial state, even though agriculture continued to be the leading occupation of the population as a whole. By a combination of peaceful and aggressive action she reached out for more territory and more raw materials. Rubber came from Malaya, manganese from India, coal and iron ore from Manchuria, petroleum from the United States and Indonesia, scrap iron and cotton from the

United States, and cotton from India. All these, added to her own resources and her leadership in raw silk production, provided a manufacturing base which enabled Japan to become the "Britain of the East" and to compete in many foreign markets with the United States and the nations of western Europe. Finally, her ambitions to dominate Asia and thrust out Western interests culminated in a widespread Pacific war in which she was decisively defeated. During the war, the Japanese navy and merchant marine were slowly destroyed and many of its industrial cities were laid waste by bombs. Under control of the Allied powers, particularly the United States, Japan has been rebuilding her factories and, bit by bit, has been allowed to re-establish many of her former manufactures.

HONSHU-KYUSHU REGION. Present-day Japan is without its former iron and steel plants in Manchuria and textile factories and other interests in China Proper. For all practical purposes it now has only one manufacturing region. It consists of several districts and manufacturing types, extending from the Tokyo-Yokohama district of Honshu to the

Fukuoka district of northern Kyushu (Fig. 346). Lesser districts are located in Honshu, part of Shikoku, and a section of southwestern Hokkaido.

The Tokyo-Yokohama district is notable for silk reeling, silk cloth, printing, small machinery, tools, and electrical equipment; its manufactures are more diversified than those of the other districts. The bulk of the manufacturing is carried on in numerous small workshops, rather than in large factories. Strung out farther west are the other main centers of Honshu's industry. Nagoya specializes in thread, yarn, and textiles, including silk, cotton, and woolen goods, as well as pottery. Osaka is Japan's major cotton textile center. Kobe, close by, is the chief shipbuilding city. Kyoto, an inland city, is noted for toys, pottery, lacquer ware and other goods requiring much care and the artistry of skilled craftsmen.

The northern margin of Kyushu, what may be called the Fukuoka-Moji district, is the heavy-industry area of Japan. Here are blast furnaces and steel mills, as well as cement, glass, and chemical plants, and shipyards. Yawata is the major steel center, a sort of Japanese Pittsburgh, but without the wealth of basic resources enjoyed by Pittsburgh. It has been very dependent on foreign scrap iron and scrap steel in its attempt to make up for the Japanese deficiency in pig iron production.

Manufacturing Regions: China

A high degree of industrialization and the creation of large manufacturing regions in China have been prevented for many reasons: overpopulation, civil war, famine, poor transportation, lack of capital, strong resistance to Western ideas and methods, to name only the chief ones. There appears to be no lessening of China's problems and there is little chance for rapid spread of industry in the near future.

CHINA PROPER. Most of China's manufacturing is located in the Yangtze Valley, from Shanghai on the east to Chungking on the west (Fig. 346). Shanghai is the big textile center, for both cotton and silk. The Hankow district makes iron and steel. During World War II, industry was greatly stimulated farther inland, in Chungking and other centers of the Szechwan Basin, because the Japanese forces held the portion of the Yangtze Valley from the Gorges to the ocean. They held not only Shanghai, but all the other key cities as well. Until China is unified and develops more industrial know-how and better transportation facilities, she will be unable to transport and combine her many raw materials and thus create manufacturing areas comparable to those of Japan or the Western world.

MANCHURIA. The bulk of Manchurian industry is located inland, in the southern part of the Manchurian Plain (Fig. 346). Under Japanese control from 1932 to 1945, the coal of the Fushun area and the iron ores of the Anshan area were combined to support an important iron and steel production. In 1945, Soviet armies occupied Manchuria and removed most of the industrial machinery. Who will ultimately control Manchuria and what will be done to develop or redevelop industry there is anyone's guess.

Manufacturing Regions: India

After long years of restiveness, India was granted her freedom from Britain in 1948. Divided into the Dominions of India and Pakistan, India is now forging ahead on her own. For many years prior to 1948, India had been slowly establishing herself in the manufacturing field. She received little encouragement from Britain; Britain needed Indian raw materials for her homeland factories and the huge Indian market for the sale of many of her finished products, especially cotton textiles. Most Indian manufactures are made in small home workshops and are consumed locally, but there is one section of the country which may now be classified as a significant industrial region. This region extends in a wide belt from Bombay on the west to Calcutta on the east (Fig. 346). Within it are several districts, the chief of which are in or near either Bombay or Calcutta. Other districts, considerably removed from the Bombay-Calcutta region, are in such cities as Madras on the Coromandel Coast and Colombo in Ceylon, with a number of others located in the upper portion of the Ganges Plain.

BOMBAY DISTRICT. Bombay is located on the edge of India's major cotton-growing area and it has long been noted for raw cotton exports to England. Year by year, Bombay has built and run cotton mills of its own until it is now the cotton cloth center of all India. With plentiful raw cotton and abundant cheap labor, plus a new bustle accompanying independence, India has practically taken over her vast home market for cotton cloth.

CALCUTTA DISTRICT. Within this area are made such key goods as manufactured jute, paper, shellac, and sealing wax. Jute manufactures occupy much the same position in Calcutta as cotton manufactures do in Bombay. On the western margin of the district increasing amounts of iron and steel are being made from local iron ore, flux, and manganese. It is this section which is envisioned as a kind of Oriental Pittsburgh (Fig. 347).

347   *SIGNS of modern India: lower part of a large blast furnace which turns iron ore into iron for use in nearby steel mill. (Government of India Information Services)*

MANUFACTURING REGIONS OF THE SOUTHERN HEMISPHERE

In world commerce, the Southern Hemisphere has been, and largely still is, a furnisher of food and raw materials for the manufacturing regions of Europe and the United States, especially the former. However, there are some places where manufacturing already has a good start and these should be noted, even in a broad and generalized treatment of the manufacturing business of the world (Fig. 336).

Australia and New Zealand

Most of the manufactured goods used by the people of Australia and New Zealand are made in Great Britain and, to a much lesser extent, in continental Europe and the United States. They are paid for mainly by wheat, butter, cheese, beef, mutton, and wool. The leading manufacturing centers of Australia itself are in the southeast, at Melbourne and Sydney (Fig. 336). Others are at Adelaide, Brisbane, and, in the southwest, at Perth. Another is at Hobart, in the southern part of Tasmania.

Australian manufactures are diversified and mainly of the lighter type. Of chief importance to other sections of the world are the making of butter, cheese, condensed milk, packed meats, and the processing of raw wool. Products for home consumption alone consist of shoes, textiles, clothing, flour, refined sugar, brewery products, small metal articles, and some iron and steel.

New Zealand's manufacturing is done both in North Island and South Island (Fig. 336). It strongly resembles that of Australia, although it is less in amount. Chief centers are Auckland and Wellington in North Island

and Christchurch and Dunedin in South Island. Products are cheese and butter, plus clothing, shoes, and some agricultural equipment. New Zealand, more a land of farms and pastures than Australia, lacks even the beginnings of an iron and steel industry.

South Africa

Like the areas just mentioned, the Union of South Africa is primarily a seller of raw materials and a buyer of machine goods. Again, it is British rather than local factories which supply most of the products. The major district centers around Cape Town; others lie along the coast to the east, as Port Elizabeth, East London, and Durban, and one, Johannesburg, lies in the interior (Fig. 336). Manufactures consist of such goods as clothing, processed foods, household equipment, books and newspapers, and a little iron and steel.

South America

In South America, as in Australia and Africa, one must look carefully to discover sections worthy of being termed manufacturing regions or districts (Fig. 336). The major South American concentrations of factories occur in what may be called the La Plata region. Important centers there are Buenos Aires, La Plata, and Rosario in Argentina and Montevideo in Uruguay. Long dependent on British coal, the La Plata region is manufacturing increased quantities of leather, shoes, cloth, paper, furniture, cement, flour, and packed meats.

In Chile, most of the factories are in the Santiago-Valparaiso district and the Concepción-Valdivia district. As in Argentina, manufacturing is increasing and it is producing a wide variety of goods, ranging from shoes and clothing to wines and smelted minerals.

The remaining industrial areas of compara-

348 *A VIEW across part of the large commercial and industrial city of São Paulo, Brazil.*
(Gendreau)

tive significance are those centering on Rio de Janeiro and São Paulo in Brazil. São Paulo particularly is becoming known more and more as an industrial city (Fig. 348). The production of textiles, clothing, machinery, cement, chemicals, and processed foods as well as the assembling of automobiles characterizes the manufacturing activities.

The foregoing discussion of manufacturing areas in the Southern Hemisphere has emphasized their small number and their small extent as compared with those of the Northern Hemisphere. To prevent misconceptions arising from this emphasis, it should be pointed out that comparatively small manufacturing areas may be of extreme importance to local regions or to the entire country in which they lie. For example, the total iron and steel production of Australia is quite small,

yet on a per capita basis it is very high. Japan became known as an important iron- and steel-manufacturing nation, but Australia makes more than three times as much steel per inhabitant as Japan ever did.

· ·

CHAPTER OUTLINE

Manufacturing Regions

Localization of manufacturing regions
   Type of culture
   Raw materials
   Power
   Labor
   Transportation
   Capital
   Markets
   The basic factors

REVIEW QUESTIONS

1. Discuss the effects of increasing industrialization on the distribution of population in the United States.

2. Using other examples than those given in the text, demonstrate that type of culture may encourage or discourage the development of manufacturing in different regions or nations over the world.

3. Is there justification for the statement that Denmark cannot become a *leading* manufacturing nation?

4. Explain the apparent paradox involved in referring to "scarcity of labor" in India.

5. Why do manufacturing regions and well-developed railroad nets go hand-in-hand?

6. Where is the greater bulk of the goods manufactured in the United States consumed?

7. What "combination" is referred to in the statement that, "Certainly no *major* industrial regions exist where this combination is not present"?

8. Give the location of the two major manufacturing regions of the world. Which one is now the leader? Why?

9. Demonstrate the critical importance of steel in our national economy.

10. What and where are the four major iron- and steel-manufacturing districts of the United States?

11. Give examples of specialization districts in the manufacture of machinery, tools, and transportation equipment.

12. How important is the automobile industry in terms of consumption of such materials as rubber, plate glass, lead, nickel, copper, and steel?

13. Why did New England, once the leader, lose its leadership in the shipbuilding industry to the Chesapeake-Delaware-Hudson region?

14. Discuss the problems of the United States shipbuilding industry in terms of meeting foreign competition.

15. On the basis of monetary value, what is the leading "product group" in our country?

16. New England once held leadership in cotton textile manufacturing. What section of the United States now leads? In what textile does New England now hold leadership?

17. What were some of the chief reasons for the rise of cotton textile manufacturing in the South?

18. Account for the position of the northern limit of the Canadian portion of the Northeast Manufacturing Region.

19. Discuss the distribution of coal and iron in relation to the West-European Manufacturing Region.

20. Why is manufacturing "more vital to Britain than to any other major nation"?

21. What is the present status (as reported by the daily press) of the utilization of Ruhr Valley coal and Lorraine iron ore?

22. Which of the important manufacturing districts of Europe are under the direct or indirect control of the Soviet Union?

23. Give examples of specialization districts within Japan's Honshu-Kyushu manufacturing region.

24. Attempt to secure recent information concerning India's progress in manufacturing, especially in the Bombay and Calcutta districts.

25. What areas or regions stand as exceptions to the fact that the southern hemisphere is mainly a "raw products hemisphere"?

SOME SUGGESTED REFERENCES

Bengtson, Nels A., and Van Royen, William, *Fundamentals of Economic Geography*, Prentice-Hall, Inc., 1950. A new edition of a standard textbook in economic geography; see particularly Chapters 27 and 28 which deal with industrial regions and selected industries of the world.

Bergsmark, Daniel R., *Economic Geography of Asia*, Prentice-Hall, Inc., 1942. A textbook which provides the general framework of Asia's economic geography, both on a regional and on a national basis. Chapters 11 through 14 are concerned with India; Chapters 20 and 21, with Japan; and Chapters 23 through 25, with China. Chapter 27 deals with Siberia and Russian Turkestan.

Colby, Charles C., and Foster, Alice, *Economic Geography*, Ginn, 1944. A treatment of the major industries and basic resources of the world's leading nations; see Chapter 4 for world commercial regions and the index for specific industries and countries.

Cressey, George B., *Asia's Lands and Peoples,* McGraw-Hill, 1944. A general geography of Asia and all of the Soviet Union; several chapters contain many references to manufacturing.

Davis, Darrell H., *The Earth and Man: A Human Geography*, 2nd ed., Macmillan, 1948. An introductory text at the college level; Chapter 38 discusses commerce and industry.

Dicken, Samuel N., *A Regional Economic Geography*, D. C. Heath and Co., 1949. A general treatment of the world's chief production regions; Chapters 34 through 37 deal with manufacturing.

Glover, John G., and Cornell, William B., *The Development of American Industries,* Prentice-Hall, Inc., 1946. A reference book on the history and economic importance of our basic industries; see separate chapters on such as the iron and steel, sugar, paper, rubber, and textile industries.

Gottmann, Jean, *A Geography of Europe,* Holt, 1950. A geography of Europe written by a European for American students; see individual chapters, such as the one on the Benelux Countries, for mention of manufacturing.

James, Preston E., *Latin America,* The Odyssey Press, 1950. A textbook on the human and physical geography of Spanish and Portuguese America; contains many specific references to manufacturing in individual Latin American countries.

Jones, Clarence F., and Darkenwald, Gordon G., *Economic Geography,* Macmillan, 1941. An introductory textbook arranged according to major occupations; Chapters 29 through 34 are concerned with manufacturing.

McCarty, Harold H., *The Geographic Basis of American Economic Life,* Harper, 1940. The "where, what, and why" of our economic activities on a regional basis; see especially Chapters 20 through 29 which deal with manufacturing and manufacturing districts.

Smith, J. Russell, and Phillips, M. Ogden, *North America,* Harcourt, Brace, 1942. A standard text on the geography of North America; use the index for references to manufacturing in the many regions discussed.

Smith, J. Russell, and Phillips, M. Ogden, *Industrial and Commercial Geography,* Holt, 1946. A geographical interpretation of the world's business; Chapter 3 discusses the fundamentals of manufacturing and other chapters discuss the various industries.

Whitbeck, Ray H., and Finch, Vernor C., *Economic Geography,* McGraw-Hill, 1941. The salient features of the economic geography of the United States and other nations; see individual countries for discussions of manufacturing.

349 "WET LAND," or "paddy" rice in an intensively cultivated portion of Java. (Corsini, Standard Oil Co. [N. J.])

CHAPTER 24

Agriculture and Animal Husbandry

No one knows when man first became a farmer; by the time he learned to keep even the most simple of records, there was mention of crops, agricultural practices, and ceremonies associated with planting and harvesting. Among the oldest of agricultural peoples are those of Egypt, India, and China, as well as those in parts of Iran, Iraq, and Afghanistan. In large sections of China, for example, well-established crop practices and intensive use of the land have been the rule for more than 4,000 years.

The first farmers were essentially gardeners, for their tools were few and crude, and they cultivated only small pieces of land. They used pointed sticks or simple wooden hoes to break the ground, planted seeds by hand, and, in the end, reaped a meager and hard-won harvest.

As time passed, more and more wild plants were tamed for use, and farming tools slowly became more numerous and more efficient. Small sickles with flint cutting edges were among the earliest harvesting tools. By 1000 B.C., sickles with metal blades were in use in Egypt. A great advance over the hoe was made when crude wooden plows were invented to help break the soil. Moreover, by this time animals had been tamed and some of them were hitched to plows to help man do his work; no longer was he completely dependent on his own limited muscle power. Despite continued advance, it was not until the nineteenth century that the metal plow was in use. The steel plow, invented in 1833, has played a large part in world agriculture because it enables man to break the tough sod of the grasslands. Formerly it was easier to clear the forests and grub out stumps than it was to tear through the tangled mat of roots present in grassland soils. Thus, new inventions not only made the farmer's work progressively easier and allowed him to increase production from land already under cultivation, but also enabled agriculture to spread more widely over the earth.

The nineteenth century was a period of great agricultural progress, just as it was a time of rapid advance in manufacturing and commerce. In fact, the connection between them was very close: new machines demanded more raw materials, many of which came from farm, ranch, or plantation; and many of the new inventions were those which facilitated farming operations and the domestic and international exchange of both raw and finished goods. The commonly used term "Industrial Revolution" actually had a twin whose name was "Agricultural Revolution." Multiple, or gang, plows, and mechanical seeders, reapers, binders, and threshers were some of the new tools provided (Fig. 350). At first, horses and mules provided most of the power for the machines, but by the end of the century many of them were engine-powered. While all this was going on, plant scientists discovered or developed new crops, some of which are able to live in colder and drier parts of the earth than was previously considered possible. Again, the result was an increase in the amount of land under cultivation.

The foregoing account might give the impression that the world's agriculture is entirely, or almost entirely, modernized or that it is chiefly an agriculture of machines and scientifically selected crops. Actually, the vast majority of the world's farms today are still run in old-fashioned and often primitive ways. This is especially true in Asia where a bit more than half the people of the world live, in the poorer sections of Europe, and in extensive portions of Africa and South America. Modern agriculture is perhaps best exemplified in the United States and sections of southern Canada.

THE SIGNIFICANCE OF AGRICULTURE

Many dwellers in the United States and other highly industrialized and urbanized countries seldom appreciate the fundamental importance of agriculture in their lives. Of course, farmers and ranchers realize its significance, but the millions of urban residents scarcely give it a thought. They get milk from the milkman, meat from the butcher, vegetables and fruits from the grocer, and bread from the baker. For them, agriculture might be an activity practiced on the moon. Only when supplies are scarce, as during a war, does production from the soil enter their minds.

Food for Man

Probably the chief concern of at least half of the people of the world is to get enough food to stay alive. The struggle for subsistence has been the lot of the majority of mankind for centuries. It is nothing new for millions of persons to starve to death in China and India in a single year. One famine year in China is estimated to have cost the lives of ten million Chinese, and this takes no account of malnutrition and disease among those many other millions who somehow stayed alive. Europe, too, has seen its share of famine, whether caused by crop failure or the ravages of war.

Admittedly, the world has a host of problems to solve. Yet, outstanding experts in world affairs state that the problem of food is the greatest of all. Hence, no matter how other activities progress, agriculture must be successful at all costs. If it is not, we are faced with a largely hungry world, one in no mood or condition to solve other serious problems. It is often said that hunger encourages endeavor, but the truth is that hunger first creates unrest, then desperation, and later complete apathy.

Food for Animals

Food for animals and food for man are not entirely separate. It is true that many domestic animals are not destined to become human food, but great numbers of them are raised specifically for human consumption. Regardless of their use, animals have to be fed and usually man has to provide their food in the form of hay, corn, oats, or some other crop. Several of the world's major crop regions have become animal regions as well. This is particularly true where population is not so great as to preclude the use of the land for the production of animal foods, to be consumed indirectly by man in the form of meat and animal fats. One good example of a crop region which has become an animal region is the United States Corn Belt. It is not only a corn belt, but a hog belt, a beef belt, and a major area of mutton and poultry production (Fig. 351). Denmark offers another example.

350 *MODERN machinery in the wheat fields near Vernon, Texas. A small "combine" is harvesting and a large "gang disc plow" is turning over the stubble and the top-soil. (Lee, Standard Oil Co. [N. J.])*

351 *BEEF cattle being fattened in a Corn Belt feed lot. These cattle were brought from western range lands to be fattened for market. (Kaufmann and Fabry Co., Chicago)*

GENERALIZED PATTERN
OF
AGRICULTURAL
AND
NON-AGRICULTURAL
REGIONS

Non-crop, non-livestock

Crop (livestock usually associated)

Livestock ranching (little, or no, crop production)

Nomadic herding (few, if any, farms or ranches)

Compressed Sinusoidal equal-area projection

352 ON THIS GENERALIZED map notice that noncrop, nonlivestock regions are mainly extremely arid or cold. Crop regions are mainly humid with long growing seasons, with some areas of irrigated or drought-resistant crops.

Ranching regions are mainly grasslands, and some mountains. Nomadic herding regions are mainly deserts, tundras, and mountains.

There almost all of the agricultural land produces feed for dairy cattle, hogs, and chickens. The result has been an astonishingly large production and export of bacon, eggs, and butter.

Raw Materials for Factories

We may appreciate the importance of crops for human food and livestock feed, but rarely do we properly connect them with industry. As pointed out in the chapter on manufacturing, the processing and manufacture of foodstuffs holds first place among United States industries. In addition, many other industries depend on farms, ranches, and plantations for raw materials. Common examples are the cotton textile, woolen, silk, leather, rope and twine, and rubber industries. Less well-known industries consume large amounts of crops in order to produce soaps, cosmetics, paints and varnishes, industrial alcohols, starches, sugars, and even medicines. Each year more industries become dependent, or partly dependent, on products obtained from the soil. One manufacturer is said to have stated that he could make an entire automobile, except the engine block, from soy beans. The statement is not so far-fetched as it sounds. Already it is possible to make such products as artificial rubber, synthetic cloth, paint and varnish, glass, and many other materials from soy beans. The chemical "breakdown" of soy beans continues and the end of possible uses has not been reached, whether for industrial or for animal and human food purposes.

LIMITING FACTORS: PHYSICAL

Agriculture is not practiced in all parts of the world, and no matter how much it continues to spread, there probably will always be parts of the world in which crops cannot be grown (except at excessive costs) and few, if any, livestock can be raised. Fig. 352 provides a generalized world view of the regions in which crops and livestock are produced; it also emphasizes those areas which are essentially noncrop, nonlivestock-producing. The extent of agriculture is determined by a number of limiting factors which operate in complex and interdependent fashion. Some of these factors are physical and some are cultural. The chief physical factors are climate, landforms, soils, drainage, native vegetation, and, in part, wild animal life.

Climate

The most fundamental limitation on the extent of agriculture is climate. Climate not only affects the spread of agriculture as a whole, but limits, often drastically, the distribution of individual crops. In Canada, for example, the northern limit of agriculture is determined by temperature, reflected in the length of the frost-free season. Agriculture is limited in the Ecuadorian Andes, except that the limit there is an upward, instead of a poleward, limit. The Sahara, except for oasis production, is devoid of crops not because of temperature conditions, but because of insufficient rainfall. In those parts of the world with a Mediterranean (Cs) climate there are some sections—sections where irrigation is not practiced—in which crops can be produced during the cool, mild winters, but not during the hot, dry summers. Again, moisture is the controlling factor, but in this instance it operates to control agriculture in a time, rather than a space, sense.

Climate sets definite limits to the cultivation of many crops. The coconut palm thrives in the tropics and invades the milder portions of the subtropics in a few places, but it cannot grow elsewhere. Essentially the same is true of bananas. Citrus fruits grow in the tropics and subtropics, but the highest quality fruit is obtained in the milder portions of the subtropics, particularly in those sections that have the Mediterranean (Cs) or the Humid subtropical (Cfa) climate. Some varieties of wheat can be grown successfully in areas with as little as 10 inches of annual precipitation, other varieties require 20, or more, inches. Such examples could be multiplied many times.

Landforms

The lay of the land constitutes another major factor in the determination of agricultural distributions (Fig. 159). The bulk of the world's agriculture is carried on in plains or undissected plateaus. Wherever surfaces are too rough, as in mountainous areas, cultivation of the land is seriously handicapped or precluded. Even in hilly regions and in too greatly dissected plains and plateaus, agriculture is restricted, not only because of the physical difficulties of tilling the land, but because of high costs of production. Only where level land is scarce does agriculture ignore in any important way the usual relationships between crops and landform conditions. In such instances, the land surface often is man-modified, as by the construction of terraces, or else crops which do not demand level land, such as certain tree, bush, or grass crops, are chosen.

Besides affecting the extent of agriculture in a general way, landforms sometimes determine the distribution of crops within localized areas. For example, there are many coastal and near-coastal valleys and basins in California where the general physical conditions are satisfactory for citrus production. Yet, the citrus groves are found only in certain parts of these valleys and basins. With occasional exception, the reason for the exact location is a landform reason; the groves lie on the middle and upper portions of alluvial fans where the surface has sufficient tilt to insure air drainage to the point where frost damage is prevented

or greatly minimized (Fig. 353). Thus, landforms, like climate, often play a large role in deciding where agriculture does or does not exist.

There is always danger of implying that the relationship between landforms and agriculture is iron-clad and immutable. Such an implication is not intended. It has been emphasized, rather, that landforms play an important part in the distribution of agriculture and that, in many instances, they set surprisingly rigid limits, even within comparatively small areas.

Soils

Another important factor in shaping the pattern of world agriculture, both in general and in detail, is soil. Soil, of course, is not divorced from climate and landforms, nor from other conditions such as drainage and natural vegetation. Yet, soils, in their own right, play a significant part in helping to determine "what crops grow where." There is, for example, the correlation between certain varieties of wheat and the distribution of chernozem soils. This is seen in the spring wheat belts of the United States, Canada, and the Soviet Union. The correlation between the black prairie soil and high corn yields in Iowa is easily recognized; again, it "takes more than soil," but soil is definitely one of the major factors. The "terra rossa" soils of São Paulo State, Brazil, have had much to do with the leadership of that area in world coffee production. Light, coarse-textured soils have enabled Maine's Aroostook County to become a leading producer of high-grade white potatoes. Likewise, the dark muck soils of sections of the glacial deposition region of southern Michigan favor the growing of commercial celery.

In a negative sense, the soilless or nearly soilless condition of many parts of the world has prevented the growth of any crops whatever. Many valley bottoms, otherwise suit-

353

CITRUS groves (chiefly orange) on an alluvial fan piedmont near Los Angeles, California. (Los Angeles Chamber of Commerce)

able for crops, are so completely floored with boulders and large gravels that they cannot be used for agriculture. In many irrigated areas bedrock, unmantled by soil, interrupts the crop pattern. In the agricultural region of southern Sweden, for example, many of the "bald spots" represent the outcropping of soilless, glaciated bedrock.

Because of recent and rapid advances in soil science and land-use practices, it is difficult to know how far to generalize regarding soil fertility. We often say, "This soil is fertile." What we should say is, "This soil is fertile, or productive, for white potatoes"; "This soil is fertile for Red Fife and other similar varieties of wheat"; or, "This soil, if supplied with phosphates and nitrates, will be fertile for oranges." In many sections devoted to intensive, commercial crops, the soil is no more than a material in which to bed the plants and to hold them as they grow. For example, parts of the Coachella Valley of southern California specialize in early ripening Thompson seedless grapes. Most of the grapes grow in what was recently no more than drifted dune sand. The dunes were leveled and vineyards planted; the desert-dry sands were irrigated and large amounts of fertilizer added (Fig. 354). The grapes feed and thrive on artificially supplied water and artificially supplied foods; the soil is literally no more than a "plant holder."

Another aspect of soils is "tear-down," as opposed to "build-up." As noted in Chapter 15, many soils have been worn out by a combination of perennial cropping and non fertilization; still others have been allowed to erode to the point of extinction or to the point where they can no longer be cultivated (Fig. 234). Such despoilage obviously affects the world pattern of agriculture, as well as the distribution of particular crops; worse, it affects the ability of the world to feed itself and provide essential raw materials.

Drainage

There are many sections of the earth where drainage conditions are such as to preclude agriculture. Most of these are the swampy or marshy lands. Some of them are small, such as "wet spots" in river flood plains, but others are comparatively large, such as the coastal

354

RECENTLY leveled dune area in a section of the floor of the Coachella Valley, California. This land is now ready for irrigation and the planting of its first crop. (R. M. Glendinning)

marshes of the Atlantic and Gulf Coastal plains, the delta of the Mississippi, or the extensive wet lands found in regions of glacial scour and deposition.

Other sections, even though not swampy or marshy, are too greatly subject to damaging floods for regular cropping (Fig. 169). Many parts of the dry lands that might be irrigated are not used because of the menace of flash floods. However, in irrigated dry lands and humid lands alike, man often takes the gamble—and suffers periodic devastations as a result. One of the major physical problems in the United States is to develop the control of surface waters, whether in individual farm fields or in entire drainage basins, to the point where crops and agricultural resources are not damaged or destroyed.

Native Vegetation

Even native vegetation has an effect on the world's agricultural pattern. As noted earlier, the grasslands greatly discouraged cultivation until the comparatively recent invention of the steel plow opened up many grasslands, such as the prairie and steppe of the United States, for a new extension of agriculture.

All of man's crops have been derived from native plants. The original location of individual native plants determined, until very recent centuries, where crops adapted from them grew. White potatoes, native to the highlands of Peru, required centuries to spread in the New World, and they were unknown in the Old World until the sixteenth century. There potatoes soon became very important in the agricultural economy of several nations, including Germany and Ireland. The so-called Irish potato actually is a historically recent immigrant to Ireland. Other wild plants which became crops in the New World and then traveled to the Old are tobacco, corn, cacao, and rubber. From the Old World to the New came wheat, sugar cane, cotton, coffee, tea, oranges, and several other crops.

Animals and Disease

Animals (including insects) and diseases of plants affect agricultural production and the distribution of many crops. The rabbit, introduced into Australia by man, has become an agricultural scourge. In some areas, deer or other large herbivores consume low-growing crops and kill orchard trees by eating the bark. Moles do great damage to crop roots. Certain birds, such as the crow, consume untold amounts of grain. Locusts can sweep an entire countryside clean of all portions of crops which grow above the ground (Fig. 355). Insects, whether the Japanese beetle or the cotton boll weevil, can decrease crop yields critically. On the positive side, insects, by insuring pollination, help the production of many crops. Some insects, by their presence or absence, determine whether certain crops can be grown at all. When the Smyrna fig was introduced to California, the trees thrived but bore no fruit. The problem was a puzzling one: climate, soil, and other physical conditions were satisfactory, but still, no fruit. The answer was discovered to be the fig wasp; it was not native to California and it was needed to insure pollination. As soon as the wasp was introduced, California fig production became successful. Fungus diseases do great damage to crops in all parts of the world. Such damage may be critical. Ecuador dropped from leadership in world cacao production to the point where she now furnishes only about 4 per cent of the supply. While the trouble was partly economic, the main reason was cacao fungus.

LIMITING FACTORS: CULTURAL

The major cultural controls affecting agriculture are cultural inheritance, plant selection and breeding, money and labor, transportation and markets, laws and other regulations, and the competition of other activities.

Cultural Inheritance

The manner of living and making a living, which is to a large extent handed down from generation to generation, exerts strong control over the distribution of agriculture as a whole and over the distribution of individual crops. To be sure, some cultures have developed in parts of the world where an agricultural economy is not possible. This is true, for instance, of Eskimo culture. However, there are other cultures which, as far as physical conditions are concerned, could have become agricul-

tural, but did not. In the South Sea Islands some groups found it so easy to obtain their food from the sea and from wild plants that they had no inclination to till the soil. Indians living in parts of Canada, where at least some agriculture could have been practiced and has in fact been introduced by the white man, chose to live by hunting and fishing, even though that living was usually a precarious one.

But there were many peoples who did learn to tame wild plants and till the soil. As they moved, they carried seeds and their agricultural practices with them. Thus, they extended agriculture as a way of living and insured a wider and wider distribution of particular crops. Rice production spread from small beginnings somewhere in southeastern Asia until, today, it is found in all parts of that continent which are physically suited to it. Cultural groups outside of Asia learned of rice production and adopted it during and following the Age of Discovery. Many other crops, such as corn, wheat, and sweet potatoes, spread in a similar way. Some crops became

355 *A CORNFIELD ruined by locusts. (Rothstein, Farm Security Administration)*

so typical of certain cultures that they named those cultures: we speak of the "rice culture" of the Orient, and the "corn (maize) culture" of Mexico. In a similar fashion, particular agricultural practices have attached their names to certain cultures, as the "milpa culture" of the Amazonian Indians, the "peasant culture" of Poland, or the "plantation culture" of the Malay Peninsula.

to drought, adapted to shorter growing seasons, or less subject to mildew and other diseases. New varieties of potatoes have been developed for particular climatic and soil conditions, as well as for resistance to disease. All such achievements affect world agriculture, either by extending it to new areas or by making it more successful in areas where it is already established.

Plant Selection and Breeding

During nearly all the time that man has practiced agriculture, the selection and breeding of plants usually have been matters of trial and error or of accident. The most recent period has seen great change. In many, but far from all, parts of the agricultural world, plant selection and breeding have been placed on a scientific basis. In addition, plant scientists roam the world seeking new plants and plant varieties which can be adapted to other than their native areas. The combination has resulted, for example, in wheats more resistant

Money and Labor

To bring land under cultivation and insure production from it, money, or capital, is usually necessary. In some instances, the amount of capital needed is small; in others, very large. The establishment of a farm in the equatorward portion of Canada's northern forest region requires comparatively little capital. The farm is small, land costs are relatively low, and many of the materials needed for fences, barns, homes, and fuel can be obtained from the forest itself. In addition, hunting and fishing help to supply food for

356   *THE ORDERLY "sea" of young banana plants on a Central American plantation.* *(United Fruit Co.)*

357

THE FIRST trickle of water moves in a section of the Coachella Branch of the All-American Canal, near the Salton Sea, California. (R. M. Glendinning)

the farm family and wild hays can be cut to help feed farm animals. Quite in contrast, a large amount of capital is needed to set up a wheat ranch in North Dakota. Land is high in price, and large acreage is necessary for successful commercial production. Several kinds of expensive machinery are needed, fertilizers must be purchased, and wages must be paid. Also, reserve funds must be available to "ride out" crop failures resulting from drought, storm, abnormally heavy precipitation, plant diseases, and occasional locust plagues—let alone times of low prices for wheat.

Even more capital is needed to start a tropical plantation (Fig. 356), especially in a new area. Land must be purchased, or leased; vegetation must be cleared away and then fought continually to prevent its return. Planting and cultivation costs are high, and fertilizer must be purchased. Added to all this, several years must elapse before there is any return on the investment. For example, from seven to nine years are necessary to bring a rubber plantation into production; during those years, expenditures are heavy and income is zero.

Some parts of the earth are so constituted that only huge investments can make them productive; government assistance as well as private capital may be necessary. This is particularly true of desert and steppe areas, which require elaborate systems of reservoirs, main canals, lateral canals, small ditches, and flood-control works, as well as ability to meet the water costs which continue after irrigation systems are completed (Fig. 357). If the agricultural use is dependent on ground water, rather than reservoirs, etc., then drilling, pumping, and maintenance costs are involved. Heavy capital outlays are also necessary to bring swamp or marsh lands into agricultural use. Expensive drainage ditches must be dug and maintained, drain pipes must be laid in the fields and, very often, pumping must be carried on. Thus, in one fashion or another, money plays a vital part in shaping the world pattern of agriculture.

Some crops and some systems of agriculture have high labor requirements, others low ones. But labor is always involved. It is closely related to money because labor must be paid for, except where the family alone can furnish all the labor needed. On the Canadian farm mentioned above, cash outlay for labor is practically nil; so is it in the rice areas of South China. But on the Dakota wheat ranch, despite wide use of machinery, labor costs are appreciable. On the tropical plantation they are still higher; even if individual wages are low, the number of laborers required is so great that the total cost is high.

The problem of labor is not necessarily

solved by money. Some regions are partly or completely deficient in the supply of labor, and either laborers cannot be found elsewhere or, if found, they will not go to the areas where they are needed. One of the major problems in producing rubber in the Amazon Basin is lack of labor within the area and the unwillingness of laborers from other regions to go there. On the other hand, in industrialized nations, particularly the United States, life in the cities has proved so attractive that man power has been drained away from the farms, without any compensating flow from the cities, thus creating a different kind of labor problem.

Transportation and Markets

The problems of handling, moving, and selling agricultural products are so great and so varied that their detailed consideration would fill volumes. Hence, the treatment here must run the risk of brevity and the dangers inherent in generalization.

If products are consumed locally transportation is easy. Most of the rice of China is eaten within a few feet or rods from where it grows. Most of Ireland's potatoes are consumed on the farms which produce them.

But with surplus production transportation becomes the paramount problem. Sugar cane, as in Cuba, must move quickly from the fields to the plants which squeeze the juice from it; otherwise the cane spoils. After the juice is obtained and processed into raw, unrefined sugar, it must travel by rail to the coast and then by ship to refineries located on the Atlantic and Gulf coasts of the United States. Bananas, as in Central America, must be picked green and moved quickly to the ports for loading into ships. Specially constructed refrigerated ships then carry them to distant ports. The ship's holds must be kept at a certain temperature and proper ship speeds must be maintained; otherwise the bananas arrive in port too ripe for handling, first in the

wholesale houses, and then in widely scattered retail establishments. California oranges must be picked at just the right degree of ripeness, hauled by truck from the groves to the packing houses, where they are culled, given a protective coating, wrapped, and boxed, and then sent in refrigerator cars to eastern markets. Without such facilities, including the refrigerator cars, a major part of California's agricultural business would be impossible. The problem of transport is particularly critical for all perishable products, whether sugar cane and bananas or oranges and truck crops. Where the proper type of transportation is not available, certain kinds of production cannot be carried on, no matter how favorable all the other factors may be.

A product such as wheat, if properly handled, is practically nonperishable; yet even wheat demands a great deal of handling and some special transport equipment and facilities. It must be hauled from the thresher to a collection point on the farm, then to the nearest railroad, where it is stored in grain elevators. From the grain elevator (Fig. 358), it must move in railroad cars to the milling centers or to ports where it is loaded into ships for export. For example, Canadian wheat from southern Manitoba travels by rail to Fort William on Lake Superior, then by lake boat to some port, such as Kingston on Lake Ontario, or Montreal on the St. Lawrence River, and then across the Atlantic to the large wheat-receiving port of Liverpool.

In addition to transportation, there is the problem of prices and the market. Obviously, there is no point in producing goods for sale and moving those goods expensively over long distances, unless there is someone to buy them in sufficient quantities and at a sufficiently high price. Price, an extremely variable thing, is the final determinant of farm production. Man could produce bananas in Greenland under artificial conditions if he could sell them for a sufficiently high price. The American Southwest could supply huge quantities of vegetable rubber, from such a plant as guayule, if the selling price were high enough. Much depends on price and the demand which lies behind it. When prices are high, even distant and inefficient areas may be able to move and sell goods at a profit. When prices are exceptionally low, even regions favored by optimum physical conditions and nearness to market may be unable to sell their goods at a profit. Thus, certain regions may produce wheat in some years and not in others; other areas produce sugar beets during certain periods and no sugar beets at other times.

Laws and Other Regulations

Under totalitarian government, the agriculture of a nation may be regimented to the point where physical controls lose much of their normal importance and where such cultural controls as cost of transportation, availability of labor, and size and character of market cease completely to have effect. Agricultural activities are of a sort and in such a location as dictated by the government. They may pay for themselves, or not. Thus, wheat may be grown in a region usually given over to corn, or cotton may be grown on land that is usually reserved for tobacco. Or, agriculture, regardless of individual crops, may be carried on in regions better adapted to grazing or forestry. Such procedures are often the result of an attempt on the part of a government to insure self-sufficiency, regardless of cost. Sometimes they result from the desire of a government to insure amounts of a given crop sufficient to be sold in large quantities to other nations, in exchange for materials lacking or available in only small amounts in

358 *TYPICAL ARRANGEMENT of railroad yard and grain elevators in Kansas City, Missouri, for handling and storing wheat. (Rotkin, Standard Oil Co. [N. J.])*

the homeland. Such drastic controls affect the agriculture of only a few nations, but some of these nations are large, large enough to be major parts of world agriculture. Notable among them is the Soviet Union.

Control of agriculture within national boundaries is not limited to totalitarian states. At times of overproduction even democratic countries may establish direct or indirect controls. Farmers may be paid not to plant particular crops and be denied certain privileges if they do not co-operate in the government's program. In other instances, a collapsed market may be artificially supported by government price-setting or by government buying in large amounts. Both of these procedures have been used at times in the United States. When the world coffee market dropped to a very low level, the coffee producers of Brazil went broke by the thousands. The Brazilian government bought huge amounts of coffee in attempts to keep up the price. Much of it was stored in warehouses, but thousands of bags were dumped into the sea or burned in locomotives in place of coal.

Agriculture may face other types of controls. In some parts of the United States, for example, agriculture is now prohibited. Some of these are sections which are not well suited to agriculture and where it has proved too expensive to maintain roads, schools, and other services. Such prohibitions are determined by local governments and are based on local zoning ordinances. Other parts of the United States, some of which are very large, are set apart as national forests and national parks. Within them, private uses of the land, including agriculture, are stringently regulated or prohibited. Sometimes state laws affect agriculture or a particular crop both within and outside the state. California, for instance, has a law which prevents the importation of avocados, so that avocado growers of other states cannot compete in California markets. Most regulations of this sort, however, represent attempts to prevent the spread of plant diseases. In other instances, the importation of certain crops is not prohibited, but the crops have to undergo rigid inspection before they are allowed entrance. This does not prevent imports, but it does set up barriers which are costly and time-consuming, however necessary some of them may be.

Agricultural products which cross international boundaries are often faced with stringent regulations as to quality, nature of packing, possibility of disease, and so on. Sometimes for political reasons the importation of a crop is prohibited from certain areas, but allowed from others. Sometimes the rules seek to prevent the dumping of cheap products on the market. Again, many of these rules represent an attempt to insure clean, high-grade, disease-free products.

In addition, tariff laws affect the movement of farm products. The tariff may be set so high as effectively to prevent imports, or just high enough to protect domestic farmers from the competition of products which can be more cheaply produced elsewhere. The United States tariff on Cuban and other foreign sugar, to mention one example, is not high enough to prevent imports, but it is high enough to enable domestic raisers of cane and especially beet sugar to meet the outside competition. What this one law accomplishes can be appreciated when one realizes that without it there probably would be no commercial cane or beet sugar raised in the entire United States.

Another arbitrary control of agriculture is exemplified by the British Stevenson Act, which was in operation from 1922 to 1928. The British felt that rubber prices were too low to meet the cost of production. Because their Far Eastern plantations dominated world rubber production, they decided to restrict output and thereby force the price to higher levels. The Stevenson Act was put into force, the British output dropped, and the price of rubber rose. Higher prices encouraged the establishment of more rubber plantations in the Dutch East Indies. By 1928, so many of these were in production that the British rubber monopoly was broken and the Stevenson Act had to be abandoned. Thus, a British regulation affected not only a phase of British agriculture, but a part of Dutch agricultural activity as well.

Many other illustrations might be given to show how laws, regulations, or agreements affect agriculture in various ways. Those already given are sufficient to indicate that the nature and distribution of agriculture are related to many factors besides climate, soils, capital, labor, transportation, and markets.

Competition from Other Activities

There are many parts of the world which are admirably suited to the production and sale of crops, but crops are not grown there. Usually, this is because the land is more valuable for other uses. In the Los Angeles metropolitan area, for instance, many thriving and profitable walnut and orange groves, as well as truck gardens, have been displaced by homes, apartments, streets and sidewalks, factories, or lumberyards. As profitable as agriculture was on these lands, it could not compete with the values established by urban land use. An interesting result is the encouragement of agriculture in areas farther removed from the metropolitan region. Much the same thing has occurred in the Detroit area and other large city regions. As the cities have grown, and as they have acquired satellite towns and cities, land in farms has become land in city blocks and in factory districts.

In a different area of California, east of Sacramento, another use of the land likewise has resulted in displacement of agriculture. Here, in several districts, huge gold dredges have chewed up many farms and left only debris-piled wastelands behind them (Fig. 299). In many parts of Texas and Oklahoma, ranches have given way to forests of oil derricks. Parts of New England have seen farm-lands become resort and recreational areas. Other sections of the country have seen mine buildings and mining dumps take the place of farm buildings and fields. Many mountain and hill valleys and basins, devoted to agriculture, have been incorporated as parts of national forests and national parks. Thus, in one manner or another, competing uses have curtailed or displaced agriculture.

TYPES OF AGRICULTURE

Agriculture is not "just farming." Both agricultural products and practices differ greatly from one region to another. The differences reflect many physical and cultural factors, ranging from location, climate, and soil to density of population, stage of economic development, general cultural background, and governmental controls. Thus, the agriculture of the United States Corn Belt is different from that of the Cotton Belt, and both differ markedly from that of the Amazon Basin or the Ganges Plain of India. Differences also occur within relatively small areas. There is great contrast, for example, between truck farming and dairy farming in southern Michigan, or between subsistence farming and plantation farming in a local section of the Philippines.

Subsistence Agriculture

PRIMITIVE. Subsistence agriculture characterizes those farming areas which consume all, or nearly all, of the products locally grown, as opposed to commercialized farming regions whose products mainly are sold and consumed "off the farm." Subsistence agriculture is of two general types: primitive and nonprimitive.

Primitive subsistence agriculture may be either migratory (shifting) or sedentary. The migratory kind, known variously as milpa, fang, ladang, chena, or caingan, is limited largely to the rainy tropics and their immediate borderlands. It is practiced where there is a great deal of room and few persons.

There are many reasons for the migratory nature of this kind of farming. Chief among them are the poor soils and the rankly growing vegetation of the humid tropics. It is easier to move than to attempt to fertilize the soils or to combat the encroaching vegetation. It is easier, likewise, to let nature restore the soil and, after this has been accomplished, to return to the use of the same plots of ground, perhaps many years later. Lesser reasons for migrating range from epidemics and insect pests to wild animal depredations and the desire to build new homes and villages rather than repair old ones.

Migratory agriculture, or shifting cultivation, as might be expected of farming that is on the move, is simple (Fig. 359). Spots of better soil are chosen near the villages and the trees are either girdled or fire-killed so that they shed their leaves and allow sunlight to reach the ground. The ground around the dead trees is loosened with a sharp stick or a simple hoe or spade and the crops are planted. As the crops grow, a weedy jungle of new plants grows along with them. The natives may or may not weed the small fields. Typical crops are corn, yams, manioc, peanuts, beans, peas, bananas, and sugar cane. After the crops are harvested and the jungle has taken over again, the field may be cleared by using machetes and fire. If the soil is worn out, the field is abandoned without clearing the brush; if not, the field may be used for two or three years. In any event, it is soon abandoned and a new field is chosen. When all the better spots of a local district are used up, the entire village may move to another district where the process is repeated. Thus this type of

359   *A NEWLY CLEARED garden in the tropical forest of northwestern New Guinea where migratory agriculture is practiced. (Archbold Expeditions of the American Museum of Natural History)*

360

PRIMITIVE agriculture of the sedentary type, in the highlands of Colombia, near Bogotá. (Collier, Standard Oil Co. [N. J.])

agriculture is migratory in two senses; it moves from one place to another within a local area and, if there is room, then moves to another area.

The sedentary kind of primitive subsistence agriculture normally occurs in areas where population is relatively dense or where climate and soil are more conducive to permanent use of the same fields. It, too, is found mainly in the tropics, but is more characteristic of hills, plateaus, and mountain basins than of the hot, wet lowlands (Fig. 360). Tools and tillage practices are simple and the crops are much the same as in migratory agriculture, except where production is carried on at elevations so great that crops like yams, bananas, and sugar cane cannot be grown. They are replaced by others, such as white potatoes and other tubers. Typical regions for sedentary subsistence farming are the equatorial Andes, the Central American highlands, western Ethiopia, and parts of the South African Plateau.

NONPRIMITIVE. The impression is often given that all subsistence agriculture is primitive and that it is limited to the tropics. This is not true. There are many sorts of subsistence agriculture which are far from primi-

tive, in the sense in which the word is normally used, and they are found in the subtropics, middle latitudes, and high latitudes, as well as within the tropics. They cannot all be discussed here, but some representative examples will be given.

Along the southern margin of the northern forests in Canada, Sweden, Russia, and other areas are numerous farms which are primarily subsistence farms. Some of them are essentially "pioneer" farms, but many of them have been too well and too long established to be called pioneer undertakings. Although farm equipment and land use practices are comparatively simple, they can hardly be termed primitive. Farms with plows, hayrakes, harrows, and permanent fences, as well as draft animals, sheep, cattle, and poultry, are not primitive, however simple they may appear. The use of new and especially adapted crops, such as particular varieties of white potatoes, as well as the latest information from agricultural experiment stations, render the term further inapplicable. Neither can the long-established and comparatively involved agriculture of such peoples as the Hopi Indians of Arizona be called primitive in any strict sense. Also, near most of the cities of the United States are large numbers of subsistence farms. Although small, they are usually very modern in appearance and farming practices. To be sure, some of them sell a few products, but not on a scale that would warrant their being called commercial farms. Many of them are run by persons who have tired of city life and have set up a family farm economy that allows them to subsist almost entirely from the land.

And, to take an entirely different sort of example, the rice farms of the Orient cannot be termed primitive, even though they represent the ultimate in subsistence agriculture (Fig. 349). These farms, if one may call them such, illustrate agricultural practices which are known to be at least 4,000 years old and are probably much older. Every bit of land that can be used is used to the utmost. Each farm family has on the average only two or two and one-half acres of land to supply it with practically all the essentials of life, as well as to pay taxes. There is little land and there are many mouths to feed. The land is worked and reworked. All possible fertilizer, including the waste products of the human body, is carefully collected and placed on the land. Rice is the king crop generally, but not entirely, because it will yield more food per acre than any other crop. The result is that these Oriental rice farms represent the height of intensive agriculture, even more than do the densely populated farming lands of Europe, whether in Poland or Belgium. Obviously such permanent and highly specialized agriculture is not primitive, despite its ancient character and the absence of modern machinery or even draft animals.

Commercial Agriculture

PLANTATION. Commercial agriculture, like subsistence agriculture, includes many different varieties. For purposes of simplicity, it may be divided into commercial plantation agriculture and commercial farming. The latter includes ranching, fruit growing, and truck gardening.

Plantation production is limited chiefly to the tropics (Fig. 356). It supplies the demand of mid-latitude consumers for such products as bananas, cane sugar, cacao, copra, coffee, tea, rubber, and many others. It is based on foreign capital, scientific knowledge, and, usually, cheap native labor. Not so many years ago the terms "plantation agriculture" and "foreign plantation agriculture" were synonymous. Today, it is necessary to distinguish between them. This is the result of the accumulation, on the part of some natives, of sufficient experience and capital to allow them to engage in plantation production of their own. One example of this is rubber production in the Malay Peninsula and the adjacent islands of the East Indies. Foreign plantations produce by far the greater amount of rubber, and a better grade of rubber, but native plantation production is improving and it is offering more competition each year. The major obstacle to native plantation production is lack of sufficient capital to buy or lease the land, clear and plant the land, fight the weeds and diseases, properly prepare and transport the products, and, far from least, to wait a number of years before the plantation is making returns on the investment. Plantation production is a large undertaking and a considerable gamble. Even if the physical and other difficulties are solved, a plantation may come into production only to find that the market for its product has collapsed and the crops cannot be sold for enough even to meet running expenses, let alone interest on investment.

COMMERCIAL FARMING. Commercial agriculture is very widespread in the subtropics, mid-latitudes, and parts of the high latitudes. It is represented by such areas as the cotton regions of India, the citrus districts of Florida and California, the truck-farming areas and the Corn Belt of the United States (Fig. 328), the Spring Wheat Belt of the United States and Canada, and the dairy region of northwestern Europe. Some varieties, notably truck farming and citrus production, make intensive use of the land and use large amounts of fertilizer. Other varieties, the Spring Wheat Belt of the United States and Canada for example, make very extensive use of the land and little use of fertilizers. Much heavy machinery is used to cultivate and harvest the crops, and land units are very large. Increased production is normally obtained by cultivating more land rather than by using the land already under cultivation more intensively.

MAJOR CROPS

The world's agriculture, whether commercial or subsistence, is based on an extremely large number of crops. Out of all the crops which man raises to feed himself and his animals, there are some which are so important as to be called key crops. The following discussion is devoted to the key crops.

Rice

This crop is the world's chief food. No one knows the exact number of rice eaters in the world, but it is certainly at least half of the earth's more than two billion inhabitants. Most of them live in the densely populated lands of the Orient, although there is a slowly increasing use of rice among the peoples of Africa and Latin America. The great bulk of the world's rice is consumed as rough, unpolished rice. This is fortunate, because the highly polished rice, such as one usually finds in the markets of the United States, has been processed to the point where most of the minerals and vitamins contained in the coatings have been removed. A diet based on polished rice is greatly deficient; one based on rough rice is less deficient than has commonly been supposed. If it were not, most of Asia's millions would not be able to exist.

The major part of the world's rice is grown in the tropical and subtropical monsoon lands of southeast Asia and the East Indies (Fig. 361). While several types of rice are grown, most of the varieties are cultivated in flooded fields called "paddies" (Fig. 349). This accounts for the designation of "wet-land" or "paddy" rice, as opposed to "dry rice" which is grown in the same manner as wheat or other "dry" grains. As the world's chief subsistence crop, nearly all rice is consumed within local producing areas. Only a few areas are able to produce a surplus. No matter how much rice the major regions grow, even two crops a year in climatically favored sections, there is barely enough, or, in some sections and in particular years, not enough. The chief surplus regions are in southern Burma, Thailand, and French Indochina. From these regions, the rice moves mainly to India, China, and Japan. That these regions are able to produce more than they need not only reflects excellent physical conditions for rice production, but also the fact that they are not as densely populated as other rice lands of the Orient. In all the Oriental rice regions, surplus or not, the way of life is so closely entwined with rice, including preparation of the land, planting of the shoots, harvesting, and threshing, that the entire culture of the people is commonly referred to as a "rice culture."

Corn

As either a subsistence or a commercial crop, corn has wide geographical range. From its original homeland in the high slopes and basins of the northern Andes and the Central American Highlands, it has spread over much of the Americas and, since the days of Columbus, to many other sections of the world. Today, it is cultivated from the equator to the margins of the northern forests and from sea level to altitudes, in the tropics, as high as eight or nine thousand feet. Moreover, corn is raised in the regions of heaviest rainfall and,

361   *ALL MAJOR rice-producing areas of the world are in southeastern Asia and the East Indies. Despite this fact, China and India, the main producers of rice, must import large quantities in order to help feed their many millions of inhabitants.*

under irrigation, in the driest deserts. There are many varieties and new ones are being developed from time to time. Each variety represents some adaptation to length of growing season, amount and distribution of rainfall, resistance to disease, or some other critical physical element.

Corn has a versatility which makes it one of the most important of all crops. It will grow and yield at least a small crop under even adverse conditions of soil and climate. Under favorable conditions, it produces heavy yields. After it is grown, it can be easily stored for either short or long periods; thus the yields of bountiful years can be used as "food in the bank" for lean years. Moreover,

it is a nutritious food for both man and his livestock. As a human food it is prepared and consumed in many forms, ranging from corn on the cob, parched corn, stewed corn, and corn meal, to hominy and special breakfast foods. From it also are made corn starch, corn syrup, corn oil, and industrial alcohol, as well as whisky. The leaves, stalks, and kernels furnish fodder for animals, and the cobs furnish corncob pipes.

Corn has played a significant role in the history of the United States. It has been said that the westward movement of our people was based on "corn and jerky." To a measurable extent this is true. The explorers and scouts carried dried corn and jerky, or dried meat, in leather pouches. These foods, plus water, enabled them to travel freely for long distances. The settlers, pushing west with their animals, wagons, and meager household furnishings, carried corn with them, and it was the initial crop to be planted on their wilderness farms. Usually it was first planted in small hills scattered among girdled trees. Corn, as a first-season crop, gave them food for themselves and their livestock. Augmented by fish and game, it provided them with a toehold while the farms were being soundly established.

The major corn-producing regions are not located just anywhere that corn will grow. They are in the regions of most favorable climate and richest soils, admitting that there are several areas well suited to corn where population is so dense that other crops of still higher yield, such as rice or potatoes, take precedence. The chief commercial regions occur in association with either the Humid Continental climate with hot summers (Dfa, Dwa) or the Humid Subtropical climate

(Fig. 362). The best corn soils are the black prairie, brown forest, or recent alluvial soils. When corn can compete economically with wheat, it yields heavily on chernozems. With proper soil management practices, commercial yields also are obtained from the yellow forest soils.

The Corn Belt of the United States (Fig. 363) leads the world. It has no close rival, either in size, yields, or the number of uses to which the corn is put. Despite the large production, little corn is exported, mainly because the Corn Belt is an animal-producing belt. About 85 per cent of the corn is used to feed and fatten livestock, chiefly hogs and cattle. Contrariwise, the Argentine corn region, producing far less, is the leading exporting region of the world. It has considerable good cornland, but fewer people and, more significantly, fewer animals to feed.

The United States Corn Belt, an area as large as France, extends from central Ohio to western Kansas and from the latitude of the Ohio Valley to that of the southern Great

MAJOR COMMERCIAL CORN REGIONS
(Areas of heavy production are shown in solid black)
← Major exports

362　*THIS MAP shows only the major commercial corn-producing regions; it does not show all regions where corn is grown. The chief commercial corn regions are in the United States, Argentina, and southern Europe. In world exports of corn, Argentina has no real rival.*

Lakes region. On the north it merges with the Hay and Dairy Belt, on the south with the Corn and Winter Wheat Belt, and on the west with the Winter Wheat Belt and part of the Spring Wheat Belt. To the east it is limited by the Appalachian Uplands. In general, the northern and western boundaries are climatic and the southern and eastern reflect soil and landform conditions. The northern limit is essentially the isotherm of 70° F. average for the three summer months. The western limit, near the 102nd meridian, is approximately the 8-inch summer season rainfall line. South and east of these two lines occurs the hot, "muggy and showery" weather which is so excellent for corn and so difficult for human beings. The eastern limit marks the beginning of the higher, rougher, and more poorly soiled Appalachian country; the southern, the rougher, more dissected lands of the Corn and Winter Wheat Belt. Here, too, soils are poorer, as one progresses from the glacial soils on the north to the nonglacial and often thin and stony soils in the south. Corn yields are higher in the western two-thirds of the Corn Belt, where the soils are mainly those of the prairie and prairie margin. These rich, dark soils, from Illinois to Iowa and Kansas are truly "the land where the tall corn grows."

The remaining major corn regions of the world lie in the northeastern part of the Argentine Pampa, the Hungarian Plain, the Walachian Plain of Romania and part of the U.S.S.R., and the portion of China where the Yangtze River and the Hwang Ho most closely approach each other (Fig. 362). Lesser, but still important, regions are in southeastern United States, the Mexican Plateau, southeastern Brazil, southern Europe, southeastern Africa, and parts of India and the East Indies. Beyond these are the countless minor corn-growing spots, such as a rain-forest farm in Brazil, a corn patch in the high Andes, or a farm in the forest of northern Minnesota.

World trade in corn is fairly simple (Fig. 362). Argentina, the only major exporter, ships most of its corn to the British Isles and other parts of western Europe. Small amounts of Hungarian and Romanian corn flow to western Europe or to the Soviet Union, and still smaller quantities move from the United States to Europe and from the East Indies to India and Japan. Actually, most of the world's corn "stays home" and most of it is fed to animals.

Wheat

The world's many varieties of wheat are descended from a cereal, or kernel-producing, grass which originally grew wild somewhere in Asia Minor. Following its domestication, it spread slowly to several different sections of Asia, Europe, and northern Africa. Kernels of wheat have been found in the wrappings of mummies from the tombs of ancient Egypt. Since 1500 it has been introduced to the Americas, South Africa, Australia, and New Zealand. Today, the kinds of wheat are very numerous; many of them are strains recently developed by plant scientists for regions of short growing season or low rainfall. Other new varieties resistant to wheat diseases have also been created.

Most of the world's wheat is grown in the mid-latitudes; lesser amounts are produced in the subtropics and the equatorward portion of the high latitudes. Wheat rarely is grown in the tropics, except in a few tropical highlands and a few small sections of irrigated lands in the tropical deserts (Fig. 364). It does better than competing crops on the dry margins in the mid-latitudes and for this reason the major commercial wheat regions tend to correlate with the cooler Semiarid (BS) and the dry-margin portions of the Moist, Mild Winter (C) and Moist, Severe Winter (D) climates. Large amounts, although not enough to meet requirements or create a surplus, are grown under distinctly humid conditions in western Europe, where the climate is Mid-latitude

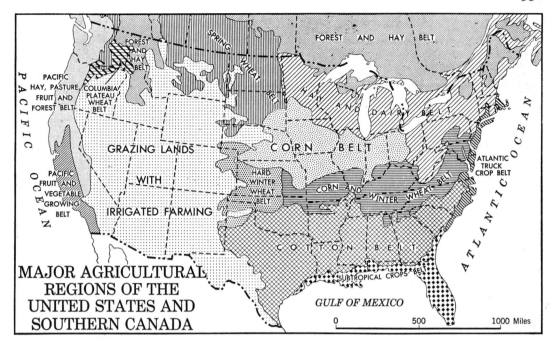

MAJOR AGRICULTURAL REGIONS OF THE UNITED STATES AND SOUTHERN CANADA

363   *THE COMBINATION of large area and wide variety in physical factors has allowed man to develop extensive and varied agricultural regions in the United States.*

Marine (Cfb). Per-acre yields there actually are higher than in the wheat belts of the United States and Canada; this is so by reason not only of climate, but of intensive agricultural practices. The commercial, surplus-producing regions of today correlate chiefly with the dark grassland soils, the black prairie and chernozem soils. The latter is said to be the best wheat soil that the earth has to offer, and it accounts for much of the agricultural wealth of such nations as the United States, Canada, U.S.S.R., and Argentina.

All the varieties of wheat may be grouped in two categories: spring wheat and winter wheat. Winter wheat is planted in the fall, grows during the winter and spring, and is harvested in late spring or early summer. Obviously, the winter wheats can be grown only in those regions which have a mild or a not-too-long-and-severe winter. Spring wheat, grown farther poleward, is planted in the spring, grows during the summer, and is harvested in the fall. Bushel for bushel, most of

the world's wheat is winter wheat, although many of the highest-grade commercial wheats are spring wheats. Because of the wide range of harvest times for winter and spring varieties, wheat, even in a given hemisphere, comes onto the market over a number of months. In the United States, for example, winter wheats grown farthest south are harvested as early as May and spring wheats grown farthest north are harvested as late as September. Thus, the United States wheat harvest lasts from May to September. Argentine wheat, grown in the Southern Hemisphere where the seasons, as compared to the Northern Hemisphere, are reversed, is harvested from early December to early February. A study of Table 23 will indicate that the combination of spring and winter wheats and the two-hemisphere production results in at least some wheat coming onto the world market in every month of the year.

Another useful twofold classification of wheat that should be noted is hard wheat and

Table 23   SEASONS OF WHEAT HARVEST IN ELEVEN COUNTRIES

Wheat is harvested somewhere in the world during each month of the year, although the total harvest period for the chief wheat-exporting nations is about six and one-half months.

	Jan.	Feb.	Mar.	Apr.	May	June	July	Aug.	Sept.	Oct.	Nov.	Dec.
CANADA							▨	▨				
ARGENTINA	▨											▨
AUSTRALIA	▨											▨
UNITED STATES						▨	▨	▨				
U. S. S. R.							▨	▨	▨			
CHILE		▦										
INDIA			▦	▦	▦							
SPAIN					▦	▦						
ROMANIA						▦	▦	▦	▦			
UNITED KINGDOM								▦	▦	▦	▦	
BOLIVIA											▦	▦

▨ Chief wheat exporters   ▦ Other selected wheat producers

soft wheat. There are many varieties of each, and some are spring wheats and some are winter wheats. In general, there are more soft wheats in the winter wheat regions and more hard wheats in the spring wheat areas; probably because of climatic requirements more than anything else, because the hard wheats need drier climates and the soft wheats need more humid climates. In comparison to soft wheats, the hard wheats have less starch and more protein, and make "stronger" dough.

Unlike corn, wheat's major use is as food for humans, although small quantities are fed to livestock, particularly poultry. Most wheat eventually becomes bread, although appreciable quantities are used for macaroni, spaghetti, pastries, and special foods, such as breakfast foods, meat substitutes, and imitation coffee. Particularly in the United States, wheat flours are very highly refined; so much so that it has been found wise to add vitamins and minerals to replace losses incident to high refinement. In many countries, whole wheat flour, producing a coarser, darker bread, is most common. Such bread may be less attractive, but it is much more nutritious. Actu-

ally, even though we in the United States are hardly able to appreciate it, only a small proportion of the world's inhabitants can afford bread or other products made from wheat. Wheat bread is unknown to most of the millions of the Orient, as well as to many who live in Africa and Latin America. Even in northern Europe, with all its wheat, the major bread is a coarse, dark and heavy, rye bread.

The chief wheat-producing nations are the United States, Canada, and Argentina, in the Western Hemisphere, and the U.S.S.R., India, China, and Australia, in the Eastern Hemisphere (Fig. 364). In some years, the U.S.S.R. leads all countries; usually it is in second place, not far behind the United States. The bulk of the wheat of the U.S.S.R. is grown in the southern part of the Russian Plain, in a large triangular area which has its base on the northern shore of the Black Sea and its apex at approximately the southern end of the Urals.

The United States wheat belts are four in number. One of them shares part of the land of the Corn Belt and of the Corn and Winter Wheat Belt (Fig. 363). Production is greatest in the area between the Mississippi and Lake Erie, usually called the Soft Winter Wheat Belt. Just to the west, and lying mainly in Kansas and western Missouri, is the Hard Winter Wheat Belt. To the north, chiefly in the Dakotas and southwestern Minnesota, is the Spring Wheat Belt. The fourth region lies in the Northwest, in the portion of the Columbia Basin east of the Cascades, mainly in southeastern Washington and northeastern Oregon. This region is ordinarily referred to as the Columbia Plateau Wheat Belt. Most of Canada's wheat is produced in the Spring Wheat Belt of the Prairie Provinces, chiefly in southern Manitoba, Saskatchewan, and Alberta. Argentina's main region is the famous Wheat Crescent which arcs around the western margin of the Pampa. Australian wheat is grown mainly in the Murray-Darling Basin, inland from Adelaide. Another region lies in the southwest, in the area between Perth and Albany. The wheat of India is concentrated in the north-

west, in the part of the Indus Plain known as the Punjab. China's wheat region occurs in the North China Plain and immediately adjacent territory. Unlike the other wheat regions noted above, China's, despite heavy production, is not a surplus region.

The major wheat-exporting nations (Fig. 364), in order, are Canada, Argentina, Australia, the United States, and the U.S.S.R. The last, although probably the leading producer, ranks low in the sale of wheat to other nations. It will be noted that the major sellers of wheat are those countries which have extensive areas of "wheat soils" and "wheat climates" (in which other crops have, so far, not competed successfully with wheat), as well as relatively sparse populations.

The heaviest flow of export wheat goes from Canada and the Argentine to the British Isles and western Europe. Other major flows are from Australia and the United States. Lesser flows are from India and the U.S.S.R., also to western Europe.

GENERAL PATTERN OF
WHEAT PRODUCTION
(Areas of heavy production are shown in solid black)
◀ Major exports

364 *THE CHIEF wheat-raising areas of the world. Note that wheat is primarily a mid-latitude crop and that the most extensive wheat regions are in the Northern Hemisphere. In general, the largest areas of* heaviest *production are in semiarid lands or the drier margins of humid lands.*

Other Grains

Rice, corn, and wheat are the key grain crops of the world. However, there are several other important grains; locally, any one of them may be of first importance. Chief among the other grains are rye, oats, and barley.

Rye production is largely concentrated in Europe (Fig. 365). It can be successfully carried on in areas where soil is too poor and climate too cold and damp for wheat. It is the source of the "black bread" which is basic in the diet of most of Europe's poorer classes. Oats, consumed by both animals and humans, are apt to be king in regions of poor soil and cool, very damp climate, even though grown in greater quantity in more favorable areas. The chief oat areas are in northwestern Europe, northern United States, and southern Canada (Fig. 365). Barley has the greatest climatic tolerance of any of the important grains. It is raised, in varying amounts, from the tropical deserts into the northern forests, but heaviest production occurs in Europe and in north central United States (Fig. 365). It is an important hay and grain crop for animals, an important human food, and some varieties are used for the making of malt. International trade in rye, oats, and barley is small; this is especially true of rye and oats.

Vegetables

The production of vegetables is so widespread and so much a part of many different agricultural systems that it is difficult to be specific about it. Vegetables appear in the "migratory" fields of the Amazon Basin and the Congo Basin, in small plots on tropical plantations, on the dikes which separate paddy fields in the rice lands, on the typical Corn Belt farm, in the forest-bordered farm of Canada or northern New England, and in many other areas. Some even are raised in underground greenhouses in a few places in the tundras of the Soviet Union.

Truly commercial production of vegetables occurs mainly in the vicinity of large cities, chiefly the large cities of the United States and Europe. Other commercial vegetable production, particularly in the United States, occurs in areas appreciably removed from large cities, but tied in very closely by means of rapid transportation which allows fresh vegetables to be placed quickly on city markets. In addition, there are many vegetable farms, whether near or far from urban areas, whose products are locally canned, quick-frozen, or otherwise processed before being sent to market. It is interesting to note that truck farms near large cities represent a very intensive use of the land, comparable to that in the densely populated areas of the Orient. Where climate allows, more than one crop is produced each year, the land is highly tilled, and large amounts of fertilizer are used. Even where the climate is humid, irrigation is often used to prevent crop failure because of a dry spell and to force the growth of the vegetables. Normally one thinks of irrigation as part of wet-land rice culture or the growth of crops in arid or semiarid regions, but it is a significant part of commercial vegetable growing in humid lands as well.

In the United States, vegetables grown only for home consumption are found chiefly to the east of the 20-inch rainfall line (Fig. 366). They are most concentrated in the area which extends from the northern part of the Cotton Belt to the southern Great Lakes and from the Mississippi to the Atlantic seaboard. In the Northwest, there are local concentrations in the Puget Sound and Willamette Valley lowlands.

Vegetables raised to sell occupy much less land than those raised for home use. Most of the commercial vegetable districts are located within or on the edge of the most densely populated part of the United States (Fig. 366). Others are located in the South and in the valleys and basins of California. These

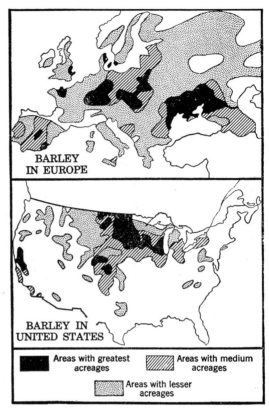

365   *MAJOR production areas of rye, oats, and barley.*

southern areas, with their subtropical climates, are able to place vegetables on the northeastern markets long before locally grown ones are available. They enjoy a lucrative off-season business. This is particularly true of the California truck districts, many of which can supply fresh vegetables all winter long.

Fruits

TROPICAL FRUITS. Within the tropical regions, with their perennial growing season, a wide variety of fruits is produced. Most of them, whether wild or cultivated, are found in the tropical humid regions, but others occur in oasis agriculture in tropical dry lands. Humid tropical fruits include coconuts, breadfruit, mangoes, oranges, and bananas. Those raised in tropical oases include dates, oranges, lemons, apricots, and grapes. With few exceptions, tropical fruits are subsistence rather than commercial products. Some coconuts are exported, but most of the commercial coconuts are shipped in the form of dried coconut meat, known as copra. Copra is an important source of vegetable oil for soaps, cosmetics, salad oils, and margarine. Copra cake is also used as a feed in regions of dairy cattle specialization. Major copra production areas are in the East Indies, particularly Indonesia and the Philippines. The oil palm,

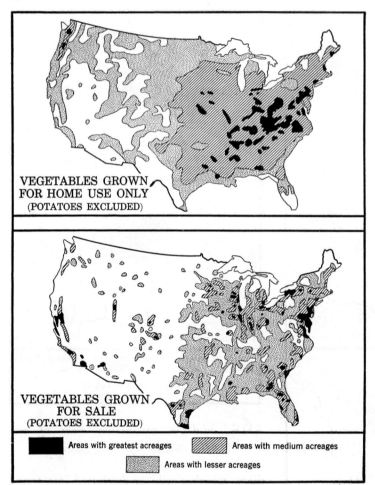

VEGETABLES GROWN
FOR HOME USE ONLY
(POTATOES EXCLUDED)

VEGETABLES GROWN
FOR SALE
(POTATOES EXCLUDED)

Areas with greatest acreages　　Areas with medium acreages

Areas with lesser acreages

366

THE GENERAL pattern *of vegetable production in the United States.*

also a tropical fruit tree, competes with coconut oil in mid-latitude markets. It bears a small, soft fruit, and oil is obtained both from the fleshy outer part and from the kernel. Chief production regions are along and near the shores of the Gulf of Guinea and in the East Indies.

Of all the tropical fruits, the banana is the one which is the most important in mid-latitude food markets. The banana long has been a major food in southern Asia, to which region it is native. More recently it has become an important food in most of the world's wet, tropical areas. However, its commercial production, almost entirely on foreign plantations, is very limited, both geographically (Fig. 367) and as to particular varieties. There

are many varieties of bananas, some edible and some not. The major edible variety of commercial bananas is the large yellow kind, the only variety commonly found in mid-latitude markets. It is grown almost entirely in hot, wet lowlands of the New World, particularly on the shores of the Caribbean. Central America, chiefly Honduras, produces more than half of all commercial bananas. Other important producers are Mexico, Jamaica, Colombia, and Cuba (Fig. 367). Most of the plantations are American owned and operated, and slightly more than half of all commercial bananas are sold in the United States. The remainder, chiefly from Jamaica and other West Indies islands, are sold in the British Isles, France, and Germany.

SUBTROPICAL FRUITS. The subtropical regions, both humid and dry, are areas of many, rather than few, fruits. These regions, in addition to fruits of their own, have become the home of fruits introduced from the tropics and the mid-latitudes. Because the subtropics have a winter season, however mild it may be, certain mid-latitude fruits, used to winters, can grow there. Likewise, the long, hot summers, coupled with no more than mild winters, allow certain tropical fruits to grow. Common subtropical fruits are oranges, grapefruit, lemons, peaches, apricots, plums, including prune plums, olives, figs, and grapes. One hears a great deal, for example, of Spanish olives, Georgia peaches, Florida grapefruit, and California oranges and grapes. Most of the commercial subtropical fruits are produced in the United States and along the Mediterranean shores of Europe, Asia Minor, and northern Africa. Lesser amounts are grown in the subtropics of the Southern Hemisphere, as in Middle Chile, the La Plata region of Argentina, southeastern Australia, and southern Africa. The subtropical portion of Asia, with its many millions of mouths to feed, cannot afford to use very much land and energy to grow fruits. From the large number of commercial subtropical fruits, the citrus fruits, olives, and grapes may be singled out for separate discussion.

Of the many kinds of citrus fruits, oranges, grapefruit, and lemons are most important commercially (Fig. 367). The orange, native to southeastern Asia, was introduced to the Mediterranean Sea region during the fifteenth century. From there it was carried, a bit later, to the New World, as well as to Australia and South Africa. Although many varieties grow in the wet tropics, it is the specially developed varieties of the subtropics which are in most demand on world markets. In

367 COMMERCIAL citrus fruits are produced mainly in regions of Mediterranean and humid subtropical climate. Commercial bananas are grown chiefly in the Caribbean area (inset map) under the hot, wet, tropical rainforest climate.

368 *THE MEDITERRANEAN region has about nine-tenths of the world's olive trees. Nearly all world olive oil exports are from the same region; Spain, Tunisia, Italy, and Algeria account for about 80 per cent.*

fact, the best varieties are grown as far poleward as the orange tree can survive. In such locations, the groves often have to be protected from winter frosts by means of such devices as heaters, smudge pots, or wind-circulating machines. Were it not for man's assistance, the orange would have a slightly smaller latitudinal range than it now has.

The major producing regions are in the Mediterranean countries, the Florida peninsula, and California (Fig. 367). Southern

China is a heavy producer, but not for export. It may come as a surprise that Spain supplies more than half of all export oranges and that its total production is second only to that of the United States. Spanish and other Mediterranean Sea Basin oranges travel to markets in western and northwestern Europe. United States oranges are consumed almost entirely at home, although attempts are being made to increase the export of California oranges. California oranges, especially the navels, are said to be able to stand long shipments because of their thick and relatively tough skins. However, production costs, including irrigation, are much higher than in such countries as Spain, Italy, and Algeria.

Commercial orange production is highly localized within the United States. The major districts are located in central Florida and in the piedmont basins and valleys of southern California and the flanks of the San Joaquin Valley of California. The extreme southern part of Texas is also becoming important. Aided by irrigation, California is able to market oranges the year around. Peak harvests for navel oranges occur in the winter and for

369 *AN OLIVE grove in the Mediterranean region of southern Europe. (Webb, Standard Oil Co. [N. J.])*

GRAPES
MAJOR VINEYARD
AREAS

Areas containing chief
vineyard acreages

Compressed Sinusoidal
equal-area projection

STATUTE MILES

370 *MOST of the world's vineyards are in the Mediterranean region of Europe, or nearby, and most of the grapes are used to make wine. Algeria leads, by far, in wine exports. Greece, Turkey, Australia, and the United States (in that order) dominate world raisin exports. Grape exports (fresh grapes for table use) originate mainly in Spain, Italy, Bulgaria, and the United States. The export raisins and fresh grapes from the United States are from California, chiefly the Central Valley.*

Valencias in the summer. Florida's orange groves, unirrigated, produce only a winter crop. Most of the districts of the world which produce oranges also grow grapefruit and lemons. In the United States, the chief grapefruit districts are in Florida, California, and southern Texas. Also, there are important areas of "desert grapefruit," particularly in the Coachella-Imperial Valley of California and the Salt River Valley of Arizona. United States lemons are grown mainly in the California citrus areas. Italy leads in world production and Spain ranks third, behind the United States.

Olives are typical of the parts of the subtropics with a Mediterranean (Cs) climate. Unlike citrus fruits, they are not adapted to the Humid Subtropical (Cfa) climate. The chief production regions occur on the shores of the Mediterranean Sea (Fig. 368). Although some olives are consumed in pickled form, both green and ripe, the main use is for oil. Olive oil has many uses, from anointing oil, soaps, and cosmetics to salad and cooking oils. It is most important as a food oil, particularly in those countries which do not produce large amounts of animal fats for table and kitchen use. Comparatively small amounts of olives are grown commercially in central Chile and central California. Spain, Tunisia, and Italy account for about 70 per cent of all olive oil exports (Fig. 369).

Grapes, like olives, are admirably suited to the portions of the subtropics with Mediterranean (Cs) climate (Fig. 370). Some species of grapes are grown in mid-latitude re-

371   *APPLE orchards, and little else, cover many square miles of the Yakima and Wenatchee Valleys of Washington. (Washington State Apple Commission, Yakima)*

gions, but most of the commercial grapes are Mediterranean both in origin and in present cultivation areas. There are three main kinds of grapes: table, raisin, and wine. Some varieties can be used for all three purposes, but, as a rule, particular varieties are grown for a single purpose. Again, the main production regions fringe the shores of the Mediterranean Sea. Other important districts occur in California and Middle Chile. There is considerable specialization by individual districts. In California, for example, the small valleys north of San Francisco Bay specialize in wine grapes, the Sacramento area in table grapes, and the Fresno district in raisin grapes. The Fresno district is the leading raisin producer of the world. Similar specialization occurs elsewhere in California, as well as in the other grape regions, whether in Spain or Chile.

MID-LATITUDE FRUITS. Most of us are best acquainted with apples, cherries, peaches, pears, plums, Concord grapes and other fruits which are produced mainly outside of the tropics and subtropics. They, too, are many, rather than few, and are grown to some extent in all mid-latitude regions, including mid-latitude dry lands where irrigation water is available. Apples, represented by many varieties, are most widespread and can be grown farther poleward than the others. Those apples grown for commercial purposes, rather than home consumption alone, come from particular, specialized districts. In the United States, for instance, famous apple districts include the Yakima (Fig. 371) and Wenatchee valleys of Washington, the Lake Ontario shore of New York State, and southern New England. The portion of Wisconsin which lies between Lake Michigan and Green Bay is a famous cherry district. The Hood River Valley of Oregon specializes in pears; the northern Chesapeake Bay region in peaches. Concord grapes, which are particularly susceptible to frost damage, are produced chiefly along the southeastern shore of Lake Michigan and the southern shore of Lake Erie.

Those two sections are so located in relation to water and prevailing wind direction that frost damage is kept at a minimum. As the land warms up in the spring, the cool winds from the lake surfaces keep the air over the land from warming too rapidly; this prevents early blossoming of the grapevines and keeps the blossoms from being "nipped" by spring frosts. Otherwise, the first warm spell would cause the grapes to blossom and spring frosts, occurring after the first warm weather, would damage or totally destroy the crop.

Sugar Cane and Sugar Beets

The tropics and the mid-latitudes together provide the world with its sugar. Practically all the cane sugar is produced in the tropics, with minor amounts in the mildest portion of the subtropics, and all the beet sugar is produced in mid-latitude regions, both humid and dry (Fig. 373). Those sugar beets grown in the dry lands are raised either under irrigation or dry-farming practices, depending on the degree of moisture deficiency locally. Pound for pound, more of the world's sugar is derived from sugar cane, although beet sugar has made tremendous gains in the past half century.

Sugar cane is native to southeastern Asia. It has spread widely to most parts of the humid tropics and to some irrigated sections of the tropical deserts. Its occurrence in a few subtropical locations, as in southern Louisiana, represents its most poleward extension. Sugar cane produces the richest juice in those parts of the tropics where a season of plentiful rain is followed by a season of abundant sunshine and less rain. Thus, despite wide tropical distribution, the major commercial cane regions are found in association with the Savanna (Aw) type of climate. While India leads all nations in production of sugar cane and cane sugar, it is a noncommercial, deficiency area. As noted previously in connection with such commodities as rice and corn in China and

wheat in western Europe, large production does not necessarily mean a surplus, especially where there are many mouths to be fed. The most important commercial cane regions are in the West Indies, East Indies, Philippines, Hawaii, Taiwan, and Brazil. Other major producers are Australia, Peru, Argentina, and Egypt. Peruvian and Egyptian cane are raised under irrigation in hot desert climates; the

372 *A FIELD of sugar beets about ready for harvesting. (U. S. Beet Sugar Association)*

combination of sufficient water and abundant sunshine insures a juice of high sugar content. Cuba (Fig. 374) is the only truly large exporter of cane sugar and Java holds second place. Other major exporters are Hawaii, the Philippines, Puerto Rico, and Taiwan. Nearly all export cane sugar is unrefined and the heaviest movements are primarily to the United States and secondarily to the British Isles. Continental Europe has developed beet sugar production to such a degree that it imports only comparatively small amounts of cane sugar.

The world's sugar beets are grown mainly in a few areas (Fig. 373). The heaviest production is found in a belt extending from the central part of the southern Russian Plain westward through Poland and Germany to northern France, with an offshoot reaching into the Hungarian Plain. The U.S.S.R. leads in production, followed by Germany, France, Poland, and Czechoslovakia. The only other major sugar beet areas are in the United States, chiefly in the western Great Plains, the Salt Lake area, California, and Michigan. Colorado is by far the leading state (Fig. 372). Beet sugar is more expensive to produce than cane sugar and it provides less sugar per acre. However, its "waste" products, the tops and pulp, help to feed domestic animals. Unlike cane sugar, the international flow of beet sugar is geographically restricted; it is limited to the countries of western and central Europe, and even there it is not of great volume. None of it moves far from the districts where it is produced.

373   *BEET SUGAR production is limited mainly to certain mid-latitude areas of the United States and Europe, and there is little international trade in beet sugar. Cane sugar is mainly a crop of the humid tropics and has a very large and important international trade, with most of it moving to the United States and western Europe. India produces more cane sugar than any other nation, yet has none to spare for export. Cuba (first, by far) and Java are the leading surplus producers.*

374 CUTTING *and hauling sugar cane on a Cuban plantation. Judging by the number of short and tall tree stumps still present in the crop area, this is "new cane land." (Eagle from American Sugar Refining Co.)*

Coffee, Tea, and Cacao

Some of the world's agricultural products are used wholly or in part for beverage purposes. Corn is used to make whisky, barley malt to make beer, rice to make rice wine, and so on. Chief among the nonalcoholic beverages are those made from coffee, tea, and cacao. All three are in sufficient demand to place them among the key agricultural commodities.

Coffee was first domesticated in the uplands of Ethiopia and was introduced to Arabia during either the fourteenth or fifteenth century. From Arabia it spread to India and the East Indies. Java became a major producer and this gave rise to the slang expression "a cup of Java." Coffee production in the New World, in Central America, South America, and the West Indies, was greatly encouraged by the inroads of fungus disease in East Indian coffee plantations. The major commercial varieties thrive best in humid tropical uplands which possess rich soils. The largest of such areas occurs in the southern part of the Brazilian Highlands, in the state of São Paulo (Fig. 375). There the combination of a tropical upland climate (see p. 128) and rich "terra rossa" soil has made possible the world's major coffee region. Thanks

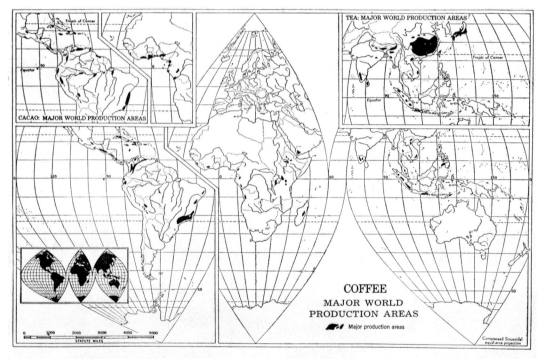

375   *COFFEE is a product of tropical mountain and hill slopes and tropical plateaus: Brazil has no close rival in world commercial coffee production. Tea* (inset map, upper right) *is a hillside crop of the Oriental tropics and subtropics: China is undoubtedly the leading producer, but India and Ceylon account for about two-thirds of tea exports. Cacao* (inset map, upper left) *is a crop of the hot, wet tropics: Africa, especially the Gulf of Guinea region, now produces about two-thirds of world cacao exports.*

chiefly to the São Paulo region, Brazil supplies as much coffee as all the other coffee regions of the world combined. Santos, the major outlet, leads all coffee-exporting ports of the world. Other important centers of coffee production occur in the plateaus and foothills of Colombia and Central America and in the foothills of Java and Sumatra. Colombia ranks second in coffee exports, but it furnishes only about one-fourth as much as Brazil. The United States imports nearly half of all export coffee; other major importers are France and Germany, with the other countries of western Europe taking smaller amounts.

The world's principal tea regions lie in southern and eastern Asia and the East Indies (Fig. 375). Tea is mainly a "hillside" crop

because it cannot be allowed to occupy land that is useful for rice or other essential Oriental foods (Fig. 376). Most of the plantations occur in areas of Subtropical Monsoon (Cw) or Humid Subtropical (Cfa) climate and, in lesser numbers, in areas of Tropical Moist (A) climates. The major export tea region is that of northeastern India, mainly in Assam. India and Ceylon together account for about two-thirds of the world's export tea and Java, Sumatra, China, and Japan for most of the remainder. More than half of the exports go to the British Isles. About one-tenth goes to the United States and lesser amounts chiefly to Canada, Australia, and the U.S.S.R. The Englishman's tea, whether consumed in the homeland or in the Dominions, supports most of the commercial tea business of the Orient.

Cacao is the source of chocolate and cocoa. It differs from tea and coffee in that it is used widely in candies, frostings, cosmetics, and some kinds of soap, as well as a beverage. Cacao is native to tropical America, but most commercial production is now in tropical Africa (Fig. 375). The chief exporter is the Gold Coast, which, with Nigeria and the Ivory Coast, furnishes about 60 per cent of the world supply. In the Americas, Brazil and the Caribbean region supply another 30 per cent. Ecuadorian production, once of major importance, is now very small. Cacao demands a "hothouse" climate; this limits it to the tropical rainforest areas or, at best, to the hottest and wettest margins of the savannas. The United States imports more cacao than any other nation, although western Europe as a whole consumes slightly more.

Cotton

Since about 1800, the world has witnessed a tremendous increase in cotton production. Before that time cotton cloth was very expensive; it was essentially the rich man's cloth. Some kinds of cloth were so costly that only royalty could afford them. An instance of this is corduroy, which means literally "the cloth of the king"; today, we think of it not as the king's cloth, but as the cloth of the workman, the hunter, and the fisherman. The great change was brought about by a series of inventions. Eli Whitney's cotton gin, invented in 1793, enabled the cotton fibers to be plucked more rapidly from the cotton seeds, to which they stubbornly adhere. It became possible for a single machine to "gin" more cotton in a day than a man could in a month. Other inventions, made during the

376 TEA PICKERS on a tea plantation in India. (Empire Tea Bureau, London)

later 1700's, enabled machine spinning and weaving of cotton to displace slow and tedious hand operations.

With cotton in great demand as the "people's cloth," production spread and increased and several regions of the earth became known more for the cultivation of the cotton plant than anything else. Today, there are more pounds of cotton produced than pounds of all other commercial fibers combined. Most of the commercial cotton is grown in Humid Subtropical (Cfa) climates, although important amounts are produced in Savanna (Aw) climates, as in the Deccan of India, in Subtropical Monsoon (Cw) climates, as in China, and in certain Arid (BW) climates under irrigation, as in Egypt and Russian Turkestan (Fig. 377). The greater bulk of the world production is short staple cotton (varieties of cotton with fibers less than one

and one-eighth inches in length); considerably lesser amounts are long staple. The latter is not only longer fiber, but is much silkier; it is used for the more expensive types of cotton cloth and for cordage in the manufacture of automobile tires. One very famous variety is Egyptian long staple.

The major cotton region of the world is the United States Cotton Belt (Fig. 363). Despite increasing competition from other regions, such as the São Paulo area of Brazil, the Cotton Belt still produces nearly as much cotton as all other regions combined (Fig. 378). The combination of relatively cheap and abundant land, cheap labor, and a Humid Subtropical (Cfa) climate enabled the Cotton Belt to become the paramount commercial region. The United States furnishes about 44 per cent of world exports, followed, in order, by India, Egypt, and Brazil. China is

377 *THE UNITED STATES, India, the U.S.S.R., China, Brazil, and Egypt produce most of the world's cotton. Chinese and Soviet Union cotton is consumed at home, but the other producers export large quantities. The United States is far in the lead as a cotton exporter, exporting a little more than India, Egypt, and Brazil combined.*

378

COTTON field and a mechanical picker in the South. Machines help the United States compete with low cost cotton-producing areas. (McCormick-Deering)

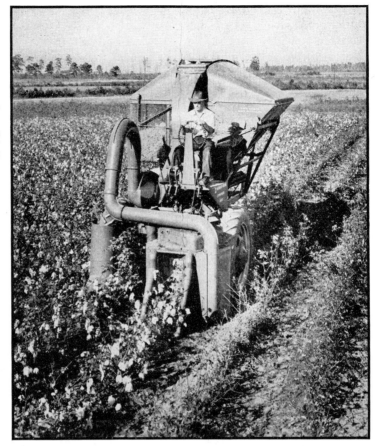

the only major producer which is not an exporter; despite her huge production, she must import cotton from India. United States export cotton goes mainly to England and secondarily to continental Europe and Japan. India's export cotton goes mainly to England and secondarily to Japan and China. Significant in world cotton production is the increase in Brazil and Russian Turkestan. United States producers are already feeling the effects of increasing exports of more cheaply grown Brazilian cotton.

Other Vegetable Fibers

The world's farms and plantations produce a wide variety of vegetable fibers in addition to cotton. Many of these are, so far, mainly of local importance, but some are well-established items in a broad world trade. Chief among the latter are flax, hemp, jute, and sisal.

Flax is grown for two main purposes: oil and fiber. Most of the "oil flax," furnishing linseed oil, is produced in dry areas. Flax used for fiber, mainly linen cloth, is grown in cool, damp regions. The leading fiber flax areas are in Europe, extending from the central Russian Plain and the eastern shore of the Baltic to northern France. Practically all linen cloth is made in the West-European Manufacturing Region.

Hemp is in demand for string, large cords, fishing lines, and thread, and finds important use in the manufacture of carpet and coarse cloth. It is grown mainly in the central part of the southern Russian Plain and from there southwestward as far as Italy. Somewhat smaller production occurs in the North China Plain and Korea.

Jute is grown almost entirely in the Ganges Delta and immediately adjacent sections of the Indian Union and Pakistan, although minor amounts are produced in French Indochina and Taiwan. It is the cheapest of the commercial fibers and is used for burlap bags (gunny sacks), carpet and linoleum base, webbing, and twine. Roughly half of the Indian production is manufactured in mills in and near Calcutta, and Calcutta long has been noted as the world's major jute port.

Sisal is used predominantly as binder twine in the world's major wheat regions. Unlike flax, hemp, or jute, sisal is derived from a drought-resistant plant. The plant is a variety of Spanish dagger. Yucatan produces about two-thirds of the world supply. Its former monopoly has been broken by production in several other regions, located chiefly in the West Indies, East Indies, the Philippines, and east Africa.

In addition to those noted above, there are other commercial vegetable fibers. One of them, Manila hemp, is produced chiefly in the Philippines. Another is kapok, used in pillows, mattresses, and life preservers. This light, resilient, waterproof fiber is obtained from the down of a tree produced commercially chiefly in Java, the Philippines, and India. It has its widest use in the United States and western Europe. Still another is ramie, sometimes called China grass. The fiber from this plant is highly adaptable for both coarse and fine cloths, as well as threads, twines, and ropes. It is waterproof and very durable. As far as physical requirements are concerned, it could be produced widely in warm, humid regions. However, labor requirements, both for cultivation and process-

379   ABOUT 98 per cent of the world's natural rubber is grown on plantations in southeastern Asia and adjacent islands. Export flow is chiefly to the United States and western Europe. The United States alone consumes about half of all the world's natural rubber.

ing of the fiber, are such as to limit its production almost entirely to its native areas in South China. It is possible that cheaper and more effective methods of growing and preparation may allow ramie to compete in the future with the major commercial fibers, even cotton.

Rubber

When Columbus came in contact with the Indians of the West Indies, he found them playing with a ball that bounced. This was the white man's introduction to rubber. During the following three hundred years rubber was little more than a curiosity. In the early 1800's it had some use as erasers and a Scotsman by the name of Macintosh learned how to apply it to cloth to make raincoats. Then, in 1839, Goodyear discovered how to vulcanize rubber and thus render it simultaneously pliable, durable, and nonsticky. However, not until the coming of the automobile and the widespread use of rubber-insulated electric wiring did demand become large. Today, rubber has myriad uses, ranging from insulation, shock pads, and battery cases to mattings, cushions, and wearing apparel, but it is the use in the automobile, especially for tires, that consumes the greater part of the production.

Except during World War II, when Japanese forces occupied the main producing regions, commercial rubber has been almost entirely natural rather than synthetic. So far, the natural vegetable rubber can be produced more cheaply than the synthetic, made from coal, petroleum, or alcohol, and it is still superior for certain purposes, although the synthetic rubber is more resistant to grease and abrasion. Following World War II, most of the synthetic rubber factories were placed in "stand-by" status for emergencies, and vegetable rubber regained much of its former control of the world rubber market.

In 1900, all commercial rubber was wild and nearly all of it came from the Amazon Basin. Most of it was obtained by tapping a native tree of the rainforest, the *Hevea brasiliensis*. At present, less than 3 per cent of commercial rubber is wild. It is collected partly in the Amazon Basin and partly from the rainforests of Africa. The latter region furnishes rubber juice, or latex, derived from vines and is referred to as liana rubber. The remaining 97 to 98 per cent of present commercial rubber is plantation grown and is obtained from southeastern Asia and the East Indies (Fig. 379).

The Far Eastern plantation production began with the introduction of hevea from the Amazon. In 1910, Brazil still held a rubber monopoly, producing nearly 90 per cent. By 1920, plantation rubber accounted for about 90 per cent and by 1930 nearly all. Plantation rubber is produced under scientific methods and it is a cleaner and higher quality product (Fig. 380). Most of the plantations are for-

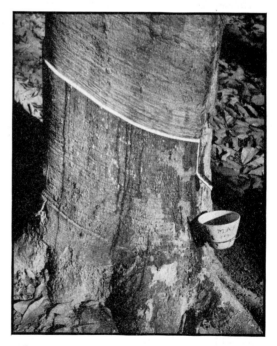

380 *NEW "tapping cut" on a rubber tree in a Malayan plantation. (U. S. Rubber Co.)*

eign owned and operated, although there is increasing production from those owned and operated by natives. The major advantage of the Far East over the Amazon or the Congo lies mainly in the availability of cheap labor, plus, of course, the fact that production is so well established there that new production elsewhere faces great difficulty in breaking into the market. The southern portion of the Malay Peninsula, under British control, is the chief producer. This region, combined with the Dutch-controlled regions in Sumatra, Borneo, and Java, produces the bulk of the world's rubber. Lesser production occurs in Ceylon, southern India, Burma, Thailand, and French Indochina. Singapore is the major collecting and export center and London is the chief financial center. The heaviest flow of export rubber goes primarily to the United States and secondarily to western Europe, including the British Isles. The United States normally uses as much rubber as all the rest of the world combined. The chief reason for this is the automobile industry with its demands for literally millions of tires. Attempts of American interests to grow rubber on plantations in Liberia and the Philippines (Firestone interests) and in the Amazon (Ford interests) have not been successful. Evidently the main problem has been that of labor, accompanied in some instances by diseases which attack the hevea trees.

So much of commercial vegetable rubber production comes from the hevea tree that other sources, however much publicized, are negligible. Some is obtained by crushing a sagebrushlike, xerophytic plant known as guayule, grown in the dry lands of northern Mexico; some is derived from another dryland plant in the Ceara area of the eastern "shoulder" of Brazil; and some from trees, other than the hevea, in the Amazon Basin. And, as mentioned above, small amounts of liana rubber are obtained from Africa. There is no indication, so far, that any other rainforest plant will threaten the supremacy of hevea, nor that any plant of the subtropics or mid-latitudes will threaten the production from the rainy tropics.

Tobacco

This is the only one of the key agricultural commodities which is, so to speak, nonessential. The others, with the debatable exceptions of tea and coffee, are either essential foodstuffs, essential raw materials for manufacturing, or both. Despite its luxury nature, tobacco is grown in many regions and it enters importantly into agricultural trade.

There are many varieties of commercial tobacco, most of which fall into the categories of cigar tobacco or cigarette tobacco. The tremendous increase in the use of cigarettes has boomed tobacco production and created a multimillion-dollar manufacturing industry as well, particularly in the United States. Tobacco is grown in the tropics, subtropics, and mid-latitudes, depending on specific varieties, and it occupies fields which range in size from "tobacco patches" to large plantations. Even where grown in small fields and in small amounts it is an important cash crop, furnishing either the major cash income or an important addition to income derived from other crops or pursuits.

Because of the many varieties, tobacco has a very wide spread climatically (Fig. 381). The St. Lawrence Valley represents tobacco's farthest poleward extension in the Americas as southern Sweden does in the Old World. In contrast, Sumatran production is virtually on the equator. Similarly, tobacco is grown in many different types of soils, ranging from deep loams to light sands. Some of the best cigarette tobaccos, where the demand is largely for light-colored, aromatic leaf, are grown on soils which naturally are light and shallow.

India, China, and the United States produce nearly equal amounts of tobacco; combined, they raise about two-thirds of all tobacco. The chief districts are widely scattered

TOBACCO
MAJOR PRODUCTION
AREAS

Major production area

Compressed Sinusoidal
equal-area projection

381 *INDIA grows more tobacco than any other nation, China possibly excepted, and United States production is nearly as great as India's—the three together grow about two-thirds of the world's tobacco. The United States has no close rival in tobacco exports, exporting about 40 per cent of all tobacco that enters foreign trade.*

in India and China; in the United States they are concentrated in a belt which runs from southern Ohio through Kentucky to northwestern Tennessee and in the Virginia-Carolinas section east of the Appalachians. Another major district extends from southern Georgia into northern Florida; and lesser districts, devoted to dark cigar tobacco, occur in the Connecticut Valley and southern Wisconsin. In addition to the major producing nations, appreciable amounts are grown in the U.S.S.R., western and southeastern Europe, Turkey, Brazil, and Java. Other production is widely scattered.

The United States is by far the leading exporter, furnishing nearly 40 per cent of the international flow. The remaining exports, with no more than 10 per cent from any one country, come mainly from Java, Greece, Bulgaria, Turkey, Brazil, and Cuba. It will be noted that, except for the United States, the leading producers are not leading exporters. For export tobacco the British Isles and western Europe are the leading consumers. The United States imports some tobacco from Turkey and southeastern Europe, chiefly for cigarette blends, and some from Java and Cuba and other West Indian islands, chiefly as cigars or cigar filler and wrapper.

ANIMAL HUSBANDRY

No one knows when man first learned to tame wild animals as sources of food, materials for clothing and shelter, beasts of burden, and for companionship. Certainly it was tens of thousands of years ago. Most of the world's domestic animals were first tamed somewhere in the heart of Asia and in northern Asia Minor. Today the distribution of livestock is extremely wide. It includes the reindeer of the tundra, the water buffalo of the Oriental tropics, the many cattle, sheep, and other animals of the mid-latitudes and subtropics, as well as the highland-dwelling yak of Tibet and the llama and alpaca of the Andes. There are few parts of the present-day, permanently inhabited world where animals of some sort have not been put to active use by human beings.

Domestic animals vary greatly in size, ranging from small fowl to hogs, cattle, horses, camels, and elephants. Domestic animals are found in greatest number in the more densely settled agricultural regions, but they use the largest amounts of land in areas of sparse population, mainly in dry lands, savannas, and tundras. Where population is extremely dense, and, at the same time, supported almost entirely by agriculture, only the smaller domestic animals can be maintained. Examples are the scavenger hogs and chickens of China. India, on the other hand, has more cattle than any other region, yet it has practically no "meat cattle" industry. The reason lies in religion. The bulk of the population is Hindu and cattle are sacred to them. The millions of cattle contribute to the overcrowding of India; they seem to be everywhere, whether in rural areas or in city streets and temples of worship. However, the cattle do furnish some milk and many are used as beasts of burden and, when they die, as a source of hides.

Domestic animals, like crops, are raised either for subsistence or for commerce. Subsistence animal industry usually is termed nomadic herding; the production of animals and animal products for sale usually is termed commercial animal husbandry. The latter includes commercial grazing, the feeding of animals on farms and in feed lots, and dairy production.

Nomadic Herding

Nomadic herding affects tremendous areas, but relatively few persons. Also, the number of animals and the amount of products obtained are small when compared with those of commercial animal husbandry. Nomadic herding, because it is migratory, demands great space. With the world a bit pressed for area suitable for crops, nomadic herding is confined to regions which are essentially nonagricultural. When human ingenuity renders formerly nonagricultural land capable of crop production, or when the stage of settlement develops from extensive to more intensive land use, migratory herding gives way.

CHIEF REGIONS. Most of the areas of migratory grazing are in cold lands or dry lands (Fig. 352). Their correspondence to most of the regions of Polar (E) and Dry (B) climates is striking, just as it is to the regions of tundra grass and steppe and desert grass supported by those climates. Within the dry land portions, the areas of migratory grazing are more likely to occur in the Semiarid (BS) climates and steppe grass than they are in the drier Arid (BW) climates and the sparser desert grass and desert shrub.

In two major regions of the earth the migratory herdsman and his flocks and herds dominate the geographical scene. One is the Eurasian tundra and certain parts of the American tundra, a one-animal economy, based on the reindeer. The other is the vast dry belt which extends from the Atlantic shore of northern Africa across Asia Minor and the heart of Asia to the plains of Manchuria. This is a multi-animal economy, based on such animals as goats, sheep, cattle, horses, and camels.

REINDEER ECONOMY. Reindeer are native to the Eurasian tundra and it is only in the past half century that they have been introduced to parts of the American tundra, in northern and western Alaska and in the Mackenzie

Delta and adjacent sections (Fig. 352). The Eskimos, primarily fishermen and hunters, have not taken readily to the herdsman's way of life and its perennial responsibilities. Quite to the contrary, the native groups of northern Europe and Asia have lived "for and by" their animals for many centuries.

The reindeer is a most useful and likable animal. Its docility and its ability to live on the tundra, whether the frozen tundra of the coldest season or the "mushy" tundra of the warmer period, make it easy to care for. From it are obtained food, clothing, shelter, and transportation. Live animals furnish milk, part of which is used to make cheese; dead animals furnish lean meat, fat, and blood, as well as skins for tents and certain clothing, and sinews and small bones for thread and needles. When the time comes to move, as it does so often in a land of scant and slow-growing pasturage, reindeer carry the family goods on their backs or pull them on crude "drags." Moving is no great chore, because possessions are, and must be, few and simple.

MULTI-ANIMAL ECONOMY. Within the second major area of the pastoral nomads (Fig. 352) the way of life is based on a comparatively large variety of animals, not only for the area as a whole, but within individual sections. Goats, furnishing milk, cheese, meat, hair, and skins, are most numerous in northwest Africa, western Asia Minor, and the Pamir Highlands. They are able to live in the sections of roughest terrain and scantiest feed. There is a saying to the effect that, "Where cattle can't live, sheep can; where sheep can't live, goats can; and where goats can't live, nothing can." Although an exaggeration, the saying contains a great deal of truth. Sheep, supplying wool, as well as mutton, have wide distribution, with more of them in Russian Turkestan than in other sections. The sections possessing the more abundant and nutritious feeds support cattle. Cattle are more numerous in the cooler portions; they are not commonly found in the African and Asia Minor portions. The great mountain arcs which comprise the Himalayas, Kunluns, Tian Shans, Altais and include, in the southern part, the Tibetan Plateau are the homeland of the yak. The yak can be ridden, used to carry burdens, pull carts, and supply meat, milk, and wool. It is very sturdy and well adapted to cold, scant feed, and high altitudes. However, it cannot live in lowlands and is seldom seen below five thousand feet. Horses are numerous and used primarily for riding, whether in traveling or in herding other animals. In some sections they furnish meat and hides, as well as mare's milk. Some of the finest riding horses in the world have been developed in this area, particularly in Arabia. In the driest and sandiest sections, whether parts of Gobi, Russian Turkestan, Arabia, or Sahara, are many camels. The ability of the camel to travel well in sand and go long distances without water or food makes it a very useful animal for peoples who must "follow the feed" and often make long journeys from one water hole to another.

Even more than the reindeer herdsmen, the nomads of central Asia, Asia Minor, and northern Africa, must be on the move. When and where feed is especially scanty, they must move day after day. Otherwise, their rude encampments may stay in one place for days or weeks at a time (Fig. 316). In the warmest and driest sections, they literally "follow the showers," which bring short-lived grasses for the animals to feed on. In some sections, mainly in central Asia, they move northward during the summer and southward during the winter. Where the grazing lands are associated with mountains, herds and flocks are driven to alpine pastures in the summer and brought back to the warmer and less stormy lowlands in the winter. Such migration thus has a vertical as well as a horizontal aspect and it represents a rather nice adjustment to seasonal atmospheric changes and to the distribution of vegetation types.

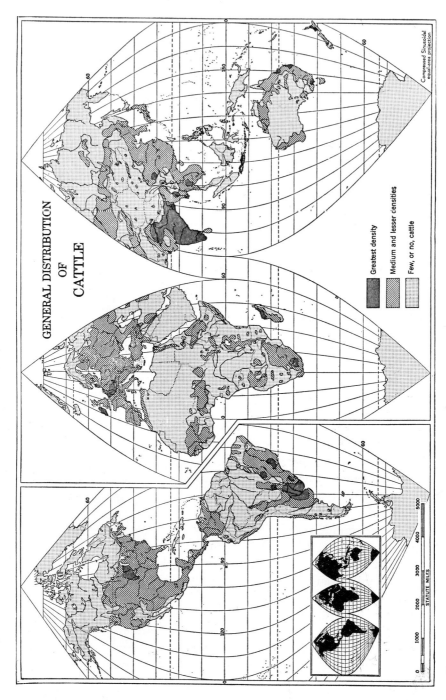

GENERAL DISTRIBUTION
OF
CATTLE

Greatest density

Medium and lesser densities

Few, or no, cattle

Compressed Sinusoidal
equal-area projection

STATUTE MILES
0   1000   2000   3000   4000   5000

382   CATTLE *are absent, or present in very small num-*
bers, in regions of long, severe cold, in deserts, and
in hot, very wet regions. India, with its hump-
backed cattle, has the greatest number, but this
situation reflects religious beliefs rather than phys-
ical or economic conditions. Cattle forming the
basis for a true cattle industry are especially con-
centrated in parts of western Europe, interior
United States, and southeastern South America.

Commercial Animal Husbandry

The parts of the earth in which animals and animal products are raised for market include the beef areas of Argentina, the sheep country of Australia, the beef and hog region of the United States Corn Belt, and the dairy regions of northeastern United States and northwestern Europe. Latitudinally, they range from the warmer edge of the northern forests and cold, wind-swept Patagonia to the margins of the rainforests. Climatically, they range from all except the coldest and the hottest humid lands to the margins of the hot deserts. Some of the regions of commercial animal husbandry are associated with highly developed agricultural areas, such as the United States Corn Belt (Fig. 351); others are the livestock ranching areas of the "wide open spaces," such as the Great Basin of the United States or the Great Plains of Argentina (Fig. 352). The chief animals raised, whether on vast ranges or in constricted pasture fields and feed lots, are beef cattle, dairy cattle, hogs, and sheep.

BEEF CATTLE. While beef cattle are raised primarily for meat, they furnish large amounts of beef extract, hides, tallow, bone and bone meal, blood meal, and hair. The better varieties are produced in the mid-latitudes and the cooler margins of the subtropics. The cattle raised in savanna regions, such as the Orinoco Llanos, furnish inferior meat and are, comparatively, more useful for other products, especially hides. Neither beef nor dairy cattle thrive in the rainier tropics, although other kinds of "cattle," such as the water buffalo of southeastern Asia and the East Indies, are well adapted. India's numerous cattle, previously mentioned as being more numerous than those of any other country, are there because of religious belief and not because they are necessarily well adapted or of major commercial significance (Fig. 382).

Argentina exports slightly more beef than all other nations combined. A mild subtropical climate, a vast area of rich soils and nearly level land, and widespread production of alfalfa, coupled with relatively sparse population, enable the Argentine Pampa to produce a large surplus. Other major beef export areas in South America are in Uruguay and the Brazilian Highlands. Australia sells abroad about the same amount of beef as Uruguay and half again as much as Brazil. Most of it comes from the eastern third of the country, partly from the humid coastal region and partly from the semiarid lands west of the Great Dividing Range. Like South America, Australia has abundant range, abundant feed, and relatively few persons to consume the meat at home. New Zealand, especially North Island, also produces a considerable surplus; enough so that she normally furnishes about 6 per cent of the world's export beef. Other producers of beef cattle, chiefly the United States and western Europe, have little or no surplus. The United States has more beef cattle than any other nation, yet home consumption is so great that there is practically no export in normal times. Many United States beef cattle, noted for their high quality, are raised on the western range lands and then transported to the Corn Belt for fattening. They are found in greatest concentration in the western part of the Corn Belt and immediately adjacent sections (Fig. 383).

At least half of the people of the world have never tasted beef; it is a high-priced food that can be afforded only by those with comparatively high purchasing power. Where poverty and dense population combine, as they do in most of the Orient, beef imports are out of the question and land at home must be used to produce foods which can be directly consumed. The large exports of beef from the Southern Hemisphere travel mainly to the British Isles. These little isles normally import about three-quarters of the world's export beef. Other importers, definitely minor, are France, Belgium, and Germany.

DAIRY CATTLE. Dairy cattle are concentrated chiefly in western Europe and the northeastern quarter of the United States. Smaller concentrations are in southeastern Canada, southeastern Australia, and New Zealand. Most dairy cows are raised in cool or cold climates which are capable of producing abundant pastures, hays, and other feeds. The dairy business began in western Europe, where the Mid-latitude Marine (Cfb) climate, with its cool, moist conditions, encouraged the growth of lush pastures and hay crops, as well as the growth of the cattle themselves. Dairy cattle there are most numerous in the coastal and near-coastal belt from southern Sweden to northwestern France and in the British Isles. Denmark and the Netherlands are particularly noted as "dairy countries."

Dairy cattle are so numerous in the portion of the United States which extends from Minnesota and Iowa to New England that the region is known as the Dairy Region, or, recognizing the importance of feed, as the Hay and Dairy Belt (Fig. 363). A part of this belt extends into the Lower Great Lakes and Upper St. Lawrence Valley sections of Canada. Both in Europe and the United States, dairy cattle are raised mainly within or next door to regions of dense population (Fig. 384). This enables the more perishable dairy products, milk and cream, to be placed quickly on the large urban markets. Butter and cheese are also produced in large amounts, but they are much less perishable and hence easier to ship. Production of dairy products outside of Europe and the United States and far away from major markets is largely limited to butter and cheese. On refrigerator ships they accomplish the long journey from Australia and New Zealand without spoilage.

Commercial dairying is a full-time job. Between the pastures and hayfields, the care and milking of the cattle, and the preparation of the milk and cream for market, the dairy farmer finds himself busy the year around. Thus, this activity and this region become

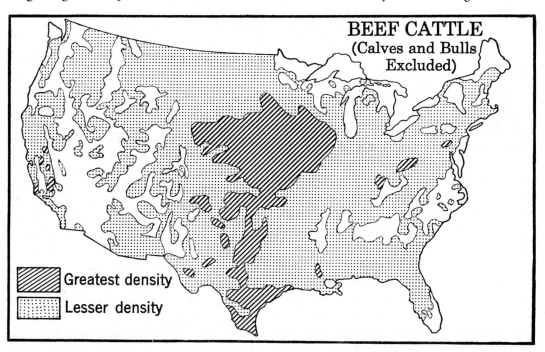

383   BEEF *cattle are raised in most sections of the United States, but they are most numerous in the western part of the Corn Belt and in parts of the Great Plains.*

384   *A TYPICAL modern dairy farm in the Hay and Dairy Belt of the United States. Note the cattle in the pasture and huge barns, milking sheds, and silo. (Milk Industry Foundation, New York)*

highly specialized, rather than diversified. Some diversification occurs in the chief dairy regions of Europe, where hog and poultry production is closely integrated with the dairy industry.

A very few nations control the export trade in dairy products. Denmark, New Zealand, and Australia account for about two-thirds of all butter exports. Denmark alone exports as many as 400,000,000 pounds of butter in a single year! And this is nearly equaled by New Zealand. Export butter, regardless of source, is consumed almost entirely by the British Isles and Germany; the former alone consumes nearly 80 per cent. New Zealand and the Netherlands supply more than half of all export cheese; the remainder is supplied chiefly by Canada and Switzerland. As with butter, most of the export cheese is sold in the British Isles and Germany, although fine cheeses to the extent of 9 to 10 per cent of the exports are sold in "luxury markets" in the United States. As noted in the discussion of beef, the tremendous production of dairy products in the United States normally does not lead to export. Again, this is a reflection of a large and "able to buy" home market.

HOGS. Hogs, or swine, are much more adaptable than either beef or dairy cattle, although some of the most highly bred varieties of hogs require much care, including scientific feeding, protection from excess sun, and inoculation against diseases. Hogs are raised all the way from the tropics to the northern forests and in lowlands and highlands alike. It is possible that China has the greatest number, but they are scavengers and their commercial significance, as opposed to their significance in local subsistence economies, rests largely on the production of bristles. Other concentrations occur in Europe, eastern United States, and southern Brazil. Hogs, regardless of type, would undoubtedly be much more widespread in the world if it were not for religious beliefs, which exclude them from large areas, particularly India, Asia Minor, and northern Africa.

Commercial hogs are produced chiefly in Europe and the United States, which account for the bulk of bacon, ham, and lard output, whether for home or export markets, and for fresh pork, which enters very little into export trade. While commercial hog production is specialized to a certain degree, it is, of course, carried on in connection with crop production and other animal industries. In the

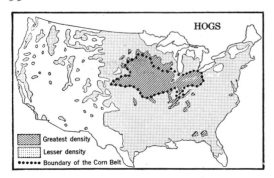

HOGS

Greatest density
Lesser density
•••••• Boundary of the Corn Belt

385 *THE CHIEF hog-producing section of the United States corresponds closely to the area of greatest corn production.*

United States, it is mainly a part of the complex crop and animal economy of the Corn Belt, where hogs consume about 42 per cent of all corn grown (Fig. 385). Corn-fed hogs furnish not only ham and bacon, but large amounts of lard as well. Hogs also occupy the corn regions of Europe, but they are most numerous in the noncorn areas. They are especially important in the dairy economy of Denmark and the Netherlands, where they are fed partly on skim milk, and in the general farming sections of Germany and Poland, where potatoes are major items in their diet. Hogs fed on potatoes and skim milk produce comparatively little lard, but they are noted for ham and bacon of fine quality.

Four countries control the bulk of the foreign trade in hog products. Denmark ranks first, followed by the United States, the Netherlands, and Poland. Danish bacon is especially famous for its high quality. The United States is the only significant exporter of lard. The European exports go largely to the British Isles and those from the United States to the Caribbean area and Central America. Unlike the other exporters, the United States consumes most of its hog products at home, whether as bacon, ham, lard, or fresh pork.

SHEEP. The mid-latitude and subtropical regions contain most of the world's sheep, although some occur in tropical highlands,

notably the Andes (Fig. 386). The tropical lowlands are not suitable for sheep: a "wool coat" and hot, wet climates do not go together. Sheep are most numerous in southern Europe, the western fringe of Europe, the British Isles, United States, Argentina and Uruguay, South Africa, and Australia and New Zealand. They are conspicuously absent from eastern Asia, mainly because of the lack of land that can be afforded for grazing. In general, sheep occupy lands which are inferior for crops and for the grazing of most animals except goats. The ability of sheep to produce both food (mutton, lamb) and clothing (skins, wool) has made them very useful, whether in dry lands and areas in the initial stages of development or in the poorer spots in regions which are well developed and generally favorable for agriculture.

A short while ago most of the world's sheep were raised either for meat or animal fiber; they were either "mutton sheep" or "wool sheep," but not both. Today, as a result of crossbreeding, many of them produce both meat and wool. In general, there is still a tendency to produce sheep primarily for wool in broad, semiarid range lands and principally for meat in more densely populated humid lands, but the distinction is disappearing as more dual purpose sheep are raised on ranges and farms alike. In the United States, there has been an increasing specialization, in some sections, in the growing of lambs. Spring lambs are marketed from such areas as Nebraska, Colorado, Wyoming, and Tennessee. California, with its mild winters, is able to market winter lambs.

Three countries monopolize the mutton export trade. New Zealand exports more than all other nations combined, accounting for about 53 per cent. Australia accounts for about 25 per cent, and Argentina about 15 per cent. Again, as for beef, butter, cheese, and ham exports, most of the mutton goes to the food-deficient British Isles. Wool exports are derived chiefly from Australia (about 37 per cent), and the remainder comes largely from

New Zealand, Argentina, Uruguay, and South Africa (Fig. 386). The wool goes primarily to the textile districts of England and secondarily to those of France, Germany, Belgium, Luxembourg, Japan, and the United States. It will be noted that the chief exporters of mutton and wool, as well as of beef, have relatively sparse populations and large amounts of semiarid grazingland or humid pastureland; and, again, that the United States, a large producer, does not enter importantly into the export trade.

ANIMAL FIBERS. Wool is the world's most important animal fiber, although it is a poor second to the leading vegetable fiber, cotton. Woolen textiles are in high demand in regions with cold winters and in those regions, even with comparatively mild winters, where there is a combination of coolness and a high degree of dampness. Thus, wool clothing and woolen blankets are in demand in Canada, northern United States, and northern Europe, as well as in the British Isles and western and interior Europe. The chief drawback to

greater consumption of woolen products is cost. Wool costs more to produce and manufacture than cotton; many persons need it, but cannot afford it, whether in the poorer sections of Europe or the still poorer sections of eastern Asia. Even in northern United States, there would undoubtedly be a greater consumption of woolen goods were the price not so high.

The second of the two major commercial animal fibers is silk. This is often discussed in connection with crop production, because the silkworms are raised on farms and fed on farm-raised mulberry leaves. Also the sale of silk is a part of farm cash income. Yet silk is strictly an animal fiber. Compared to wool, silk production is highly localized (Fig. 387). Also, silk textiles are so high in price that they are in demand in only a few luxury markets. Silk is one of the most ancient items of trade. It was a compact, high-value commodity in the earliest trade within the Orient itself. Later, it played the same role in trade between the Orient and Asia Minor and the

Chief wool producing areas
Wool exports
Greatest concentrations of sheep
Medium concentrations of sheep
Few, or no sheep

GENERAL DISTRIBUTION OF SHEEP

386 THERE are comparatively few sheep in hot, wet areas, in hot, arid areas, or in areas of long-extended or perpetual cold. Most of them are to be found in the mid-latitudes and subtropics (including steppes as well as humid regions). A few nations dominate world wool exports, with Australia in a commanding position.

387   *CHINA probably produces more raw silk than Japan, but Japan produces a better grade and leads the world in raw silk exports. The United States is chief importer of raw silk and leads in silk textile manufacturing.*

Orient and Europe. The most famous of the ancient trade routes which wound across Asia from China to southeastern Europe was called the Silk Road, although it was no more than a caravan route.

Silkworms can be raised in most subtropical regions, but nearly all the commercial production occurs in the milder parts of Japan and China. The decisive consideration in raw silk production is very cheap labor. The silkworms must be carefully raised and fed and the unwinding of the fine fibers from the cocoons produced by the worms is a laborious and highly expert process. The worms actually are raised in the farmhouses of the Japanese and Chinese peasants, where they receive as much care as though they were human infants (Fig. 388). Japan produces about 55 per cent of all commercial raw silk, as compared to China's approximately 30 per cent. The silkworm industry, technically known as sericulture, has been placed on a much more scientific basis in Japan, and Japanese silk generally is higher in quality than Chinese.

Most of the raw silk of commerce is manu-

388

JAPANESE feeding mulberry leaves to silkworms. (Cheney Brothers, New York) factured in those countries of the world able to buy luxury textile goods. Some silk textiles are manufactured in Japan and China for export, but most of the commercial raw silk moves to factories in the United States and western Europe. The United States alone makes about 30 per cent of all commercial silk cloth. In Europe, the chief manufacturer is France.

The animal fibers, particularly silk, are meeting an increasingly stiff competition from certain vegetable and mineral materials. Artificial silk in the form of rayon and nylon has become of major importance, whether for "silk" stockings, dresses, or underclothing. Real silk cannot compete in price with these more cheaply made materials. Rayon is made from wood pulp and cotton linters, and nylon from coal, limestone, and water. Another competitor which may soon affect animal fiber production, and cotton fiber output as well, is glass. Modern science has already learned how to make light and flexible glass cloth which is hardly distinguishable from certain silk, rayon, and cotton cloth. It has the major advantage of being fireproof and it may win very wide use before long, especially for drapes, curtains, wall hangings, carpets, upholstery cloth, and decorations used in crowded public places, where sudden fire has many times taken a heavy toll because of the use of highly inflammable paper or cotton decorations and furnishings.

Despite new substitutes which appear from time to time, the demand for domestic animals and their products continues to increase. Particularly in regard to meat, dairy products, and wool, commercial animal husbandry faces a favorable future. It is difficult to foresee a time when the keeping of animals, whether as a source of food or of industrial raw materials, will become unimportant.

CHAPTER OUTLINE

Agriculture and animal husbandry

The significance of agriculture
  Food for man
  Food for animals
  Raw materials for factories
Limiting factors: physical
  Climate
  Landforms
  Soils
  Drainage
  Native vegetation
  Animals and disease
Limiting factors: cultural
  Cultural inheritance
  Plant selection and breeding
  Money and labor
  Transportation and markets
  Laws and other regulations
  Competition from other activities
Types of agriculture
  Subsistence agriculture
    Primitive
    Nonprimitive

  Commercial agriculture
    Plantation
    Commercial farming
Major crops
  Rice
  Corn
  Wheat
  Other grains
  Vegetables
  Fruits
    Tropical fruits
    Subtropical fruits
    Mid-latitude fruits
  Sugar cane and sugar beets
  Coffee, tea, and cacao
  Cotton
  Other vegetable fibers
  Rubber
  Tobacco
Animal husbandry
  Nomadic herding
    Chief regions
    Reindeer economy
    Multi-animal economy
  Commercial animal husbandry

Beef cattle
Dairy cattle
Hogs
Sheep
Animal fibers

REVIEW QUESTIONS

1. Discuss some of the effects of the Industrial Revolution on agriculture. Have these effects been strongly felt wherever agriculture is practiced?

2. Give some examples to show that agriculture and manufacturing are now closely related in many parts of the world.

3. What are the major physical factors which "limit" agriculture? Can any of these factors be modified by man?

4. Is there justification for considering cultural inheritance as a limiting factor to agriculture? Discuss.

5. Do you know of any significant recent developments in plant selection and breeding? See what you can find out, for example, about hybrid corn and its implications.

6. Should we spend millions of dollars to irrigate or drain lands for crop production, when other lands which do not require irrigation or artificial drainage could be brought into production or, if in production, could be made more productive? What is your opinion? Why do you hold it?

7. In the area in which you live, is there competition with agriculture on the part of other land uses?

8. Compare and contrast types of subsistence agriculture with types of commercial agriculture.

9. Describe the general agricultural economy of your home area or, if you live in a large urban area, the agricultural area that is closest to your home. What is it like? Why is it that way? What are the trends?

10. What are the world's chief food crops? Where is the major commercial production region of each one?

11. Why did corn play such an important part in the Westward Movement in our country?

12. Discuss the physical requirements for large scale commercial corn production.

13. Contrast wheat and corn in terms of what happens to them after harvesting.

14. Determine the location of the chief *surplus* wheat-producing regions of the world. What enables them to produce significant surpluses? Where are these surpluses sent? Why?

15. Can you account for the fact that international trade in barley is very small?

16. Are most of the world's vegetables raised for sale or for home consumption?

17. What enables the vegetable-producing areas of California to compete with vegetable-producing areas located in the chief consuming regions of the United States?

18. Where are the world's major citrus fruit production areas? With what types of climate do they correlate?

19. The United States could grow enough sugar beets to satisfy its sugar needs. Why doesn't it do so?

20. Trace the geographical shifts in commercial coffee production. Are there any good reasons why Brazil should stand out so sharply in world coffee production?

21. Why do we not grow the tea we use in this country rather than import it from Asia?

22. What happened in the past that changed cotton from the "King's cloth" to the "people's cloth"?

23. Why did commercial rubber production shift from the Amazon Basin to southeastern Asia? Why is rubber in such great demand, particularly in the United States?

24. See if you can determine the present status of "synthetic versus natural rubber."

25. What are the chief domestic animals?

26. In general, what types of climate occur in the regions of nomadic herding?

27. What are the factors responsible for Argentina's leadership in beef exports?

28. Comparatively few of the world's people consume appreciable quantities of meat. Why is this?

29. Where is our Hay and Dairy Belt? How do you account for its existence?

30. We commonly speak of "corn-fed" hogs. Are there any important hog-producing regions where the feed is not corn?

31. Explain the statement, in reference to hogs raised in the United States Corn Belt, that, "Everything is used but the squeal."

32. Cotton textiles are much cheaper than wool textiles. Why, then, is there such a large world demand for wool?

33. Why is there so much mention of the decreasing importance of silk?

SOME SUGGESTED REFERENCES

Bengtson, Nels A., and Van Royen, William, *Fundamentals of Economic Geography,* Prentice-Hall, Inc., 1950. Chapters 8 through 14 of this standard textbook on world economic geography discuss, either briefly or in considerable detail, various phases of the geography of agriculture.

Colby, Charles C., and Foster, Alice, *Economic Geography,* Ginn, 1944. In this book on the industries and resources of the world, see individual chapters dealing with specific agricultural commodities, such as Chapter 9, Coffee: a Product of Tropical Uplands.

Davis, Darrell H., *The Earth and Man: A Human Geography,* 2nd ed., Macmillan, 1948. An introductory college textbook; Chapters 29 through 33 discuss grazing, primitive agriculture, Oriental agriculture, Western agriculture, and plantation agriculture.

Dicken, Samuel N., *A Regional Economic Geography,* D. C. Heath and Co., 1949. This textbook on the world's major production regions contains several chapters on grazing, herding, and dairying, as well as on particular crop regions.

Farmers in a Changing World, Yearbook of Agriculture 1940, U. S. Department of Agriculture, 1940. Written by several experts; sample chapters are "The Farmer's Changing World," "The City Man's Stake in the Land," "The New Range Outlook," "Farm Tenancy," and "Science and Agricultural Policy."

Food and Life, Yearbook of Agriculture, 1939, U. S. Department of Agriculture, 1939. A book by many authors, discussing topics ranging from food habits and human nutrition to the feeding of dairy cattle and sheep.

Jones, Clarence F., and Darkenwald, Gordon G., *Economic Geography,* Macmillan, 1941. Parts 4 and 5 of this textbook on world economic geography contain chapters on animal industries and agricultural activities, as well as chapters on individual crops.

Smith, J. Russell, and Phillips, M. Ogden, *North America,* Harcourt, Brace, 1942. A standard textbook on North American geography; see such individual chapters as those on the Cotton Belt, Corn Belt, Winter Wheat Belt, and the Great Plains Ranch Region.

For world agricultural regions, see the following:

Baker, Oliver E., "Agricultural Regions of North America," *Economic Geography,* Vols. 2-9 (1926-1933).

Jonasson, Olof, "Agricultural Regions of Europe," *Economic Geography,* Vols. 1 and 2 (1925 and 1926).

Jones, Clarence F., "Agricultural Regions of South America," *Economic Geography,* Vols. 4-6 (1928-1930).

Shantz, Homer L., "Agricultural Regions of Africa," *Economic Geography,* Vols. 16 and 17 (1940 and 1941).

Taylor, Griffith, "Agricultural Regions of Australia," *Economic Geography,* Vol. 6 (1930).

Van Valkenburg, Samuel S., Cressey, George B., and Hall, Robert B., "Agricultural Regions of Asia," *Economic Geography,* Vols. 7-10 (1931-1934).

389   *THE FAMOUS old mining town of Ouray, Colorado, in the northern part of the San Juan Mountains. It is located in a lead-, zinc-, silver-, and gold-mining district. (Corsini from Standard Oil Co. [N. J.])*

CHAPTER 25

Mining and Mining Regions

The securing of minerals from the earth, like the production of crops from the soil, predates any historical record. Thus, there is no way of ascertaining what man or group of men first engaged in mining. Certainly it was a long time ago, probably at least 250,000 years and maybe 1,000,000. Certainly, too, the first mining was extremely simple, hardly more than the tearing loose of weathered rock fragments, the digging into a hillside, or the scraping up of unconsolidated earth materials. Mining implements were hands and sticks, and minerals sought were salt for food and flinty rocks for primitive tools and weapons. The shaping of the flinty rocks may be thought of as man's first attempt at manufacturing, unless the fashioning of pointed and fire-hardened sticks or the shaping of crude receptacles from clay should be considered as the earliest beginnings of "making things by hand." In any event, crude mining started man on the manufacturing road, just as modern mining has helped him to continue along that road.

It is from such remote origins that present-day mining, with its use of many minerals and intricate techniques, has developed. Modern mining and modern mining communities bear as little resemblance to their ancient forerunners as do modern men to their initial ancestors, except in those very few parts of the world where primitive mining survives and where primitive people still live in what approximates a Stone Age economy.

SIGNIFICANCE OF MINING

Like agriculture, animal husbandry, and many other human activities, mining leaves its imprint on lands and cultures. The sharpness of the imprint has varied greatly with time, location, and people, but mining has produced great changes within many areas of the earth and widespread changes in the affairs of man.

In the Past

The earliest mining affected only a few local areas and a few persons. The visible results were small holes and scratched surfaces and, somewhere close by, piles of flint, clay, salt, and rough building stone. There were no mining settlements as such. Rather, there were a few places where persons, engaged primarily in other activities, such as hunting and collecting, gathered minerals and used them to minor degree. Some cultures, like those based on pastoral nomadism or migratory agriculture, were not of a nature to include mining of any sort. This is true of a few cultures which exist to this very day; for example, the Indian cultures of the Amazon Basin or the Bushman culture of parts of Australia.

Those people who, somehow, were able to recognize the possibilities of minerals and engage in mining found that they were thereby able to do more things and that they could move farther afield with greater ease and safety. Mining, however simple, made them stronger and enabled them to spread into new areas, often at the expense of other peoples who did not know how to mine and use minerals or, for some reason, did not practice what they knew. Peoples with stone axes and flint spearheads and arrowheads held a distinct advantage over those who used only clubs, sharpened sticks, or loose rocks. Those who knew how to quarry rock for building stone and make bricks from clay had a "home and fortress" advantage over those who did not. And, a long time later, those who learned to mine and use coal and to mine and smelt ores, found themselves possessed of power, tools, and machines which greatly transformed their lives and the lives of peoples with whom they came in contact.

Mining supplied many of the commodities of early trade. At first it consisted mainly of goods like spearheads, arrowheads, salt, stone bowls, pottery, or beaten pieces of "free" copper (Fig. 390). Later, precious stones became items of trade and still later, gold, silver, copper, tin, bronze, and iron. Before long, "regular" mining districts and mining settlements had come into existence and international competition for their control became strong—even to the point of war and conquest. Egyptian trade dealt importantly in gold, copper, and turquoise at least 5,000

390

IMPLEMENTS and ornaments of beaten "free" copper made by American Indians. These were discovered in graves and were in use prior to 1492. (Copper and Brass Research Association, New York)

391

PROSPECTORS "panning" for gold in a section of Canada's Yukon Territory (National Film Board, Canada)

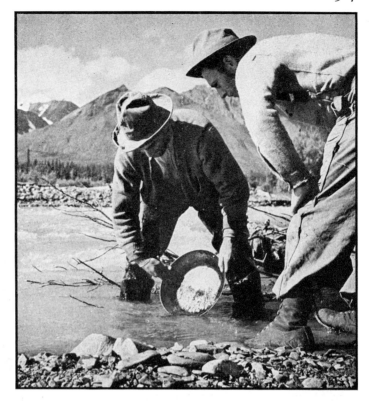

years ago, and it was part of Egyptian policy to reach out and secure mining districts in such areas as Cyprus, the Sinai Peninsula, and Ethiopia. Early overland trade between Egypt and India was based largely on gold and gem stones. Phoenician trade was involved partly in exploring for and marketing the mineral products of areas scattered from Cyprus to Sardinia and Spain to Cornwall. The mines of Greece, furnishing silver and lead, played a large part in her strength and trading activities. The Roman Empire seized and traded in many metals, particularly gold, silver, copper, mercury, and iron. Much later, following the emergence of Europe from the Dark Ages, minerals, particularly gold and silver, were major items in the trade with the New World.

The search for minerals and the hope of controlling mining regions have accounted for much of the exploration of the world. Contrary to many of the storybooks, most of the great explorers set out not for high adventure but rather to find new regions rich in mines and minerals or to seek new trade routes for bringing minerals and other riches to the home country. Many a lesser explorer, often a lone prospector, has opened up rich portions of the earth merely because he envisioned himself as the owner of a prosperous mine or mining district (Fig. 391). Men have searched for many things and have explored for many purposes; it would be interesting to know just how much of the earth's surface has been discovered, explored, and even mapped in detail as a by-product of the search for mineral riches; certainly it is a large portion.

Mining played a major part in the growth of nations and empires. Sometimes the growth was based on mining in the homeland or on mining done in far-flung, but homeland-controlled, colonies, or both. The strength and wealth of the Spanish Empire rested in large measure on Spanish mines. Mineral wealth paid for armies and navies which, in turn, enabled Spain to reach out and find and control the mines of the New World. As long as Spain was able to produce enough gold and silver or to obtain them elsewhere, the Spanish Empire remained invincible. The mines of Britain, the mineral wealth seized from Spanish galleons, and, later, the mines of Canada, South Africa, and Australia, supplied strong sinews to the British Empire.

The Industrial Revolution, both in its inception in England and in its spread to many other parts of the world, was to a great extent based on mining. British ironstone and British coal furnished iron and energy for making and running the machines which fabricated the goods, goods which themselves were often of mineral origin. German coal was the main basis of German iron, steel, and chemical manufacturing. Without abundant iron ore and coal, let alone the many other resources, mineral and otherwise, the United States hardly could have become the greatest manufacturing nation of the world. Minerals made large-scale manufacturing possible. The demands of such manufacturing have steadily increased the spread of mining and mining settlements over the earth.

In the Present

Mining plays an increasingly larger role in human affairs. Even though many sections have been "mined-out," mining districts today are larger and more numerous than at any previous time. Mining as a human activity affects more persons than ever before. Also, the variety of mineral products is greater than even a few years ago. It is significant to note that the present world powers are those with major mining regions in the homeland, especially mining regions which produce large amounts of both coal and iron ore. If, as some claim, there are only two world powers, the United States and the Soviet Union, it is

pertinent to remember their homeland production of petroleum as well as of coal and iron ore. However, no major nation is completely self-sufficient in mineral resources, but some are strong enough to reach out for larger supplies. Therein lies continued danger and a continued problem: will the "reaching out" be done peacefully, or on the basis of armed strength?

In the present period of uneasy international relations, the significance of mining is difficult to overestimate. This is not to ignore the basic importance of other major human activities, such as agriculture, animal husbandry, lumbering, manufacturing, or communication and transportation. In the modern world these activities depend heavily on mining. Were mining suddenly to cease, the productive apparatus of modern civilization would be largely paralyzed and major populations would face imminent starvation. Without sufficient supplies of coal and petroleum, the populations of the industrial regions would lack heat for their homes and energy to run the factories. Without iron and other metals, modern vehicles—ships, railroad cars, autotrucks, planes, etc.—could not be repaired or replaced; without coal and petroleum they could not run. Without the mineral products which are used in farm machinery, the chief surplus food regions— the most critical food regions of all—could not produce their essential bounty.

In time of war, minerals, both metallic and nonmetallic, assume even greater and more critical importance. Then there is the need for factories to run faster than ever, for transportation equipment to function more efficiently, for mechanized agriculture to produce more food than before. Moreover, there is increased need for the essential minerals used in instruments and machines of war. An insufficiency or a complete lack of even one mineral may spell the difference between victory and defeat. The Allies could hardly have been victorious in either World War I or World War II without huge supplies of petroleum and petroleum products, or manganese, or copper, or many another minerals. Now, with the atomic bomb in existence, deposits of uranium-bearing ores have become extremely important. Thus, in war or peace, there is small likelihood that mining will decrease in significance.

MINING REGIONS

Chapters 16, 17, and 18 dealt with the chief mineral resources of the world, and the maps accompanying those chapters dealt with the distribution of mineral resources. If the maps were transparent and were laid one on top of another, the resultant compounding of patterns would constitute the total pattern of mineral resource regions. By omitting those portions of the mineral resource regions in which actual mining operations are not important, a map of major present-day mining regions is obtained. The result, somewhat generalized, is shown in Fig. 392.

Northern Hemisphere

Most of the mining regions are located north of the equator. Moreover, most of them are in the United States and Europe. The area in which mining is a major activity is a bit larger in the United States than in Europe, but Europe has a greater number of mining regions. Asia has a considerable number of mining regions, most of them recently developed, at least as far as modern large-scale mining is concerned. The mining regions of Asia are likely to increase in both size and number until they rival those of the United States and Europe.

The largest single mining region of North America extends from the heart of Mexico into Canada (Fig. 392), much of it rough, mountainous terrain. The remainder, largely hill and plateau country, consists mainly of dry lands, which pose difficult problems of water supply both for domestic use and for mining and ore processing. This great mining

Note: This is not a map of mineral resources, but a map of the general areas within which actual mining operations are numerous.

Compressed Sinusoidal equal-area projection

392 *MINING is a well-developed industry on all continents.*

region contains hundreds of mining settlements, large and small, producing such minerals as copper, lead, zinc, silver, gold, molybdenum, and vanadium. To the west, in parts of coastal and near-coastal California, are important petroleum fields.

East of the Rockies lie smaller and more numerous mining regions (Fig. 392). In central United States, they extend, with major breaks, from Lake Superior to the Gulf. The Lake Superior mining region specializes in iron ore, although copper is still important in one section. The more southerly regions are devoted primarily to the mining of coal and petroleum, with lead and zinc important in the tristate area (adjacent parts of Kansas, Missouri, and Oklahoma), and sulphur significant along the Gulf Coast. In eastern United States, mining settlements are numerous in large portions of the Appalachian Highlands. The greater bulk of them are coal-mining towns. In southeastern Canada, a major mining region extends from eastern Lake Superior to the border of Maine. Nickel, gold, and asbestos are typical mineral products of this region. The remaining mining regions of North America are widely scattered. Their products range from Alaskan copper, Klondike gold, and the zinc of Flin Flon (a mining town northwest of Lake Winnipeg) to Nova Scotian coal and Newfoundland and Labrador iron ores.

The largest and most important mining region of Europe extends from northeastern France and western Germany into Poland (Fig. 392). Lorraine iron ore and Ruhr and Saar coal dominate this region, although other important products include lead, zinc, copper, and potash. To the north are the iron-mining regions of Sweden and to the west the iron- and coal-mining regions of Great Britain. To the south and southwest are coal and bauxite-mining regions in France; iron ore, zinc, and silver-mining regions in northern Spain; and copper, lead, silver, and mercury-mining regions in southern Spain. Also, chiefly in Yugoslavia, is an important mining region devoted to production of lead, zinc, bauxite, and copper. To the east are the remaining mining regions of Europe. They are almost entirely in the Soviet Union and include particularly the iron ore and coal-mining region near the Black Sea, the coal-mining region just south of Moscow, the Caucasus petroleum region, and the iron ore, zinc, manganese, chromium, and platinum-mining region of the Urals.

The major mining regions of Asia lie chiefly in Siberia, India, China, and Japan (Fig. 392). Newest and most rapidly developing is the elongated region which extends from north of Lake Balkhash to east of Lake Baikal. Within it are many mining towns producing coal, zinc, copper, iron ore, and gold. There also has been recent, marked development in India's mining regions, especially the one near Calcutta. Here manganese, coal, iron ore, zinc, and copper are important. Farther south is another region producing manganese, gold, and chromium. China's chief mining region is in the south. It produces several minerals, particularly tungsten, lead, zinc, tin, silver, and some manganese. Northern China has a much smaller mining region based primarily on the coals of Shansi and Shensi provinces. The Manchurian mining region is one of coal and iron ore. Between India and China is the mining region of central Burma, producing silver, tin, lead, zinc, petroleum, and rubies. Far to the south is the chief mining region of the Malay Peninsula. There the tin mines of the Federated Malay States are most important, although there are others which produce gold and tungsten. Japanese mining regions cover much of Honshu and parts of Kyushu and Hokkaido. Significant minerals are copper, lead, zinc, coal, and some iron ore and manganese. In Asia Minor, far to the west, are the petroleum-producing regions of Iran, Iraq, and Arabia and the chromium mines of Turkey.

Northwest Africa and northern South America contain the only other major mining regions of the Northern Hemisphere (Fig. 392). Mining activities in the former are based on phosphates, iron ore, lead, zinc, and manganese. Those of the latter include the platinum, gold, and silver-mines of Colombia, the oil fields of Venezuela, and the bauxite, gold, and silver-mines of British and Dutch Guiana.

Southern Hemisphere

Active mining operations are much less extensive in the Southern Hemisphere than in the Northern Hemisphere (Fig. 392). Despite this, some of the mining areas are quite large and a few of them, like those of Africa, promise much for the future.

The chief mining region south of the equator in the Americas extends from southern Ecuador to the southern part of middle Chile. In an east-west direction, it reaches from the Pacific coast into the highlands of the Andes. This rich region is a producer of many types of metals, including copper, iron, silver, lead, zinc, tin, tungsten, and vanadium. In addition, there is some coal, petroleum, and natural nitrates. Another region far to the east, in the hinterlands of Rio de Janeiro, yields iron ore, diamonds, silver, manganese, and some nickel. A small region in southern Brazil, not far from Uruguay, produces some coal.

Africa's largest mining region occupies parts of the Union of South Africa and Rhodesia. Gold and diamonds are particularly important, but there is a wide variety of other mineral products, including silver, platinum, copper, tin, lead, zinc, manganese, chromium, and coal. Farther north, in Northern Rhodesia and the southern portion of the Belgian Congo, is another region noted for its copper, radium ore, and diamond mines.

Australia possesses three regions in which mining is important. The largest, in the southeastern part, furnishes gold, silver, iron ore, and coal, as well as some copper, tin, lead, zinc, manganese, chromium, molybdenum, and tungsten. In the northeast is a region which yields chiefly silver, copper, and some tin. In the far southwest, gold is the chief product, although some copper is mined also.

The two relatively small mining regions of New Zealand produce some gold, silver, and coal. One of them is located in the narrow finger of North Island and the other in the northwestern strip of South Island.

MINING'S IMPRINT ON THE LAND

The degree to which mining becomes part of the geographical scene varies greatly from one mining area to another and from one type of mining to another. It is always a visible part of the landscape while it is being carried on, and in some places its effects on the surface of the earth are permanent.

Pits, Debris Piles, and Special Structures

Where open-pit mining is practiced, as in the Mesabi Range of Minnesota, huge depressions are created (Fig. 276). These great pits are very conspicuous while mining activities continue, and they remain afterward as permanent, man-made landforms. Upon abandonment, some of them fill with water to become artificial lakes and ponds. Sometimes, open-pit mining is accompanied by the stacking up of mammoth piles of waste earth materials, as in the copper-mining districts of Arizona. Such "dumps" also become more or less permanent features of the landscape (Fig. 393). Near the copper mines, other dumps, consisting of waste materials from the processing of the ore, are more permanent than the stamp mills and smelters with which they are associated.

393   *MINES and mine dumps in Cochise County, Arizona. Here the mine dumps (light-colored materials at right) are relatively small; often such dumps cover large areas of the mining countryside. (Ransome from U. S. Geological Survey)*

In districts of shaft mining or tunnel mining, as in the Marquette Range of northern Michigan or the anthracite region of eastern Pennsylvania, the shaft houses and other associated structures and stock piles are the major surface indicators of the activity carried on within the earth (Fig. 280). When the structures and stock piles disappear, the holes leading down or back into the earth are all that remain, except where so much material was removed from within the earth that parts of the surface sank to form permanent depressions. Where this happens, mining leaves another indelible mark on the land (Fig. 394).

394

DEPRESSIONS, usually occupied by swamps or ponds (similar to the pond in this photo), sometimes result from removal of minerals from below the surface. The tall concrete structures are shaft houses over deep iron-ore mines in northern Michigan. (Cleveland-Cliffs Iron Company)

Where mining is done with a pump, as in the sulphur districts of Texas, the salt districts of Michigan, or the petroleum districts of California, Texas, or Oklahoma, derricks are the main mark of mining activities (Fig. 271). This kind of mining leaves virtually no marks behind when it is finished: once the resources are used up and the derricks and pumps removed, there is practically no physical evidence left.

Other surface marks of mining are of many sorts. Most of them are readily apparent as long as mining continues, but they soon disappear when mining stops. Among them are truck roads, aerial tramways, conveyor belt lines, railroad tentacles, pipe lines, and storage tanks.

Mining Towns

Compared to settlements based on other activities, such as agriculture, manufacturing, or commerce, mining settlements are temporary affairs. Some of them last no more than a few months or years. Others may exist for several decades. Their longevity depends on many, often unpredictable, forces; for example, the amount and quality of the resource, the cost of mining, the location of markets, the market price, the use of substitutes, and whether the world is at peace or war. Eventually, most mining settlements die and become "ghost towns" (Fig. 395). Then their deserted buildings and streets fall into ruin and become objects of curiosity to the occasional visitor. If dying mining settlements have favorable locations, they may be gradually transformed into other types of settlement. For example, a settlement born because of local mineral resource may decline as a mining town, but become part of an agricultural settlement. This has happened in many areas, as in parts of the Sacramento Valley "gold country" of California.

Occasionally, a dead mining town is reborn. Modern machinery may give access to ores previously inaccessible. New processes may allow low-grade ores, formerly nonprofitable, to be mined and marketed at a profit; or, they may render profitable the reworking of old dumps, or "tailings." War, with high prices and perhaps government subsidy, may reestablish operations which are uneconomical in times of peace. Mining settlements prob-

395 *A "GHOST TOWN" in Wyoming. The present appearance of the once thriving gold-mining camp of Atlantic City in the Wind River Country. (Collier from Standard Oil Co. [N. J.])*

ably face more "unpredictables" than settlements of any other kind.

Mining towns vary considerably in size, although most of them are small, with populations measured in the scores or hundreds of persons. Some are so small that they hardly merit the name "town." In the American West, for example, the term is applied to settlements of no more than half a dozen habitations clustered about a single general store near a mine shaft. Fig. 396 shows such a "town." In contrast, full-fledged cities also are called mining towns, Butte, Montana, for example.

Where the resource being exploited is large and profitable, mining settlements normally are "company towns." That is, they are controlled and owned by a single company or corporation. Many of those established within recent years are model towns possessing graded streets, running water, electricity, and up-to-date sanitary facilities. Company towns usually include the company store, motion-picture theater, hospital, hotel, bunkhouses, and individual family dwellings (Fig. 397). The older company towns usually are worn and weather-beaten, their plan is quite haphazard, and they have few, if any, modern conveniences (Fig. 398). Where the mining operations are small, the company often attends only to the mine and the town is left to shift for itself.

Many, if not a vast majority, of the world's mining towns are crowded into small areas because they are located in hilly or mountainous country where there is little level land to build upon or spread out upon. Their frequency in areas of rough terrain reflects the fact that mineral resources usually are easier to discover and obtain in regions where erosion and crustal deformation have exposed the bedrock or allowed no more than a broken and patchy mantle of regolith to accumulate.

....

CHAPTER OUTLINE

Mining and mining regions

REVIEW QUESTIONS

1. Evaluate the statement, "Mining owes its origin to the Industrial Revolution."
2. Evaluate the statement, "Mining in the world at present is entirely a matter of large operations and modern machinery."
3. Discuss the importance of mining in relation to the development of Western civilization.
4. Mineral products are important items in international trade. Is this something relatively new, or are there significant historical precedents?
5. Is there any validity to the notion that demand for minerals was responsible for the exploration of the earth? Discuss.
6. Is it true that "present world powers are those with major mining regions in the homeland. . ."? Support your answer.
7. "The small number of important mining regions in Asia is a reflection of Asia's mineral poverty." Discuss.
8. What are the chief mining regions of Africa? What are the chief minerals mined in them?
9. Compare the world map of mining regions in this chapter with the world map of manufacturing regions in Chapter 23. What conclusions do you draw from the comparison?
10. What are the visible landscape expressions of coal mining? Are these expressions relatively similar, or do they differ considerably from one coal mining area to another?
11. What occupations other than mining often result in "ghost towns"?

396

THE SMALL silver- and lead-mining town of Goodsprings, Nevada. Such towns are difficult to see from a distance because they seem to merge with the desert landscape. (R. M. Glendinning)

397

THE COMPANY town, or "camp," of an oil company in Texas. (Corsini from Standard Oil Co. [N. J.])

398

A SMALL company town crowded into a narrow valley bottom in one of West Virginia's coal-mining sections. (Raymond E. Murphy)

12. A large proportion of the world's mining communities lies in areas of considerable relief. What is the reason for this?

(See also the questions at the ends of the chapters on mineral resources—Chapters 16, 17, and 18.)

SOME SUGGESTED REFERENCES

Davis, Darrell H., *The Earth and Man: A Human Geography*, 2nd ed., Macmillan, 1948. A college textbook which emphasizes man and his major activities; see especially Chapter 35 which discusses mining, particularly in the United States.

Finch, Vernor C., and Trewartha, Glenn T., *Elements of Geography: Physical and Cultural*, 3rd ed., McGraw-Hill, 1949. Chapters 26 and 27 of this standard textbook deal with minerals and mining.

Jones, Clarence F., and Darkenwald, Gordon G., *Economic Geography*, Macmillan, 1941. An economic geography organized according to major occupations; Chapters 21 through 27 discuss minerals and mining operations.

Parkins, Almon E., and Whitaker, J. Russell, *Our Natural Resources and Their Conservation*, Wiley, 1939. Twenty-three authors discuss, in this book, the many aspects of the use of resources and the associated problems, particularly in the United States. See Chapters 16 and 17 for a treatment of minerals, including their significance.

Whitbeck, Ray H., and Finch, Vernor C., *Economic Geography*, McGraw-Hill, 1941. A topical-regional introductory textbook in world economic geography; Chapter 14 is on mineral industries; in addition, see index for references to mining in different countries.

See also the references listed at the ends of the chapters on mineral resources—Chapters 16, 17, and 18.

CHAPTER 26

Utilization of Forests

....

Within recent years great social and political pressure has been exerted for the protection and wise use of existing forests and for the re-establishment of forests which have been destroyed. This pressure has been generated by the belated recognition that forest resources are limited. Clearly forests and forest products are still vital, despite the ever-increasing use of minerals for heating, constructing buildings, and manufacturing. Even in this so-called Age of Metals, men still depend on forests and forest products.

GENERAL SIGNIFICANCE OF FORESTS

Despite thousands of years of use and abuse, forests constitute one of the chief geographical patterns of the present day. Their readily visible presence is especially marked in the northern portions of North America and Eurasia and in the rainier parts of the tropics (Fig. 400). All in all, forests of one sort or another cover about one-fourth of the earth's land surface, an extent greater than that of the world's deserts and nearly as great as all deserts and steppes combined. However, the area in what is classified as "productive" forest is only about one-sixth to one-seventh of the land surface.

The full utility of forests is seldom recognized or appreciated. Most persons think of forests only in terms of lumber supply or perhaps in terms of pulp for newspapers and magazines. Hence it is necessary to stress the manifold uses of the world's forests.

Foods, Spices, and Medicines

From time immemorial man has turned to the forest for part or all of his food; today, many primitive and semiprimitive peoples still depend heavily on the forests for food. The dependence is generally twofold: the forest furnishes such products as fruits, nuts, and roots; it also supplies edible insects, snakes, birds, fish, and game animals. There are, for example, many native tribes in the rainforests of Africa, South America, southeastern Asia, and the East Indies, which depend almost entirely on the vegetable and animal products of the forest for their livelihood. The same is true for a number of native groups who live in the northern forest regions of Canada and Siberia (Fig. 401).

Where agriculture is practiced in forested areas, the farmer still turns to the forest for what it can offer. Thus, the migratory farmer of the Amazon Basin seeks out forest fruits and game to add to the products of his small clearing. In similar fashion, the farmer of the warmer parts of the northern forests depends

399   *SCENE along the Redwood Highway, north of San Francisco, California. The redwoods here are the coastal redwoods (Sequoia sempervirens). The tall redwood in the center of the scene is about 150 feet in height. (Gabriel Moulin from American Forest Products Industries)*

upon wild berries, a few tree fruits, and fish and game to augment his food supply. In the Great Lakes region and eastward practically to the Atlantic, the Indians obtained sugar from the sweet sap of the maple tree; today, in some of the "sugar-bush" areas, the white man has developed the production of maple sugar into an important local enterprise. Where domestic animals occur, the forest furnishes forage for them, either in the form of browse from trees and bushes, grass from forest-protected glades, or mast from nuts and roots.

While many of the spices which season and preserve foods are now produced on farms or plantations, some of the supply still is obtained from the forests, either from parts of trees or from bushes and vines which can exist only in the presence of numerous trees. Examples are pepper, cloves, nutmeg, ginger, and cinnamon. Chicle, one of the bases for chewing gum, also comes from the forest.

Scores of forest plants, both trees and smaller growth, furnish substances used in both primitive and modern medicine, either for the cure of disease or the alleviation of pain. Again, many of the plants are now farm and plantation products, but wild collection from the forest is still important. Here one may mention such items as cinchona bark for quinine, coca leaves for cocaine, kola nuts for stimulants, white pine bark for cough medicines, and timbo roots for rotenone to relieve muscular spasm (as well as to use in insecticides). Indians of the Canadian forest even use spruce needles to make a medicinal tea.

Fuel

How much of the world's population depends mainly on trees for fuel cannot be stated accurately, but it is most of the world, and authorities estimate that about half of the world's wood output is used for fuel. In the tropics, wood, or charcoal made from wood, is practically the only fuel. Because of the cli-

mate, such regions require fuel primarily for cooking rather than for heating. In middle and higher latitudes, wood is widely used for both cooking and heating: tremendous quantities are burned merely to heat homes in climates where the winters are especially long and severe. A farmer or town dweller in southern Canada uses from 15 to 25 cords of wood each winter, merely to keep his home warm. The same applies to farmsteads, villages, and towns in much of northern United States and Europe and, in somewhat lesser degree, in the South and in southern Europe. When one realizes that 15 cords of wood represent a pile 4 feet wide, 4 feet high, and 120 feet long, one can begin to appreciate how much wood is consumed by literally millions of homes. It is estimated that some 63,000,-000 cords of wood are used annually for fuel in the United States alone, even though the chief sources of energy for heating and cooking are coal, natural gas, petroleum, and hydroelectricity.

Construction Materials

The use of trees as a source of piling, beams, and lumber of many sizes and shapes is well known. In those parts of the world where trees of "stick-timber" size are present, or readily brought in, most buildings, wharves, bridges, and other structures are of wood. Where forests are not present, or are greatly depleted, lumber is scarce and high in price. In these regions, wood is reserved for smaller items, such as furniture, sills, panelings, and certain tools and household utensils. There are some areas with purchasing power sufficiently high to allow large lumber imports from distant production regions. A good example of this is the Los Angeles metropolitan region. Here all except the larger buildings are constructed primarily of wood, despite the fact that all the lumber must be imported, most of it from the forests of northern California, Washington, and Oregon, which are

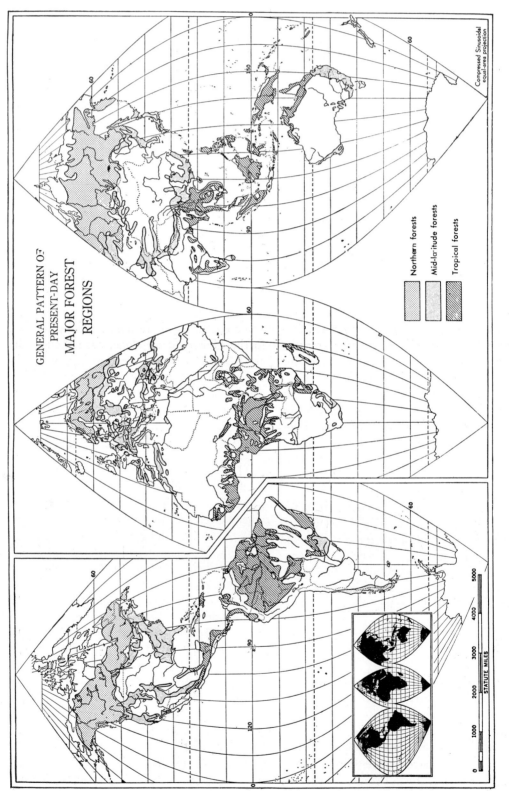

GENERAL PATTERN OF PRESENT-DAY MAJOR FOREST REGIONS

Northern forests

Mid-latitude forests

Tropical forests

Compressed Sinusoidal equal-area projection

STATUTE MILES

400 *PATTERN of present-day major forest regions. This figure should be compared with Plate VII.*

401

INDIAN trappers of the northern forest of Quebec Province returning to winter camp with beaver they have just secured from their trap line. (National Film Board, Ottawa. Canada)

from 600 to 1,700 miles away. Lumber in Los Angeles is not cheap, even though much of the haul is by water.

In recent years, many new wood-processing techniques have been perfected, which have increased the utility of wood for building and many other purposes. Wood is now impregnated and made fireproof and termiteproof. Plywood, or laminated wood, can now be made nearly as hard as steel. It is used for building walls, panels, trimmings, containers, furniture, boats, and a wide variety of small articles.

Paper & Other Cellulose Materials

During the nineteenth century, paper made from rags gave way to paper made from wood pulp, that is, from trees. The result was less expensive paper and a tremendous increase in paper consumption, not only for writing paper, newspapers, and magazines, but also for bags, cartons, separators, and packings. The greatest increase in the use of paper made

from the cellulose fibers of trees, particularly spruce trees, has come since 1900. This has further emphasized the importance of forests and the serious depletion of the forests of the United States. At present, the United States produces somewhat more than half of all the world's paper, yet must depend on foreign sources, mainly Canada, for much of its pulp-wood supply.

The cellulose materials derived chiefly from trees are also used for the manufacture of rayon, plastics, and explosives. Present demands for cellulose for other than paper uses are so great that many areas previously logged-over for lumber are now being combed for the wood which the original lumbermen left behind. In some areas, stumps and even partly burned or partly rotted logs are being utilized.

Game Protection

Forests, particularly if they are not too dense, furnish habitats for many species of

402

AN EXAMPLE of a forest (a mixture of dense and more open growth) that is an excellent game habitat— near Lutzen, Minnesota. (Shaler E. Aldous from U. S. Fish and Wildlife Service)

game animals and game birds (Fig. 402). Forests also protect streams and, hence, game fish. There are parts of the world where such game and fish are worth literally millions of dollars each year. Examples are to be found in much of northeastern United States, parts of the Appalachian Uplands, and the mountainous regions of the West. Game attracts hunters and fishermen, who spend huge sums for licenses, equipment, transportation, guides, food and housing. While some of the money is spent in cities and some goes into state treasuries, much of it goes to the local inhabitants. The amount is often sufficient to largely support permanent populations, some of them in areas which might otherwise have to be abandoned.

Water Conservation

The surest way to squander water resources and to encourage flood damage in a forested region is to remove the forest. Forests break the impact of torrential rains; they shade snow on the ground and enable it to melt slowly. Forest undergrowth and forest litter prevent rapid surface runoff and encourage more water to sink into the ground. In one fashion or another, they reduce floods and insure the preservation of underground water supplies (Fig. 403). These things are significant not only within the forested areas themselves, but often many miles away; many a section, for example, has been struck by disastrous floods whose origin lay in deforested regions upstream. In addition, forests help to hold the soil in place, so that it does not move with every rain to glut the valleys or to choke and clog streams which flow into other areas. For such reasons, forests should be preserved or even re-established over many parts of the earth. If they had nothing but water and soil conservation to contribute, their maintenance still would be worth the cost.

Scenery and Recreation

Forests are also important just to be in and to look at. They are cool and restful; they please the eye and the spirit and help to restore energy to tired bodies. The truth of this is attested by the millions who vacation in them each year and by the many thousands who go to forest sanitariums to regain their health. Again, all this has economic importance, for vacationers and health seekers spend millions of dollars annually to be among the trees.

MAJOR FOREST REGIONS OF THE WORLD

There are three major forest regions in the world: the tropical forests, the mid-latitude forests, and the northern forests (Fig. 400). Their distribution correlates with the definitely humid climates. The tropical forests are found chiefly in regions with 60 inches or more of average annual precipitation; the mid-latitude forests chiefly in regions of 20 or more inches; the northern forests mainly in regions of 10 or more inches. It will be remembered that, in general, the effectiveness of a given amount of precipitation increases with increased latitude. Thus, 10 inches of average annual precipitation is sufficient to insure a humid climate—a climate sufficiently humid to insure the growth of trees—in the higher latitudes. In the somewhat warmer mid-latitudes, with increased evaporation, at least 20 inches are necessary. In the tropics, with their high evaporation rates, at least 60 inches normally are needed, except where swampy conditions prevail or where soils locally are highly retentive of moisture.

The Tropical Forests

The area occupied by the tropical forests today does not differ greatly from that of the past, except that removal has been complete,

403 SEVERE gullying on unprotected land. Note the lack of gullying on the surface protected by the tree. Tehachapi area, California. (U. S. Forest Service)

or nearly so, in large parts of southeastern Asia, such as India and Java (compare Fig. 400 and Plate VII). However, most of the tropical forests and tropical forest margins have suffered considerably in quality and density because of grazing, migratory agriculture, and fires. That the tropical forests have not greater commercial importance is largely a reflection of the many difficulties of exploiting them. These difficulties include distance from major markets; competition from more favorably located forest regions; inadequate labor supply; hot, wet climates; health problems; and a world lumber demand which is mainly for softwoods rather than tropical hardwoods. However, the tropical forest regions are large and contain approximately one-half of the world's productive forest area, and the day may come when these forests will be more actively and more extensively utilized.

Roughly one-third of the world's hardwood forests are tropical hardwood forests located in South America, mainly in Brazil. They sweep across the Amazon Basin from the Atlantic to the slopes of the Andes and from the northern edge of the Brazilian Uplands into and across much of the Guiana Highlands to the margins of the plains of the Orinoco Basin. Other similar forests occur in parts of the Brazilian Uplands, along the southeast coast of Brazil, and in much of western Colombia. Elsewhere in the Americas, they occur chiefly along and near the Caribbean shore, from Colombia to the Gulf of Mexico, and in parts of the West Indies. Africa possesses about one-sixth of the world's hardwood forests, practically all of which are tropical. Most of them lie in the area between the Gulf of Guinea and the equatorial mountain and lake district and along the northern shores of the Gulf of Guinea. In Asia, the bulk of the tropical hardwood forests is found in the southeastern corner, from Burma to French Indochina and south into the Malay Peninsula. The remainder of those in the Eastern Hemisphere are in the East Indies, chiefly in Sumatra, Borneo, Celebes, and

New Guinea, and in scattered patches along the northern fringe of Australia.

The Mid-latitude Forests

The mid-latitude forests have suffered more from the ax, saw, and fire than the tropical forests. At present the mid-latitude forests comprise only a small part of the world's forested area (compare Fig. 400 and Plate VII). In China Proper, the removal has been almost complete except in the hilliest sections of the south. In Europe and the United States, all except the higher and the rougher sections have been largely cleared or at least logged heavily, although there are many forests or woodland areas in the lowlands, mainly in the form of farm wood lots, forest strips along some of the steep valleysides, or relatively extensive stands in swampy or very sandy areas. Also, there now are many man-made forest districts, where trees are raised as a kind of crop, as in parts of Europe and portions of our South. The mid-latitude forests are "mixed"—a mixture of hardwoods and softwoods. Admitting many exceptions, where soils are sandy there are apt to be "solid stands" of conifers; where soils are high in clay there are apt to be hardwood stands. But, in general, any large mid-latitude forest area usually contains both softwood and hardwood varieties. Most of the mid-latitude forest was removed to make way for crops, although it also served as fuel, fencing, lumber, etc. In many sections, the forest was merely in the way and most of it "went up in smoke." For example, the early settlers in Ohio, Indiana, and southern Michigan cut and burned great piles of black walnut just to get rid of it. Today, black walnut is very scarce and almost "worth its weight in gold."

What is left of the mid-latitude forests is chiefly in the United States and Europe. Those of the United States are mainly in the Appalachian Uplands, the western mountains, the northern Great Lakes states and

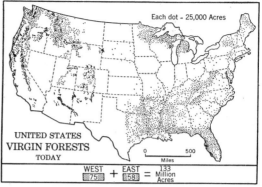

404 *THESE TWO maps, including the bar graphs at the bottom, indicate what has happened to the virgin forests of the United States since Colonial days.*

parts of the Atlantic and Gulf Coastal plains. Those of Europe are also mainly in uplands and a few lowland sections, especially in the north. The major occurrence is in a broken belt from Spain to central western Russia and east into Siberia. Elsewhere in the Northern Hemisphere they are chiefly in widely scattered hilly and mountainous areas, from the Caucasus to South China and northward into Korea, and in parts of Manchuria, and Japan. The Southern Hemisphere had little mid-latitude forest to begin with, and it too has been greatly altered by burning and cutting.

The Northern Forests

Most of the remaining forests outside the tropics are in high latitude regions of the Northern Hemisphere (Fig. 400). In North America they lie chiefly on the poleward side of the 50th parallel; in Eurasia chiefly poleward of the 55th parallel. They extend northward until they gradually break down and merge with the tundras of the Arctic. In a few places, they actually send fingers which stretch to embayments of the Arctic Ocean, as for example, in the delta of the Mackenzie River. The northern forests are predominantly coniferous, although hardwoods are not uncommon along the warmer margins. Mid-latitude market demands have eaten heavily

into these forests, especially in Canada and Europe. In area the northern forest lands are equal to about three-quarters of the tropical forest area. In wood content, however, their reserve is much less than that of the tropical forests because the northern forests are patchy and broken and trees are comparatively small, except along the warmer margins where growing conditions are better than in the middle and northern portions. Very often the trees are of pulpwood size rather than lumber size. Replacement by new growth is very slow because of the shortness of the growing season.

FOREST REGIONS OF THE UNITED STATES

Forests originally covered nearly half of what is now the United States. These were the virgin forests (Fig. 404). They swept almost unbroken from the Atlantic to the prairies of the far interior and from the Gulf into Canada. Farther west, they occupied large sections of the central and northern Rockies, parts of the Colorado Plateau, and an extensive area in the Cascades, Sierra Nevada, and the Coast Ranges. Today, the eastern virgin forests are more than 90 per cent removed and those of the west about half removed. The entire virgin forest, eastern and western combined, is now about 90 per cent depleted and what virgin-forest areas remain have been seriously robbed of certain types of trees. Depletion of United States forests is most marked in the Corn Belt and east to the Atlantic and in the eastern half of the Cotton Belt. It is least marked in the western mountain and hill regions, the northern fringe of the country from Minnesota to Maine, the southern Appalachian Uplands, and the sandier and swampier portions of the Gulf Coastal Plain. Most of the depletion has occurred within the past one hundred years and much of it within the past seventy years. Large areas which were cut over and burned over have grown new forests, but the new timber is generally inferior to that of the virgin stand. Considering the present, manifold utility of the forests, the sad state of their depletion, and the added fact that most of the forests of the United States which furnish crucially important saw timber still are being cut with little or no regard for future crops of trees, one can readily appreciate the need for more rational cutting. It is estimated that the present cut of saw timber exceeds growth by 50 per cent.

The major forest regions of the United States, as designated by the United States Forest Service, are five in number: the Mixed Northern Forest Region, the Central Hardwood Forest Region, the Southern Mixed Forest Region, the Rocky Mountain Forest Region, and the Pacific Coast Forest Region (Fig. 405).

The Mixed Northern Forest

The Mixed Northern Forest extends chiefly from Minnesota to Maine and from the latitude of the northern Great Lakes to that of the southern Great Lakes. In addition, it sends a narrow finger southward along the higher and cooler parts of the Appalachian Uplands (Fig. 405). Its major remnants,

mingled with areas of new but inferior growth, are chiefly in the northern Lake region, the Adirondacks, northern Maine, and the southern Appalachians (compare Figs. 404 and 405). Dominant, or "key," species of trees are spruce, balsam fir, hemlock, cedar, pine, birch, poplar, beech, and maple.

It is generally agreed that the northern and the rougher sections of this forest region are better suited to the growth of trees than to any other use. Already there are some national forests, as well as some under control of state and local governments, but the percentage of the original area under such control is small. As is usually true, it is much easier to destroy a resource than it is to replace it or substitute for it.

The Central Hardwood Forest

The main body of the Central Hardwood Forest Region (Fig. 405) extends from the southern margin of the Great Lakes to the Cotton Belt and from all except the higher parts of the Appalachian Uplands to the interior prairies. An eastern portion, east of the higher parts of the Appalachians, extends as a strip from southern New England to northern Georgia. In the northern half this strip extends to the Atlantic; in the southern half it lies considerably inland. The western fringe of the forest region extends from Canada to Mexico. This is the forest-prairie transition: fingers of the forest reach westward along the damp valley bottoms. Fingers of the prairie originally reached eastward along interstream areas.

So much of the Central Hardwood Forest Region has proved to be excellent for agriculture that there is little forest cover left (compare Figs. 404 and 405). Most of the region has become the Corn Belt and the Corn and Winter Wheat Belt; a great deal of it was cleared merely to make way for fields of corn. The chief remnants of mature forest growth, and the chief areas which should be reforested, are in the rougher sections, particularly in major portions of such states as Kentucky, Tennessee, and Missouri. Dominant trees are oak, hickory, chestnut, maple, elm, yellow poplar, and some pine.

The Southern Mixed Forest

Much of the Southern Mixed Forest Region (Fig. 405) has become the Cotton Belt, and another portion has become the Subtropical Fruits Belt and the southern part of the Middle Atlantic Truck Crops Belt (compare Figs. 405 and 363). Even so, about half of the South is still in forest of one type or another. The region extends from the Atlantic to the southern part of the hardwood forest-prairie transition, noted above, and from the Gulf to the Corn and Winter Wheat Belt. Dominant trees are yellow pines, oak, cypress, tupelo, red gum, and swamp maple. The last four occur in damp or wet sections, particularly in river flood plains and the northern edge of the Mississippi Delta. Their largest occurrence is in the broad flood plain of the

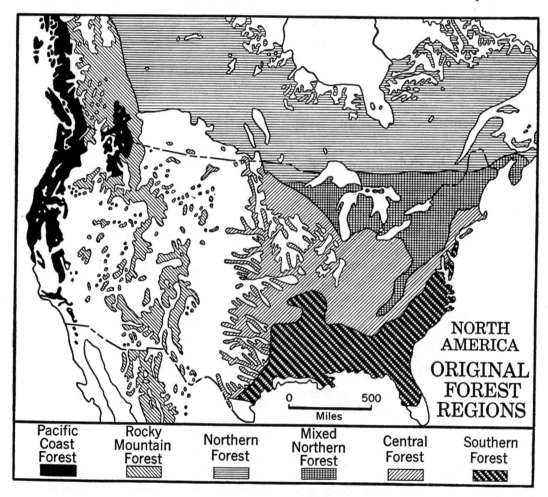

Pacific Coast Forest | Rocky Mountain Forest | Northern Forest | Mixed Northern Forest | Central Forest | Southern Forest

405 THE original *forest regions of the United States and parts of Canada and Mexico (after U. S. Forest Service). It will be noted that except, chiefly, for the arid and semiarid sections, forests covered most of the United States.*

Mississsippi River, from the Delta to the mouth of the Ohio. The chief remnants of the original Southern Mixed Forest are in the Mississippi drainage area and in Florida (compare Figs. 404 and 405). More is left of this forest than of the Mixed Northern Forest and much more than of the Central Hardwood Forest. By reason of its ability to grow new trees rapidly, the Southern Mixed Forest Region probably has more to offer than any other forest region of the United States, with the possible exception of the northern part of the Pacific Coast Forest Region. Many believe that eventually it will become our major forest reserve. Already there are numerous sections in which trees are planted and harvested as though they were ordinary crops. Undoubtedly this practice will become more general, especially on those lands which are nonoptimum or definitely submarginal for agricultural purposes.

The Rocky Mountain Forest

The Rocky Mountain forests are mainly in the central and northern Rockies, separated by the broad gap of the Wyoming Corridor (Fig. 405). They lie far from the main lumber-consuming markets of eastern United States and far from the ports and shipping facilities of the Pacific coast. Because of their comparative isolation and the difficulty of locating and logging the characteristically scattered mountain stands, they have survived largely intact to the present. However, most of the interior West has "boomed" in recent years and this has meant a more rapid cut of the mountain forests, to serve not especially the mountain areas but rather the populations of growing Western towns and cities.

Huge portions of the Rocky Mountain Forest Region have been incorporated in national forests and national parks (Fig. 406). Some individual national forests are larger than some of the smaller eastern states. Thus, many of the forests of the Rockies will be preserved

and used rationally and many an adjacent lowland area will have essential protection of its domestic and irrigation water supplies and of its mountain-located hydroelectric power resources. These large forest reserves also insure a steady flow of lumber from such typical trees as spruce, Douglas fir, and yellow pine.

The Pacific Coast Forest

The Pacific Coast Forest Region occupies the Sierra Nevada, the Cascades, and the Coast Ranges north of San Francisco (Fig. 405). It is much less patchy in distribution than the Rocky Mountain Forest Region and timber growth is heavier at lower elevations, including some valley lowlands. At first glance, this forest region appears to be largely untouched. Forested slopes meet the eye in almost any direction, and they stand up too abruptly and cover too much of the view to be ignored. Closer examination reveals widespread removal in the more accessible areas and tremendous "burns" in nearly all areas. One would hardly speak of this forest as consisting of remnants, yet it is already more than half destroyed. The dominant tree north of California is the Douglas fir. Others are spruce, red cedar, and yellow pine. In the California section, the coastal redwoods, the famous *Sequoia sempervirens*, occur along and near the shore in what is often referred to as the fog belt. Farther inland are the yellow pine and sugar pine, with some interior redwoods, the *Sequoia gigantea*, on the western slopes of the Sierra Nevada where they occur as redwood patches in what is generally a sugar pine and yellow pine forest. The California forests have suffered greatly from cutting and fire. They are located closer to major West-coast markets, are generally drier than the forests of the heavy precipitation belt of Washington and Oregon, and are closer to great numbers of people, many of whom

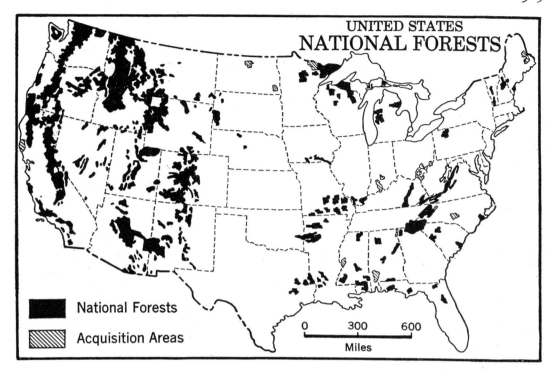

406 *THIS MAP shows only the National Forests of the United States (not National Parks and National Monuments). The mountainous and plateau West contains most of such forests, although the number is slowly increasing in the East.*

have never learned to be careful with fire.

As in the Rockies, national forests and national parks are numerous (Fig. 406). This offers considerable hope for the Pacific Coast Forest Region; however, fire is no respecter of man's boundary lines and each year thousands of acres of national forest, as well as of private forest, go up in smoke. Much of the private forest land, logged or now being logged, should be reforested and given greater protection. Nowhere else in the United States is there so much land "all in one piece" which should be devoted permanently to forest cover, both for wood and for the many other uses which forests serve. The Pacific Coast Forest Region is now our chief reserve of trees of saw-timber size. It contains about half of all timber trees in the nation (Fig. 407). It would be complete folly to use it in such a manner that it might cease to contribute importantly to the national economy.

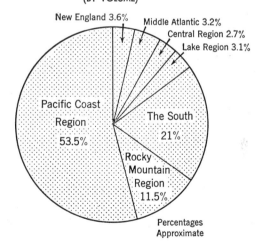

UNITED STATES DISTRIBUTION OF TIMBER OF SAW-TIMBER SIZE TODAY
(BY VOLUME)

407 *THE WEST, especially the Pacific Coast region, contains most of the trees of saw-timber size today.*

LUMBERING

Large-scale commercial lumbering has developed only in the past century or century and a half. Prior to the early 1800's operations were crude and small. There were a few small sawmills in Europe as early as the middle of the 1300's, but most of the world's lumber was cut and used close to home and mainly shaped by the ancient methods of splitting and hewing logs. Some of it was produced by pitsawing. This method utilized a pit or, sometimes, a slightly elevated platform. The logs were placed over the pit or on the platform. Two men, one standing below and the other above, operated a long, two-handled saw which "whipped" logs into planks and boards.

Shortly after 1800 sawmills became numerous in Europe and the era of modern lumbering began. Steam power as well as water power was used, new machinery was invented and utilized, and mills grew to greater size. Methods of logging and getting the logs to the mills slowly improved and the products of the mills began to move longer distances

as land and water transportation facilities increased and as the forests closest to markets were used up. The great changes in lumbering kept pace with those in agriculture, animal husbandry, and manufacturing. Lumbering, too, was caught up in the Industrial Revolution. By 1840, the "lumber boom" was on in the United States, generated and maintained by the great westward surge of population.

In the United States

Lumbering in the United States had its beginnings along the Atlantic seaboard, particularly in New England, in the early 1600's. As the better and more accessible stands of the East were used up, the loggers began a westward march through the Mixed Northern Forest Region (Fig. 408). The center of production shifted from New England to New York and then to Pennsylvania; by 1890 it was in the Great Lakes region, and by 1910 that region was practically "logged off." The chief demand then, as now, was

408

MODERN pulpwood operations in a section of the Mixed Northern Forest Region. The big "stick timber" is largely gone and the cut is now "smaller stuff." (American Forest Products Industries)

409

LOGGING with modern machinery, Olympic Peninsula, Washington. (Eagle from Standard Oil Co. [N. J.])

for softwood lumber, and it was the stands of pine which suffered first and most heavily. In the wake of the "pine cutters" came the "hardwood cutters," both leaving great slashings and burns and abandoned lumber towns. The loggers stopped their westward trek and turned south. By the time they turned in this direction the Central Hardwood Forest Region was largely a thing of the past. It had made way for many thousands of farms and hundreds of hamlets, villages, and towns, as well as a few great cities. Thus, the loggers, except for those who went to the Pacific Coast Forest Region, jumped over the Central Hardwood Forest Region and began their work in the Southern Mixed Forest.

The Southern Mixed Forest Region came into its own with the beginning of the present century and for some twenty years it was the center of lumbering operations. Again, the softwoods suffered most, especially the extensive pine stands on the more sandy lands, but hardwoods were also being cut in large numbers and used for more purposes than previously. The several varieties of southern oak were in particular demand for use in furniture and railroad ties. Today the southern forest still furnishes roughly half of the United States lumber supply, although much of the recent cut is based on second-growth and, in some sections, third-growth timber. Second-growth timber also is responsible for a large part of the supply obtained from what is left of the forest resources of the Northern Mixed Forest Region. Only in the Pacific Coast and Rocky Mountain Forest Regions is second-growth timber unimportant.

The lumber boom in the Pacific Coast Forest Region began during World War I (Fig. 409). The Rocky Mountain forests, scattered and mainly inaccessible, were by-passed. The jump to the Pacific coast brought into major production a region located far from the chief lumber markets of the United States. Either by land or water, it was a long expensive haul to eastern markets. But softwood lumber was still in greatest demand and it was the Northwest which now had the only large supply. The markets, including growing

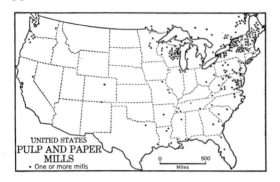

UNITED STATES
PULP AND PAPER
MILLS
• One or more mills

0   500
Miles

410   *THE GENERAL distribution of the combination pulp and paper mills of the United States and adjacent Canada.*

foreign markets for United States lumber, were able to pay the rising costs, and from the Pacific Coast Forest Region moved the greatest flow of softwood lumber that the world had ever witnessed. Most of it moved, and still moves, to the eastern part of the United States, but large amounts traveled to rapidly growing southern California and to Australia, the Orient, South America, and Europe. At present, the Pacific Coast Forest Region possesses about half of all remaining saw timber in the United States.

Looking to the future, it is pertinent to note that the South possesses the largest area suitable for forests. This area comprises about 30 per cent of all the land in the United States that is suitable for, and should be used for, forest purposes. The South's closest rival in this respect is the Pacific Northwest, where only about 16 per cent of United States land suitable for forests (and not better for other purposes) lies. On the basis of land and climate suitable for forests, it is easy to understand why the South may be expected to continue furnishing about half of the United States timber supply.

In addition to the cutting of trees for lumber, American forests have already been heavily cut for pulpwood. It is pulpwood that supports the modern paper industry and furnishes wood fibers for such products as

rayon, cellophane, wallboard, and certain explosives. World demand for paper, both for newsprint and containers, has increased by leaps and bounds since 1900. Inasmuch as the most of the world's paper is made from wood, the forests have been subjected to an additional drain. In many areas, the pulpwood cutters have finished up what the sawtimber cutters left behind; they also have utilized previously untouched forests which were not suitable for lumber, but whose small trees are satisfactory for pulp.

Until the early 1920's, nearly all wood pulp produced in the United States was processed in the Northern Mixed Forest Region. Northern spruce was practically the only source of pulpwood and it was obtained from sources within or very close to the Northeastern Manufacturing Region. Today, nearly half of the wood pulp secured in the United States comes from the South and the Pacific Northwest. Spruce still furnishes the material for more than half our wood pulp, but much of it is imported from southeastern Canada and some from northwestern Europe. Newer techniques of manufacturing have allowed the use of balsam fir, western hemlock, southern yellow pine, and southern poplar. Most of the mills which transform pulpwood into wood pulp are located in the source regions (Fig. 410). This is because pulpwood itself is bulky and of low value, while wood pulp is more concentrated, easier to handle and ship, and of comparatively high value. Some of the mills which make wood pulp also make paper, but much paper is manufactured in mills which are located in or near the large cities of northeastern United States, particularly in those which do the most printing and make the largest numbers of paper bags and cartons. Such mills draw not only on distant sources of paper pulp but also depend greatly on wastepaper. Paper mills are concentrated particularly in a belt that begins in New England and extends to the northern edge of Chesapeake Bay, though they are numerous as far west as the Mississippi (Fig. 411).

In Europe

Nearly all of Europe was once covered with forests (see Plate VII). In terms of climate, soil, and drainage conditions, trees represented the natural cover for most of the land. Widespread removal first began in the Mediterranean and in the eastern and southeastern portions of the Continent. As Europe developed, particularly as agriculture spread and towns and cities became numerous, forest destruction increased rapidly, except in the northern forests of what are now Norway, Sweden, Finland, and Soviet Russia. Today, virgin forest occurs only in the north or in some of the highlands. Much of Europe, unlike other forested portions of the earth, has practiced scientific forestry for more than a century. This is especially true in western Europe, where the pinch of insufficient wood and lumber supplies was felt first. Scientific methods have included reforestation, particularly of areas not well suited to other uses. Some sections have more trees now than they had fifty or one hundred years ago. Europe has recognized the importance of forests for many purposes. There a forest, or even the smallest patch of trees, is seen as a very valuable thing. Rules and regulations concerning forest use are stringent and rigidly enforced. Nothing is wasted; small branches and twigs are carefully gathered and bundled and, ordinarily, each tree cut down means several young trees planted in its place. The contrast between forest use in Europe and the United States is startling. The United States is just beginning to grasp the significance of forests; it has barely reached the stage Europe was in a century ago.

The proportion of land in forest varies widely from one section of Europe to another. Finland is about seven-tenths forest. No other country in the world is so much a land of forests, forest workers, and forest products. About eight-tenths of Finland's exports are forest products, ranging from beams, lumber,

UNITED STATES
PAPER MILLS
. One or more mills (these are not pulp mills)

0   500
Miles

411   *THE GENERAL distribution of the paper mills (mills which do not produce wood pulp or other necessary raw materials) in the United States and adjacent Canada. These mills are much more concentrated in or near large cities than are the combination pulp and paper mills (Fig. 410).*

and pulpwood, to paper, safety matches, and other small wooden articles. Sweden is more than half forested, and is second only to Finland in her dependence on trees. European Russia is about one-third forested; Germany, about one-fourth; and France, about one-fifth. Less than one-twentieth of England is in forest cover. Except in the north of Europe, the present forests are mainly man-planted and man-tended; the virgin forests disappeared long ago.

Despite some imports, mainly from the United States and Canada, Europe's forests have been sufficient to take care of its needs in normal times. The chief consuming area has been in the west and south; the chief supplying areas have been in the north and east. The major exporters have normally been those east of a line drawn between Sweden and Norway, Poland and Germany, and Yugoslavia and Italy. Chief among them were Soviet Russia, Finland, and Sweden. The major importers, all west of the line just mentioned, were Great Britain, Germany, France, and Italy. As a result of war and postwar conditions and reconstruction needs, Europe's former self-sufficiency in timber is greatly upset and western Europe is much more dependent on imports from Canada and the United States than ever before.

Like the United States, Europe draws upon her forests for pulpwood, as well as for lumber and fuel. Most of the pulp is processed in the supply areas of the northern forest and in Germany. About half of it is manufactured in Sweden and Finland alone. Paper manufacture, again like the United States, is concentrated in the more densely populated regions, either in or near the large printing centers. Germany leads, followed by Great Britain; together they usually make a bit more than half of all Europe's paper. Germany is the only country in Europe which is outstanding in the manufacture of both wood pulp and paper.

Outside the United States and Europe

The United States produces a little more than four-tenths of the world commercial lumber supply; Europe produces nearly three-tenths. The two combined thus produce a bit more than seven-tenths. This emphasizes not only the importance of the two main producers, but also the comparatively insignificant production by the remainder of the world.

Canada contributes important amounts of wood to the world total, but her annual cut is only about one-tenth that of the United States. In the southeast, pulpwood predominates, while lumber is most important in the Pacific Coast Forest Region. Soviet development of lands east of the Urals is resulting in an increasing timber cut along and near the Trans-Siberian railway and along the many north-flowing rivers which thread their way through the northern forest. Here too, as in Canada and in the world as a whole, the wood obtained is almost entirely softwood. Farther east, Japan produces significant

amounts of both hardwoods and softwoods from her predominantly hilly and mountainous lands. China, although woefully deficient in forests, is still able to produce some lumber from the more rugged lands of the south and southwest. The remaining world timber cut occurs chiefly in widely scattered parts of the tropical forests. The nontropical parts of the Southern Hemisphere never did possess substantial forest resources. Chile is the only country that carries on major lumbering operations and then only in small sections of her south.

As pointed out previously, about half of the world's present forest area is in the rainy tropics. The difficulties of lumbering in tropical forests, plus the long haul to major markets and the fact that the demand is primarily for softwood, have left these vast hardwood forests largely untouched. Most of the timber that is obtained is for special purposes. So far, such trees as teak, mahogany, Philippine mahogany ("false mahogany"), ebony, and Spanish cedar have been most sought after. "Sought after" is a good way to express the matter, for most of the tree species of the tropical forests do not occur in solid stands, but here and there in among a wide variety of other tree species. Thus, logging has been of the "selective" type, rather than the "over-all" or general "slash-logging" type practiced in mid-latitude and northern forests. Teak is obtained from southeastern Asia, mainly from Burma, Thailand, French Indochina, and Java. It is hard, heavy, durable, and highly resistant to attacks of boring insects. Most of it is used in small boats or in the wooden parts and trimmings of large vessels.

Mahogany comes chiefly from Central America and the islands of the Caribbean. Because of its hardness and durability and its capacity to take a smooth, lustrous finish it is in demand for furniture. The somewhat similar Philippine mahogany is also used for certain types of furniture, particularly on the West coast of the United States. Ebony is a very hard, almost black, wood. It is used chiefly for chests, carved figurines, and the backs of such articles as hair brushes and hand mirrors. The best ebony is obtained from the forests of southeastern Asia; other ebony or ebonylike woods are secured from central Africa and the West Indies. Spanish cedar, unlike the bulk of tropical woods, is soft and easy to work. In addition, it is light and highly fragrant. Its qualities make it useful for such things as interior trim, closet linings, chests, cigar boxes, and pencils. It is widely produced in the tropical forests, particularly in the Caribbean region, central Africa, and southeastern Asia.

Naval Stores and Tannin

Naval stores represent another group of products secured from forests, a group obtained by tapping, rather than cutting down, trees. Naval stores are pine pitch or resin and the rosin and turpentine derived from the resin. Their name goes back to the days of wooden ships, when large amounts of pine pitch and pitch products were needed to render wooden vessels waterproof and to protect them and their gear from wear and the elements. Pine forests in many sections of the world were tapped to enable merchantmen and ships of war to sail the seas. Today, only a few regions specialize in naval stores and the stores themselves are used mainly for other than ship purposes.

The two major production regions for naval stores are in our South and in the Landes region of southwestern France. United States output comes chiefly from Georgia, Florida, and Alabama. The Landes district is a good example of "much made from nothing." Formerly it was a barren sandy area; now it is a scientifically managed pine forest furnishing a permanent "crop" of pitch. The pine forests of the sandy lands of our South have not been so well managed. However, scientific methods are becoming more prominent: proper care of the trees and careful methods

of tapping are putting more sections on a permanent production basis, as well as increasing the yield per tree (Fig. 412). The resin obtained by tapping is collected in barrels and hauled to local distilleries where the turpentine is distilled from it, leaving a residue called rosin. While naval stores are still consumed in the small-boat industry, most of them now go as semiraw materials to the large manufacturing districts. Turpentine is used in a wide variety of paints and varnishes, and rosin in chemicals, soaps, polishes, and paper surfacers.

The securing of vegetable tanning solutions, unlike naval stores, requires destruction of the plant. Sometimes, leaves, twigs, nuts, and other fruits are used as a source of the tannic acid solutions, but usually it is either the bark or the wood, or both, that furnishes the necessary material. If wood is used it must be chipped or ground before being soaked to obtain its tannin. Oak bark, still in common use, is one of the older sources. Other major sources are hemlock bark, chestnut bark, and quebracho wood. In the United States, oak bark and hemlock bark are of major importance. Most of the oak bark is obtained from the forests of the southern Appalachians and most of the hemlock bark from the remnants of the Mixed Northern Forest, especially in the northern Great Lakes region. The United States leather industry also depends on foreign sources of tannin, particularly quebracho extract from Argentina. Quebracho is a tree of very hard wood (its name means "axbreaker") which grows only in the Chaco region of northern Argentina and adjacent portions of Paraguay. Its tannin content is about double that of hemlock bark. Formerly, whole logs were sent to the United States and Europe, but now most of them are ground up and the solution obtained in scores of small mills located on the banks of the Rio Paraguay. The extract is readily shipped by river boat to Buenos Aires and thence abroad by ocean vessels. In the leather centers of the United States and Europe, the

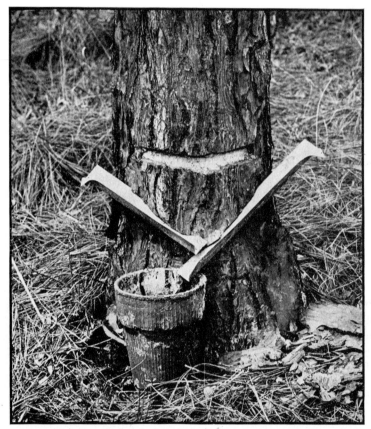

412

SCIENTIFIC tapping of a pine tree for resin for naval stores. (Florida Forest Service, courtesy American Forest Products Industries)

quebracho extract is mixed with that from oak bark and hemlock bark. Mineral tanning solutions are now used in the production of more than half the leather made in the United States, but the remainder is based on vegetable solutions supplied from forest trees, such as American oak and hemlock or Argentine quebracho.

. . . .

CHAPTER OUTLINE

Utilization of forests

General significance of forests
  Foods, spices, and medicines
  Fuel
  Construction materials
  Paper and other cellulose materials
  Game protection
  Water conservation
  Scenery and recreation
Major forest regions of the world
  The tropical forests
  The mid-latitude forests
  The northern forests
Forest regions of the United States
  The Mixed Northern Forest
  The Central Hardwood Forest
  The Southern Mixed Forest
  The Rocky Mountain Forest
  The Pacific Coast Forest
Lumbering
  In the United States
  In Europe
  Outside the United States and Europe
  Naval stores and tannin

REVIEW QUESTIONS

1. Explain and substantiate the statement that, ". . . this is still very much a 'world of wood.' "
2. Distinguish between "forest" and "productive forest."
3. List and discuss the ways in which forests are significant.
4. Describe the general pattern of distribution of the three major forest regions of the world.
5. Compare and contrast general climatic conditions in the world's three major forest regions.
6. What is meant by a "mixed forest"?
7. Name and locate the forest regions of the United States. Give examples of dominant or "key" tree species in each region.
8. Which of the United States forest regions is physically so constituted as to be able to grow trees most rapidly? Why this region?
9. About how long has it taken to nearly wipe out the virgin forests of the United States? Where is most of the remaining virgin forest in this country today? Why is it in that area?
10. Trace briefly the history of lumbering, including geographical shifts, in the United States.
11. What sections of the United States supply nearly all of our commercial lumber at present?
12. Why are most of the wood pulp mills located near pulp wood supplies while most of the paper mills are located in or near large cities, especially in northeastern United States?
13. What is meant by "timber cropping"?
14. Western Europe has been far ahead of the United States in the practice of scientific forestry. Why?
15. Where are the surplus and deficiency areas of Europe as far as forest products are concerned?
16. Why are certain tropical woods sought after? Why is their cost comparatively high?
17. Is world demand primarily for softwood or hardwood? Explain.
18. Discuss the nature and methods of production of naval stores.
19. What is tannin? Comparatively, are mineral or vegetable tannins increasing in importance?
20. It is estimated, on the basis of cubic feet of wood alone, that the forest regions of the United States are now growing about as much wood as is needed. Why, then, is so much heard about decrease in our lumber resource?

SOME SUGGESTED REFERENCES

Forest Resources of the World, Division of Forestry and Forest Products, Food and Agricultural Organization of the United Nations, 1948. A short, modern report on the world forests.

Forest Trees and Forest Regions of the United States, Miscellaneous Publication 217, U. S. Department of Agriculture, 1936. An illustrated pamphlet describing the trees, forests, and forest regions of our country, including Alaska, Hawaii, and Puerto Rico.

Forests and National Prosperity: A Reappraisal of the Forest Situation in the United States, Miscellaneous Publication 668, U. S. Department of Agriculture, 1948. A brief report on forests, forest conditions, and forest products.

Glover, John G., and Cornell, William B., *The Development of American Industries,* Prentice-Hall, Inc., 1946. The history and economic significance of our major industries; Chapters 5 and 6 discuss lumbering and the pulp and paper industries.

Jones, Clarence F., and Darkenwald, Gordon G., *Economic Geography,* Macmillan, 1941. World economic geography by chief occupations; see Part III for discussion of forest industries, including wood cellulose industries.

Lumber Production in the United States, 1799-1946, Miscellaneous Publication 669, U. S. Department of Agriculture, 1948. A report, including statistics, on lumber production in our country from the end of the 18th century to the present period.

Parkins, Almon E., and Whitaker, J. Russell, *Our Natural Resources and Their Conservation,* Wiley, 1939. See especially Chapters 1, 5, 10, and 11 of this book by many authors on the nature, use, and abuse of our natural resources.

Trees, Yearbook of Agriculture, 1949, U. S. Department of Agriculture, 1949. A large, illustrated book, by many authors, dealing with topics ranging from famous trees and forest types to uses of wood and future timber requirements.

United States Pulp and Paper Industry, Trade Promotion Series, No. 182, Bureau of Foreign and Domestic Commerce, 1938. The title well describes the reference.

413   *FOOD from the sea—in this instance herring by the thousands. Here a scoop net is lifting herring from a net which is still in the water of one of the inlets of Canada's western coast. (National Film Board, Ottawa, Canada)*

CHAPTER 27

The World's Fisheries

....

Through the ages fishing has grown from rude and simple beginnings into a world-wide industry with complex apparatus and installations. The earliest known records of China, Mesopotamia, and Egypt indicate that fishing was an important occupation and that certain groups of persons specialized in obtaining food from adjacent waters. The Bible contains many references to fishing and fishermen. The folklore of the Eskimos and the South Sea Islanders is replete with tales of fishing and of the mighty fishermen whose cunning and heroism enabled them to wrest from the sea its bounty. The history of Norway and several other countries of western Europe is entwined with fishing and the voyages of the fishing fleets. Much of the story of early New England is one of fish, fishing vessels, and fishermen. Large sections of the Pacific coast of North America are seldom thought of without salmon fisheries coming to mind. Even in ordinary conversation the always interesting topic of fishing trips and of the "big one that got away" emphasize that fishing continues to manifest its importance in the lives of many men. Dependence upon the earth's waters as a source of both food and raw materials for manufacture is increasing. Obtaining what the waters had to offer has in the past been a matter for individuals or small groups; today, it involves a relatively important segment of the whole population, especially in maritime areas.

NATURE, LOCATION, AND VALUE OF FISHERIES PRODUCTS

The commodities which man obtains from the oceans, seas, lakes, and streams are more numerous and varied than is commonly supposed. Some are animal, some vegetable, and some mineral. Primarily, it is the animal products which are under discussion in this chapter, although some vegetable products are mentioned. Notice was taken earlier in this book of certain minerals obtained from the sea, such as salt and magnesium. All the activities associated with the securing of animal and vegetable products from the earth's waters come under the heading of *fisheries,* even though it is obvious that vegetable materials are not fish, nor are some of the animals, such as seals and whales. Fisheries products include fish, clams, oysters, lobsters, shrimp, eels, turtles, seals, and whales; they also include pearls, sponges, coral, shells, and seaweed.

Most of the fisheries are widely scattered: some are in fresh water, others in salt water; some are in very shallow water, some in comparatively deep water; some are in warm water, others in cold water. The water areas, mainly on continental shelves, from which

PRINCIPAL FISHING AREAS

Principal Commercial Fishing Areas

Other Important Fishing Areas

Sponge Fishing Areas

Pearl Fishing Areas

Sinusoidal equal-area projection.

414 *NEARLY ALL the world's principal fisheries products are obtained in ocean areas with approximate depths of 0-600 feet (0-100 fathoms). Compare this figure with Fig. 208 which shows the depths mentioned.*

the products themselves are obtained are called *fishing grounds*. The chief ones are, as a rule, on the fringes of the land masses which have the widest continental shelves (Fig. 414). Certain of the fishing grounds are called *fishing banks*. Well-known examples are the Grand Bank near Newfoundland and the Dogger Bank of the North Sea. Water depths over the major banks range from as little as 20 to 40 feet to as much as 300 to 600 feet. Some fishing is carried on in still deeper waters, but this is "open-sea," rather than "banks," fishing. The most important banks are located where both warm and cold currents meet to bring a wide variety of fish food into one relatively restricted area. For example, the Grand Bank is supplied with a great variety of minute plants and animals (known collectively as *plankton*) brought by the cold Labrador Current and the warm Gulf Stream.

At any given time, there is a large range in value among the many different kinds of fisheries products. Pearls are far more valuable than shells; fur seals tremendously more valuable than hair seals; pound for pound, sponges are worth more than seaweed; codfish are worth more per pound than herring, and so on. The total value of fisheries products is not known. There are no statistics for all the noncommercial fishing so important in the lives of such peoples as the Eskimos, the Canadian Indians, the South Sea Islanders, the hunter-fishermen of the Congo, or many others. Nor can dollars-and-cents value be attached to the millions of sport fish which are caught each year. The figures which are available for the world's commercial fisheries indicate, for a representative year, a value of about $800,000,000. The annual value of United States fisheries (Alaska included) usually ranges from $100,000,000 to $150,000,000.

The leading fishing nations, in order, are Japan, United States, Soviet Union, United Kingdom, and Norway. In the first one and the latter two, fishing is comparatively more important among the chief occupations, and it occupies a greater percentage of the population. Its comparative importance in these three countries is a reflection, more than anything else, of meager agricultural resources and, hence, a greater dependence on the sea for food. Japan is more dependent on the bounty of the sea than is any other major nation.

USES OF FISHERIES PRODUCTS

No single statement to the effect that fisheries supply fish and that fish are used for human food can do justice to the multitudinous products of the world's fisheries. The wide variety in fisheries products leads to many uses—and new uses are constantly appearing.

Human and Animal Foods

The utilization of fisheries products for human food leads all other uses. The amount consumed varies greatly from one nation to another and from one local group to another. It also varies with general economic conditions. When meat is scarce and high in price, the consumption of fisheries foods increases provided they are or can be made available. Disregarding primitive peoples, consumption normally is high in such nations as Japan, China, Norway, United Kingdom, and the Catholic countries of Europe. It is comparatively low in such countries as the United States, Mexico, Australia, and Argentina.

Food fish, including cod, mackerel, halibut, herring, salmon, and many others, as well as such "fish" as oysters, clams, crab, lobster, shrimp, caviar, and even octopus, are prepared for consumption in many forms (Fig. 415). These include fresh, frozen, salted, dried, smoked, pickled, and canned foods. From the livers of such fish as the cod, halibut, and shark come high-vitamin oils. Other fish supply lard substitutes. Seaweed furnishes vegetable food, in Japan for example, and also agar-agar, which is used in ice-cream mixes and salad dressings.

Livestock and poultry are fed large amounts of fish meal and fish cake. These foods are high in essential proteins, as well as fats.

Other Uses

Fish oils, including whale and seal oils, are used in the manufacture of soaps, cosmetics, special lubricating oils, and margarine. They supply certain ingredients of many paints and varnishes. Also, they are used in the manufacture of linoleum, leathers, waterproofing compounds, and glues.

Fertilizer is prepared in the form of fish powder and fish cake. Seaweed furnishes potash fertilizer and iodine.

Shells supply material for inlaid tables, combs, and brushes, as well as for curios and certain kinds of costume jewelry. They also furnish millions of so-called "pearl" buttons. Real pearls are used for jewelry, and coral for curios and necklaces. Sponges are used for cleaning, surgical, and wall-finishing purposes. In one way or another, the modern fisheries industry allows little to be wasted. Before long, waste of any sort may be a thing of the past.

MAJOR FISHERIES OF EURASIA

Fishing on a local and subsistence basis has been widespread in the world from time immemorial. Fishing on a large and truly commercial scale began in Europe. Of all the continents Europe is most intimately associated with salt water. Not only are there marine coasts on three sides, but there are many large and deep-reaching embayments which extend far inland from the open oceans. Europeans have always been intensely aware

415

LOBSTERS from the waters of the North Atlantic. (National Film Board, Ottawa, Canada)

416   *FISHERMAN and boat near Norway's rocky and nearly barren coast. (Norwegian National Travel Office)*

of the sea and the foods it has to offer. It was only natural that they learned how to build sea-going fishing boats that enabled them to secure more fish than could be obtained by fishing from the shore or in the streams and lakes. Thus, incidentally, Europeans laid the basis for later navies and commercial fleets. To the European peoples, ability to move over the sea gave a start toward development of sea lanes which have become world routeways. In addition, several parts of western Europe, such as rocky Norway and Brittany and sandy Denmark, had such meager agricultural resources that the inhabitants were, in a sense, forced to the sea for at least part of their livelihood (Fig. 416). Fishing operations led to the first real knowledge of the Mediterranean Sea. Fishing paved the way for the forays and explorations of the Vikings. Fishing fleets, particularly from France and Portugal, began making annual voyages across the Atlantic to the Newfoundland banks almost on the heels of John Cabot. Some of the earliest arguments over control of North America revolved around the possession of fishing grounds.

Western Europe

While fishing is carried on across most of Europe, in streams and lakes as well as adjacent seas, it is most important along or relatively near the shores of western Europe (Fig. 414). The chief fishing grounds are in the North Sea, along the coast of Norway, and around Iceland. Others of importance are in the Baltic Sea, the waters west and south of the British Isles, the Bay of Biscay, and far to the north, the White Sea. As noted earlier, the chief fishing nations of western Europe are the United Kingdom and Norway. Their annual catch is about the same, although the United Kingdom usually holds a slight lead. Germany is third, with about half the catch of the leaders. The three combined account for nearly half the total catch of western Europe.

The waters fringing western Europe provide many kinds of fish; chief among them are herring, mackerel, cod, and haddock. Herring is the most important.

Fishing operations are conducted in a very efficient and scientific manner. The vast ma-

417 *FISHING boat of the North Atlantic. (Parks from Standard Oil Co. [N. J.])*

jority of the vessels, whether large or small, are powered by steam, gasoline, or Diesel engines, and many different types of nets and other gear are used (Fig. 417). Shore installations are equipped to carry out rapidly many different processes, such as salting, smoking, canning, oil extraction, or fish-meal preparation (Fig. 418). Experts in fish life are employed to advise the fishermen, and airplanes are often used to locate the schools of fish.

The Mediterranean Sea

The Mediterranean lost, long ago, its one-time leadership in Europe's fishing business, although the tuna and mackerel catches are important. Many of its fishing grounds are badly overfished and modern techniques and scientific knowledge are not widely used. Many Mediterranean countries, like Spain, Italy, and Greece, are so sorely pressed for food that fish, regardless of size and future propagation needs, are caught wherever possible and even in the smallest quantities.

Japan

The extensive fishing grounds of western Europe are matched on the far opposite side of Eurasia by those directly next to or near Japan (Fig. 414). Japan is the world's chief fishing nation, and the bulk of the catch is taken from waters south of Japan and Korea. Even more than in western Europe, the meager agricultural resources, accompanied by high population densities, force great reliance on the resources of the sea. In addition to waters near the homeland, the Japanese fish far afield, not only in the North Pacific, but in the waters of Antarctica and the South Seas. Their total harvest from the ocean, based on tons of fish secured, probably accounts for about 40 per cent of the world's annual total.

Japanese fisheries produce a greater variety of products than those of Europe. Among them are sardines, salmon, cod, mackerel, tuna, shark, and bonito, as well as shellfish, cuttlefish, and crabs. The manufacture of fish oils and fish meals is a prominent corollary of the fisheries. In addition, the Japanese secure pearls and coral from tropical waters and whales from Arctic and Antarctic waters. Cultured pearls are also produced in pearl-oyster "farms" located in shallow waters along the southerly portion of the homeland. Seaweed is harvested in large quantities. It is an important vegetable food for humans, as well as a source of fertilizer, animal fodder, iodine, and stuffing for certain types of upholstery.

The equipment of the Japanese fisheries industry combines the ancient and the very new. Most of the boats are small and depend on sail power (Fig. 419). The larger vessels, which range far waters, have powerful modern engines and are equipped to stay at sea for months at a time. Not only do they possess refrigeration facilities, but some of them are huge floating factories which can catch,

418 *FISHING station and fleet, Lofoten Islands, Norway. (Norwegian National Travel Office)*

process, and pack either thousands of cases of salmon and crab or whole whales. As with Europe, the fishing industry taught Japan to build and operate boats, and to explore ever more distant waters, and laid the basis of a huge navy and merchant marine— most of which was destroyed during World War II.

Other Fisheries

Other Eurasian fisheries occur along the eastern, southeastern, and southern coast of Asia. Their westernmost extension is found in the Persian Gulf and the Red Sea (Fig. 414). Even combined they are of less importance than the Japanese fisheries. Nearly all of them are coastal rather than deep-water ones. Fishing vessels are small and of ancient design and they engage in fishing primarily for subsistence rather than for commerce. Some pearls are obtained along the southern coast, especially in the Persian Gulf and the Red Sea. The latter also furnishes some sponges.

Inland from the Asiatic coasts, as in Europe, fish are secured from numerous rivers and a few lakes and interior seas. Eastern China is particularly dependent on stream and pond fish for some of its food. Much farther north, portions of the large Siberian rivers, especially in southern Siberia, are sources of fresh-water fish. Among the inland water bodies, Lake Baikal (fresh) and the Aral and Caspian seas (both saline) are worth noting.

MAJOR FISHERIES OF THE AMERICAS

North America has rich fishing grounds on three of its sides: Atlantic coast, Pacific coast, and the Gulf Coast-Caribbean-Bahamas area (Fig. 414). Inland fisheries, of far less value,

are widespread; those of the Great Lakes and the Mississippi and its tributaries are most significant. The North American ocean fisheries, coastal and deep-water, are controlled chiefly by the United States and Canada. Together, they probably produce somewhat less than half the annual tonnage of the Japanese fisheries. The United States, including Alaska, produces about four times the tonnage of Canada, about two-fifths the tonnage of Japan, and less than half the tonnage of Europe.

South American fisheries are comparatively minor (Fig. 414). In fact, nowhere in the Southern Hemisphere are there fishing grounds as large or as well supplied with fish and fish food as those in the Northern Hemisphere. Some coastal fishing occurs on both eastern and western sides of South America (that on the western side is more important), especially in the colder waters of the south. Whales are obtained in the adjacent waters of Antarctica and the Falkland Islands. Stream fishing, mainly noncommercial, is important in the Amazon River, the Paraná River, and their tributaries.

United States

The commercial fisheries of the United States began with Plymouth Colony in the early 1600's. In fact, Plymouth sent a cargo of fish, preserved by salting, to England as early as 1624. Plymouth also traded in fish with other settlements, including the Dutch colony of New Amsterdam. The importance of fish as food and as a profitable trade item resulted in the establishment of many fishing villages and towns and in the spread of the industry to new and more distant fishing grounds. The success of the New England fisheries encouraged the development of fishing activities farther south, at many places along the entire Atlantic coast. When the thirteen colonies became the United States, fishing rights were retained not only in the

419 *JAPANESE coastal fishing is carried on with small boats and only the simplest equipment. (Natori from Black Star)*

waters near the States, but also in those of the Newfoundland banks.

The Atlantic fisheries of the United States extend from the Grand Bank of Newfoundland to Florida (Fig. 414). They are both less and more important than in the past: less important because they occupy a smaller place among all present-day occupations; more important because the annual catch and annual value of the catch is greater than in the past. As in most other commercial fisheries of the world, modern boats and gear have made larger catches possible, both in deep-water and shallow-water fishing grounds. Also, modern methods of processing and marketing, including a greatly increased sale of "iced" and quick-frozen fish to markets located far inland, permit large catches to be disposed of quickly. Fishing ports are strung from Portland, Maine, to Jacksonville, Florida, but the major ones are Boston, Gloucester, and Baltimore. The leading fishing grounds extend from the latitude of Virginia northward to the Grand Bank (Fig. 420). Typical products are cod, halibut, haddock, herring, and mackerel, as well as oysters, clams, and lobsters. Farther south, men-

haden, mullet, bass, bluefish, among others, are obtained; these have less value for food purposes, but are used in the preparation of fish-meal fertilizer, fish-meal and fish-cake animal feeds, and fish oils. The menhaden is a particularly good source of oil and fertilizer.

The warm waters of the Gulf Coast-Caribbean-Bahamas region supply a wide variety of commercial fisheries products. Included are mackerel, mullet, red snapper, flounder, sheepshead, oysters, some pearls, shrimp, and sponges. Gulf of Mexico shrimp, which grow comparatively large, are of increasing importance. The major sponge-fishing region of the world is in the waters of the Bahama Islands, those of the east and west coasts of Florida, and those to the north of Cuba and Haiti. Recently, widespread sponge disease, plus the manufacture of synthetic sponges, has greatly injured the sponge industry. The fishing industry as a whole centers in a few major ports located here and there from Jacksonville, Florida, to Galveston, Texas. Despite the variety of products, these warm-water fisheries are much less valuable than those of the Atlantic, especially the northern Atlantic, section.

Pacific-coast fisheries of the United States

have, in general, increased greatly in value within recent years. Some commercial fishing has been practiced there for approximately a century. Salmon, nearly all canned, leads by a wide margin. It is obtained in immediate coastal waters and river mouths all the way from northern California to southern Alaska (Fig. 421). The heaviest catch is in Alaskan waters and the bulk of it is canned, almost as soon as caught, in small cannery towns which bustle with activity during the summer "salmon run" and are practically deserted the rest of the year. Large amounts also are canned in the cities of Seattle and Portland. The numbers of salmon have declined, particularly in the southern section, and the future of the industry is precarious. Unwise fishing practices, based on the impulse to "get rich quick" and the idea that "there will always be plenty of salmon," plus pollution of the river spawning grounds, the damming of rivers, and widespread river logging operations, are major factors in the decline. As salmon fishing has declined somewhat, tuna fishing has increased. Like salmon, tuna is marketed almost entirely in canned form. California produces nearly all the tuna "pack" in the United States, and Los Angeles is the chief tuna port and canning center. Other important commercial fish taken along or near the West coast include pilchard (sar-

dines), herring, and mackerel. The major fishing ports of the Pacific coast are San Diego, Los Angeles, Monterey, San Francisco, Portland, and Seattle, as well as the many small and scattered cannery towns of southeastern Alaska (Fig. 422). It is pertinent to note that the Pacific-coast fisheries supply the greater bulk of canned and otherwise preserved fish produced in the United States.

On the basis of value, the Pacific-coast fisheries, including Alaska, account for about 43 per cent of United States production; excluding Alaska, they account for some 32 per cent. New England accounts for about 23 per cent of the United States-Alaska total and all the Atlantic fisheries (New England included) for about 43 per cent. Total values, then, are about the same for both the Pacific-coast fisheries (Alaska included) and the Atlantic-coast fisheries. The Gulf Coast-Caribbean-Bahamas fisheries produce about 9 per cent of the value of United States-Alaska fisheries.

Inland fisheries account for some 6 per cent of the value of United States-Alaska fisheries. Nearly all the inland production is from the Great Lakes and the Mississippi River. While these fresh-water fisheries are comparatively insignificant, it may be surprising to learn that their production equals slightly more

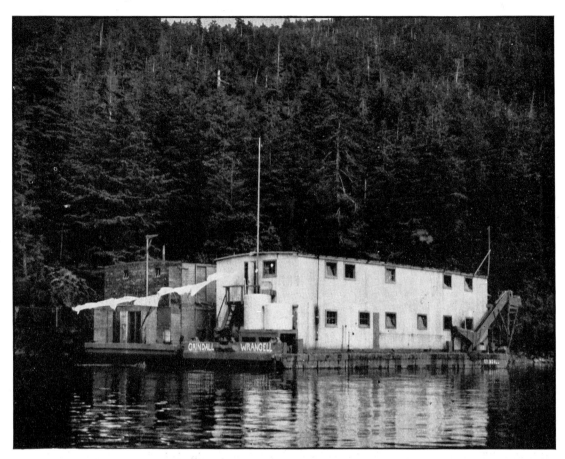

421 *A FLOATING salmon cannery in one of the many coves along the steep, forested shore of southeastern Alaska. (H. C. Scudder from U. S. Fish and Wildlife Service)*

422 *FISHING vessels and canneries at Los Angeles Harbor, California. The canneries shown handle chiefly tuna, sardines, and mackerel. (U. S. Fish and Wildlife Service)*

4 2 3 *THE "FUR-seal islands," the Pribilofs, lie in the eastern Bering Sea at about 57° N.*

than half the value of the famous Alaskan fisheries. The production of the Great Lakes fisheries alone is equal to nearly half that of Alaska. Also, the average price per pound received for Great Lakes fish is higher than in any of the other United States-Alaska fisheries. The chief fish are herring, trout, perch, chub, and whitefish. The Lower Lakes account for most of the catch, but Lake Superior is famous for its trout and whitefish, which command high prices in the hotel and restaurant trade. Some of them, packed in ice, are shipped by express and airplane to cities as far away as New York and San Francisco. The greater portion of all Great Lakes fish is sold fresh in large cities located along or near the Lower Lakes. Nearly 2,000 small craft, known as "fishing tugs," carry on the Lakes fisheries. They operate both from small towns and fishing villages and from large city ports. Seldom do they travel more than a few miles

from their home docks. The total catch is declining. Again, it is the old story of overfishing, insufficient protection of small, young fish, and pollution of waters. Added difficulties are the spread of certain fish diseases and the recent invasion of the lakes by a kind of sea lamprey, an eellike creature that fastens itself to a fish's side and feeds until the fish dies. The Mississippi River fisheries supply local towns and cities with such products as catfish, carp, and buffalo. They also contribute important amounts of mussels (river clams) which are used chiefly for buttons and "pearl" inlays. Mussels also contribute a few "river pearls."

A separate and unique portion of the United States fisheries is carried on in the Pribilof Islands. This is the fur-seal industry. The Pribilofs are in the Bering Sea about 250 miles west of the Alaskan Peninsula and a like distance north of the arc made by the

Aleutian Islands (Fig. 423). From the Pribi-lofs come practically all of the world's fur-seal pelts. Ruthless, uncontrolled exploitation nearly wiped out the fur-seal herds; by 1910, herds which formerly numbered approxi-mately 2,500,000 had been reduced to about 125,000. In 1911, the United States succeeded in obtaining an international agreement for the controlled hunting of the fur seals. Under this agreement only a certain number of the bachelor seals were killed each year and the annual take was apportioned as follows: United States, 70 per cent; Japan, 15 per cent; Canada, 15 per cent. Japan withdrew from the compact in 1941, and under present agreement between the United States and Canada, the United States reserves 80 per cent and Canada 20 per cent. Management of the Pribilof seals has worked so successfully that today they number close to 3,000,000 and the annual take is about 125,000 pelts or "skins"—a take comparable to that of more than half a century ago. St. Louis, Missouri, is the major world market for fur-seal pelts.

Canada

Of various Canadian fisheries, it is the ocean fisheries, both shallow and deep-water, that are of chief commercial importance (Fig. 414). The major fishing grounds lie near Newfoundland, Nova Scotia, and Labrador, in the Gulf of St. Lawrence, and along the shore of British Columbia (Figs. 414, 420).

Salmon is king in the west and cod in the east. For the past half century, or slightly more, salmon has exceeded cod in value (Fig. 424). Other important fish on both coasts are herring and halibut. Some seals (not fur seals) are hunted in Hudson Bay. Total Canadian fisheries production normally has a value about one-third that of the United States-Alaska fisheries.

Newfoundland, first of the British colonies in the New World, long has been synony-mous with good fishing. Fishing still occupies approximately one-third of the population, including practically all the population of the Labrador coast. Meager agricultural resources,

424 DRYING cod on flakes (racks) in a Nova Scotia fishing town. (National Film Board, Ottawa, Canada)

combined with the abundance of fish in the nearby sea, have kept fishing in a position of great prominence. Within recent years, both forest products and mineral products have exceeded fish in value. Even so, fishing still is relatively much more important in Newfoundland than in other Canadian provinces and the United States and, perhaps, relatively more important than in any other part of the world. The chief fish are cod, herring, and halibut; there are a few salmon, and seals are hunted off the Labrador coast.

OTHER FISHERIES

In addition to the world fisheries discussed in the preceding pages there are others which should at least be mentioned. These are the whale, seal (nonfur), and pearl fisheries.

Commercial whaling began as a near-shore activity in Europe nearly a thousand years ago. Since then it has spread into deep waters and across all the oceans. Whaling reached its peak during the nineteenth century and then went into decline when petroleum and petroleum products largely supplanted whale oil and when metals and synthetic materials came to replace whalebone in women's apparel. But decline did not mean oblivion. Some demand continued for whalebone in clothing and for use in mechanical brushes; the oil is used in soaps, leather preservatives, special lubricants, and edible fats; the meat is used as human food; and the "waste" is processed as meal and cake for animal feed, poultry feed, and fertilizer. Following World War II, the shortage of edible and industrial fats and oils, as well as meat, gave new encouragement to the whaling industry.

Modern whaling is carried on by large, intricately equipped ships quite unlike the sailing whalers of the past century. While some whales are still towed to port and processed in shore "stations," many of them are processed at sea in huge factory ships (Fig. 425).

Some whales still are captured in Arctic waters and in the North Atlantic and North Pacific, but most of them are now found in commercial numbers only in the Antarctic Ocean and along the southwestern coast of Africa (Fig. 414). Norwegian vessels continue to dominate the whaling industry; others are mainly British, Japanese, and Argentine.

Seal fisheries, in addition to the fur-seal industry previously mentioned, are carried on mainly in the Arctic Ocean, the Hudson Bay-Labrador Coast region, and the portion of the Antarctic Ocean near South America. Like whales, many of the varieties of nonfur seals have become extinct, or nearly so. Those of present commercial importance are obtained chiefly in northern waters and are mainly of the group known in the trade as "hair seals." These seals are sought for their oil and hides. The oil is used primarily for special lubricants and industrial dressings and the hides for the manufacture of such goods as shoes, handbags, and luggage. The industry is dominated by Russian, Norwegian, and British sealers.

FISHING SETTLEMENTS

The human settlements associated with fishing vary greatly from one place to another. Those of a more primitive sort are small and simple. They are represented by such as the South Sea Island fishing village and the Eskimo fishing village of northwest Greenland. Some of them are seasonal and temporary, like the summer fishing encampment of the Indians in the portion of Canada west of Churchill. Equipment is simple, usually no more than small boats, spears, and crude nets. Processing, too, is simple. Fish not immediately consumed may be dried, salted, or smoked, but there are no special buildings or machinery. Likewise, there are no problems of market price, transportation, or special handling.

Nonprimitive fishing settlements are quite

425 *A NORWEGIAN "whaler" and a bountiful "catch." (Norwegian Official Photo)*

different, whether they are comparatively simple or highly complex. Their function is to supply commercial, rather than subsistence, fish. Some of them are small and simple, like the fishing villages of rocky Labrador (Fig. 426) or those found in parts of northern Norway, but, no matter how small, they possess specialized gear and processing grounds or buildings and they are connected with the channels of world trade. Somewhat larger settlements are very highly specialized as to gear, processing equipment, and types of wharves. They also are well integrated with the world's transport system, including sometimes even air service. Examples are to be seen in Norway's Lofoten Island towns and villages (Fig. 418), the fishing towns of the Bay of Biscay Coast of France, or the whaling and sealing stations of the Falkland Islands (Fig. 427). Some of the highly specialized settlements are, in a sense, seasonal. A good example is seen in the typical cannery town of southern Alaska, which comes to life when the salmon starts to run.

Today, the most important fishing centers can hardly be called fishing settlements. The handling of fish is only one of many economic activities. All of the intricate operations involved in receiving, processing, and distributing fish and fish products represent but a small part of the total commercial and industrial work performed by large seaport cities. One can hardly refer to Boston as a fishing settlement, or Baltimore, or New Orleans. The same is true of Los Angeles, even though that city or, rather, its harbor section, is the leading fishing center of the United States. Fishing, like so many other occupations, has become largely mechanized and urbanized. Commercially at least, fishing is now chiefly a "big-town" and "big-city" enterprise, despite the fact that the fish or other fishery products may be secured many miles away.

••

CHAPTER OUTLINE

The world's fisheries

Nature, location, and value of fisheries products
Uses of fisheries products
  Human and animal foods
  Other uses

426 *A SMALL fishing village in northern Labrador, seemingly lost in the maze of inlets and glaciated rocks so typical of the Labrador coast. (Photo from Alexander Forbes:* Northernmost Labrador Mapped from the Air, *American Geographical Society)*

REVIEW QUESTIONS

1. Why is the term "fisheries" somewhat inappropriate and ambiguous?
2. List the commercial products obtained from the earth's waters, excluding mineral products.
3. Locate the chief fishing regions of the Americas. How do these correlate with water depths?
4. What are plankton and why are they important?
5. How does the annual value (in dollars) of world fisheries compare with the annual value of automobiles made in the United States?
6. Which nations are the leading fishing nations of the world?
7. Why are sea products such a major item in the diet of the Japanese?
8. Where are Europe's major fishing areas? What two countries lead in Europe's fishing industry?
9. Discuss the significance of fishing in the development of New England and its business.
10. What are the chief commercial uses of cod? Of menhaden?
11. Are there any major reasons for the recent decline in the United States sponge fisheries?
12. What are the major problems of the Great Lakes fisheries?
13. Discuss the fur-seal industry.
14. Contrast the "old" and the "new" in world whaling activities. What nations dominate the whaling industry?

15. Why is it that today's chief fishing ports cannot be referred to as "fishing settlements"?

16. See if you can find recent articles on the future importance of the sea and of fresh waters in terms of food supply for man.

SOME SUGGESTED REFERENCES

Ackerman, Edward A., *New England's Fishing Industry,* University of Chicago Press, 1941. Historical, economic, and social aspects of our fisheries of the Northeast, from southern New England to the Bay of Fundy.

Bengtson, Nels A., and Van Royen, William, *Fundamentals of Economic Geography,* Prentice-Hall, Inc., 1950. A new edition of an introductory textbook in economic geography; see Chapter 17 which discusses the economic significance of the sea.

Glover, John G., and Cornell, William B., *The Development of American Industries,* Prentice-Hall, Inc., 1946. Our basic industries and their history and economic significance; the fishing industry is discussed in Chapter 4.

Jones, Clarence F., and Darkenwald, Gordon G., *Economic Geography,* Macmillan, 1941. The world's economic geography as based on a study of major occupations; Chapters 3, 4, and 5 deal with subsistence hunting and fishing and with commercial fishing of fresh waters, sea coasts, banks, and open seas.

Parkins, Almon E., and Whitaker, J. Russell, *Our Natural Resources and Their Conservation,* Wiley, 1939. See Chapters 19 and 20 which discuss wild life and fisheries.

Smith, J. Russell, and Phillips, M. Ogden, *Industrial and Commercial Geography,* Holt, 1946. Basic resources and industries of the world; fisheries are discussed in Chapter 20.

U. S. Bureau of Fisheries, Washington, D. C. Various publications.

427   *A WHALING station in the Falkland Islands. (British Information Services)*

428 ROUTES over the land, on the water, and through the air create a world-wide net of increasingly closer weave which ties together all the parts of the human habitat. At the top, the Rock Island Railroad roundhouse at El Reno, Oklahoma. (Rotkin from Standard Oil Co. [N. J.]) Below, a moonlight view of the east side of New York Harbor with Brooklyn at the upper left and the channel to the Atlantic in the center background. (Corsini from Standard Oil Co. [N. J.])

CHAPTER 28

The World Pattern of Routes

The endless variety of both physical and cultural elements of the human habitat from place to place suggests, at first thought, a sharp separation of the individual parts of the world. There is real danger of overemphasizing this notion of separateness. Actually, the whole human habitat is a single mosaic in which each tile contributes its bit to the overall effect. It is the world pattern of routes, above all other patterns, that holds the pieces together. The pattern of routes is like the visible part of the matrix in which the individual tiles of a mosaic are set. Though routes appear superficially to be separators, their function, like the material which holds one tile to the others in a mosaic, is to unite the whole—to tie together the great variety of the human habitat into one world pattern.

The present world pattern of routes has evolved through the whole of human history; it reflects man's efforts, successes, and failures in overcoming the handicaps of distance and barriers and in passing from simple to complex economic stages. Early man depended upon his own muscles to move about over the surface of the earth, primarily in search of his food. His routes were irregular, perhaps radiating from his shelter throughout the area in which he hunted, or leading from his shelter to a source of water. His routes were limited by the distance which he could conveniently cover on foot. With the taming of animals which could be used as beasts of burden and

with the invention of navigation, range of movement became greater and routes more definitely fixed—a pathway from the dwelling to a fishing site on a lake or river, or the river itself when used to get from one hunting ground to another.

Routes followed by one group of people gradually extended to link up with those of neighboring groups. Overland roads for vehicles took the place of trails for men and animals. River routes formed links between land routes; then water routes were extended first to cross inland seas and later to cross open oceans. Artificial waterways, canals, amplified the natural water routes. Steam power brought the railroad. The internal-combustion engine speeded movement overland and later brought air travel. At each step, the existing pattern of routes was amplified both in more intensive local coverage and in its wide extent. Always the result was the closer tying together of the whole human habitat, the creation of one modern world mosaic from the scattered fragments of the prehistoric world.

The world pattern of routes is made up of lines of transportation and communication over the land, on the water, and through the air. The lines on the land leave permanent traces whether they are paths, trails, roads, or railroads. On the water, inland waterways, both natural and artificial, are essentially as clearly marked as roads, but nothing permanent marks the passage of a ship over a sea or ocean. Nor is there a visible trace of passage through the air. Yet, both ocean and air routes become as well marked as roads, for they exist because they link two places on the surface of the spherical earth. The shortest route between any two such points occurs along a great circle. As near as is physically possible and economically feasible, ships and aircraft follow these great circle routes.

INTERCONTINENTAL ROUTES

Ocean Routes

The great highways of the oceans and seas exist despite the lack of visible markings. Just as surely as though the way were marked by a broad expanse of pavement, a ship sailing from a port on the eastern coast of North America to one in northwestern Europe follows, within broad limits, the course of the ship which preceded it. In so far as it is possible, this course is a great circle on the ocean's surface because a great circle is the shortest distance between any two points on the globe. Similarly, certain other parts of the world's oceans become regularly traveled routes which can be indicated with exactness upon the map (Fig. 429).

Well-defined ocean routes were not so prominent in the past when a far larger proportion of ocean traffic was handled by "tramps," those cargo-carrying vessels that plied from port to port where cargo was available. Nowadays, the role of the tramp steamer has dwindled; regular cargo services exist and vessels ply back and forth between fixed termini. Thus by far the greater part of transocean traffic has been funneled into a few outstanding routes. These routes are the great strands which tie the densely settled portions of the human habitat together.

THE NORTH ATLANTIC ROUTE. The shape of the North Atlantic basin and the directions of the North American and European coastlines are such that the routes from all ports on one side of the ocean to those on the other side follow essentially the same course—a great-circle route across the North Atlantic. For example, ships from the ports of the southeastern United States must follow closely along the coast northward for some distance if they are to follow the shortest route to western Europe.

This convergence of shipping lanes to form the North Atlantic route and the nature of the lands at each end of it easily explain its rank as the most used route in the world. Surplus raw materials, partially manufactured goods, and some wholly manufactured commodities flow eastward from industrial eastern North America and from its regions of surplus agriculture in the interior of the continent. Back from even more densely peopled northwest Europe flow manufactures, both complete and partial, and a few food items. In addition, millions of people have followed the route, the millions that moved westward from overcrowded Europe to help fill the empty interior of a new land in the past and since then the smaller stream returning, mostly for temporary visits or for business negotiations.

In winter, the North Atlantic route is exceedingly stormy for, at that season, it lies athwart the zone of contact between Polar and Tropical air masses. Storm follows storm, with gale-force winds whipping the sea into tremendous waves and lowering temperatures below the freezing point. At all seasons, though somewhat more frequently in summer and autumn than at any other time of year, fog is a hazard on the Newfoundland Grand Bank where the warm Gulf Stream encounters the cold Labrador Current. In summer, icebergs drifting southward from more northerly seas make necessary continued patrolling of the waters along this route so that the hundreds of ships that ply the track may be warned and escape danger. Despite these handicaps, the North Atlantic route has be-

429 *THE GREAT ocean routes stand out as clearly as though they were highways across the land.*

come the highway for a large share of the world's total shipping tonnage. This route serves nearly half of the world's principal ports.

THE MEDITERRANEAN-ASIATIC-AUSTRALIAN ROUTE. The route which is second to the North Atlantic water highway is the one leading from northwestern Europe to the densely settled areas of the Middle and Far East. This is known as the Mediterranean-Asiatic-Australian route. From the North Sea it leads through the Strait of Gibraltar and on to the eastern end of the Mediterranean Sea. Then by means of the man-made Suez Canal, it reaches into the Red Sea and through that into the Arabian Sea. Branch routes diverge to the eastern coast of Africa, to the Persian Gulf, and to the ports of western Pakistan and India (Fig. 429), but the main track

leads on to Ceylon. There, two branches open out, one to southern Australia and the other through the Strait of Malacca past Singapore to the East Indies and the coastlands and islands of the eastern Asiatic fringe.

This route is much longer than the one which links the lands on either side of the North Atlantic. Furthermore, local traffic contributes heavily to the total which flows along it, primarily because the route follows close to the land throughout much of its course. For example, the exchange between the eastern and western ends of the Mediterranean and, at least prior to World War II, the flow between Japan and the East Indies were significant elements in total volume. This route has often been called the "life line of the British Empire" for it tied industrial Britain to a large portion of her overseas dominions and colonies. Along it lie nearly all the different kinds of lands from the tropics to the higher middle latitudes; it has one terminus in areas of Western industrial economy and the other in the center of Oriental agricultural economy. Yet, the flow along it is smaller than that across the North Atlantic: southeastern Asia is a region of relatively little surplus production and the buying power of that region is still low in comparison to that at either end of the North Atlantic route.

OTHER MAJOR OCEAN ROUTES. Prior to the cutting of the Suez Canal, the way to the East lay around the Cape of Good Hope in southern Africa or around Cape Horn at the southern tip of South America. The Cape of Good Hope route is still important as one of the major routes of the world; economic and political ties between northwestern Europe and southern Africa are sufficiently close to provide considerable traffic.

The Europe to eastern South America route diverges from the Cape of Good Hope route off the Saharan coast of Africa. Along it flow the manufactured goods of northwestern Europe and the agricultural surpluses of southeastern South America. Though this route continues southward to "round the Horn," volume traffic on it decreases materially south of Buenos Aires. The eastern South America to eastern North America route has been far less significant in the past than the one leading from South America to Europe, but it nevertheless is one of the prominent world routes.

The North America to western South America route owes its prominence to the Panama Canal. Before the canal was constructed, the water route between the Atlantic and Pacific seaboards of North America had to follow the difficult way around Cape Horn. Now, the Panama Canal provides a cutoff and, in addition, allows easy contact of both eastern and western North America with all the coastlands of South America. Still further, the coastlands of Middle America and the islands of the Caribbean are easily

accessible to the arms of this Y-shaped route (Fig. 429).

The tremendous expanse of the Pacific Ocean is spanned by two main ocean highways. The North Pacific route swings far to the north, close to the Aleutian Islands and more than a thousand miles north of the Hawaiian Islands, to provide the shortest course between the ports of western America and those of eastern Asia. The North America to Australasia route cuts boldly southwestward from west-coast ports by way of the Hawaiian Islands to stretch the 7,000-mile distance to New Zealand and Australia. Secondary routes make a crossroads station of the Hawaiian Islands. But the volume which flows over the Pacific routes is far less than that of the previously mentioned ones, except under the stress of war. The routes are "marked out," but they have not become the heavily traveled "Main Streets" of world transportation.

The eight routes that have been listed form the skeleton of ocean transportation (Fig. 429). From all of them, there are almost innumerable branches. The coastwise shipping of most every maritime nation merges with the main flow along one of these eight routes in some parts of its course. About the edges of all of the continents except Antarctica and the Arctic fringes of North America and Eurasia, oceans and seas are well-used routes. Even the Arctic fringe of Eurasia is subject to sporadic use: the Arctic Sea route from northern European Russia to eastern Asiatic Russia has been used in summer since 1936. The coastal fringes feed to the main ocean highways which, in turn, link together the permanently inhabited parts of the globe.

Air Routes

The last quarter century has seen the addition of the airway to the ocean route as a means of intercontinental transportation. A growing net of airways has spread over much of the whole human habitat and has been projected over an even greater part, particularly since the close of World War II. And flights along existing routes have multiplied, thus linking the continental areas even more closely together than before.

GENERAL FACTORS IN AIR-ROUTE LOCATION. Like a ship crossing an ocean, an airplane leaves no visible trace of its passage. The atmosphere extends alike over land and sea. Passage through it is possible in any direction. It would seem, therefore, that there would be no restricting influence to the development of air routes between any two points on the earth's surface. Further, it might appear that there would be no tendency to establish regular channels of flight now that long-range aircraft have been developed. But air routes have become more or less fixed just as have ocean routes. Some examination of the causes must here be made.

Economic reasons help to account for the close-knit appearance of the air net over some parts of the world and its fragmentary nature in others. Airplanes of the present day travel at speeds scarcely conceived twenty-five years ago. Though their size has increased greatly in the same period, they can carry only relatively small loads as compared with ocean vessels. In addition, much of an airplane's carrying capacity has to be used to transport the huge loads of fuel necessary to drive it at high speed over long distances. Thus, the airplane's use normally must be restricted to the transport of human beings or of goods of great value per unit weight. Here, then, is a restriction placed upon the location and growth of intercontinental air routes.

The highly industrialized and commercialized portions of the world, northwestern Europe and northeastern North America, are certainly the chief destinations for high-value goods. In most instances, these same regions are likewise the origin. It is in these regions, too, that human travel, either for business or for recreational purposes, is most common. Hence, northwestern Europe and northeastern North America constitute prominent foci for the strands of the intercontinental air net (Fig. 430). The strands themselves are heaviest over the North Atlantic basin.

PRINCIPAL INTERCONTINENTAL
AIR ROUTES
1950

430 *TODAY'S intercontinental air net has as its prominent foci northwestern Europe and northeastern North America.*

Southward from both the North American and European foci, air routes lead to South America and Africa. Western North America and Asia are tied across the North Pacific. By way of the Hawaiian Islands, North America is likewise tied to the southwest Pacific area, to New Zealand and Australia, and to Asia. Finally, from northwest Europe routes extend to southern and eastern Asia, thus completing the girdling of the globe (Fig. 430). In general, the pattern of air routes corresponds closely to the distribution of areas most influenced by Western industrial civilization.

SPECIFIC FACTORS IN AIR-ROUTE LOCATION. The growth of air routes is affected not only by economic developments, but also by certain technical difficulties peculiar to air travel. The most critical periods in any airplane flight are, ordinarily, the take-off and the landing. Adequate facilities, especially a large cleared area suitably surfaced and with unobstructed approaches, are essential at both ends of a flight. Intercontinental aircraft need ports just as ocean vessels do. These ports must be located where both passengers and high-value goods are available in quantity. Essentially this means a location in or near great cities or groups of cities. Commercial centers were already established and the flow lines of both passengers and goods to them were well fixed before the airplane came into being. It is to these centers that airports have had to be attached. The terminal points of significant intercontinental air routes were, thus, fairly well predetermined.

Yet, the very places on the earth's surface which are the most logical terminal points for air routes combine many difficulties for efficient air operation. In the first place, space in the world's great cities is at a premium. Usually, this means relegation of the airport to a location at some distance from the city's center. Local transportation which will make movement easy and rapid between the urban center and the airport becomes an essential.

Even if easily accessible space is available, the mere presence of the city imposes physical obstacles to approach and departure. Tall buildings and power lines suggest two of these; the smoke of heavy industrial plants is another.

Then, too, since cities date from an earlier period in transportation history, presence of a good ocean harbor may have outweighed other features of site. Level land is often not present except at some distance from the urban center. Yet, despite this difficulty, it is where the break between overland and ocean routes provides a collecting and distributing center that air routes must be tied down to earth.

Local weather conditions must also be taken into account in the detailed location of air routes. Weather phenomena like frontal activity, visibility, and icing conditions are troublesome. Man is not yet able to control the weather. In two ways, however, he has sought to overcome its effects. First, progress has been made in understanding atmospheric conditions and probable atmospheric changes. Second, even greater progress has been made by numerous inventions to cope with unfavorable weather conditions. Deicing and pressurizing equipment, radio, radar, and the like have all made air transport possible in extremely adverse weather.

Yet, even now, weather causes flight cancellations or changes of destination in midflight. Where regularly followed air routes become well established, subsidiary airfields or emergency landing fields must be available. It is in the areas of industrial economy, such as northeastern North America and northwestern Europe, that airfields are most numerous.

Meteorological observations are more plentiful and more complete on either side of the North Atlantic and along the great route followed by ocean shipping between North America and Europe than in any other part of the world. Despite the fact that this part of the atmosphere is a zone of intensive cyclonic activity and hence a zone of extremely variable weather, it is nevertheless better understood than almost any other portion of the earth's atmospheric blanket.

National frontiers present another obstacle to international air routes. The segment of the atmosphere above a country is considered to lie within the jurisdiction of that country. Once an ocean vessel clears port, it may proceed on any determined course across the open ocean. Movement over the world's oceans, except in the immediate vicinity of the coast, is recognizedly open to ships of all nations. Airplanes, however, if they fly the shortest course, often have to pass over, perhaps more literally through, the domain of different nations.

For example, the route from New York to Europe leads to the British Isles or, by way of the Azores, to Portugal. Newfoundland's location, close to main great circle routes across the North Atlantic, makes it a logical junction point. Gander, Newfoundland, is truly an international air-route junction. Nevertheless, one country—Canada—has sovereignty over the port and all of its approaches. Thus, it is easy to see that great international air routes are vulnerable in a way that ocean transportation is not.

INTRACONTINENTAL ROUTES

Where the great transoceanic routes by air or sea reach the continental edges, they join networks of routes leading inland, networks which tie even the most remote fixed human habitation into the world transportation pattern. Roads, waterways, and railroads exist as visible evidences of the flow lines of people and goods. Airfields indicate the most recent addition to the transport scheme. All of these forms, with the vehicles which move along

them, are among the more prominent man-made features on the land. In this respect alone, intracontinental transportation is immediately different from intercontinental, which has as its major evidence only the urban terminal ports.

The culture of the inhabitants of an area, largely their economy and the stage of development within that economy, determines the nature of the network of routes and the intensity of its use. To the self-sufficient farmers of South China, for example, roads are of little significance. The few that exist are mere tracks or paths leading from the villages to the fields. They are not main-traveled thoroughfares between large urban centers, nor do large quantities of goods flow along them. On the other hand, to an industrial society like that in the northeastern United States, first-class highways with many surfaced and unsurfaced feeders, numerous railroads, and a growing system of air lines are "musts." Along all of these, as well as along inland waterways, flow the necessaries upon which industrial life is based. Food and raw materials for manufacture constantly travel inward to the urban centers, and manufactured goods move outward with similar constancy. The net of transportation must not only be of the highest quality; it must also be closely woven.

The location of any route is subject to the strong effects of both the physical and the cultural elements of the habitat. Since its function is to tie together two given points, any route follows the most direct path feasible between those two points. The obstacles which force deviation from the straight line path are numerous. Some of them are physical features like steep slopes, swamps, or lakes; others are man-made like property lines or international boundaries. Nevertheless, whether it is the rude footworn path of the Chinese farmer or the wide, gleaming pavement of the most modern superhighway, the straight line trajectory is the goal.

Roads

FUNCTION. The main function of the road is to *facilitate* the movement of human beings and their goods from one place to another on the face of the earth. This means different things to different groups of people. The needs of the migratory farmer of the Amazon forest are met by a crude system of pathways from his jungle-crowded garden patch to his dwelling, from a fishing place along a river to his dwelling, and from a hunting or collecting place in the forest to his dwelling. Perhaps animal trails through the areas of lighter forest are also roads for him, for they lead him to and from the places where he can supplement his meager agriculture. All of these pathways are his "roads"; the function of them all is to facilitate his movement.

In the intensive industrial region of northwestern Europe, as in that of northeastern North America, the "road"—it may be a magnificently paved and boulevarded highway—has essentially the same function. The differences between the primitive path and the modern highway are differences in magnitude and not in function. For the migratory farmer, it is not important that his roads connect with those of other groups or go beyond the area of his immediate use. But for the people of a modern industrial center, the roads must extend beyond the confines of the immediate area in which the center is located. They must extend far enough and in a sufficiently tightly connected design to make possible the accumulation of huge supplies and the distribution of equally huge amounts of manufactured produce.

Until relatively modern times, the road developed and operated primarily on a local scale. Perhaps the first departure from this was the conception and creation of the famous system of Roman roads. In the days of the Roman Empire, surfaced roads were built throughout much of western and southern Europe, all of them focusing eventually on the city of Rome itself. Main trunk lines led from that city to all major parts of the empire and to key points on the frontier. The function of this system was to facilitate movement, but primarily troop movements. The roads welded together the territory throughout which Roman military authority extended.

With the decline of the Roman Empire, the road system became the line of movement of armies despoiling the lands formerly under Roman control. Later, the system fell into disuse and decay. For a long period, roads again served only local areas. Later still, particularly in the seventeenth and eighteenth centuries, roads became the framework for the spread of political control, a device for the centralizing of power, as in the creation of the modern French state. Yet, through these many centuries, the prime function—to facilitate the movement of peoples and goods for short distances—did not change. When the spread over larger areas became necessary for carrying on a certain way of life, long-distance transportation by road developed.

PATTERN OR DESIGN. Landforms, water features, vegetation, and soil all have their effect upon the position of the road upon the land. Similarly, features of the cultural milieu, the locations of settlements, the system of land survey, the type of economy, and intangibles like law have equally strong effects upon the location of the road in any given area.

Relief features stand out perhaps more prominently than any others in controlling road location. Roads across mountain ranges, for example, are fixed in part by the location of low sections of the crest line, the passes, like Brenner Pass in the Alps. Not only the low section of the crest line, but access to it determines where the road is to go. As has previously been pointed out, a wide glacial trough leads back into the Alps from the plain of the Po River in Italy and gives easy access to the pass. Likewise, another glacial trough leads northward from the pass itself to the hill zone of the Alpine Foreland of southern

Germany and Austria. Thus, the easiest gradient across the whole width of the Alps provides the obvious line to be followed and practically fixes the road's location (Fig. 332).

Other features of the physical setting, like swamps, marshes, and lakes, all contribute to the location of a specific roadway. A jog may indicate avoidance of land which is seasonally flooded, or it may lead around a patch of exceptionally clayey soil where passage would be easy in dry weather, but almost impossible in wet. Roads often depart from the direct route to approach an easy river crossing instead of a difficult one. Many of the roads which had their origin in early days avoided wooded areas and chose instead to follow from one open grassy area to another. No really significant reason appears nowadays why this should have been so. In earlier days, however, when political power extended only over small areas and even within them was not too strong, as, for example, in the Europe of the Middle Ages, there was no policing of the highway. As a result, woodland often gave cover to highwaymen. Travel was dangerous and wherever possible the road led across country in which nothing offered cover for ambush.

But features of the physical setting have by no means been the only elements influencing the location of roads. The existence of a market town offering commercial facilities for a considerable countryside formed a focus toward which roads led, subject always to the physical barriers to be overcome. Sometimes the design was planned, as in the building of the system of *Routes Nationales* in France (Fig. 432). There, the great system of highways which radiated to all parts of the nation from Paris was primarily a planned way of expanding royal influence to all parts of the territory nominally subject to the French king. The road was in this instance a political and military device. The pattern imposed was the radial one, the one by which everything was directed toward the seat of government, Paris.

431 *TYPICAL road pattern for an area of rectangular land survey. Note how the pattern breaks in the northeastern corner of the map where lakes and a swamp appear. Note also the departure from rectangularity induced by the stream in the southwestern part of the map.*

In the Midwest and West of the United States, a cultural element was in large part responsible for the road pattern which developed. The rectangular land survey, used in the Northwest Territory and later in the area which became our western states, created a gridlike pattern (Fig. 431). Even in this area departures from the rectangular pattern are numerous where it became necessary to avoid certain water or landform features or where settlement preceded survey. Yet, over much of the land, the roads extend straight for miles on end and are crossed at right angles by other equally straight roads. The motor age has brought some modification, for high speeds and right-angle turns are not compatible. Where sharp turns occur on main-traveled roads, they are being replaced by wide, sweeping curves.

QUALITY. Early roads were essentially tracks marked on the land by the passage of men, beasts of burden, and primitive vehicles. There was no idea of road construction, nor were there special works like bridges, culverts, fills, and cuts. There was no special or organized effort to maintain the road once it came into being. In rare instances roads were paved locally, as by the Incas in Peru, but far and away the greater part of the roads were simple, natural tracks across the land.

To the Romans belongs the credit for the first constructed roads in areas of Western civilization; to them likewise belongs the credit for the development of the first road system. Heavy rock foundations, causeways, bridges, and culverts were introduced to make the roads passable at all times of the year. And pavement of the stone-block type created a new and less ephemeral feature on the land. The highway net which the Romans spread through western and southern Europe was more firmly fixed than any of the roads which preceded it and more completely knit together. Then, too, the roads were maintained during the whole period of ascendancy of the Roman Empire. Maintenance was planned, not haphazard. Even after the decline of the empire had set in, as has been suggested previously, many of the Roman roads were maintained locally. So well were they built, and in many places so well were they kept up, that they form the base of many of the modern roads of Great Britain, Belgium, France, and Italy.

By and large, however, road systems declined during the Middle Ages. It was not until near the end of the fifteenth century, and then in France only, that any attempt was made at organized road maintenance. In France, Louis XI created *Les Postes Royales,* which was actually a system of relay stations along routes traveled by royal messengers. The creation of this system brought to the forefront the notion of road-surface improve-

ment and road maintenance. From that time on, the quality of a road became the object of greater and greater care.

The toll road was one of the early devices introduced to better the quality of the road. Private individuals or companies were given the right to charge for travel over a certain length of highway in return for maintaining the highway in the best possible condition. As often as not, this "best possible condition" was little better than earlier cross-country tracks (Fig. 433). Yet, the system of toll roads did develop commonly used ways that were more extensive than any local network. And where travel was sufficiently heavy, it led slowly to improvement.

Not until the coming of the automobile, however, was progress in road improvement rapid. Higher speed of travel and longer distances to be covered—in short, greater mobility—brought the demand for more and more surfaced roads, and for surfaces of greater and greater smoothness. It is really only in this century that road systems have been built to tie together areas which are relatively far apart.

GENERAL WORLD PATTERN. A network of high-quality roads for a large area is, of course, best illustrated in the United States. The great number of motor vehicles in the United States as compared with the rest of the world suggests a reason. Nearly half of the approximately 3,000,000 miles of roads in the United States are classed as surfaced roads. The remainder are the ordinary dirt roads of rural areas. Of the roads with some type of surface, such as gravel, crushed stone, macadam, or any of the other types of surfacing, only about 200,000 miles are the highest-quality, hard-surfaced type (Fig. 434). Thus, despite the fact that U. S. roads are the best in the world, somewhat less than seven per cent of all roads in the country have the high-quality surface which we commonly think of as a usual feature of our roadway system.

The highest density of roads is encountered in Japan. Great Britain, Denmark, France,

432 *THE BASIC road pattern of France, radiating from Paris to all parts of the country. This map shows only the main* Routes Nationales.

Ireland, and Belgium follow in order. All of these countries are small in area; they are comparable to individual states in the United States. When large areas are considered, two great areas of high road density stand out above all others: the United States and northwestern Europe (Fig. 435). The net loosens to fray out in widely spaced strands in eastern and southern Europe on the one hand and in Canada and Mexico on the other.

In Asia, the eastern and southern fringe areas, like Japan and parts of China in the east and sections of the Dominions of Pakistan and India in the south, include some areas of tightly woven road net. From these, isolated stringers reach out toward the interior. A few lines cross the continent to connect with the European pattern in the U.S.S.R.

Of the other continents, Africa shows a fairly dense road net in the Atlas lands and in the Cape region. Elsewhere long stringers

433

HIGHWAY 32 near Townsend, Wisconsin, as of 1908. Roads like this one were the "superhighways" of early automobiling days. (Automobile Old Timers, Inc.)

crisscross the continent at wide intervals. In South America, a high density marks the Rio-São Paulo area of Brazil, most of Uruguay, and the Argentine Pampa. Along the coasts over the rest of the continent, an occasional road reaches back from coastal settled regions to a nearly empty interior. Southeastern Australia is the focal region on that continent though there the net is less tightly woven than in other centers mentioned.

Where human beings live in a commercial or an industrial economy, an elaborate net of roadways is a necessity. Where human groups exist in an economy which is self-sufficient, the road net is fragmentary. The stage of cultural and economic development largely determines both the density and the quality of the network of roads.

434 *CLOVERLEAF intersection of two modern American highways in New Jersey near the George Washington bridge helps to carry heavy automobile traffic efficiently. (Rotkin from Standard Oil Co. [N. J.])*

435 *A GENERALIZED world map showing relative density of the net of motorable roads.*

Waterways

Men have been using rivers and lakes as natural routes for ages. Today, rivers and lakes still remain almost the only highways in some of the less densely peopled parts of the world. For example, the Amazon River is the only real "road" throughout a large part of the South American continent. At the same time, rivers and lakes remain very important in the transportation system of the most highly industrialized regions of the world. To be sure, artificial works like canals have been introduced to by-pass obstructions like falls and rapids. And it is a far cry from the small and hazardous dugout of the tropical forest dweller to the huge vessels of modern design which ply certain of the world's great inland waterways like the Great Lakes.

Waterways are most useful today in the movement of bulky goods of low value per unit weight and of goods which make no call upon speedy transportation. In North America, the magnificent waterway of the Great Lakes, previously discussed in Chapter 13, is an essential link between the Midwest, with its supplies of mineral and agricultural raw materials, and the manufacturing regions of the East, with their huge demands for "food" for both human beings and machines. The thousands of tons of iron ore from the Lake Superior mining region are brought, to the coal of the Appalachian region cheaply and efficiently (see Chap. 17). So likewise are huge tonnages of wheat brought from farms to the eastern milling and shipping centers. By use of this waterway other lines of transportation are freed to move other goods, many of them requiring faster means of conveyance. Similarly, the Rhine River with its navigable tributaries and associated canals is still, as it has been for centuries, a main artery of transportation in western Europe. The Yangtze River still funnels the produce of interior China to the coast, where there is access by ocean routes to the industrial regions of the world.

Likewise where new land or relatively sparsely populated land is being opened either for exploitation or for settlement, the waterway is a cheap, ready-made route. The early opening of the interior of the United States was facilitated by the existence of the widespread system of the Mississippi and its tributaries. The produce of frontier farms could be floated downstream to New Orleans and the needed goods brought back upstream by river boat. Again, the exploitation of the Congo forest was greatly facilitated by the presence of an extensive network of water routes. Even today, in the opening of northern Siberia by the U.S.S.R., water routes are the only practical expedient yet available. The great northward-flowing rivers of Siberia, the Ob, the Yenisei, and the Lena, though unnavigable for much of the year because of ice, are the best routes from the Trans-Siberian Railway northward or from the Arctic coast southward. By far the most used waterways of the modern world are those of northwest Europe (Fig. 436). A plains surface in this region of humid climate without too severe winters provides many rivers which are not seriously interrupted by falls or frozen for extended periods. Flow in most of them has been regularized and the courses have been straightened and deepened. The Seine, the Meuse, the Rhine, the Moselle, the Ems, the Elbe, the Oder, and the Vistula are the main ones giving access to the Atlantic or to its marginal seas, the North and Baltic. Not too far from the headwaters of all of these streams, the Danube offers a line which leads to the Black Sea and thus to the Mediterranean. Between the northern rivers, canals were easily built linking the whole North European Plain. By means again of a canal, the northern rivers were linked to the southward-flowing Rhone and through it to the Mediterranean. A whole network of waterways fills in the parts of this general pattern so that few sections of European industrial regions are far from water transportation of some sort.

MAIN WATERWAYS OF
NORTHWEST EUROPE

436 *WATERWAYS are vital in the transportation pattern in northwestern Europe.*

In the United States, waterways play a smaller role. The Great Lakes, of course, are an exception. There are, in addition, a few canals, like the New York State Barge Canal, which links the Hudson River with the Great Lakes. Important too is the main stem of the Mississippi River and some of its tributaries, especially the Ohio. Beyond that, there is the system of coastal waterways leading from Long Island Sound to the Gulf Coast. But, throughout the greater part of the country, roads and railroads carry the loads.

Railroads

All peoples have roads of some sort. Waterways too are used by primitive peoples as well as by the most advanced or complex civilizations. But the railroad is the distinctive transportation feature of Western industrial civilization.

The railroad made possible the movement of huge volumes of goods over long distances at high speeds. Through the use of railroads, industrial nuclei could draw their raw materials for manufacture and their foods from areas increasingly larger and increasingly farther away. And the products of the industrial centers could be distributed in volumes and at speeds previously unattainable.

Railroads are little over a century old, but it is hard to imagine just how our present-day great cities could exist, how any sizable urban agglomerations could have existed, without them. Other means of transportation have, at least in the United States, taken over much of the local business from the railroads. Motor trucks, busses, and airplanes have taken over the functions of the railroads for short hauls and for small hauls. The railroad, however, remains as the long-distance method of shipping the bulk of the world's industrial goods.

RAILROADS IN THE UNITED STATES. From a scant 5,000 miles in 1840, the railroads of the United States have been extended so that

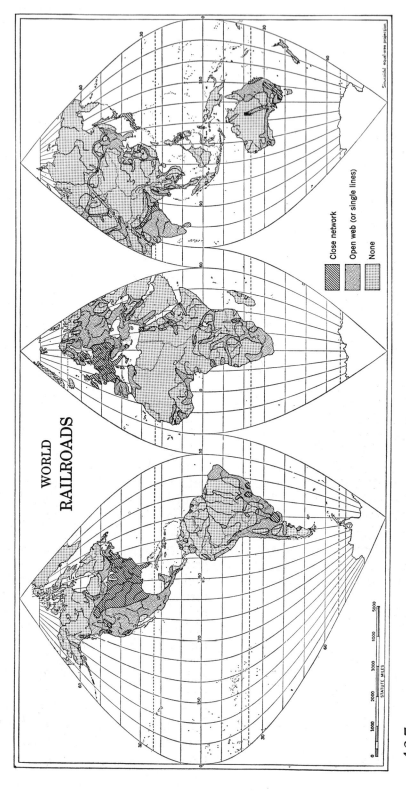

WORLD
RAILROADS

Close network

Open web (or single lines)

None

Sinusoidal equal-area projection

1000   2000   3000   4000   5000
STATUTE MILES

437   *A GENERALIZED world map showing relative density of railroads.*

there are now nearly 250,000 miles of line. The first steam locomotive in regular service began its operations in December of 1830 on a six-mile line from Charleston to Hamburg in South Carolina. From this small beginning, American railroads have grown so that they now make up about one-third of all the railroads in the world (Fig. 437).

The rail net (Fig. 438) focuses upon the industrial northeastern part of the country. Nearly all of the eastern seaboard region is crossed by lines linking the large eastern cities and extending inland from them. Notable concentrations cross the Appalachian system by the Hudson-Mohawk corridor in the north and by more devious routes between Philadelphia and Pittsburgh. Once the rough land of the Appalachians is crossed, the net of lines becomes denser in the interior plains, with a major focus at Chicago. To the south and west of that city a relatively closely woven net spreads over the land as far as the 100th meridian except for the rough land of the Ozark Highlands. Then quite suddenly the rail net frays out and only a few long stringers stretch across the plain, mountain, and plateau country of the west to link Pacific-coast centers with the east. It is in the humid east that rail lines are most numerous and most evenly spaced over the whole surface.

The pattern of rail lines does not reveal their true significance from one region to another within the United States. A line may be single track or multiple track; it may carry one train per hour or one train per week. When the distributions of these elements are added to the pattern, it can be clearly appreciated that rail traffic counts most heavily in the Northeastern Manufacturing Region.

RAILROADS IN THE REMAINDER OF NORTH AMERICA. Canadian railroads seem almost to be extensions of the net within the United States. The route between Buffalo and Detroit is an example as is also the northward extension of the Hudson Valley lines to Montreal. Southern Ontario and the middle St. Law-rence Valley in the east have closely woven nets.

The second concentration of rail lines in Canada is that of the so-called Prairie Provinces, from Winnipeg in Manitoba in a wide-sweeping belt westward through the wheat-producing lands of Saskatchewan and Alberta.

There are finally the cross-continent lines between the Pacific and Atlantic coasts. These lines hold together the widely separated, more highly populated parts of the Dominion. From them extend a few long tentacles like that to Prince Rupert on the British Columbian coast, Churchill on Hudson Bay, and Moosonee on James Bay.

The Mexican rail net is fragmentary. It is best developed in the vicinity of Mexico City. Lines lead from that center to the Gulf Coast at Veracruz and Tampico. Likewise, lines lead northward to join with railroads of the United States along the Texas and Arizona boundaries.

RAILROADS IN EUROPE. Northwestern Europe has an even closer network of rail lines than the United States (Fig. 437). It was, of course, in England that the world's first railroad was built and operated in 1825. As industrialization spread from England to the northwestern part of the Continent, railroads quickly followed. An increasingly widely spaced net extended eastward across the Plain of North Europe to fray out toward the Ural Mountains. The net likewise thins out southward and southeastward from the North Sea shores to become especially thin in the Iberian and Balkan areas.

Over much of Europe, the handicaps of rugged terrain are absent. Only in the Alps are there serious landform obstacles, and, even in those mountains, great engineering feats like the Saint Gotthard, Simplon, or Mont Cenis tunnels extended rail communication tying Italy closely to northern Europe. In extreme northern Europe, the almost complete absence of railroads reflects the low density of population.

RAILROADS
IN THE
UNITED STATES

0 200 400 600
Miles

438 *THE RAIL net in the United States is most nearly complete in the northeastern quarter of the country. It is fragmentary in the rougher lands of the East, in the drier Great Plains, and in the mountain and plateau country of the West. For other relationships, compare this map with Figs. 337 and 363.*

439 *THE RAILROADS of France converge on Paris.*

Two features distinguish the European railroad pattern. First, railroads came after the land was thoroughly settled, so that they followed already existing routes. Hence, the effect of the railroad was to increase the importance of existing centers of manufacture and commerce rather than to create new ones. For example, the supremacy of Paris among French cities was already established well before the railroad era. The fact that rail lines over the whole country converge toward Paris has strengthened that city's position so that no other French city even approaches it in size, in importance as a center of manufacturing, or as the commercial and economic heart of the country.

The second feature of the European rail pattern is the fact that railroads radiate from capital cities in each country as, for example, in France (Fig. 439). The railroad has been developed throughout Europe with military needs in mind. Each country, faced with the military needs of the nineteenth century, sought ease of access from the capital city to

all points on the frontier. Military convenience became the leading influence in the development of railroads within each of the
separate countries of the continent. International routes were, of course, made available, but they were relatively few in number
and their planning and construction were
secondary to the internal lines. Further, difficulty of articulation of one country's net
with another's became a problem with the
use of different rail gauges by different countries. For example, most of the railroads of
France are standard gauge (rails four feet
eight and one-half inches apart) while much
of the railroad system of Spain is broad
gauge (rails five feet five and three-quarters
inches apart).

RAILROADS IN ASIA. The tremendous expanse of Asia has hardly been penetrated by
the railroad. Only in a few sections of the
continent is the pattern sufficiently intensified
to be called a net. Western influence has
created the net in those places where one
exists.

On the west, Asiatic railroads are linked
to the frayed edge of the European pattern.
One thin strand was early extended eastward
from Moscow across Siberia to the Pacific
coast at Vladivostok (Fig. 437). Later, under
Soviet regime, other lines were built linking
with the Trans-Siberian Railway to bring the
newer mining and industrial areas of the
Central Urals, Kuznetsk, and the like into
closer touch with the European portions of
the U.S.S.R.

Throughout Japan, railroads came with industrialization. It is there more than in any
other part of the Asiatic sphere that the railroad is a common means of transportation.
In Manchuria, Korea, and northern China
there are lines which are really amplifications
of the eastern end of the Trans-Siberian line.
The peninsula of India has as completely developed a pattern as is to be found on the
Asiatic mainland. The broad lowland of the
Ganges is the most intensively covered part

of India. An east coastal network centers
upon Madras. Bombay and Karachi are
termini in the west. Over the Deccan Plateau
stretches a net which is less intense than that
of the Ganges Lowland, but which ties the
parts of the peninsula together.

RAILROADS IN THE OTHER CONTINENTS. Of
the other continents, South America is perhaps best equipped with railroads, though it
has no truly continental development. Three
networks stand out clearly in the east coast
regions: they center on Rio de Janeiro, São
Paulo, and Buenos Aires. All have tentacles
reaching toward the interior and there are
weak links between the three nets. In Chile,
a north-south line extends nearly the whole
length of the central valley and from it lead
spurs eastward into the Andes and westward
to the Pacific. Beyond these few, the railroads
of South America are mostly isolated lines
reaching from a port into the interior or from
one navigable portion of a river to another.

In Africa, two areas have moderately well
developed rail patterns. The French have tied
together their North African lands of Morocco, Algeria, and Tunis with an east-west
line stretching the whole length of the Atlas
lands. From this, skeletal spurs lead from the
coast into the desert. In the Union of South
Africa, the more humid lands of the Cape
Town area, Natal, Orange Free State, and
Transvaal are closely joined by railroads. The
main line northeastward from Cape Town
leads ultimately by way of the Rhodesias to
the important mineral region of Katanga in
southeastern Belgian Congo. From this main
line, spurs lead to coastal termini like Port
Elizabeth and Durban in the Union, and
Beira and Lourenço Marques in Mozam-
bique.

In Australia, the greater development is in
the southeast, between Adelaide, Melbourne,
Sydney, and Brisbane. A smaller net centers
on Perth in the southwest. And a single line
ties the two together. Elsewhere, long fingers
reach from ports toward the interior.

Air Lines

The density of scheduled-flight air lines is greatest in the most highly urbanized portions of the earth, as in the United States (Fig. 440). The commercial operation of air lines has so far dealt mainly with passengers and with mail. Speed has been the great asset; limited load capacities, the greatest handicap. As has previously been stated, it is in the urbanized portions of the earth that both passengers and mail are plentiful enough to ensure economic operation of the air lines.

Here and there other means of transportation are so costly as to make air transport economically feasible. For example, the trip from the coast of Colombia up the Magdalena River Valley and into the eastern Andes to the capital city of Bogotá is so time consuming when made by rail and river that the air line can compete successfully. Still passengers and mail make the bulk of the cargo. Similarly, travel to such places as Elizabethville in the Katanga of the Belgian Congo is so time consuming by surface routes that the airplane offers, in the end, the most efficient transport agent. Airplanes can and do function over such sparsely populated areas as northern Canada or Alaska where other means of transportation are lacking. Still, the function of bulky-goods carrier remains for other than air transport. Of course, the recent so-called airlift connection between the American Zone in Germany and the American-controlled part of Berlin was carried on as an emergency military function, not as a normal commercial venture.

Other Transportation Forms

To the roads, waterways, railroads, and air lines of intracontinental transportation must

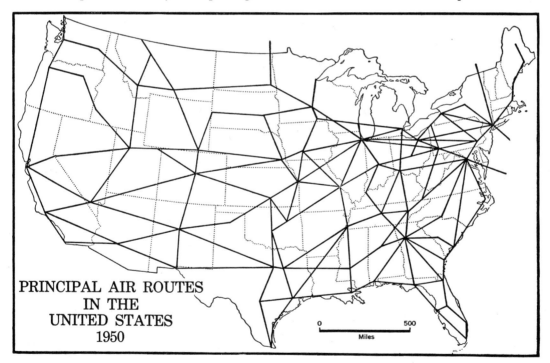

PRINCIPAL AIR ROUTES IN THE UNITED STATES 1950

0   500   Miles

440   *THIS MAP shows only the principal air routes in the United States. Many other lesser routes tie into this main pattern. Note the closer spacing in the Northeastern Industrial Region.*

be added such forms as pipe lines, telephonic and telegraphic wires, cables and power lines, and radio in its various types. Pipe lines carry natural gas and oil from the producing fields to the consuming areas, as from the mid-continent and Texas-Oklahoma fields to the urban northeast. Again, it is the urban areas of the world, especially those of the United States, which have brought this transport agent into being. In the same way, the industrialized portions of the world have brought wires and cables into use for transportation purposes—transportation of electric energy and electric impulses.

There has come likewise the transmission of words and images with and without the use of wires. These forms of communication are primarily a part of the industrial urban way of life; they are most numerous and most commonly used in North America and northwestern Europe. Yet, they too are stretching out to new regions, tying those fragments of the human habitat into closer and closer relation with one another.

THE WORLD PATTERN OF TRANSPORTATION AS A FEATURE OF WESTERN CULTURE

By one means or another, the great number of fragments of the human habitat have come to be more and more closely linked, largely as a result of the development and spread of Western culture. In the early periods of human history, the people of one small part of the world spread over increasingly larger areas until they came in contact with other groups. Through contact, a limited habitat came to be more than an isolated fragment.

For example, a weak tribe of south European peoples once occupied the "Hills of the Tiber" in west central Italy. Through centuries, they extended their little world beyond the hills on which they settled, through the Italian Peninsula, across the mountain barrier of the Alps, and even across the water barrier of the English Channel. All of this they welded together, the greater part of western Europe and northern Africa, into the Roman Empire. They used "roads" to do it—the land road and the route provided by the Mediterranean Sea.

From the western European base, the nations which were the descendants of the Roman Empire sought out overland "roads" to the Orient. Later they ventured out onto the "Western Sea." Water routes supplanted land roads and brought more of the human habitat into the European, the Western, sphere. At the same time, Western economy underwent radical changes and became the industrial economy. A need was present for continued expansion over still more of the world; the need of supplying increasing urban populations with food for themselves and raw materials for their machines. The means of linkage between the parts of the world were the roads, the waterways, the railroads, and, newest of all, the airways. Thus the transportation pattern of the world grew to its present form.

Imperfect though it still is over many parts of the world, this pattern has profoundly affected our concept of the whole human habitat. For Western people especially, the world is no longer a jumble of little pieces separated from one another by unknown voids; it is a mosaic of great variety of detail in some portions and of great coarseness in others, but all held together in a matrix, the visible evidence of which is the world transportation pattern.

CHAPTER OUTLINE

The world pattern of routes

REVIEW QUESTIONS

1. Why do most ships crossing the North Atlantic Ocean follow essentially the same course?

2. Why is the North Atlantic route the most traveled intercontinental route in the world?

3. Locate each of the major ocean routes on an outline map of the world.

4. What conditions account for the location of intercontinental air routes?

5. In what parts of the world are intercontinental air routes most numerous and most frequently flown? List some of the reasons.

6. What are some of the factors which place detailed limitations upon the location of air routes?

7. Why are the patterns of intracontinental routes of different quality, intensity, and design in different parts of the world?

8. What is the main function of the road? Illustrate by specific reference to different parts of the world.

9. What factors contribute to the determination of road pattern in various parts of the world? Give specific examples.

10. Where were the first constructed roads within the areas of Western civilization? What was their prime purpose?

11. What part of the world has the densest network of high-quality roads for a large area? For a small area?

12. With what kinds of areas are high-quality roads normally associated? Why?

13. What waterway is of major significance in the United States today? What gives it the importance which it has? Explain.

14. Suggest some reasons for the greater importance of waterways generally in Europe than in the United States.

15. In what parts of the world are there relatively dense networks of railroads? With what other distributions may that of railroads be associated?

16. Describe the main features of the railroad pattern of North America.

17. What two features distinguish the European railroad pattern?

18. Describe the distribution of railroads in Asia.

19. In what parts of the world is the intensity of scheduled-flight intracontinental air lines greatest? Give some of the reasons for this distribution.

20. What are some of the transportation forms other than those of road, waterway, railroad, and air line?

21. From the point of view of Western civilization, what is the significance of the world transportation pattern?

SOME SUGGESTED REFERENCES

Belloc, Hilaire, *The Road,* Harper & Brothers, 1926. A classic short study of the origin and development of the road in general and of English roads in particular; nontechnical and primarily for the general reader; beautifully and effectively written.

East, William Gordon, *An Historical Geography of Europe,* rev. ed., Methuen & Co., Ltd., 1948. Settlement geography, political geography, and economic geography of Europe in the past, from the time of the Roman Empire to the late nineteenth century; especially useful for the study of routes.

Frederick, John H., *Commercial Air Transportation,* rev. ed., Richard D. Irwin, Inc., 1947. A standard text on commercial air transportation in the United States; discusses routes, equipment, regulations, problems, services, and actual operations of United States air transportation.

Holbrook, Stewart H., *The Story of American Railroads,* Crown Publishers, 1947. A readable, popular account of railroads in the United States from early railroading days to the present;

somewhat dramatic in places, but essentially sound historically, with some geographical information.

Smith, J. Russell, and Phillips, M. Ogden, *Industrial and Commercial Geography,* 3rd ed., Holt, 1947. A standard text in economic geography; about one-quarter of the book concerned with trade and trade routes.

Van Zandt, J. Parker, *The Geography of World Air Transport,* Brookings Institute, 1944. A brief but highly suggestive discussion of the geographic factors involved in the development of the world air-route pattern.

PART FOUR

Concluding Remarks

441 *ROUND-UP time on the grassy, monotonous plain of the Argentine Pampa, the very model of a geographic region. (Earl Leaf from Rapho-Guillumette, New York)*

CHAPTER 29

Regions and the Regional Concept

A region is any portion of the earth's surface delimited or recognized for any particular purpose. There are many kinds of regions, large and small, geographic and nongeographic. Any individual region, regardless of its kind, possesses some unifying elements or combination of elements. A state, such as one of the United States, is one type of region—a political region. Its area is determined by its political boundary and its basic unity is an outgrowth of the state constitution and state laws. A country, such as France, is another example of a political region. The trading area of a city is a kind of region; it is one that is economic rather than political in nature. The part of Europe occupied by the Magyars is an ethnic region. The territory under the Tennessee Valley Authority is a planning region (Fig. 442). The Brooks Range of Alaska is a landform region; so is the Manchurian Plain; and the Massif Central of France. The chernozem belt of the United States and Canada is a soil region. Regions may be of widely different sizes. The State of Rhode Island is just as much a political region as is the State of Texas. The trade area of Bennington in Vermont is an economic region just as much as is the trade area of New York City, though much smaller. Many examples could be given to show that a region is any area delimited or recognized for any particular purpose. But, what is a geographic region?

GEOGRAPHIC REGIONS

The geography of any area is comprised of physical and cultural elements. A geographic region is an area in which there is some conspicuous unity in the expression of these elements. The essential unity may rest primarily upon one or more dominant physical elements or on one or more dominant cultural elements, or both. Climate is the dominant element in the distinction of Sahara as a geographic region. The regions of the Black Hills or the Pyrenees are distinguished first and foremost by landform conditions. Basic to the regionality of the Great Swamp of western Siberia is the drainage. The concept of the "Moslem World" or Moslem Region is based on cultural similarities, highlighted by a well-established and militant religion. A smaller and somewhat more clearly defined cultural region is the "Mormon Country," which centers on Salt Lake City (Fig. 443). The regionality of the United States Corn Belt rests on close and very complex interrelationships among many elements, from climate and soils to agriculture and animal husbandry. Much the same is true of the Argentine Pampa.

The dominance of one or a few elements in establishing the essential unity of a given geographic region must not be misinterpreted.

There are many elements in a regional complex. All the elements must be recognized and the significance of their mutual relationships appreciated. To say that the Sierra Nevada is a geographic region because it is all mountains is only a "starter." Needed are many other understandings, such as the type of mountains involved, the difference between the glaciated and the unglaciated parts, the vertical zonation of vegetation and climate, the differences between the windward and lee sides, the seasonal changes, the pass routes, the human use of the natural resources, the distribution of population, and so on. The whole association is necessary, no matter how important the major landform condition may be in and of itself and no matter how greatly this condition affects and is reflected in other conditions. Neither could one appreciate or establish the regional character of the Pampa by a consideration merely of the basic unity partly created by landforms and climate. Both are unifying factors, but so are soils, natural vegetation, the Spanish cultural background, the railroad pattern, and several other factors.

Geographic regions are of many different sizes, as witness the Sahara, the Central Valley of California, or the Lake St. John Lowland. Large ones are usually divided into several subregions but even the smallest usually have at least two subregions. In the Lake St. John Lowland, for example, it is necessary to recognize at least two subregions. One is the clay soil portion, chiefly in farms and rather densely populated; the other is the sand and swamp portion, little utilized and only sparsely populated (Fig. 48). These represent intraregional differences, yet they are both parts of a region whose general unity rests primarily on conditions of landforms, climate, and settlement by French-Canadian farmers.

Major Geographic Regions

The term "major geographic regions," as here used, refers to the largest and most generalized of the geographic complexes which are usually recognized for the world as a whole. The Tropical Rainforest Lands, the Mediterranean Lands, and the Tundra Lands are examples (Fig. 444). Because, on such a large scale, more conditions are related, directly or indirectly, to climate than to any other single element, these regions are essentially climatic. Yet, they are more than climatic regions, for within them there is general uniformity in many other physical conditions, such as soils and natural vegetation, and some degree of similarity in the cultural aspects, such as types of land use and land-use

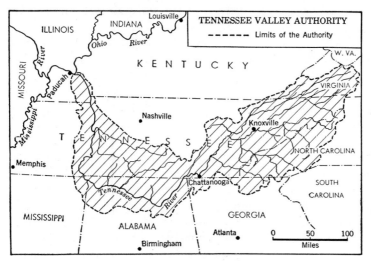

442

THE "planning region" of the Tennessee Valley Authority. The TVA is a separate United States Government corporation, holding certain planning authority within the drainage basin of the Tennessee River—a basin containing roughly 40,000 square miles, nearly 7,000,000 persons, and including parts of eight states.

problems. As time goes on and there is an increasing spread and interchange of cultural traits, including modes of making a living, there is an ever-growing similarity in the cultural geographic expression of these major geographic regions, even though it is not as marked, and probably never will be, as the general uniformity found in the physical expression. In order to be more specific, and to show to what degree the idea of "major geographic regions" possesses utility in helping one to understand the whole earth, it may be useful to discuss one major region as an example.

THE NORTHERN FOREST LANDS: AN EXAMPLE. The Northern Forest Lands, as the name implies, are limited to the Northern Hemisphere (Fig. 444). They have their greatest extent in Eurasia, where they sweep from the eastern edge of the Norwegian mountains to the mountains of eastern Siberia and beyond, in places, to the Pacific. To the north they are barely cut off from the Arctic Ocean by the Tundra Lands and to the south they reach Humid Mid-latitude Continental Lands on the east and west and the Dry Lands in the interior.

In North America, the Northern Forest Lands occupy most of Canada and parts of interior Alaska. The major extent is from the eastern foot of the Canadian Rockies to southern Labrador and Newfoundland. As in Eurasia, they are transitional with the Tundra Lands on the poleward margins and with either Dry Lands or Humid Mid-latitude Continental Lands on the equatorward margins, as well as being transitional along some parts of their margins with the Mountain Lands.

The most conspicuous feature of the Northern Forest Lands is the vegetation which gives them their name. It is largely a coniferous forest in which spruce, balsam fir, and cedar are dominant trees, although birch and poplar are common. Along the equatorward margin, where the growing season is longer, there are some pines and a considerably greater admix-

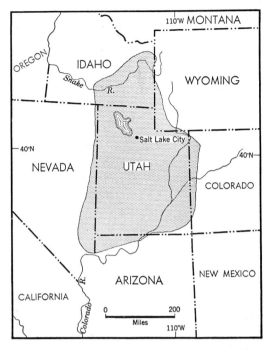

443 THE "Mormon Country" (shaded area) lies mainly in Utah and centers on Salt Lake City. (From sketch map by J. E. Spencer)

ture of broadleaf trees, such as poplar, birch, and maple. Trees are generally taller along this margin and constitute a major regional resource, being exploited for both lumber and pulpwood. The farther north one goes, the smaller the trees, and the fewer the species. Hardiest of all are spruce, birch, and willow. However, where they interfinger with or, in some places, invade the tundra, they are hardly trees; the spruces become mere bushes and the willows and birches become matted, vinelike masses which hug the ground. Much of the forest is broken and patchy, especially in the parts which have been subjected to continental glacier scour. Such parts are often more lakes, ponds, and exposed bedrock than forest (Fig. 130). There are also extensive relatively open swamps, many of which are muskegs, possessing only a few trees and a low cover of bushes, hummocky mosses, and wild cranberry vines.

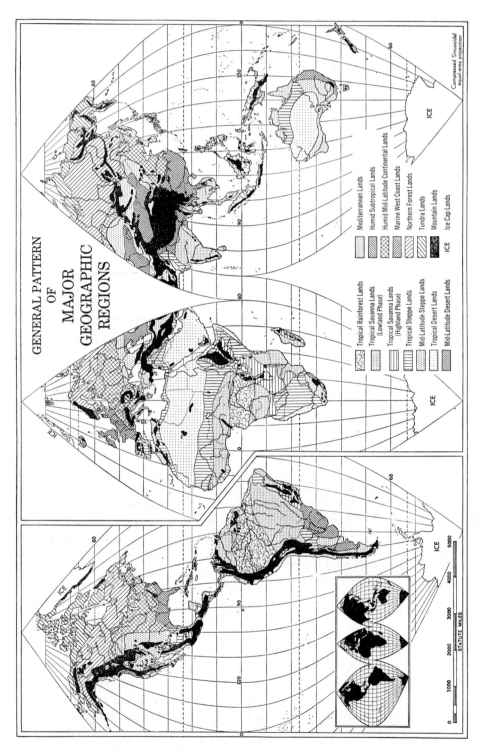

GENERAL PATTERN
OF
MAJOR
GEOGRAPHIC
REGIONS

Tropical Rainforest Lands
Tropical Savanna Lands (Lowland Phase)
Tropical Savanna Lands (Highland Phase)
Tropical Steppe Lands
Mid-Latitude Steppe Lands
Tropical Desert Lands
Mid-Latitude Desert Lands

Mediterranean Lands
Humid Subtropical Lands
Humid Mid-Latitude Continental Lands
Marine West Coast Lands
Northern Forest Lands
Tundra Lands
Mountain Lands
Ice Cap Lands

Compressed Sinusoidal
equal-area projection

STATUTE MILES
0   1000   2000   3000   4000   5000

444   THIS generalized map represents one way, one only, of recognizing the larger component complexes which together comprise the geography of the land masses.

'This map is, in reality, a summary statement of the variety within the human habitat. See discussion of "Major Geographic Regions" in the text.

Except in areas which have been over-hunted, overfished, or very recently burned, wildlife usually is abundant. It ranges from large to very small animals and includes those of the land, water, and air. In the Canadian portion, for example, there are moose, deer, black bear, wolf, fox, otter, mink, muskrat, and rabbit. In the lakes and streams are trout, pike, and pickerel. Among the birds are ducks, geese, loons, owls, partridge, and several varieties of small songbirds. Many of the birds, especially the waterfowl, are migratory. And last, but far from least, are the insects which make life almost unbearable for man and animals during the warmer season. Most numerous of all are the swarms of mosquitoes. They are not the disease-carrying type, but their bites are sharp and they cause intense itching and swelling. It has been said, and truly, that one of the chief handicaps to human settlement in the Northern Forest Lands is not the climate, but the mosquitoes.

The climate of these forestlands is characterized by long, cold, snowy winters and short, cool, rainy summers. It is the Subarctic (Dfc, Dfd, Dwc, Dwd) climate (Plate V). Precipitation is greatest along the warmer margins and very scant on the colder margins.

However, it is all very effective, whether summer rain or winter snow, for the temperature conditions are such as to preclude rapid evaporation. A very important part of the climate is the marked seasonal change. There are essentially two seasons, summer and winter. What might be called fall and spring are very short seasons of quick change from either summer to winter or winter to summer. During the long winter season the streams and lakes are covered with thick ice and drifted snow, and the forest is snow-mantled, even though the snow mantle becomes very thin on the tundra margin. When summer comes for its short stay, the snow melts away, the ice on the lakes turns gray and finally disappears, and the ice on the stream pushes and grinds along in the "breakup."

These Northern Forest Lands have long been the home of the hunter, trapper, and fisherman. The past few centuries have seen the native trapper and white trapper alike seeking furs for the great fur markets of the United States and Europe. Trading posts, to which the trappers bring their furs and from which they receive supplies, often are the only nonnative settlements to be found in vast territories (Fig. 445). Mining towns are

445 *HUDSON'S Bay Company post at Moose Factory Island, James Bay, Canada. A typical winter scene at one of the scattered and remote fur-trading posts of the north country. (National Film Board, Canada)*

found in a few places, as are "river stations" which are located along the large north-flowing rivers. On the warmer margins, the lumberman has cut down large sections of the forest for lumber and pulpwood. The same margins have also seen the farmer follow close on the heels of the lumberman to create what are still largely wilderness farms. The airplane has wrought truly startling changes in the way of life of the people of the Northern Forest Lands. Distances which formerly required weeks of travel, by canoe in summer or dog sledge in winter, are now covered in a few hours. These lands have literally jumped from very primitive to the most advanced methods of travel, without, for the most part, any intervening stages marked by the use of roads and railroads (Fig. 446).

The foregoing short, and far from complete, description of the Northern Forest Lands as one of the major geographic regions of the world suggests the utility of the major regional concept. If all such regions are studied, one by one, and compared and contrasted with one another, it becomes possible to build up a general knowledge which serves as a broad base for the understanding of world geography as a whole. It is *one* way of appreciating "in complex" the outstanding physical and cultural elements of the earth. The accompanying map (Fig. 444) shows all the major geographic regions of the world. A considerable knowledge of any one of them may be acquired by noting its distribution on Fig. 444 and then comparing that distribution with those shown on the world maps of climate, landforms, soils, natural vegetation, population, industrial areas, crop distributions, and so on (Plates I-IX). For example, it can be quickly ascertained that the Humid Subtropical Lands of the United States possess a Humid Subtropical (Cfa) climate,

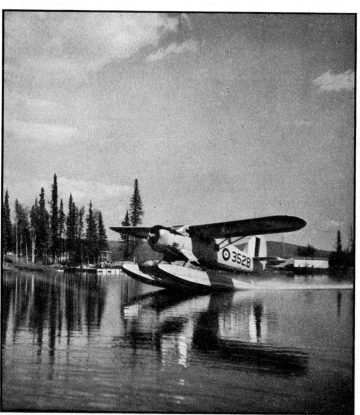

446

PONTOONS in summer and skis in winter allow the use of the many lakes of the Northern Forest Lands as landing fields for aircraft. They carry passengers, mail, and freight to and from "the outside." (Royal Canadian Air Force photo)

lateritic soils (as far as mature soils are concerned), and that most of them are plains. In addition, it will be found that these lands are predominantly agricultural, that cotton is one of the major crops, and that some parts, relatively small as yet, have become industrialized. The foregoing represents a small sampling of the general geographical understanding that can thus be obtained.

Lesser Geographic Regions

Following the study of major geographic regions, it is useful to change the scale of inquiry and examine smaller regions in considerable detail; for example, the Columbia Plateau, the United States Cotton Belt, the North China Plain, or the Argentine Pampa. These are parts of major geographic regions. Again, if all of them were studied, the world would be "filled in" much as one completes a picture puzzle by recognizing the pieces and fitting them together. Following is a brief discussion of the Pampa as one of the smaller geographic regions of South America.

THE ARGENTINE PAMPA: AN EXAMPLE. The Pampa occupies the most southern portion of South America's Humid Subtropical Lands (Figs. 444, 447). Its eastern margin is marked by the pronounced bulge of the coastline south of Buenos Aires. The northern end of the bulge is about at the head of the La Plata estuary and the southern end at the port of Bahía Blanca. If one draws another bulge, beginning the line at Bahía Blanca and bending it westward and then back eastward approximately to Santa Fe on the Paraná River, the opposite margin of the Pampa is defined. Between the two bulges, or arcs, is the low-lying and nearly level Pampa plain whose monotonous surface is broken only by the low hilly groups of the so-called Pampa Ranges in the south. The region's considerable size is shown by the approximately 500-mile distance from Santa Fe to Bahía Blanca and a similar distance from eastern to western margin.

447 THE *Argentine Pampa, with its fertile soils, nearly level land, and mild, humid climate, is one of the world's great food baskets.*

The climate of the region is chiefly Humid Subtropical (Cfa). Summers are long and hot and winters short and cool. Rainfall is usually plentiful at all seasons, with somewhat more in the warmer six months than in the cooler six months. Average annual precipitation is about 40 inches in the east and close to 20 inches in the west, where the Pampa gives way to the Great Plains with their Semiarid (BS) climate. As in many other humid regions, droughts are not uncommon and they constitute one of the major causes of crop failure; "drought years" are most frequent in the southern and western parts of the Pampa. All in all, the Pampa climate is similar to that of the United States Cotton Belt, though slightly cooler in both summer and winter seasons.

The Pampa is well named, for a pampa is a grassland. About all the Spanish explorers saw, mile after mile to the horizon, was tall prairie grass; little wonder that they named it *the* Pampa. There is still much speculation as to why the Pampa was a grassland. Considering the climate, one would expect a forest such as that which grew in our South. That the environment is not unfavorable to trees is proved by their successful introduction in the towns and cities and on many of the ranches.

The combination of a mild humid climate and abundant humus derived from grass roots has produced, in general, a black prairie soil which grades into chernozem in the western and somewhat drier portion. These soils have developed from transported materials, partly stream alluviums and partly loess. In sections where the Pampa plain is especially low and smooth, there are soils which are waterlogged either part or all the year. Most of them occur within the shallow, and poorly defined, drainage basin of the Rio Salado (Fig. 447). Because the Pampa soils are deep and highly porous, waterlogged conditions develop only where the surface is so low that it lies near or actually intersects the ground water table. The porosity also accounts for the near lack of surface streams, streams which otherwise would be numerous in an area as humid as the Pampa.

The major physical conditions of the Pampa provide a wealth of natural resources in one way and a lack of those resources in another. Landforms, soils, and climate, both in nature and extent, comprise a basic wealth of inestimable value. In contrast, the lack of mineral resources, particularly coal, petroleum, and iron ore, and the lack of forests, as a source of lumber and fuel, represent a kind of basic poverty. This combination of resources makes for agricultural wealth and limits industry.

Prior to the arrival of Europeans, the Pampa was no more than a wild, grassy plain inhabited by a sprinkling of Indians who lived chiefly by hunting. Today, it is one of the major agricultural regions of the world. The transformation has required nearly four centuries but most of the changes have taken place since about 1850. As in so many other grassland areas, the outstanding features of the cultural geography are of historically recent origin. They have been made possible by many things, including immigration, modern agricultural machinery, modern breeds of livestock, pumps and windmills to furnish water from the ground, fencing, roads and railroads, and demands for more and more food on the part of the mid-latitude areas of the Northern Hemisphere, particularly the British Isles and the western fringe of continental Europe.

For the first two and three-quarter centuries of settlement, almost entirely by Spaniards, the northern part of the Pampa was taken up in large ranches devoted to the "open-range" grazing of cattle, horses, and sheep. Meanwhile the central and southern parts were practically untouched "Indian Country." Good land was so plentiful in the north that there was no need to attempt to use the wet lands of the Rio Salado district or to penetrate beyond them to good land farther south. Europe was far distant and there was no way of selling the products of the ranches except as wool, hides, and tallow. Livestock, especially cattle, was inferior, as was the meat obtained from it. In addition there were no refrigerator ships to carry fresh meat to faraway markets. Then the changes began. Railroads started shortly after 1850 and were well spread over the whole Pampa by 1910. Scrub cattle were replaced by high-grade beef cattle, chiefly after 1880. The refrigerator ship made its appearance in 1877. Beginning in 1857 there was an increasing stream of immigrants from Italy, Spain, and other countries of western Europe, and later, from such eastern European countries as Russia and Poland. It was these immigrants, working mainly as tenants and sharecroppers, who turned the Pampa into a large producer of beef, alfalfa, wheat, corn, and allied crops. The land came into more intensive use and various parts of the Pampa began to specialize in various types of production. From all these changes the new and modern Pampa emerged. Landholdings are still large, but the old days of the open-range ranches have disappeared.

Within the present-day Pampa there are several fairly well defined production regions (Fig. 447). The area adjacent to Buenos Aires has become a combination dairy-product and truck-crop belt. Its existence not only reflects fertile soils and mild climate, but also the ever-increasing demand for food on the part of a large urban population. To the northwest of Buenos Aires and west and south of Rosario is a corn belt. This area is the leading surplus corn area of the world; its leadership rests on favorable physical conditions, little consumption of corn within the area, either by man or animals, and a large and steady market for corn in western Europe. South of the two regions just mentioned is a large area devoted to grazing of beef cattle. This area occupies the heart of the Pampa and extends from the Atlantic's edge for two-thirds of the distance across the entire Pampa plain. It is mainly a pasture area, rather than a crop production region in the ordinary sense. In its southern part, not far east and north of Bahía Blanca, sheep are numerous. The remaining production region is the famous Wheat Crescent, which makes a broad arc from the southern edge of the Pampa to the section west of Santa Fe. Its western margin, which slightly invades the region of Semiarid (BS) climate is, for all practical purposes, the inland boundary of the Pampa. The atmospheric conditions and the dark fine-textured soils are excellent for wheat; these advantages, plus the large size of the Crescent and only minor consumption by relatively sparse population, enable the region to rank second only to Canada in world wheat exports.

All of the production regions of the Argentine Pampa merge with one another on their margins and it is difficult to draw any hard

and fast lines between them. Likewise, the Pampa itself merges with other areas, particularly the dry lands to the west and the scrub-covered Chaco to the north or northwest. Only where the Pampa plain meets the sea is it possible to draw a definite line of separation.

Serving the Pampa and acting as "connectors" with the outside world, are the cities of Santa Fe and Rosario on the Paraná River, Buenos Aires and La Plata on the La Plata estuary, Mar del Plata on the southeast coast, and Bahía Blanca on the bay of the same name. The railroads fan out from Santa Fe and Rosario, and serve the Pampa plain (Fig. 447). Buenos Aires is the major focus of railroads, a fact which partly explains its commanding position in the life and business of the Pampa, both at home and abroad.

Buenos Aires has become a city of nearly three million persons. It is a truly modern city and one of the most beautiful in the world (Fig. 448). In Argentina, "all roads lead to Buenos Aires." About one out of every five Argentinians lives in Buenos Aires, a sufficient index of its importance not only as a political and economic center, but also as the social and educational nerve center of the country. If the United States had any comparable single city, it would have to combine the functions of Washington, New York, and Chicago, and have a population of about 30 million inhabitants!

The foregoing regional analysis of the Pampa is of course far from complete, but it serves to express the idea of "lesser" geographic regions, as opposed to "major" geographic regions of the world.

THE UTILITY OF THE REGIONAL CONCEPT

The chief advantage of the regional treatment is that it "leaves together" elements which actually occur together. It provides a

448 *A VIEW of Buenos Aires, the hub of Argentine life, showing the Plaza del Congreso and the Capitol. (Gendreau)*

reasonably complete understanding of areas as they exist in complexes comprised of many elements. In addition, it enables the student of geography to compare and contrast the many different areas which together make up the world scene—a scene of much variety and appreciable change from time to time. The systematic study of the elements of geography, one by one, is absolutely fundamental. There is the basic and initial need for the study of climate as such, landforms as such, population as such, cultures as such, and so on through all the elements. But all this, to possess full geographic reality, must be followed by a study of wholes, in which the elements are seen in their true relations to each other and not simply as separate elements. By a very rough analogy, geography may be compared to an automobile engine. To comprehend the engine one must take it apart. He must learn the appearance and nature, as well

as the function, of each part. But, if he stops there, he still has no real knowledge or appreciation of the engine. At that stage, the engine has become nothing more than a helter-skelter collection of parts strewn on the garage floor. It has to be put together and operated before it is a real engine and before one can appreciate it as a functioning complex. Moreover, it must be taken apart and put together again before it can be compared with other types of automobile engines. In similar fashion, geographic data may well be examined, element by element, and then studied in combination—in a definite area, whether the area be one of the major or minor components of the world scene. Thus regional geography becomes significant and useful; in regional geography the notions of "physical scene" and "human scene" merge to become the "areal complex," a full measure of the nature of man's habitat.

CHAPTER OUTLINE

Regions and the regional concept

REVIEW QUESTIONS

1. What is a region?
2. What is a geographic region?
3. Many persons claim that any region (any kind of region) is a geographic region. Is there justification for this point of view?
4. Give examples of different types of geographic regions.
5. As used in this chapter, what is meant by the term "major geographic region"?
6. Using the world maps in the front of this book and other maps in the several chapters, describe the outstanding geographical characteristics, both physical and cultural, of the Hot Desert Lands (as shown on Fig. 444).
7. Describe the physical complex of some large or small area with which you are personally familiar.
8. If it were your job to discuss the human (or cultural) geography of Switzerland, what elements or conditions would you consider?
9. Using all source material available to you in this book, present a geographical interpretation of the Bolivian Plateau.

SOME SUGGESTED REFERENCES

Finch, Vernor C., "Geographical Science and Social Philosophy," *Annals of the Association of American Geographers,* Vol. 29, No. 1 (March, 1939): 1-28. The greater part of this article is concerned with regions and the regional approach in geography.

Hartshorne, Richard, "The Nature of Geography," *Annals of the Association of American Geographers,* Vol. 29, Nos. 3 and 4 (September and December, 1939): 171-658. Pages 426 to 541 of this treatise on geography and its nature discuss regional geography and associated concepts and problems.

White, C. Langdon, and Renner, George T., *Human Geography,* Appleton-Century-Crofts, Inc., 1948. An introductory textbook which stresses geography as human ecology; Chapter 41 is devoted to a discussion of the region as a geographic unit.

449   THE "PRETZEL," *Kew Gardens, Long Island, New York. How different from
the crossroads of yesteryear! (Wide World Photo)*

CHAPTER 30

The Varied and Changing Scene

Modern man's knowledge of his world is relatively thorough. To be sure, some portions of the earth are still unmapped and many others inadequately mapped. Also, many problems of living and making a living on the earth are only vaguely recognized or are far from solution. But, by and large, the earth is well understood and the earth as man's habitat is fully appreciated. As man sizes up his present-day world, he can hardly fail to see its amazing variety or fail to be aware of its changing appearance.

VARIETY AND CHANGE IN THE PHYSICAL SCENE

The physical variety of the earth is such that no two parts are identical. This presents man with many opportunities and with many problems: opportunities to live and gain a livelihood in different fashions; problems of how best to meet physical conditions as they occur in a given region or in all regions. As bewildering as the physical variety may be, close examination soon indicates certain broad comprehensible patterns. The complexities of the air resolve themselves into recognizable types of weather and climate. The variations of the land surface itself become identifiable kinds of major and minor landforms. The details of natural vegetation merge to produce major vegetation associations (Plates IV, V and VII). Finally, the various types of climate, landforms, natural vegetation, and others, themselves combine to constitute certain physical complexes of one size or another. Thus, one gains a working notion of such environments as the world's Dry Lands, Mountain Lands, Northern Forest Lands, or Tropical Rainforest Lands—ultimately one gains a grasp of the physical earth as a whole (Fig. 444). Or, on a more detailed scale, one gains insight regarding the physical setup of such areas as the Argentine Pampa, the Paris Basin, or the Central Valley of California.

Men often refer to "the unchanging physical scene." The reference reflects the shortness of the individual life span and general unawareness of such change as does take place, often in a single lifetime. In terms of one man's life there are many conditions which change only a little: the Rocky Mountains "stay there," the climate of England remains the same; the state of Iowa still has its black prairie soil; glacial lakes continue to dot the Laurentian Shield. Yet, the Rockies represent only one temporary phase in the succession of landforms of that particular segment of the earth's crust; England's climate has been different in the past and undoubtedly will be different in the distant future; Iowa's black prairie soil is, in terms of earth's history, only a fleeting phase of the regolith; the glacial lakes of the Laurentian region are being filled with sediment and aquatic vegetation, many of them already have become swamps and some of the swamps have become dry land (Fig. 450). The vast majority of the major changes in the physical scene result from processes that accomplish their work very slowly—slowly in terms of the common man's concept of time.

formed appreciably by one storm. Rapidly or slowly, the physical complex changes.

In addition to the physical changes wrought naturally, there are many more caused by man himself, particularly in those areas where he has lived a long time and in sizable numbers. In extensive areas he has wiped out forests or turned seas of grass into seas of wheat. He has brought water to deserts and trans-

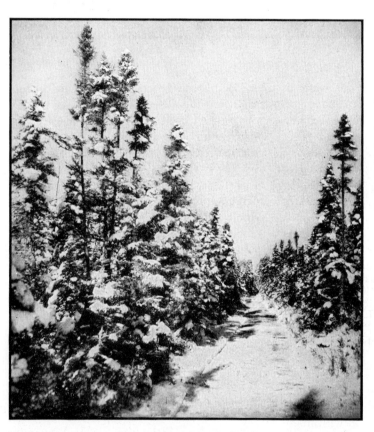

450

A MINNESOTA spruce-swamp which has resulted from the filling in of a former glacial lake. (Minnesota Department of Conservation)

However, there are some which occur with comparative rapidity, especially in localized areas. A flash flood in the desert may carve a large arroyo within a few hours. Faulting of the earth's crust may create a new escarpment within a few minutes (Fig. 451). A fire set by lightning may devastate hundreds of square miles of forest in a matter of days. River channels change position overnight and the local character of a shore may be trans-

formed sterile wastes into densely populated garden lands. He has leveled hills and filled valleys, drained marshlands and constructed huge reservoir lakes (Fig. 452). In large metropolitan areas, he has changed virtually everything, including the conditions of the lower atmosphere. Too often, he has wrought destructive change, as witness farmlands eroded beyond possibility of cultivation (Fig. 261), fire-blackened wastes of former forest-

45¹

AIR view of a recent fault scarp, which may be seen as the pronounced line extending from upper left to lower right, near Indio, California. The parts of the scarp which cross canyon mouths are buried by alluvial materials washed from the hills. (Spence Air Photos, Los Angeles)

lands, and "dried-out" regions of lowered water tables and dwindling streams. Unthinkingly or by design, man has played a large part in changing the physical world.

VARIETY AND CHANGE IN THE CULTURAL SCENE

Just as no two parts of the earth are physically identical, no two parts are culturally identical. Again, man is presented with opportunities and with problems: opportunities to share the best from many cultures; problems of what to do when cultures clash with one another or fail to function when transferred to new environments. Like the physical variety, cultural variety often seems bewilderingly complex—perhaps the term "cultural complex" has much deeper meaning than the term "physical complex." Yet on one scale or another, or with one objective or another, we can grasp the manifold cultural patterns and their individual elements.

We may recognize Western as opposed to Oriental cultures, primitive as opposed to advanced cultures, machine as opposed to non-machine cultures, nomadic as opposed to sedentary culture, and so on. In a more re-

45²

A SECTION of reclaimed land in the Pontine Marshes along the west coast of Italy, near Rome. (Burton Holmes from Ewing Galloway)

453A *MAN and his works dominate the landscape in some sections of the world: San Francisco seen from the air. (Gendreau)*

stricted sense, we may recognize rice culture as opposed to maize culture, or hoe culture as opposed to plow culture. All of these cultures, singly and intermixed, provide the variety of the earth's cultural scene. Geographically, they appear as populations of different patterns, densities, and "races," as various types of structures, settlements, major occupations, and ways of transportation and communication, and as different types of land-use complexes (Fig. 453). Certainly, the variety in the cultural scene at least matches the variety in the physical scene. If it is a variety more difficult to grasp, there is good reason, for it

is fraught with many elements which do not readily lend themselves to quantitative measurement and with changes which are, more often than not, disconcertingly rapid.

Until the Age of Exploration and the Industrial Revolution, cultural change was relatively slow. Ideas, persons, and goods moved at a snail's pace. Some cultures were so isolated that they grew and gave their particular impress to the land for thousands of years before the rest of the world was aware of their existence. Within the past 150 to 200 years, change has been the order of the day and man has witnessed greater change than took place

453B *IN OTHER parts of the world man's presence is only slightly noticeable: Vermont village. (Newell Green)*

within the preceding 2,000 years. Some areas have been affected much more than others, but there is hardly a region, no matter how remote, that has not changed, or been forced to change, its way of life to some degree.

spread like wildfire and persons and goods are sped across land and sea at ever increasing rates. The results are to be seen almost everywhere. Grasslands, long stubbornly resistant to the hoe and wooden plow, have capitulated

454   *NIGHT view in modern Pittsburgh (a far cry from little Fort Pitt of Colonial days) showing blast furnaces and steel mills along the steep, crowded banks of the Monongahela River. In the left background the lighted tops of two tall buildings mark the position of Pittsburgh's famous "Golden Triangle," where the Monongahela and Allegheny join to form the Ohio River. (Jones and Laughlin Steel Corp.)*

Change has been so rapid for the earth as a whole that cultural evolution has been replaced by cultural revolution.

The growth and application of technology lies at the root of the rapid changes occurring in the present-day world. Ideas can now

to the steel plow and tractor-drawn gang plow; deforested areas are replanted and placed under scientific management; regions of subsistence farming become highly specialized commercial farming districts; open rural countryside becomes a crowded city (Fig.

454); airplanes serve regions which have never seen a highway or a railroad; and automobiles provide economic and social mobility for whole populations.

In today's world, political boundaries change; empires decline; mass population movements occur; whole systems of land use are modified; nationalism clashes with internationalism; the released energy of the atom promises man a better way of life—or threatens to annihilate him. In one fashion or another, all these changes affect the cultural scene; coupled with the variety and transformations in the physical scene they present us with a fascinating, even though often disconcerting, world.

Appendices

A. MAP PROJECTIONS

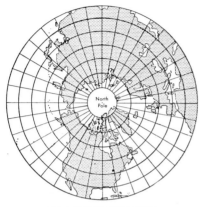

AN AZIMUTHAL PROJECTION
(ALSO EQUAL-AREA)

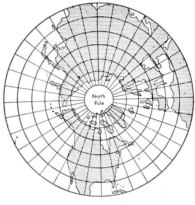

AN EQUIDISTANT PROJECTION
(ALSO AZIMUTHAL)

A CYLINDRICAL PROJECTION

A POLYCONIC PROJECTION

**GOODE'S INTERRUPTED HOMOLOSINE
PROJECTION**

A "BUTTERFLY TYPE" PROJECTION
(BARTHOLOMEW'S REGIONAL)

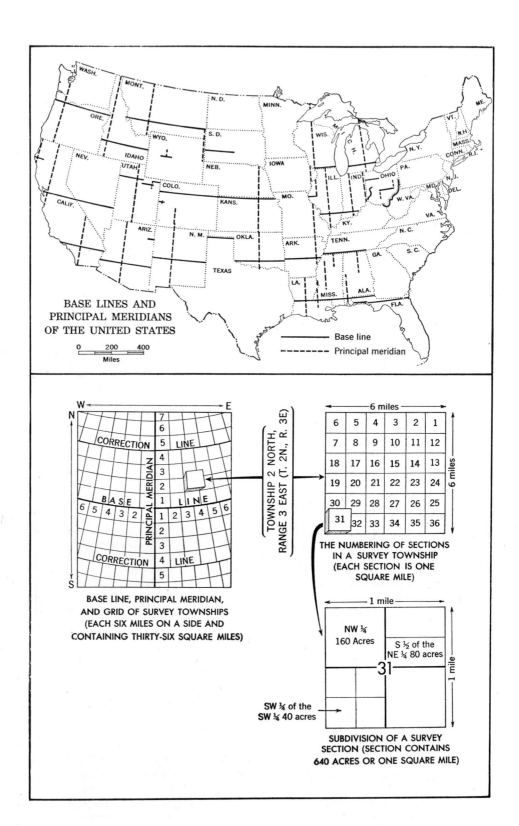

BASE LINES AND
PRINCIPAL MERIDIANS
OF THE UNITED STATES

0   200   400
Miles

——— Base line
––––––– Principal meridian

TOWNSHIP 2 NORTH,
RANGE 3 EAST (T. 2N., R. 3E)

BASE LINE, PRINCIPAL MERIDIAN,
AND GRID OF SURVEY TOWNSHIPS
(EACH SIX MILES ON A SIDE AND
CONTAINING THIRTY-SIX SQUARE MILES)

THE NUMBERING OF SECTIONS
IN A SURVEY TOWNSHIP
(EACH SECTION IS ONE
SQUARE MILE)

NW ¼
160 Acres

S ½ of the
NE ¼ 80 acres

SW ¼ of the
SW ¼ 40 acres

31

SUBDIVISION OF A SURVEY
SECTION (SECTION CONTAINS
640 ACRES OR ONE SQUARE MILE)

B. CLIMATE

Part I The Köppen Classification of Climates

ORIGIN. The most commonly used classification of climates is that devised by a German meteorologist, Wladimir Köppen (1846-1940). As early as 1900, Köppen suggested a climatic classification based on plant cover. It was in 1918, however, that he first formulated the actual scheme. In its major aspects, this original plan has not been altered though there have been many minor modifications. The final form specified by Köppen himself appeared in 1936 as a section of a five-volume work, "Handbook of Climatology," of which Köppen was one of the editors.

GENERAL FEATURES. The Köppen classification deals with the two climatic elements which are most obviously significant to man as he attempts to live and make a living on the face of the earth. These two elements are temperature and precipitation. Long-time records of each are available for numerous and widely scattered places on the earth. When these records are analyzed, it is found that certain outstanding combinations regularly occur. For example, some places show a combination of "hot and moist"; others are "hot and dry"; still others are "cold and moist"; and so on through many temperature and moisture combinations. It is such recognized combinations, or types, that constitute the Köppen "system" of climatic classification.

This system recognizes five *major* categories. To each of these a letter symbol is given. One of the major categories, for example, is expressed by the letter A, which signifies moist climates that are perennially hot. Subdivisions are made within each of the major classes, and each of these in turn is given a letter symbol. One of the subdivisions of the A climates is Af. The addition of the f indicates one special type of A climate, one which is not only hot and moist, but moist to the degree that there is no season of true drought at any time during the year.

The type of climate, or the *climate-formula,* to use Köppen's designation, is expressed as a combination of two or more letters. The letters are defined specifically as well as generally. Thus, direct measurements of degrees of heat and amount of moisture are provided.

In the use of the complete system, many detailed differences can be indicated by the addition of as many letter symbols as apply to the measurements at hand. For purposes of a general world survey, the subdivisions of the climatic types usually involve a third letter. Thus, a given climate may be symbolized as Cfa. The third letter in this instance signifies hot summers, and it, too, is capable of exact definition in a quantitative fashion. To go beyond a third symbol is, *for general purposes,* unwise and cumbersome.

SIGNIFICANCE OF THIS CLASSIFICATION. The Köppen classification of climates is extremely useful, first, because it is a quantitative and wholly objective device for the categorization of observed climatic phenomena. As has been indicated, it makes use of temperature and of precipitation amounts and of temperature and precipitation distribution through the year. These are measurable facts which are commonly observed over a large part of the earth's surface. When the Köppen definitions are applied to the observed facts, there is no question as to which category those facts represent. Given a set of climatic statistics, any individual, no matter from what part of the world he may come, can arrive at the proper *climate-formula* for his own, or any other, climate. The classification thus provides a sort of climatic Esperanto, or an international climatic shorthand.

Second, the Köppen classification is an extremely useful geographic tool for world or continental study. The definitions are stated in exact amounts which are capable of accurate representation on maps. It is therefore possible to construct maps on which the areas of different climatic types may be specifically delimited. From these maps, direct comparisons between one part of the world and another, or between one part of a continent and another, may be made. Further, these comparisons are standardized by the quantitative nature of the definitions. On a world-wide or a continental scale, the patterns disclosed by a map of climatic types are basic to an understanding of the variety which exists. It must here be noted, however, that the classification is of much less value in disclosing significant patterns within smaller areas.

Third, the Köppen classification is easy to apply. It does not require any special knowledge, either of meteorological details or of mathematical processes. It can, therefore, be used by nonspecialists fully as easily as it can by professional students.

Finally, the Köppen classification has come into such common use throughout the world that it may now be considered a standard. Nearly all of the many current classifications of climate are variants of the Köppen system. In some variants, names have been substituted for combinations of letter symbols. Thus, it is fairly common to speak of an Af climate as a Tropical Rainforest climate: of a BW climate as a Desert or Saharan climate; and of a Cs climate as a Mediterranean climate. In other variants, there have been different definitions proposed for those of Köppen while the main framework remains unaltered. Whether they be descriptive-type variations or definition variations, no one of the alternative classifications has had the world-wide acceptance which has been accorded the Köppen system *as a useful geographic tool*. This is not to suggest that there are no weaknesses in the Köppen system—for example the definitions specify types that are far too broad for purposes of climatological research. But despite difficulties of this sort, the system remains an extremely useful and a widely accepted tool for geographers.

PLAN OF THE CLASSIFICATION. *Major categories.* The five major categories of climate are given the letter symbols A, B, C, D, and E. Climates which are moist and are always hot, showing no appreciable seasonal changes of temperature, are designated the A climates. Those in which potential evaporation exceeds precipitation, dry climates, are given the symbol B. Moist climates in which there is a definite, though mild, winter are called C climates. Moist climates with severe winters use the letter D. And climates which have no summer season are known as E climates. For convenient reference, a tabular summary of general meanings of all symbols is given in Tables A and B in this part of the appendix. In addition, exact definitions for each symbol are given in Part II of this appendix. The method of determination of the climatic symbol represented by any set of temperature and precipitation statistics is included in Part III of this appendix.

The choice of the particular letters is purely arbitrary. It should be noted that the first letter symbol in the classification is always a capital letter. This is important because, in the definition of subdivisions of the major categories, some of the letters are used again, but they are always written or printed as small letters.

The A, C, and D climates are moist; that is, they are climates in which, regardless of the temperature, there is normally no problem of insufficient precipitation. In contrast to these three, the E climates are so cold that the problem of moisture is not significant. Only in the B climates do we find, as a normal condition, the problem of moisture deficiency.

Moisture deficiency, or dryness, must be defined on a sliding scale. Efficiency of precipitation, from the point of view of the cover of vegetation which it produces, is closely related to the rate of evaporation. More water will evaporate at high temperatures than at low ones. If evaporation is high, water available for plants is decreased. Hence, the amount of precipitation which is adequate for plant growth in a cool area is altogether insufficient in an area of constantly high temperatures. Likewise, an area which receives most of its precipitation during the warm growing season when the evaporation rate is high must have more water available than an area where most of the precipitation comes during the cooler season when evaporation is low. If evaporation records were kept as frequently and as accurately as are those of temperature and precipitation, it would be possible to determine directly the location of the line along which evaporation equals precipitation. This would permit exact definition of the boundary between climates which are moist and those which are dry. Unfortunately, records of evaporation are few in number and the points of observation are widely scattered. For these reasons, it has been necessary to introduce into the classification a definition which is not predicated upon a single amount of precipitation, but which is in reality a crude estimate of evaporation. This definition makes allowance for temperature, for yearly precipitation, and for seasonal distribution of precipitation.

Subdivisions of the major categories. The B climates are subdivided into arid climate which is represented by the secondary symbol W, and semi-arid climate which is represented by the secondary symbol S. These are written as capital letters when they are used with B and they have no tie with the letters w and s as those are used with the A, C, and D types. Beyond the classification as arid or semi-arid, a further difference within the B climates is made in terms of temperature; those dry climates which are always hot use the symbol h and those which are cold or have a pronounced winter season use the symbol k.

In each of the A, C, and D types, the second symbol is one which specifies the nature, the amount, and the distribution of precipitation through the year. There are three possibilities so far as the distribution of precipitation throughout the year is concerned; either the precipitation is rather evenly spread through the year, or it is concentrated in the cooler part of the year, or it is concentrated in the warmer part of the year. The symbol which indicates an even spread through the year is f; that which indicates concentration in the cooler part of the year is s; and that which shows concentration in the warmer part of the year is w. Theoretically, any of the three might be used following the first letter of the climate-formula. Actually, s occurs so infrequently with either A or D that it may be omitted so far as those two major categories are concerned. Within the A climates, another letter, m, is used to indicate an intermediary position between f and w.

Only in the C and D climates is a third symbol essential to the generalized world pattern. Since in those two categories the nature of the winter and of the summer have great effect upon the vegetation, the symbols should indicate the nature of each of those seasons. The first letter does this in part; the third letter completes the statement. Three of the letters used in third place characterize the summer and one of them, the winter. Where the summers are long and hot, the symbol a is used; for short and warm summers, b is used; for very short and cool summers, c is the symbol; and where winters are excessively cold and severe, the symbol d is used.

Within the climates which have no true summer, E, a distinction is made between regions of continuous frost, F, and those in which temperatures are occasionally high enough to permit a spotty vegetation cover of tundra, T.

SUMMARY OF TYPES. *Generalized description.* In summary, twenty-four climatic types are recognized. These are listed in Table A in this part of the appendix, each with a generalized résumé of its major features. Table B shows the relationship between the major categories and their subdivisions. It also indicates the relative position within the whole scheme of each of the types.

Equivalent climatic types. It is common practice to refer to climatic types by descriptive names, as has been done in the body of this text, or by names of places in which the climates occur. For convenience, certain of these equivalent names are listed in Table C of this part of the appendix. It should be pointed out that, even though they are rough equivalents, the descriptive or place-name climatic types lack the uniformity and convenience of detailed, standard definition which the Köppen types possess.

Table A TABULAR SUMMARY OF TWENTY-FOUR MAIN CLIMATIC TYPES OF THE KÖPPEN SYSTEM

Af	Always hot, always moist climate	Csa	Mild winter, rainy winter climate with long, hot, droughty summers
Am	Always hot, seasonally excessively moist climate	Csb	Mild winter, rainy winter climate with short, warm, droughty summers
Aw	Always hot, seasonally droughty climate	Dfa	Severe winter, always moist climate with long, hot summers
BSh	Semiarid, hot climate	Dwa	Severe winter, summer rainy climate with long, hot summers
BSk	Semiarid, cool or cold climate	Dfb	Severe winter, always rainy climate with short, warm summers
BWh	Arid, hot climate	Dwb	Severe winter, summer rainy climate with short, warm summers
BWk	Arid, cool or cold climate	Dfc	Severe winter, always moist climate with very short, cool summers
Cfa	Mild winter, always moist climate with long, hot summers	Dwc	Severe winter, summer rainy climate with very short, cool summers
Cfb	Mild winter, always moist climate with short, warm summers	Dfd	Severe winter, always moist climate with short summers and excessively cold winters
Cfc	Mild winter, always moist climate with very short, cool summers	Dwd	Severe winter, summer rainy climate with short summers and excessively cold winters
Cwa	Mild winter, summer rainy climate with long, hot summers	ET	Polar climate with very short period of plant growth
Cwb	Mild winter, summer rainy climate with short, warm summers	EF	Polar climate in which plant growth is impossible

Table B RELATIONSHIP BETWEEN THE MAJOR CATEGORIES OF CLIMATE AND THEIR SUBDI-
VISIONS

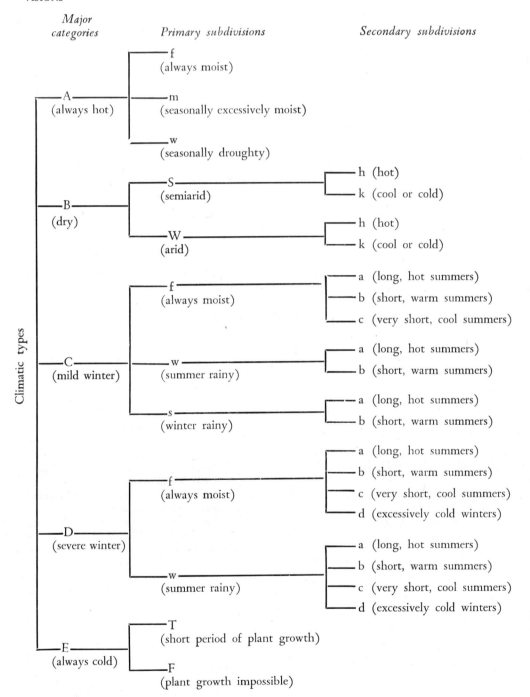

Table C SOME CLIMATIC TYPE EQUIVALENTS

Type name used in this text	Köppen type	Place name example
Tropical rainforest	Af	Amazon
Tropical monsoon	Am	Malabar
Savanna	Aw	Sudan
Semiarid	BSh and BSk	Lower Rio Grande and Northern Great Plains
Arid	BWh and BWk	Tarim Basin and Sahara
Humid subtropical	Cfa	Gulf States
Mid-latitude marine	Cfb and Cfc	Northwestern Europe
Subtropical monsoon	Cwa	South China
Tropical upland	Cwb	Ethiopia
Mediterranean	Csa and Csb	Mediterranean
Humid continental with hot summers	Dfa and Dwa	Iowa and North China
Humid continental with warm summers	Dfb and Dwb	Northern Great Lakes and Northern Manchuria
Subarctic	Dfc, Dwc, Dfd, Dwd	Central Canada, Amur Lowland, and Northeastern Siberia
Tundra	ET	Northern Alaska
Icecap	EF	Greenland

Part II Definitions of Climatic Symbols

PRIMARY TYPES

A Average temperature of the coolest month 64.4° F. or over

B Precipitation less in inches than the amount .44t − 8.5 when it is evenly distributed through the year; or less than the amount .44t − 14 when it is concentrated chiefly in winter; or less than the amount .44t − 3 when it is concentrated chiefly in summer. In all of these amounts, t equals average annual temperature in degrees F. These amounts are worked out in Table D. See note regarding meaning of "concentrated" in Table D

C Average temperature of the warmest month over 50° F. and of the coldest month between 64.4 and 26.6° F.

D Average temperature of the warmest month over 50° F. and of the coldest month 26.6° F. and below

E Average temperature of the warmest month below 50° F.

SECONDARY TYPES As they occur with A

f Precipitation of the driest month of the year at least 2.4 inches

w Precipitation of the driest month of the year less than the amount shown in Table E

m Precipitation of the driest month of the year less than 2.4 inches, but more than the amount shown in Table E

As they occur with B

W Precipitation for the year less than half the amount shown in the definition for B. See Table D.

S Precipitation for the year less than the amount shown in the definition for B, but more than half that amount. See Table D.

As they occur with C and D

s Precipitation for the driest month of the summer half of the year less than 1.6 inches and less than ⅓ the amount which falls in the wettest month of the winter half of the year

w Precipitation of the driest month of the winter half of the year less than 1/10 the amount which falls in the wettest month of the summer half of the year

f Precipitation not satisfying the definitions for s or w

As they occur with E

T Average temperature of the warmest month of the year between 50° F. and 32° F.

F Average temperature of the warmest month 32° F. or below

TERTIARY TYPES *As they occur with B*

h   Average annual temperature 64.4° F. or above
k   Average annual temperature below 64.4° F.

As they occur with C

a   Average temperature of the warmest month 71.6° F. or above

b   Average temperature of the four warmest months 50° F. or above, and average temperature of the warmest month below 71.6° F.

c   Average temperature of from one to three months 50° F. or above, and average temperature of warmest month below 71.6° F.

As they occur with D

a   Same as with C
b   Same as with C
c   Same as with C
d   Average temperature of the coldest month below −36.4° F. (*Note:* a, b, and c do not specifically exclude d, *but* when d can be used, do *not* use a, b, or c.)

Table D

This table gives the amount of precipitation in inches at the boundary between the B climates and the other primary types for each average annual temperature from 32° F. to 90° F., and for the three possible distributions of rain through the year.

Average annual temperature	Precipitation concentrated chiefly in winter (.44t − 14)	Precipitation evenly distributed through the year (.44t − 8.5)	Precipitation concentrated chiefly in summer (.44t − 3)
32	.08	5.58	11.08
33	.52	6.02	11.52
34	.96	6.46	11.96
35	1.40	6.90	12.40
36	1.84	7.34	12.84
37	2.28	7.78	13.28
38	2.72	8.22	13.72
39	3.16	8.66	14.16
40	3.60	9.10	14.60
41	4.04	9.54	15.04
42	4.48	9.98	15.48
43	4.92	10.42	15.92
44	5.36	10.86	16.36
45	5.80	11.30	16.80
46	6.24	11.74	17.24
47	6.68	12.18	17.68
48	7.12	12.62	18.12
49	7.56	13.06	18.56
50	8.00	13.50	19.00
51	8.44	13.94	19.44
52	8.88	14.38	19.88
53	9.32	14.82	20.32
54	9.76	15.26	20.76
55	10.20	15.70	21.20
56	10.64	16.14	21.64
57	11.08	16.58	22.08
58	11.52	17.02	22.52
59	11.96	17.46	22.96
60	12.40	17.90	23.40
61	12.84	18.34	23.84
62	13.28	18.78	24.28
63	13.72	19.22	24.72
64	14.16	19.66	25.16
65	14.60	20.10	25.60
66	15.04	20.54	26.04
67	15.48	20.98	26.48
68	15.92	21.42	26.92
69	16.36	21.86	27.36
70	16.80	22.30	27.80
71	17.24	22.74	28.24
72	17.68	23.18	28.68
73	18.12	23.62	29.12
74	18.56	24.06	29.56
75	19.00	24.50	30.00
76	19.44	24.94	30.44
77	19.88	25.38	30.88
78	20.32	25.82	31.32
79	20.76	26.26	31.76
80	21.20	26.70	32.20
81	21.64	27.14	32.64
82	22.08	27.58	33.08
83	22.52	28.02	33.52
84	22.96	28.46	33.96
85	23.40	28.90	34.40
86	23.84	29.34	34.84
87	24.28	29.78	35.28
88	24.72	30.22	35.72
89	25.16	30.66	36.16
90	25.60	31.10	36.60

Note: Precipitation is said to be concentrated in summer when 70% or more of the average annual amount is received during the warmer six months. It is concentrated in winter when 70% or more is received in the cooler six months. If neither season receives 70% of the annual total, the precipitation is considered to be evenly distributed. Division of the year into six-month periods is made between March and April on the one hand and between September and October on the other.

APPENDICES

Table E

This table gives the amount of precipitation in inches during the driest month of the year along the boundary between Am and Aw climates for differing amounts of yearly precipitation. If the amount in the driest month is 2.4 inches or more, the symbol f is used; if the amount in the driest month is between 2.4 and the amount shown in this table, the symbol m is used; and if the amount in the driest month is less than that shown in this table, the symbol w is used.

(All figures in inches)

Total yearly precipitation	Precipitation in driest month	Total yearly precipitation	Precipitation in driest month
38.5	2.40	57.5	1.64
39	2.38	58	1.63
39.5	2.36	58.5	1.60
40	2.34	59	1.58
40.5	2.32	59.5	1.56
41	2.30	60	1.55
41.5	2.29	60.5	1.53
42	2.26	61	1.51
42.5	2.24	61.5	1.48
43	2.22	62	1.47
43.5	2.20	62.5	1.45
44	2.18	63	1.42
44.5	2.16	63.5	1.41
45	2.14	64	1.38
45.5	2.12	64.5	1.36
46	2.10	65	1.34
46.5	2.08	65.5	1.33
47	2.07	66	1.30
47.5	2.04	66.5	1.28
48	2.02	67	1.26
48.5	2.00	67.5	1.24
49	1.98	68	1.22
49.5	1.96	68.5	1.20
50	1.94	69	1.18
50.5	1.92	69.5	1.15
51	1.90	70	1.13
51.5	1.88	70.5	1.11
52	1.86	71	1.10
52.5	1.85	71.5	1.08
53	1.82	72	1.06
53.5	1.80	72.5	1.03
54	1.78	73	1.02
54.5	1.77	73.5	1.00
55	1.75	74	.98
55.5	1.73	74.5	.96
56	1.70	75	.94
56.5	1.68	75.5	.92
57	1.66	76	.90

Total yearly precipitation	Precipitation in driest month	Total yearly precipitation	Precipitation in driest month
76.5	.88	88	.42
77	.86	88.5	.40
77.5	.84	89	.37
78	.81	89.5	.36
78.5	.80	90	.34
79	.78	90.5	.32
79.5	.76	91	.29
80	.74	91.5	.28
80.5	.72	92	.26
81	.70	92.5	.24
81.5	.68	93	.22
82	.66	93.5	.20
82.5	.63	94	.18
83	.61	94.5	.16
83.5	.59	95	.14
84	.58	95.5	.11
84.5	.56	96	.09
85	.54	96.5	.07
85.5	.51	97	.06
86	.50	97.5	.04
86.5	.48	98	.02
87	.46	98.5	.00
87.5	.44		

Note: If the total yearly precipitation is 197 inches, there can be two whole months without rain and the symbol m can be used; if the yearly amount is 295.5 inches, three months may be dry; etc. The symbol m signifies that the dry period is compensated by excess rain at another time whereas w indicates a lack of compensating amounts. Hence, the dividing amount in the driest month becomes smaller as the total for the year becomes larger.

Part III The Determination of Climatic Types

GENERAL PROCEDURE. *Primary types.* In order to determine the climatic type at a given place, it is necessary to have available average temperatures for every month and for the year as well as average precipitation for each month and for the year. When these statistics are at hand, the actual classification can most easily be accomplished by following the routine procedure stated below. It is essentially a process of elimination.

To determine the first letter of the climate-formula, proceed according to the following questions.

1. Is the average temperature of the warmest month below 50° F.? If it is, the climate is of the E type; if it is not, proceed to the second question.
2. Is the amount of precipitation less than the amount specified as the limit of the B climates in Table D? If it is less, the climate is of the B type; if it is not, proceed to the third question.
3. Is the average temperature of the coolest month 64.4° F. or above? If it is, the climate is of the A type; if it is not, proceed to the fourth question.
4. Is the average temperature of the coldest month between 64.4° F. and 26.6° F.? If it is, the climate is of the C type; if it is not, or, in other words, if the average temperature of the coldest month is below 26.6° F., the climate is of the D type.

Thus by following through a sequence of, at most, four questions, it is possible to determine which one of the five primary climatic types is represented by any set of temperature and precipitation statistics.

Secondary types. Once the primary type is determined, similar routines are followed to obtain the second and third letters of the climate-formula. Secondary characteristics of each of the main types are most easily determined by applying the following questions.

1. If the climate is of the E type, is the average temperature of the warmest month over 32° F.? If it is, the secondary symbol is T; if it is not, the secondary symbol is F.
2. If the climate is of the B type, is the yearly precipitation over one half the amount specified as the limit of the B climates in Table D? If it is, the secondary symbol is S; if it is not, the secondary symbol is W.
3. If the climate is of the A type:
   a. Is the precipitation of the driest month 2.4 inches or more? If it is, the secondary symbol is f; if it is not, refer to the next question.
   b. Is the precipitation of the driest month more than the amount specified in Table E? If it is, the secondary symbol is m; if it is not, the secondary symbol is w.
4. If the climate is of the C or D types:
   a. Is the driest month of the year in the summer six-month period and is its precipitation

less than 1.6 inches? If both conditions are satisfied, proceed to question b; if either is not satisfied, proceed to question c.
   b. Is the precipitation of the driest month of summer less than ⅓ that of the wettest month of winter? If it is, the secondary symbol is s; if it is not, the secondary symbol is f.
   c. Is the precipitation of the driest month of winter less than ⅒ that of the wettest month of summer? If it is, the secondary symbol is w; if it is not, the secondary symbol is f.

Tertiary types. Tertiary characteristics of each of the C and D climates are determined most easily as follows. If the climate is of the C or D type, apply the following questions.

1. Is the average temperature of the coldest month below −36.4° F.? If it is, the symbol is d; if it is not, proceed to the next question.
2. Is the average temperature of the warmest month 71.6° F. or above? If it is, the symbol is a; if it is not, proceed to the next question.
3. Are the average temperatures of four warmest months 50° F. or above? If they are, the symbol is b; if they are not, the symbol is c.

APPLICATION OF THE PROCEDURE OF CLASSIFICATION. *First example.* The first example is Maracaibo, Venezuela. The statistics are given below.

Beginning with the primary types, we must first ask the question, "Is the average temperature of the warmest month below 50° F.?" The warmest month is August, with an average of 84.4°. This is well above 50° and hence the type cannot be E. We have eliminated one of the primary types.

Second, we must ask the question, "Is the amount of precipitation less than the amount specified by definition as the limit of the B climates?" It is simplest here to refer to Table D. To use the Table, we must know three things about the place in question. These are: (1) the average annual temperature, (2) the average annual precipitation, and (3) the distribution of the precipitation through the year. For example, does 70% or more of the precipitation come in the winter six months? Does 70% or more come in the summer six months? Or does 70% come in neither season?

Items 1 and 2 are given in the statistics: Maracaibo has an average annual temperature of 82.3° F., and an average annual precipitation of

	J	F	M	A	M	J	J	A	S	O	N	D	Year
Temp.	80.7	81.0	81.2	82.5	83.2	83.5	84.1	84.4	83.5	82.0	81.3	81.0	82.3
Prec.	0.1	0.1	0.3	0.5	2.4	1.6	1.4	1.3	3.3	4.3	2.5	0.4	18.2

18.2 inches. To secure the necessary third item requires the application of simple arithmetic.

The warmer six months at Maracaibo are April through September. During these months, the precipitation in inches is as follows: April, .5; May, 2.4; June, 1.6; July, 1.4; August, 1.3; and September, 3.3. The total for this season is 10.5 inches. Since the total for the year is 18.2 inches and that for the warmer six months is 10.5 inches, the amount which falls in the cooler six months must be 18.2 minus 10.5, or 7.7 inches. The summer, or warmer season, precipitation is 10.5 inches; the winter, or cooler season, precipitation is 7.7 inches. Is either of these amounts equal to or more than 70% of the total for the year? Seventy per cent of 18.2 is 12.74. Since neither the warmer season precipitation nor that of the cooler season is equal to or greater than 70% of the total, the precipitation is considered to be evenly distributed throughout the year.

Now, the three items necessary for the use of Table D are available: average annual temperature, 82.3° F.; average annual precipitation, 18.2 inches; and evenly distributed precipitation. Consulting Table D we find in the first column average annual temperatures in whole numbers. The nearest to 82.3 is 82. The third column is headed "Precipitation evenly distributed through the year." We follow down this column until we come to the figure on the same line as 82 in the first column. That figure is 27.58. Now we can answer the question, "Is the amount of precipitation less than the amount specified by definition as the limit of the B climates?" The precipitation at Maracaibo (18.2 inches) is less than the limit figure (27.58 inches). Hence, Maracaibo has a B climate.

We need go no further with the primary types for no set of statistics will fulfill the requirements for more than one. The task is now to determine the secondary symbol.

For the second symbol, only one question is necessary. "Is the yearly precipitation over one half the amount specified in Table D?" The amount specified in Table D in this instance is 27.58. One half of that is 13.79. Is the annual precipitation at Maracaibo (18.2 inches) over one half the amount (13.79 inches) specified in Table D? It is and hence the secondary symbol is S. Maracaibo thus has a BS climate.

Second example. As a second example of the application of the procedure of classification, the statistics for Iloilo in the Philippine Islands may be examined below.

We follow the same order as in the example of Maracaibo. First, is the average temperature of the warmest month below 50° F.? It is not; therefore the type is not E. Is the precipitation for the year less than the amount specified for the limit of the B climates? We must know three things to answer this question: (1) the average annual temperature; (2) the average annual precipitation; and (3) the distribution of precipitation through the year. The warmer six months at Iloilo is the period of April through September. In that season, 60.8 inches of rain fall. Since 88.7 inches fall during the whole year, the amount in the cooler season is 88.7 minus 60.8, or 17.9 inches. Seventy per cent of 88.7 is 62.09. Neither the amount which falls in the warmer season nor that which falls in the cooler season is equal to or more than 62.09. Therefore, the precipitation may be considered to be evenly distributed through the year. Referring to Table D, we find 81 in the first column. Opposite it in the third column is 27.14. This represents the amount of precipitation which, under these conditions of temperature, limits the B climates. The amount of precipitation at Iloilo is more than 27.14; therefore, the climate at Iloilo is not B.

We proceed to the next question. "Is the average temperature of the coolest month 64.4° F. or above?" The coolest month at Iloilo has an average temperature of 78.0° F. This is above 64.4° F. and, therefore, Iloilo has an A climate.

There is a threefold division within the A climates. We must now discover into which of these three Iloilo fits. The first question is "Is the precipitation for the driest month 2.4 inches or more?" The driest month at Iloilo has 1.3 inches of rain. The answer to the question is in the negative and consequently the symbol f does not apply. The second question asks "Is the precipitation of the driest month more than the amount specified in Table E?" In order to use that Table, we must know the average annual precipitation and the precipitation of the driest month. At Iloilo, the average annual precipitation is 88.7 inches; the precipitation of the driest month is 1.3 inches. On Table E in the column headed "Total yearly precipitation,"

	J	F	M	A	M	J	J	A	S	O	N	D	Year
Temp.	78.0	78.5	80.0	80.7	82.3	81.3	80.5	80.7	80.0	80.0	79.7	78.8	81.0
Prec.	2.4	1.8	1.3	1.6	5.9	10.5	16.3	13.8	12.7	10.3	7.7	4.4	88.7

the figure 88.5 can be found. This is the figure closest to 88.7. Opposite it in the column headed "Precipitation of the driest month" is the figure .40. Returning to the question, we can see that the precipitation of the driest month at Iloilo (1.3 inches) is more than the amount specified in Table E (.40 inch). Therefore, the symbol m can be used. The climate at Iloilo is of the Am type.

Part IV   Selected Climatic Statistics

NORTH AND MIDDLE AMERICA AND THE CARIBBEAN AREA

1. San Juan, Puerto Rico

	J	F	M	A	M	J	J	A	S	O	N	D	Year
Temp.	75	75	75	77	79	80	80	80	80	80	78	76	78
Prec.	4.1	3.0	3.0	4.1	5.2	5.4	5.8	5.9	6.0	5.7	7.0	5.4	60.6

2. Miami, Florida

	J	F	M	A	M	J	J	A	S	O	N	D	Year
Temp.	66	68	72	74	79	81	82	82	81	77	73	69	75
Prec.	3.3	2.5	2.8	3.1	5.9	7.9	7.2	7.3	9.9	9.2	2.4	2.2	63.7

3. Port-au-Prince, Haiti

	J	F	M	A	M	J	J	A	S	O	N	D	Year
Temp.	78	78	79	80	81	83	84	84	82	81	80	78	81
Prec.	1.2	2.7	4.1	6.7	8.0	4.0	2.7	4.8	7.7	7.4	4.2	0.9	54.4

4. Acapulco, Mexico

	J	F	M	A	M	J	J	A	S	O	N	D	Year
Temp.	78	78	79	80	83	83	83	81	81	83	80	79	81
Prec.	0.6	0	0	0	1.7	16.5	6.0	6.3	14.7	5.9	1.9	0.7	54.3

5. Veracruz, Mexico

	J	F	M	A	M	J	J	A	S	O	N	D	Year
Temp.	70	71	74	78	81	81	81	81	80	78	75	71	77
Prec.	1.0	0.6	0.5	0.6	1.7	11.4	13.0	10.7	12.0	5.7	3.1	1.0	61.3

6. Medicine Hat, Canada

	J	F	M	A	M	J	J	A	S	O	N	D	Year
Temp.	13	16	28	45	55	63	69	67	56	45	30	19	42
Prec.	0.6	0.6	0.6	0.7	1.6	2.5	1.8	1.4	1.2	0.6	0.7	0.7	13.0

7. Goodland, Kansas

	J	F	M	A	M	J	J	A	S	O	N	D	Year
Temp.	29	33	40	50	59	70	77	74	66	54	41	30	52
Prec.	0.3	0.6	1.0	1.8	2.5	2.8	2.7	2.5	1.6	1.0	0.6	0.6	18.0

8. San Diego, California

	J	F	M	A	M	J	J	A	S	O	N	D	Year
Temp.	54	55	56	58	61	64	67	69	67	63	59	56	61
Prec.	1.8	2.0	1.5	0.6	0.3	0.1	0.1	0.1	0.1	0.3	0.9	1.8	9.6

9. Mexico City, Mexico

	J	F	M	A	M	J	J	A	S	O	N	D	Year
Temp.	54	57	61	63	65	64	62	62	61	59	57	55	60
Prec.	0.2	0.3	0.5	0.7	1.9	4.1	4.5	4.3	4.1	1.6	0.5	0.3	23.0

10. Phoenix, Arizona

	J	F	M	A	M	J	J	A	S	O	N	D	Year
Temp.	50	54	60	67	75	84	90	88	82	70	59	52	69
Prec.	1.0	0.7	0.6	0.4	0.1	0.1	1.3	1.0	0.7	0.5	0.8	0.7	7.9

11. La Paz, Mexico

	J	F	M	A	M	J	J	A	S	O	N	D	Year
Temp.	63	65	68	71	74	78	82	84	82	79	72	66	74
Prec.	0.2	0.1	0	0	0	0	0.4	1.2	1.4	0.6	0.5	1.1	5.5

12. Cairo, Illinois

	J	F	M	A	M	J	J	A	S	O	N	D	Year
Temp.	44	47	57	67	76	85	88	87	81	70	56	46	67
Prec.	3.9	3.2	4.1	3.9	3.8	3.9	3.0	3.0	2.9	2.8	3.6	3.3	41.4

13. New York, New York

	J	F	M	A	M	J	J	A	S	O	N	D	Year
Temp.	30	31	38	49	59	69	75	73	66	55	44	34	52
Prec.	3.3	3.3	3.5	3.3	3.5	3.4	4.1	4.4	3.4	3.4	3.6	3.3	42.5

14. *Washington, D.C.*

	J	F	M	A	M	J	J	A	S	O	N	D	Year
Temp.	33	35	42	53	64	73	77	75	68	57	45	36	55
Prec.	3.1	3.1	3.5	3.3	3.7	3.7	4.3	4.1	3.3	3.1	2.6	3.0	40.8

15. *San Antonio, Texas*

	J	F	M	A	M	J	J	A	S	O	N	D	Year
Temp.	53	55	63	69	75	81	83	83	79	70	61	54	69
Prec.	1.4	1.6	1.8	2.7	3.2	2.7	2.5	2.6	3.5	2.0	2.2	1.8	28.0

16. *Montgomery, Alabama*

	J	F	M	A	M	J	J	A	S	O	N	D	Year
Temp.	48	51	58	65	73	80	82	81	76	66	56	49	66
Prec.	5.1	5.5	6.4	4.3	3.8	4.2	4.7	4.2	2.9	2.4	3.1	4.5	51.1

17. *Sitka, Alaska*

	J	F	M	A	M	J	J	A	S	O	N	D	Year
Temp.	30	32	35	40	46	51	55	55	51	44	37	33	42
Prec.	7.1	6.8	5.6	5.4	4.3	3.5	4.0	7.1	9.7	11.7	8.8	7.4	81.4

18. *St. Paul, Minnesota*

	J	F	M	A	M	J	J	A	S	O	N	D	Year
Temp.	12	15	28	46	58	67	72	70	61	48	31	19	44
Prec.	0.9	0.8	1.4	2.4	3.4	4.1	3.5	3.5	3.4	2.0	1.4	1.0	27.8

19. *Albany, New York*

	J	F	M	A	M	J	J	A	S	O	N	D	Year
Temp.	23	24	33	47	59	68	72	71	63	50	39	28	48
Prec.	2.6	2.5	2.7	2.7	3.5	4.0	4.1	3.8	3.4	3.4	3.0	2.7	38.4

20. *Dubuque, Iowa*

	J	F	M	A	M	J	J	A	S	O	N	D	Year
Temp.	20	23	35	49	60	70	75	72	64	52	37	25	48
Prec.	1.5	1.4	2.2	2.6	3.9	4.5	3.7	3.4	4.0	2.5	1.9	1.5	33.1

21. *Edmonton, Canada*

	J	F	M	A	M	J	J	A	S	O	N	D	Year
Temp.	6	12	22	40	51	57	61	59	50	41	26	14	37
Prec.	0.8	0.7	0.8	0.9	1.7	3.1	3.2	2.4	1.3	0.7	0.7	0.8	17.1

22. *Toronto, Canada*

	J	F	M	A	M	J	J	A	S	O	N	D	Year
Temp.	22	23	30	42	53	63	69	67	60	48	37	27	45
Prec.	2.8	2.7	2.4	2.5	2.8	2.7	2.9	2.8	3.1	2.4	2.8	2.6	32.5

23. *Halifax, Canada*

	J	F	M	A	M	J	J	A	S	O	N	D	Year
Temp.	23	23	30	39	49	58	65	65	58	49	39	28	44
Prec.	5.5	4.9	4.9	4.6	4.1	3.7	3.8	4.5	3.6	5.2	5.5	5.3	55.6

24. *Duluth, Minnesota*

	J	F	M	A	M	J	J	A	S	O	N	D	Year
Temp.	10	13	24	38	48	58	66	65	57	45	29	17	39
Prec.	1.0	1.0	1.5	2.1	3.4	4.4	3.9	3.5	3.7	2.7	1.5	1.2	29.9

25. *Norman, Canada*

	J	F	M	A	M	J	J	A	S	O	N	D	Year
Temp.	−19	−13	−2	19	41	54	59	54	41	24	−1	−15	20
Prec.	0.4	0.5	0.6	0.5	1.1	1.3	1.8	1.9	1.0	0.8	0.4	0.4	10.7

26. *Churchill, Canada*

	J	F	M	A	M	J	J	A	S	O	N	D	Year
Temp.	−21	−17	−2	17	30	44	54	52	41	27	6	−11	18
Prec.	0.6	1.1	1.1	1.0	0.9	2.0	1.8	2.4	2.6	1.3	1.2	0.8	16.8

27. *Father Point, Canada*

	J	F	M	A	M	J	J	A	S	O	N	D	Year
Temp.	9	10	22	34	44	53	58	56	49	41	30	17	36
Prec.	2.5	2.4	2.4	1.9	3.0	3.6	2.9	3.2	3.1	3.3	2.9	2.8	34.0

28. *Upernavik, West Greenland*

	J	F	M	A	M	J	J	A	S	O	N	D	Year
Temp.	−7	−10	−7	6	25	35	41	41	34	25	14	1	17
Prec.	0.4	0.4	0.6	0.5	0.6	0.6	1.0	1.1	1.0	1.2	1.1	0.5	9.0

SOUTH AMERICA

29. *Medellín, Colombia*

	J	F	M	A	M	J	J	A	S	O	N	D	Year
Temp.	71	72	71	71	71	71	71	71	71	69	69	70	71
Prec.	2.7	3.5	3.3	6.6	7.7	5.5	4.1	4.6	6.2	6.9	5.2	2.5	58.8

30. *Santos, Brazil*

	J	F	M	A	M	J	J	A	S	O	N	D	Year
Temp.	76	78	76	73	69	66	66	66	67	69	73	76	71
Prec.	10.4	9.2	8.1	6.8	6.1	2.4	4.4	4.6	5.6	6.1	7.8	7.0	78.5

31. *Manaus, Brazil*

	J	F	M	A	M	J	J	A	S	O	N	D	Year
Temp.	80	80	80	80	80	80	81	82	83	83	82	81	81
Prec.	9.2	9.0	9.6	8.5	7.0	3.6	2.2	1.4	2.0	4.1	5.5	7.7	69.8

32. *Rio de Janeiro, Brazil*

	J	F	M	A	M	J	J	A	S	O	N	D	Year
Temp.	79	79	78	75	72	70	69	70	70	72	74	77	74
Prec.	4.9	4.8	5.2	4.3	3.1	2.3	1.7	1.7	2.6	3.2	4.1	5.4	43.3

33. *Coquimbo, Chile*

	J	F	M	A	M	J	J	A	S	O	N	D	Year
Temp.	64	64	62	59	57	54	54	54	55	57	59	62	58
Prec.	0	0	0	0	1.1	1.5	1.1	0.5	0.2	0	0	0	4.4

34. *Lima, Peru*

	J	F	M	A	M	J	J	A	S	O	N	D	Year
Temp.	73	74	74	70	66	63	61	61	61	63	66	70	67
Prec.	0	0	0	0	0	0.1	0.2	0.4	0.4	0.4	0.2	0.1	1.8

35. *Buenos Aires, Argentina*

	J	F	M	A	M	J	J	A	S	O	N	D	Year
Temp.	74	73	69	61	55	50	49	51	55	60	66	71	61
Prec.	3.1	2.8	3.9	4.8	2.8	2.0	2.1	2.2	2.9	3.3	4.0	4.0	37.9

36. *Puerto Montt, Chile*

	J	F	M	A	M	J	J	A	S	O	N	D	Year
Temp.	60	58	56	52	50	46	46	46	47	51	54	57	52
Prec.	4.6	4.4	5.9	7.4	10.6	10.0	10.8	9.3	6.3	5.5	5.5	5.4	85.7

37. *Mar del Plata, Argentina*

	J	F	M	A	M	J	J	A	S	O	N	D	Year
Temp.	67	66	64	59	53	47	46	47	50	53	59	64	56
Prec.	2.1	3.1	3.1	3.1	1.9	2.4	2.1	1.8	2.6	2.4	2.6	2.7	29.9

38. *Santiago, Chile*

	J	F	M	A	M	J	J	A	S	O	N	D	Year
Temp.	69	67	62	57	51	46	46	49	52	57	62	67	57
Prec.	0	0.1	0.2	0.6	2.4	3.3	2.8	2.1	1.3	0.5	0.2	0.2	13.7

39. *Tucumán, Argentina*

	J	F	M	A	M	J	J	A	S	O	N	D	Year
Temp.	77	75	72	66	60	54	54	57	64	69	73	75	66
Prec.	6.3	7.5	5.5	3.1	1.2	0.6	0.3	0.5	0.6	2.3	4.2	5.9	38.0

EUROPE

40. *Astrakhan, U.S.S.R.*

	J	F	M	A	M	J	J	A	S	O	N	D	Year
Temp.	19	21	32	49	64	73	78	75	64	50	38	26	49
Prec.	0.5	0.3	0.4	0.5	0.6	0.7	0.5	0.5	0.5	0.4	0.4	0.5	5.8

41. *Turin, Italy*

	J	F	M	A	M	J	J	A	S	O	N	D	Year
Temp.	33	37	46	54	61	69	74	73	65	54	43	35	54
Prec.	2.2	1.6	2.3	4.4	4.8	4.2	2.3	2.6	2.8	3.6	2.6	1.6	35.0

42. *Trieste*

	J	F	M	A	M	J	J	A	S	O	N	D	Year
Temp.	39	41	47	54	62	69	74	73	66	58	49	43	56
Prec.	2.2	2.3	2.8	2.9	3.7	4.1	3.7	3.7	4.0	4.7	3.6	3.4	41.1

43. *Paris, France*

	J	F	M	A	M	J	J	A	S	O	N	D	Year
Temp.	37	39	43	51	56	62	66	64	59	51	43	37	51
Prec.	1.4	1.1	1.4	1.5	1.9	2.1	2.0	1.9	1.9	2.1	1.9	1.6	20.8

44. *Dublin, Eire*

	J	F	M	A	M	J	J	A	S	O	N	D	Year
Temp.	40	41	42	45	49	55	58	57	54	48	44	41	48
Prec.	2.2	1.9	1.9	1.9	2.1	2.0	2.6	3.1	2.0	2.6	2.9	2.5	27.7

45. *Reykjavík, Iceland*

Temp.	30	30	31	36	43	49	52	51	46	39	34	30	39
Prec.	3.9	3.3	2.7	2.4	1.9	1.9	1.9	2.0	3.5	3.4	3.7	3.5	34.1

46. *Frankfort on the Main, Germany*

Temp.	32	36	41	49	57	63	66	64	58	49	41	35	49
Prec.	1.5	1.4	1.7	1.2	1.9	2.2	2.6	2.2	1.9	2.1	1.8	2.0	22.5

47. *Edinburgh, Scotland*

Temp.	38	39	40	45	49	55	58	57	54	47	42	39	47
Prec.	2.0	1.8	1.7	1.5	1.9	2.4	2.7	3.0	2.5	2.4	2.3	2.3	26.5

48. *Athens, Greece*

Temp.	48	50	53	58	66	74	80	80	73	66	57	52	63
Prec.	2.1	1.8	1.3	0.9	0.8	0.6	0.3	0.6	0.7	1.4	2.9	2.5	15.9

49. *Coruña, Spain*

Temp.	49	50	52	55	58	62	64	64	62	57	53	50	57
Prec.	2.7	3.5	3.2	2.9	2.0	1.4	0.9	1.1	1.7	3.1	3.5	3.5	29.5

50. *Granada, Spain*

Temp.	44	48	52	58	63	70	77	77	70	60	51	44	59
Prec.	2.0	1.7	2.2	2.1	1.8	0.8	0.1	0.2	1.1	1.8	1.9	1.9	17.6

51. *Lisbon, Portugal*

Temp.	51	52	55	58	62	67	71	72	69	63	57	51	61
Prec.	3.4	3.3	3.4	3.1	1.8	0.6	0.2	0.2	1.3	2.4	3.6	4.3	27.6

52. *Bucharest, Romania*

Temp.	26	31	41	52	62	69	73	72	64	53	40	31	51
Prec.	1.2	1.1	1.5	1.7	2.3	4.3	2.2	2.2	2.0	1.6	1.6	1.2	22.9

53. *Odessa, U.S.S.R.*

Temp.	25	28	35	48	59	68	73	71	62	52	41	31	49
Prec.	0.9	0.7	1.1	1.1	1.3	2.3	2.1	1.2	1.4	1.1	1.6	1.3	16.1

54. *Oslo, Norway*

Temp.	25	26	31	41	51	60	63	60	52	42	33	27	43
Prec.	1.1	1.1	1.3	1.3	1.7	1.9	2.8	3.5	2.4	2.5	1.9	1.7	23.2

55. *Moscow, U.S.S.R.*

Temp.	12	15	23	38	53	62	66	63	52	40	28	17	39
Prec.	1.7	0.9	1.2	1.5	1.9	2.0	2.8	2.9	2.2	1.4	1.6	1.5	21.6

56. *Stockholm, Sweden*

Temp.	27	26	30	38	48	57	62	59	53	43	35	29	42
Prec.	1.4	1.3	1.3	1.5	1.5	1.7	2.4	2.9	1.9	1.8	1.9	1.9	21.5

57. *Tromsö, Norway*

Temp.	26	24	27	32	39	47	52	51	44	36	30	27	36
Prec.	4.3	4.4	3.1	2.3	1.9	2.2	2.2	2.8	4.8	4.6	4.4	3.8	40.8

58. *Arkhangelsk, U.S.S.R.*

Temp.	7	9	19	30	41	54	60	57	47	35	22	12	33
Prec.	0.8	0.7	0.8	0.7	1.0	1.5	2.2	2.1	2.0	1.5	1.1	0.8	15.2

59. *Vardö, Norway*

Temp.	22	21	23	30	35	42	48	48	43	35	28	24	33
Prec.	2.6	2.8	2.1	1.7	1.4	1.6	1.7	2.0	2.4	2.5	2.5	2.6	25.9

60. *Angmagssalik, East Greenland*

	J	F	M	A	M	J	J	A	S	O	N	D	Year
Temp.	18	16	19	25	34	41	45	43	38	30	23	20	29
Prec.	3.3	2.0	2.4	2.4	2.4	2.1	1.9	2.4	3.7	5.7	3.3	2.8	34.4

AFRICA

61. *Nouvelle Anvers, Belgian Congo*

Temp.	79	80	79	78	78	78	77	78	78	77	77	77	78
Prec.	4.1	3.5	4.1	5.6	6.2	6.1	6.3	6.3	6.3	6.6	2.6	9.3	67.0

62. *Freetown, Sierra Leone*

Temp.	81	82	82	82	82	80	78	77	79	80	81	81	80
Prec.	0.6	0.5	1.1	5.4	14.8	21.3	36.8	39.6	32.5	15.2	5.3	1.3	174.4

63. *Banana, Belgian Congo*

Temp.	80	81	82	80	79	75	73	73	76	79	80	80	78
Prec.	2.1	2.3	3.7	6.1	1.9	0	0	0.1	0.1	1.6	5.9	4.7	28.5

64. *Mombasa, Kenya*

Temp.	80	80	82	81	78	77	75	76	77	78	79	80	79
Prec.	0.8	0.9	2.3	7.8	13.7	3.6	3.5	2.2	1.9	3.4	5.0	2.2	47.3

65. *Kimberley, Union of South Africa*

Temp.	76	75	72	64	56	50	51	56	62	68	73	76	65
Prec.	2.8	3.0	2.8	2.0	0.7	0.5	0.1	0.3	0.2	0.8	2.1	2.9	18.2

66. *Gorée, French West Africa*

Temp.	69	66	68	69	72	78	81	82	82	82	78	72	75
Prec.	0	0	0	0	0	0.9	3.6	9.9	5.2	0.7	0.1	0	20.4

67. *Cairo, Egypt*

Temp.	54	57	63	70	77	82	84	83	78	75	66	59	71
Prec.	0.3	0.2	0.2	0.2	0	0	0	0	0	0.1	0.1	0.2	1.3

68. *Swakopmund, Southwest Africa*

Temp.	61	63	63	60	61	59	57	55	56	58	59	62	59
Prec.	0	0.1	0.2	0	0	0	0	0	0	0.1	0	0.2	0.6

69. *Cape Town, Union of South Africa*

Temp.	69	70	68	63	59	56	55	56	57	61	64	67	62
Prec.	0.7	0.6	0.9	1.8	3.9	4.4	3.5	3.3	2.2	1.6	1.1	0.8	24.8

70. *Algiers, Algeria*

Temp.	53	55	58	61	66	71	77	78	75	69	62	56	65
Prec.	4.2	3.5	3.5	2.3	1.3	0.6	0.1	0.3	1.1	3.1	4.6	5.4	30.0

71. *Pretoria, Union of South Africa*

Temp.	72	71	68	63	57	53	52	57	63	68	69	71	64
Prec.	5.5	3.9	3.5	1.1	0.6	0.2	0.1	0.2	1.1	1.8	3.7	4.2	25.9

ASIA AND ADJACENT ISLANDS

72. *Legaspi, Philippine Islands*

Temp.	78	78	80	82	83	82	81	81	81	81	80	79	81
Prec.	15.2	13.0	7.7	5.4	5.3	8.8	10.1	7.2	10.2	13.0	17.3	18.7	131.9

73. *Manokwari, New Guinea*

Temp.	78	78	79	79	79	79	79	79	79	80	80	79	79
Prec.	10.8	10.7	13.0	11.1	7.8	8.3	6.0	5.3	5.1	4.2	6.6	10.6	99.5

74. *Medan, Sumatra*

Temp.	75	77	78	79	79	78	78	78	77	77	76	76	77
Prec.	5.4	3.9	4.1	5.2	7.0	5.2	5.2	6.9	8.7	9.8	10.1	8.9	80.4

75. *Yap, Caroline Islands*

	J	F	M	A	M	J	J	A	S	O	N	D	Year
Temp.	80	80	80	81	81	81	80	80	80	81	81	81	81
Prec.	7.0	6.8	4.9	5.2	9.6	10.8	16.6	16.2	13.4	11.8	10.1	8.9	121.3

76. *Batavia, Java*

	J	F	M	A	M	J	J	A	S	O	N	D	Year
Temp.	78	78	79	80	80	79	79	79	80	80	79	79	79
Prec.	11.9	13.4	7.9	5.6	4.1	3.7	2.6	1.6	2.8	4.5	5.7	7.6	71.4

77. *Moulmein, Burma*

	J	F	M	A	M	J	J	A	S	O	N	D	Year
Temp.	76	79	84	85	83	80	79	79	80	81	79	76	80
Prec.	0.2	0.2	0.5	2.8	20.0	37.8	45.2	42.8	28.1	8.5	2.2	0.3	188.6

78. *Colombo, Ceylon*

	J	F	M	A	M	J	J	A	S	O	N	D	Year
Temp.	79	80	81	82	82	80	80	81	80	79	80	79	80
Prec.	3.2	1.9	4.7	11.4	12.1	8.4	4.5	3.8	5.0	14.4	12.5	6.4	88.3

79. *Bombay, India*

	J	F	M	A	M	J	J	A	S	O	N	D	Year
Temp.	75	75	78	82	85	82	80	79	79	81	79	76	79
Prec.	0.1	0	0	0.1	0.5	20.6	24.6	14.9	10.9	1.8	0.5	0.1	74.1

80. *Tehran, Iran*

	J	F	M	A	M	J	J	A	S	O	N	D	Year
Temp.	34	42	48	61	71	80	85	83	77	61	51	42	62
Prec.	1.2	0.9	2.4	0.9	0.4	0	0.4	0	0.1	0.1	1.2	1.3	8.9

81. *Tashkent, U.S.S.R.*

	J	F	M	A	M	J	J	A	S	O	N	D	Year
Temp.	30	34	47	58	70	77	81	77	67	54	43	36	56
Prec.	1.8	1.4	2.6	2.6	1.1	0.5	0.1	0.1	0.2	1.1	1.4	1.7	14.6

82. *Delhi, India*

	J	F	M	A	M	J	J	A	S	O	N	D	Year
Temp.	58	62	74	86	92	92	86	85	84	79	68	60	77
Prec.	1.0	0.6	0.7	0.3	0.7	3.2	8.4	7.4	4.4	0.4	0.1	0.4	27.6

83. *Karachi, Pakistan*

	J	F	M	A	M	J	J	A	S	O	N	D	Year
Temp.	65	68	75	81	85	87	84	82	82	80	74	67	78
Prec.	0.6	0.3	0.1	0.1	0	0.4	3.2	1.8	0.7	0	0.2	0.2	7.6

84. *Tokyo, Japan*

	J	F	M	A	M	J	J	A	S	O	N	D	Year
Temp.	37	38	44	54	62	69	75	78	72	61	50	41	57
Prec.	2.0	2.6	4.3	5.3	5.9	6.3	5.6	4.6	7.5	7.2	4.3	2.3	57.9

85. *Shanghai, China*

	J	F	M	A	M	J	J	A	S	O	N	D	Year
Temp.	38	39	46	56	66	73	80	80	73	63	52	42	59
Prec.	2.2	2.3	3.4	3.8	3.7	6.5	5.5	5.9	4.7	3.2	1.7	1.2	44.1

86. *Hankow, China*

	J	F	M	A	M	J	J	A	S	O	N	D	Year
Temp.	39	40	49	61	71	78	84	83	76	65	54	43	62
Prec.	2.1	1.1	2.8	4.8	5.0	7.0	8.6	4.6	2.2	3.9	1.1	0.6	43.8

87. *Benares, India*

	J	F	M	A	M	J	J	A	S	O	N	D	Year
Temp.	60	65	77	87	91	89	84	83	83	78	68	60	77
Prec.	0.7	0.5	0.3	0.1	0.6	5.5	12.5	11.2	6.5	2.2	0.2	0.2	40.5

88. *Darjeeling, India*

	J	F	M	A	M	J	J	A	S	O	N	D	Year
Temp.	40	42	50	56	58	60	62	61	59	55	48	42	53
Prec.	0.8	1.1	2.0	4.1	7.8	24.2	31.7	26.0	18.3	5.3	0.2	0.2	121.7

89. *Pekin, China*

	J	F	M	A	M	J	J	A	S	O	N	D	Year
Temp.	24	29	41	57	68	76	79	77	68	55	39	27	53
Prec.	0.1	0.2	0.2	0.6	1.4	3.0	9.4	6.3	2.6	0.6	0.3	0.1	24.8

90. *Irkutsk, U.S.S.R.*

	J	F	M	A	M	J	J	A	S	O	N	D	Year
Temp.	−5	1	17	35	48	59	65	60	48	33	13	1	31
Prec.	0.6	0.5	0.4	0.6	1.2	2.3	2.9	2.4	1.6	0.7	0.6	0.8	14.6

AUSTRALIA AND NEW ZEALAND

91. *Darwin, Australia*

	J	F	M	A	M	J	J	A	S	O	N	D	Year
Temp.	84	84	84	84	82	79	77	79	83	85	86	85	83
Prec.	15.2	13.5	9.6	4.1	0.6	0.1	0.1	0.1	0.5	2.0	4.7	9.8	60.3

92. *Hall's Creek, Australia*

	J	F	M	A	M	J	J	A	S	O	N	D	Year
Temp.	86	85	83	78	71	66	64	69	76	84	87	87	78
Prec.	5.7	4.8	3.0	0.8	0.4	0.2	0.2	0.1	0.2	0.6	1.5	3.3	20.8

93. *Alice Springs, Australia*

	J	F	M	A	M	J	J	A	S	O	N	D	Year
Temp.	83	82	77	73	60	54	53	58	66	74	79	82	70
Prec.	1.7	1.7	1.2	0.7	0.6	0.6	0.4	0.4	0.4	0.7	1.0	1.5	10.9

94. *Marble Bar, Australia*

	J	F	M	A	M	J	J	A	S	O	N	D	Year
Temp.	93	92	90	84	75	68	67	71	78	84	90	92	82
Prec.	2.6	3.2	1.9	0.9	0.7	1.1	0.6	0.2	0	0.2	0.4	1.3	13.1

95. *Auckland, New Zealand*

	J	F	M	A	M	J	J	A	S	O	N	D	Year
Temp.	66	66	64	61	57	54	52	52	55	57	60	63	59
Prec.	2.6	3.3	3.0	3.5	4.6	5.0	5.0	4.2	3.7	3.6	3.4	2.9	44.8

96. *Melbourne, Australia*

	J	F	M	A	M	J	J	A	S	O	N	D	Year
Temp.	68	68	65	59	54	50	49	51	54	58	61	65	59
Prec.	1.8	1.8	2.1	2.2	2.1	2.0	1.8	1.8	2.4	2.6	2.2	2.2	25.0

97. *Hobart, Tasmania*

	J	F	M	A	M	J	J	A	S	O	N	D	Year
Temp.	62	62	59	55	51	47	46	48	51	54	57	60	54
Prec.	1.8	1.6	1.7	1.9	1.8	2.2	2.1	1.8	2.1	2.2	2.4	1.9	23.5

98. *Adelaide, Australia*

	J	F	M	A	M	J	J	A	S	O	N	D	Year
Temp.	74	74	70	64	58	54	52	54	57	61	67	71	63
Prec.	0.7	0.8	1.0	1.7	2.7	3.1	2.6	2.4	2.1	1.7	1.1	0.9	20.8

99. *Mackay, Australia*

	J	F	M	A	M	J	J	A	S	O	N	D	Year
Temp.	80	79	77	74	68	64	62	64	68	73	77	79	72
Prec.	15.0	13.7	15.4	7.3	4.4	2.7	2.3	0.9	1.1	2.4	2.7	7.3	75.2

INDIAN OCEAN

100. *Kerguelen Island*

	J	F	M	A	M	J	J	A	S	O	N	D	Year
Temp.	44	45	39	39	35	37	33	34	33	34	39	41	38

C. AREAS AND POPULATIONS OF THE COUNTRIES OF THE WORLD [1]

Name of continent and state	Area (In sq. mi.)	Population (In thousands)	Persons per sq. mi.
World total	**58,087,756**	**2,341,154**	**44.9 ***
AFRICA	11,596,043	187,494	16.2
Belgian colony and trusteeship	925,094	14,748	
† British colonies, dependencies, protectorates, and trusteeships	3,916,650	68,647	
Egypt	383,000	19,528	51.0

* In computing the world density the area of Antarctica is omitted.
† Includes as military trustee areas Libya, Eritrea, and Italian Somaliland.
[1] From 1950 *Britannica Book of the Year*. Reprinted by permission of the publishers.

Name of continent and state	Area (In sq. mi.)	Population (In thousands)	Persons per sq. mi.
AFRICA (Cont.)			
Ethiopia	350,000	8,000	22.9
French colonies, trusteeships, protectorates, department and metropolitan area	4,258,070	49,301	
Liberia	43,000	1,600	37.2
Portuguese colonies	794,959	11,502	
South-West Africa (mandate of Union of South Africa)	317,725	369	1.2
Spanish colonies and protectorate	134,763	1,537	
Tangier, International Zone of	232	150	646.6
Union of South Africa	472,550	12,112	25.6
ANTARCTICA	6,000,000	uninhabited	
ASIA (exclusive of U.S.S.R.)	10,593,048	1,242,986	117.3
Afghanistan	270,000	12,000	44.4
Arabian desert	193,000	largely uninhabited	
Bhutan	18,000	300	16.7
British colonies, dependencies, protectorates, protected state and independent state under British protection	248,861	9,993	
Burma	261,749	17,000	64.9
Ceylon, Dominion of	25,332	7,177	283.3
China (35 provinces, including Formosa, Kwantung and South Manchurian railway, Manchuria, and Tibet)	3,876,956	463,493	119.6
French overseas territory and associated states	272,552	25,794	
India, Dominion of	1,243,886	342,114	275.0
Iran	634,413	17,000	26.8
Iraq	116,600	4,794	41.1
Japan (1948)	146,690	82,466	562.2
Jordan, Hashemite Kingdom of	34,750	400	11.5
Korea	85,225	29,239	355.6
Kuwait	9,000	120	13.3
Lebanon	3,470	1,208	348.1
Mongolian People's Republic	580,158	850	1.5
Nepal	54,000	6,910	128.0
Netherlands Indies (Indonesia)	735,000	76,360	103.9
Oman and Masqat	65,000	830	12.8
Pakistan, Dominion of	337,524	73,321	203.1
Palestine (including Israel)	10,159	2,000	196.9
Philippines, Republic of the	115,600	19,234	166.4
Portuguese colonies	8,876	1,496	
Qatar	4,000	16	4.0
Saudi Arabia	597,000	6,000	10.1
Siam	198,272	17,666	89.1
Syria	72,560	3,750	51.7
Trucial Sheiks	16,000	105	6.6
Turkey	296,185	19,750	66.7
Yemen	31,000	1,600	51.6

Name of continent and state	Area (In sq. mi.)	Population (In thousands)	Persons per sq. mi.
AUSTRALIA and OCEANIA	3,304,620	11,697	3.5
Australia	2,974,581	7,581	2.5
Australian dependency, territory and trusteeships	183,557	1,216	
British colonies, dependencies, condominium, protectorate, and protected state	24,670	496	
French colonies	9,199	106	
New Zealand	103,416	1,840	17.8
New Zealand dependencies and trusteeship	1,652	94	
United States possessions, territory and trusteeship	7,545	364	
EUROPE (exclusive of U.S.S.R.)	1,908,096	385,390	202.0
Albania	10,629	1,175	110.5
Andorra	174	5	28.7
Austria	32,388	6,953	214.7
Belgium	11,774	8,603	730.7
British colonies and dependencies	124	330	
Bulgaria	42,796	7,100	165.9
Czechoslovakia (1947)	49,330	12,409	251.6
Denmark (excl. Greenland, incl. Faeroe Islands)	17,109	4,220	246.7
Eire	26,602	2,997	112.7
Estonia	18,357	854	46.5
Finland (including Åland Islands)	130,159	3,958	30.4
France	212,737	41,500	195.1
Germany (1937 area, 1939 population)	181,742	69,317	381.4
Germany (1946)	143,245	65,911	460.1
Greece (including Aegean Islands)	51,182	7,960	155.5
Hungary	35,893	9,165	255.3
Iceland	39,768	139	3.5
Italy (1948)	116,235	45,706	384.6
Latvia	25,395	1,650	65.0
Liechtenstein	61	13	213.1
Lithuania	25,173	2,353	93.5
Luxembourg	1,010	292	289.1
Monaco	0.6	21	35,000.0
Netherlands	12,868	9,955	773.6
Norway (including Spitzbergen)	149,486	3,185	21.3
Poland (pre-World War II)	149,922	35,339	235.7
Poland (1946)	120,359	23,900	198.6
Portugal (incl. Azores and Madeira Islands)	35,413	8,402	237.3
Romania	91,654	15,873	173.2
San Marino	38	12	315.8
Spain (including Canary Islands)	194,945	27,761	142.4
Sweden	173,390	6,925	39.9
Switzerland	15,940	4,609	289.1
Trieste, Free Territory of	293	345	1,177.5
United Kingdom	93,667	50,213	536.1
Vatican City	0.5	1	2,000.0
Yugoslavia (after Sept. 15, 1947)	98,826	15,752	159.4

Name of continent and state	Area (In sq. mi.)	Population (In thousands)	Persons per sq. mi.
U.S.S.R. (1939)	8,173,557	170,467	20.9
‡ U.S.S.R. (1949 area, 1948 pop. est.)	8,436,121	193,000	22.9
NORTH AMERICA	9,387,294	214,824	22.9
British colonies and dependencies	21,172	2,690	
Canada	3,847,597	13,636	3.5
Costa Rica	19,238	825	42.9
Cuba	44,217	5,295	119.8
Danish colony (Greenland, including ice cap)	840,000	21	0.03
Dominican Republic	19,129	2,214	115.7
El Salvador	13,176	2,100	159.4
French territory and departments	1,206	601	
Guatemala	45,452	3,717	81.8
Haiti	10,748	3,500	325.6
Honduras	59,160	1,326	22.4
Mexico	767,168	24,447	31.9
Netherlands overseas territory (The Netherlands Antilles)	403	160	397.0
Nicaragua	57,145	1,173	20.5
Panama (excluding Canal Zone)	28,575	764	26.7
United States	3,022,387	150,000	49.6
United States possessions	590,521	2,355	
SOUTH AMERICA	6,862,534	105,763	15.4
Argentina	1,079,965	16,300	15.1
Bolivia	416,040	3,922	9.4
Brazil	3,286,170	48,900	14.8
British colonies and dependencies	97,161	392	
Chile	286,323	5,704	19.9
Colombia	439,714	10,777	24.5
Ecuador	104,510	3,362	32.2
French department (French Guiana)	34,740	35	1.0
Netherlands overseas territory (Surinam)	54,291	210	3.9
Paraguay	157,047	1,270	8.1
Peru	482,258	8,061	16.7
Uruguay	72,172	2,330	32.3
Venezuela	352,143	4,500	12.8

‡ Areas and populations of Baltic republics included in 1949 and 1948 U.S.S.R. totals.

D. ONE HUNDRED CONTOUR MAPS WHICH ILLUSTRATE SPECIFIC LANDFORMS AND DRAINAGE CONDITIONS

The maps listed here represent "A Set of One Hundred Contour Maps That Illustrate Specified Physiographic Features," as issued by the United States Geological Survey, Washington, D. C. The Geological Survey is in the process of revising this list and issuing a group of new maps showing unusual physical features in shaded relief. However, the revision will probably not be completed before 1952. The maps in the present list are still quite adequate for the study of landforms. The list contains many maps which are already available in college and university libraries, or in separate map collections in such institutions. Others may be obtained from the Director of the United States Geological Survey. A few titles are out of print and are not scheduled for reissue.

The following listing is divided into two parts, List A and List B. List A contains contour maps, by name, in alphabetical arrangement. Under the name of each contour map is a list of landforms and drainage features which appear on the map. List B is arranged according to specific landform and drainage features (such as fiord, tidal flat, terminal moraine, etc.) and the maps on which these features appear are listed by name below the major heading.

List A

Antietam, Md.-Va.-W. Va.
Braided stream
Dissected peneplain
Intrenched meander
Intrenched stream
Mature topography
Ridges due to hard rocks
Valley excavated in soft rocks
Water gap or narrows
Wind gap or pass

Aransas Pass, Tex.
Barrier beach
Beach, abandoned
Lagoon or coastal lake
Offset barrier beach
Recurved or hooked spit
Sand dunes
Tidal marsh
Truncated headland
Wave-cut cliff
Winged headland

Atlanta, Ga.
Consequent stream (southeast part)
Dissected peneplain
Dome of crystalline rock
Early mature drainage
Early mature topography
Intrenched stream (Chattahoochee)
Migrating divide (between Chattahoochee and Atlantic drainage)
Monadnock
Rock sculpture controlled by exfoliation

Avon, Ill.
Cut-off meander or oxbow lake
Ground moraine (plain)

Avon, Ill. (Cont.)
Plain (of ground moraine)
Stream meander
Stream prematurely aged by valley filling
Youthful drainage
Youthful topography

Ballarat, Calif.-Nev.
Alluvial slope, possibly including planed rock slope
Alluvium-filled valley (all valleys)
Bolson basin (same as above)
Canyon or gorge
Mountain not glaciated
Nonglaciated or v-shaped valley
Playa
Rugged or youthful mountain
Sand dune (Saline and Death Valleys)
Sand wash
Valley due to dislocation of the rocks

Baton Rouge, La.
Flood plain
Lateral drainage diverted by flood-plain deposits (Bayou Fountain)
Natural and artificial levees
Plain (of erosion)
Stabilized stream (Mississippi River)
Stream meander
Swamp or marsh

Bright Angel, Ariz.
Canyon or gorge
Cliff
Contrast between surfaces formed in different cycles of erosion
Dissected plateau

Bright Angel, Ariz. (Cont.)
Encroachment of younger upon older drainage
Hanging valley
Intrenched stream
Mesa (Shiva Temple)
Migrating divide (south of the river)
Nonglaciated or v-shaped valley
Old drainage (on plateau)
Old topography (on plateau)
Plateau
Rejuvenated stream
Rock sculpture controlled by fractures (Bright Angel Creek Valley)
Rock terrace
Stream piracy (on plateau)
Waterfall or rapid
Youthful drainage
Youthful topography

Buck Hill, Tex.
Alluvial slope, possibly including planed rock slope
Canyon or gorge
Escarpment
Mesa
Plain
Youthful drainage

Cape Henry, Va.
Barrier beach
Drainage blocked by barrier beach
Drowned valley
Estuary (Lynnhaven Bay)
Foreland (Cape Henry)
Sand dune
Swamp or marsh
Wave-formed plain

Everett, Pa. (Cont.)
  Water gap or narrows (Bedford and Mount Dallas)
  Zigzag ridges
Fargo, N. Dak.-Minn.
  Intrenched meander
  Intrenched stream
  Lake plain (Glacial Lake Agassiz)
  Youthful drainage
  Youthful topography
Fayetteville, W. Va.
  Canyon or gorge
  Cliff (top of gorge)
  Dissected plateau (northwestern part)
  Intrenched meander
  Intrenched stream
  Mature drainage (northwestern part)
  Mature topography (northwestern part)
  Plateau
  Waterfall or rapid (Kanawha Falls)
Fond du Lac, Wis.
  Delta
  Drumlin (southeastern part)
  Escarpment
  Glacial lake and pond
  Ground moraine
  Infantile drainage
  Swamp or marsh
  Terminal moraine
Fort Payne, Ala.-Ga.
  Anticlinal valley (Big Wills Creek)
  Canyon or gorge (Little River Gulf)
  Escarpment (east front of Lookout Mountain)
  Old drainage (Coosa Valley)
  Old topography (Coosa Valley)
  Plateau
  Ridges due to hard rocks
  Stream meander
Genoa, N. Y.
  Delta
  Dissected plateau modified by glaciation
  Ground moraine
  Spit
  Youthful drainage (parallel)
  Youthful topography
Gilbert Peak, Utah-Wyo.
  Comb ridge or cleaver
  Disappearing stream
  Glacial cirque
  Glacial col
  Glacial lake and pond
  Glaciated or trough valley
  Hanging valley
  Kettlehole
  Matterhorn peak
  Mountain modified by alpine glaciation
  Solution basin and sinkhole
Glacier National Park, Mont.
  Alpine or valley glacier

Glacier National Park, Mont. (Cont.)
  Canyon or gorge
  Cliff (bordering glacial cirques)
  Comb ridge or cleaver
  Continental or subcontinental divide
  Delta (St. Mary)
  Dissected alluvial slope (Milk River Ridge)
  Fault-line scarp (east front of mountains)
  Glacial cirque
  Glacial lake and pond
  Glaciated or trough valley
  Glacier
  Hanging glacier
  Hanging valley
  Matterhorn peak
  Mountain modified by alpine glaciation
  Mountain range
  Nonglaciated or v-shaped valley (southwestern part)
  Rugged or youthful mountain
  Waterfall or rapid
  Wind gap or pass (Gunsight, Swiftcurrent, etc.)
Grass Creek Basin, Wyo.
  Anticlinal valley (Grass Creek Basin)
  Cuesta
  Dissected alluvial slope
  Mature topography
  Ridges due to hard rocks
  Ridges due to the erosion of an anticline
  Stream terrace (Cottonwood Creek)
Greylock, Mass.-Vt.
  Canyon or gorge
  Escarpment
  Glacial lake and pond
  Ground moraine
  Hanging valley
  Mountain modified by continental glaciation
  Mountain peak, isolated
  Plateau
  Valley excavated in soft rocks
Henderson, Ky.-Ind.
  Alluvium-filled valley
  Development or shifting of meander
  Dissected plain
  Flood plain
  Lateral drainage diverted by flood-plain deposits
  Mature topography
  Stream meander
  Underfit stream (Canoe Creek)
  Youthful drainage
Hollow Springs, Tenn.
  Contrast between surfaces formed in different cycles of erosion
  Dip slope (Plateau of the Barrens)
  Dissected plateau
  Early mature drainage

Hollow Springs, Tenn. (Cont.)
  Early mature topography
  Encroachment of younger upon older drainage
  Migrating divide (western edge of plateau)
  Nonglaciated or v-shaped valley
  Old drainage (on plateau)
  Old topography (on plateau)
  Plateau
  Solution basin and sinkhole
Honomu, Hawaii
  Canyon or gorge
  Consequent stream (all streams)
  Hanging valley
  Rock stack
  Volcanic cone
  Waterfall or rapid
  Wave-cut cliff
  Youthful drainage
  Youthful topography
Hot Springs and vicinity, Ark.
  Dissected peneplain
  Intrenched stream
  Mature topography
  Ridges due to hard rocks
  Ridges due to the erosion of an anticline
  Ridges due to the erosion of a syncline
  Valley excavated in soft rocks
  Water gap or narrows
  Zigzag ridges
Houghton, Mich.
  Delta (Sturgeon and Pilgrim Rivers)
  Drainage deranged by ice sheet
  Glacial lake and pond
  River valley, abandoned
  Sand dune
  Swamp or marsh
  Terminal moraine
  Wave-cut cliff
  Youthful drainage
  Youthful topography
Interlachen, Fla.
  Lake in solution basin
  Lake plain
  Meander scar
  Solution basin and sinkhole
  Stream prematurely aged by valley filling (Oklawaha River)
  Swamp or marsh
Joplin district, Mo.-Kans.
  Alluvial slope
  Dissected plateau
  Early mature topography
  Flood plain
  Intrenched meander
  Intrenched stream
  Waterfall or rapid (Grand Falls)
Kaaterskill, N. Y.
  Beheaded stream (Gooseberry and Schoharie Creeks and Beaver Kill)
  Escarpment
  Glacial lake and pond

Kaaterskill, N. Y. (Cont.)
Ground moraine
Late mature topography (lowland)
Mature topography (upland)
Migrating divide
Mountain modified by continental glaciation
Rock terrace (on escarpment)
Stream piracy (see Beheaded stream)
Trellis drainage (lowland)
Wind gap or pass

Kalamazoo, Mich.
Drainage deranged by ice sheet
Glacial lake and pond
Infantile drainage
Infantile topography
Kame
Kettlehole
Pitted outwash plain
Stream prematurely aged by valley filling (Kalamazoo River)
Stream terrace
Swamp or marsh
Terminal moraine
Underfit stream (Kalamazoo River)

Kilmarnock, Va.
Bay bar
Beach, abandoned
Cut-off meander or oxbow lake
Dissected plain (upland)
Drowned valley
Estuary
Land-tied island or tombolo
Meander scar (Meachim Creek)
Recurved or hooked spit
Tidal marsh
Wave-formed plain (upland)
Wave-formed terrace

Kimmswick, Mo.-Ill.
Contrast between surfaces formed in different cycles of erosion
Cut-off meander or oxbow lake
Development or shifting of meander
Dissected plateau (upland)
Flood plain
Lateral drainage diverted by flood-plain deposits
Mature topography (upland)
Meander scar
Natural and artificial levees
Solution basins and sinkhole
Stream terrace (Meramec River and Sandy Creek)
Unsymmetrical stream (upland in Missouri)

Knoxville, Iowa
Cut-off meander or oxbow lake
Dissected plain
Early mature drainage
Early mature topography
Flood plain
Stream meander

Lake Placid, N. Y.
Glacial lake and pond
Ground moraine (in valley)

Lake Placid, N. Y. (Cont.)
Mountain modified by continental glaciation
Stream prematurely aged by valley filling (Saranac River)
Swamp or marsh
Water gap or narrows (Wilmington Notch)
Wind gap or pass
Youthful drainage

Lake Providence, La.
Cut-off meander or oxbow lake
Development or shifting of meander
Flood plain
Natural and artificial levees
Swamp or marsh

La Porte, Tex.
Drowned valley
Infantile drainage
Intrenched stream
Meander scar
Mud spring (mud volcano), extinct
Natural and artificial levees
Stabilized stream
Wave-cut cliff

Loveland, Colo.
Artificial lake (for irrigation)
Canyon or gorge
Consequent stream (on plain)
Cut-off meander or oxbow lake
Hogback
Old drainage (on plain)
Old topography (on plain)
Plain
Ridges due to hard rocks
Ridges due to the erosion of an anticline
Ridges due to the erosion of a syncline
Stream meander
Valley excavated in soft rocks
Water gap or narrows
Wind gap or pass

Lower Matanuska Valley, Alaska
Braided stream
Glacial cirque
Glacial lake and pond
Glaciated or trough valley
Glacier
Hanging valley (western part)
Intrenched stream
Kettlehole
Ridges due to the erosion of a syncline
Stream terrace
Terminal moraine
Youthful drainage

Malaga, Wash.
Canyon or gorge
Cliff
Dip slope
Escarpment
Meander scar
Plateau (eastern part)
Rock terrace

Malaga, Wash. (Cont.)
Stream terrace (along Columbia River)
Underfit stream (Moses Coulee)
Waterfall or rapid

Manitou, Colo.
Alluvial fan or cone (The Mesa)
Alluvial slope
Artificial lake (municipal water supply)
Canyon or gorge
Contrast between surfaces formed in different cycles of erosion
Glacial cirque
Monadnock (Pikes Peak)
Mountain peak, isolated
Mountain modified by alpine glaciation
Nonglaciated or v-shaped valley
Plain
Swamp or marsh
Terminal moraine

Marysville Buttes and vicinity, Calif.
Alluvial fan or cone (at West Butte and Sutter)
Alluvial slope, possibly including planed rock slope
Alluvium-filled valley
Cut-off meander or oxbow lake
Dissected volcanic cone
Distributary stream
Flood plain
Infantile drainage
Natural and artificial levees
Plain
Stream meander
Swamp or marsh
Wedge segments of volcanic cone, outlined by erosion

Meriden, Conn.
Drainage deranged by ice sheet
Escarpment
Fault-line scarp
Kettlehole
Artificial lake
Rock sculpture controlled by fractures (Hanging Hill, etc.)
Stream terrace
Terminal moraine (Southington)
Valley excavated in soft rocks
Youthful drainage

Mesa Verde National Park, Colo.
Canyon or gorge
Cliff
Consequent stream (southward-flowing)
Contrast between surfaces formed in different cycles of erosion
Dip slope (old plateau surface)
Dissected plateau
Early mature topography
Escarpment (north face of plateau)
Migrating divide

Milton, W. Va.
Dissected peneplain
Dissected plateau
Intrenched meander

Milton, W. Va. (Cont.)
  Intrenched stream
  Mature drainage
  Mature topography
  Meander migrating downstream
    (most meanders)
  River valley, abandoned (Teays
    Valley
  Stream piracy (Trace and Sleepy
    Creeks)
  Underfit stream (Mud River)
Monadnock, N. H.
  Dissected plateau modified by gla-
    ciation
  Drainage deranged by ice sheet
  Glacial lake and pond
  Ground moraine
  Hanging valley
  Monadnock
  Mountain peak, isolated
  Mountain modified by continental
    glaciation
  Swamp or marsh
Monticello, Ky.
  Dissected peneplain
  Dissected plateau (southeast cor-
    ner)
  Early mature drainage
  Early mature topography
  Flood plain
  Intrenched meander
  Intrenched stream
  Mature drainage (southeast corner)
  Mature topography (southeast cor-
    ner)
  Meander migrating downstream
  Meander scar
  Monadnock (Chapel Hill, etc.)
  Solution basin and sinkhole
Montpelier, Idaho-Wyo.-Utah
  Alluvial slope
  Alluvium-filled valley (Thomas
    Fork Valley)
  Bay bar
  Consequent stream
  Cut-off meander or oxbow lake
  Early mature topography
  Escarpment
  Fault-line scarp
  Intrenched meander
  Lake plain
  Solution basin and sinkhole
  Stream meander
  Subsequent stream
  Superimposed stream
  Swamp or marsh
  Terrace formed by silted-up lake
    basin, partly excavated later
  Underfit stream (Bear Lake out-
    let)
  Valley due to dislocation of the
    rocks
Mount Desert, Maine
  Fiord (Somes Sound)
  Glacial lake and pond
  Mountain modified by continental
    glaciation

Mount Desert, Maine (Cont.)
  Recurved or hooked spit (Meadow
    Point)
  Rock sculpture controlled by frac-
    tures
  Spit (Hadley Point, etc.)
  Swamp or marsh
Mount Hood, Oreg.-Wash.
  Alpine or valley glacier
  Braided stream
  Canyon or gorge
  Cliff
  Dissected plateau
  Glacial cirque
  Glacial lake and pond
  Glacier
  Hanging glacier
  Hanging valley
  Landslide
  Landslide lake
  Mature topography
  Mountain peak, isolated
  Volcanic cone (Mount Hood)
  Waterfall or rapid
Mount Mitchell, N. C.
  Continental or subcontinental di-
    vide (Blue Ridge summit)
  Contrast between surfaces formed
    in different cycles of erosion
  Encroachment of younger upon
    older drainage (Blue Ridge
    summit)
  Intrenched meander (northern
    part)
  Intrenched stream (northern part)
  Late mature topography
  Migrating divide (Blue Ridge
    summit)
  Mountain not glaciated
  Subdued or old mountain
  Wind gap or pass (Swannanoa
    Gap)
Mount Rainier National Park, Wash.
  Alpine or valley glacier
  Braided stream
  Comb ridge or cleaver
  Early mature topography
  Glacial cirque
  Glacial col
  Glacial lake and pond
  Glaciated or trough valley
  Glacier
  Hanging glacier
  Hanging valley
  Matterhorn peak
  Medial and lateral moraines
  Mesa
  Mountain modified by alpine gla-
    ciation
  Mountain peak, isolated
  Nunatak
  Rock sculpture controlled by frac-
    tures
  Volcanic cone
  Wedge segments of volcanic cone,
    outlined by erosion
  Wind gap or pass (Chinook Pass)

Mount Riley, N. Mex.
  Alluvial slope, possibly including
    planed rock slope.
  Dissected alluvial slope
  Mountain peak, isolated
  Volcanic cone (western part)
  Youthful drainage
Naples, N. Y.
  Delta (streams entering Canan-
    daigua Lake)
  Dissected plateau, modified by
    glaciation
  Drainage deranged by ice sheet
  Glacial lake and pond
  Glaciated or trough valley
  Ground moraine
  Mature topography
  River valley, abandoned
  Stream prematurely aged by valley
    filling
  Swamp or marsh
  Terminal moraine (above Naples)
  Underfit streams (Cohocton River
    and Naples Creek)
  Youthful drainage (parallel)
Nashua, Mont.
  Alluvium-filled valley
  Cut-off meander or oxbow lake
  Dissected plain (south of Missouri
    River)
  Flood plain
  Glacial lake and pond
  Mature topography (south of Mis-
    souri River)
  Plain
  Stream meander
  Stream prematurely aged by valley
    filling (Milk River)
  Underfit stream (Milk River)
  Youthful drainage (north of Milk
    River)
  Youthful topography (north of
    Milk River)
Natural Bridge, Va.
  Intrenched meander
  Intrenched stream
  Meander migrating downstream
  Mountain not glaciated
  Natural bridge
  Ridges due to hard rocks
  Ridges due to the erosion of a
    syncline
  Solution basin and sinkhole
  Synclinal stream
  Valley excavated in soft rocks
Niagara River and vicinity, N. Y.
  Beach, abandoned (ridge at Dick-
    ersonville)
  Canyon or gorge
  Escarpment (above Lewiston)
  Ground moraine
  Plain
  Waterfall or rapid
Oberlin, Ohio
  Beach, abandoned (various
    "ridges")
  Intrenched meander
  Intrenched stream

Oberlin, Ohio (Cont.)
Wave-cut cliff
Youthful topography

Oelwein, Iowa
Contrast between a surface deeply covered with drift and one which has only a slight cover of much older dissected drift
Dissected plain (northeastern part)
Ground moraine (southwestern part)
Mature drainage (northeastern part)
Mature topography (northeastern part)
Plain (southwestern part)
Youthful drainage (southwestern part)
Youthful topography (southwestern part)

Ogallala, Nebr.
Braided stream
Lake in dune area
Sand dune
Youthful drainage
Youthful topography

Olancha, Calif.
Alluvial slope (eastern part)
Alluvium-filled valley (eastern part)
Block mountain
Bolson basin (eastern part)
Canyon or gorge
Encroachment of younger upon older drainage
Escarpment (eastern part)
Fault-line scarp (eastern part)
Glacial cirque (northern part)
Glacial lake and pond
Glaciated or trough valley (Kern Canyon)
Hanging valley
Migrating divide (eastern part)
Mountain modified by alpine glaciation (northern part)
Mountain not glaciated (southern part)
Nonglaciated or v-shaped valley
Plateau

Oyster Bay, N. Y.
Barrier beach
Bay bar (Bar Beach)
Drowned valley
Land-tied island or tombolo
Recurved or hooked spit (Plum Point)
Spit (Matinecock Point)
Terminal moraine
Wave-cut cliff
Winged headland (Oak Neck)

Palmyra, N. Y.
Beach, abandoned (of Glacial Lake Iroquois)
Drainage deranged by ice sheet
Drumlin
Ground moraine (southern part)
Infantile drainage
Infantile topography

Palmyra, N. Y. (Cont.)
River valley, abandoned (southern part)
Swamp or marsh

Passadumkeag, Maine
Braided stream due to inequalities in its bed
Drainage deranged by ice sheet
Esker ("horsebacks")
Glacial lake and pond
Infantile drainage
Swamp or marsh

Pawpaw, Md.-W. Va.-Pa.
Dissected peneplain (900 to 950 feet altitude)
Intrenched meander
Mature drainage
Mature topography
Meander migrating downstream
Ridges due to hard rocks
Ridges due to the erosion of a syncline (Purslane Mountain and Sideling Hill)
River valley, abandoned (opposite Pawpaw)
Solution basin and sinkhole
Trellis drainage
Valley excavated in soft rocks
Water gap or narrows (at Lineburg)

Peeples, S. C.-Ga.
Cut-off meander or oxbow lake
Flood plain
Plain
Solution basin and sinkhole
Stream meander
Stream prematurely aged by valley filling
Underfit stream

Peever, S. Dak.-Minn.
Continental or subcontinental divide
Intrenched meander
Glacial lake and pond
Kettlehole
Plain
River valley, abandoned (Glacial Warren River)
Stream meander
Stream terrace
Swamp or marsh
Terminal moraine
Underfit streams (Jim Creek and Minnesota River)
Youthful drainage

Pittsburgh, Pa.
Dissected plateau
Intrenched meander
Intrenched stream
Mature drainage
Mature topography
Migrating divide (main divides all migrating northward)
Nonglaciated or v-shaped valley
River valley, abandoned (in Pittsburgh and back of McKeesport)

Pittsburgh, Pa. (Cont.)
Stream meander (Youghiogheny River from Buenavista to Versailles)
Stream terrace
Unsymmetrical stream

Playas, N. Mex.
Alluvial slope, possibly including planed rock slope
Alluvium-filled valley
Bolson basin (Playas Valley)
Playa (bottom of Playas Lake)
Playa lake

Point Reyes, Calif.
Barrier beach (on Drakes Bay)
Bay bar
Block mountain (Inverness Ridge)
Delta (head of Tomales Bay)
Distributary stream (on delta)
Drainage blocked by barrier beach
Drainage deranged by faulting
Drowned valley (Tomales Bay)
Estuary (Tomales Bay and estuaries off Drakes Bay)
Hanging valley
Intrenched stream (Walker Creek)
Lagoon or coastal lake
Nonglaciated or v-shaped valley
Offset barrier beach
Rock stack
Sand dune
Truncated headland
Valley due to dislocation of the rocks (Tomales Bay and Olema Creek Valley, San Francisco earthquake rift)
Wave-cut cliff
Wave-formed terrace

Port Valdez district, Alaska
Alpine or valley glacier
Bay bar
Braided stream
Delta
Distributary stream
Fiord (Port Valdez)
Glacial outwash plain
Glacier
Hanging glacier
Hanging valley
Ice-dammed glacial lake
Medial and lateral moraines (on glaciers)
Nunatak
Recurved or hooked spit
Tidal flat
Tidewater glacier (Shoup Glacier)

Quincy, Wash.
Cliff
Dip slope
Escarpment
Infantile topography (lake plain)
Lake plain
Stream terrace
Waterfall, abandoned

Ravenswood, W. Va.-Ohio
Dissected peneplain
Flood plain
Intrenched meander

Ravenswood, W. Va.-Ohio (Cont.)
Mature drainage
Mature topography
Meander migrating downstream (Ohio River)
Meander scar (at Letart)
River valley, abandoned (at Racine)
Stream terrace

Redlands, Calif.
Alluvial slope
Alluvium-filled valley
Braided stream (Santa Ana, Wash.)
Canyon or gorge
Contrast between surfaces formed in different cycles of erosion (northern part)
Encroachment of younger upon older drainage (northern part)
Fault-line scarp (front of mountain)
Mountain not glaciated
Nonglaciated or v-shaped valley
Rugged or youthful mountain
Sand wash

Reelfoot Lake, Tenn.-Mo.-Ky.
Delta
Dissected peneplain
Early mature topography
Earthquake lake
Flood plain
Natural and artificial levees
Stream meander

Rehoboth, Del.
Barrier beach
Drowned valley
Estuary
Lagoon or coastal lake
Offset barrier beach
Plain
Sand dune
Solution basin and sinkhole
Thorofare or tidal runway.
Tidal marsh
Truncated headland (Rehoboth Beach)

Rochester east, N. Y.
Barrier beach
Bay bar
Beach, abandoned (Ridge Road)
Canyon or gorge
Delta (Irondequoit River)
Drowned valley
Intrenched stream
Kame
Kettlehole
Lagoon or coastal lake
Swamp or marsh
Terminal moraine
Waterfall or rapid (Rochester)
Youthful drainage
Youthful topography

St. Albans, Vt.
Bay bar
Beach, abandoned (east of lake)
Delta (Missisquoi River and Mill Run)

St. Albans, Vt. (Cont.)
Distributary stream (Missisquoi delta)
Intrenched stream
Natural and artificial levees
Spit (Stephenson Point)
Swamp or marsh
Waterfall or rapid (Highgate Falls)
Wave-formed terrace

St. Croix Dalles, Wis.-Minn.
Canyon or gorge
Glacial lake and pond
Infantile drainage
Infantile topography
Kame
Kettlehole
Stream terrace (at Taylors Falls)
Swamp or marsh
Terminal moraine
Waterfall or rapid (St. Croix Falls)

Seattle, Wash.
Cut-off meander or oxbow lake
Delta
Distributary stream
Flood plain
Glacial lake and pond
Spit
Stream meander
Stream prematurely aged by valley filling
Tidal flat
Wave-cut cliff

Standingstone, Tenn.
Disappearing stream
Dissected peneplain (1,000 and 1,900 feet altitude)
Dissected plateau (edge of plateau)
Intrenched meander
Intrenched stream
Plateau (Cumberland Plateau)
Solution basin and sinkhole

Stockton, Utah
Alluvial fan or cone (of Ophir Creek)
Alluvial fan or cone, abandoned (of Soldier Creek)
Alluvial slope
Alluvium-filled valley
Bay bar, abandoned (north of Stockton)
Beach, abandoned (northeast of Stockton)
Bolson basin (Rush Valley)
Canyon or gorge
Cliff (in Dry Canyon)
Lake plain (all below 5,250 feet)
Mature topography (mountain)
Mountain not glaciated
Nonglaciated or v-shaped valley
Playa (floor of Rush Lake)
Playa lake (Rush Lake)
Recurved or hooked spit, abandoned (Stockton)
Rugged or youthful mountain
Swamp or marsh
Valley due to dislocation of the rocks

Stockton, Utah (Cont.)
Wave-cut cliff, abandoned (northeast of Stockton)
Waved-formed terrace (northeast of Stockton)

Stryker, Mont.
Comb ridge or cleaver
Drumlin
Escarpment
Glacial cirque
Glacial col
Glacial lake and pond
Glaciated or trough valley
Matterhorn peak
Mountain modified by alpine glaciation
Swamp or marsh

Tehama, Calif.
Alluvial fan or cone (Mill and Antelope Creeks)
Alluvial slope
Alluvium-filled valley
Canyon or gorge
Contrast between surfaces formed in different cycles of erosion (northeastern part)
Distributary stream (on fans)
Fault-line scarp (base of mountain)
Flood plain
Infantile topography
Nonglaciated or v-shaped valley
Valley due to dislocation of the rocks
Youthful topography

Van Horn, Tex.
Alluvial fan or cone (Victoria Canyon)
Alluvial slope
Alluvium-filled valley
Block mountain (Sierra Diablo)
Bolson basin (Salt Flat)
Canyon or gorge
Cliff (eastern face of Sierra Diablo)
Cuesta (Sierra Diablo)
Escarpment (eastern front of Sierra Diablo)
Fault-line scarp (eastern foot of Sierra Diablo)
Mountain not glaciated
Playa (floor of Salt Lake)
Playa lake (Salt Lake)
Valley due to dislocation of the rocks

Washington and vicinity, D. C.-Md.-Va.
Braided stream
Canyon or gorge
Delta (creeks below Alexandria)
Delta, abandoned
Dissected peneplain (east of Potomac and Anacostia Rivers)
Drowned valley
Early mature topography
Estuary (Potomac River)
Fall line (through Washington, from northeast to southwest)
Flood plain

Washington and vicinity, D. C.-Md.-
Va. (Cont.)
Intrenched meander
Intrenched stream
Meander scar
Rejuvenated stream (Potomac
River)
Stream terrace (below Great Falls)
Swamp or marsh
Tidal flat
Waterfall or rapid (Great and Lit-
tle Falls)
Waukegan, Ill.-Wis.
Extended stream (streams east of
Chicago & Northwestern Ry.)
Kame
Kettlehole
Lake plain (higher part of Wauke-
gan and Zion City)
Stream prematurely aged by val-
ley filling
Swamp or marsh
Terminal moraine
Terrace formed by silted-up lake
basin, partly excavated later
(same as lake plain)
Wave-cut cliff (south of Wauke-
gan)
Wave-cut cliff, abandoned (north
of Waukegan)
Wave-formed terrace (lower part
of Waukegan and Zion City)
Youthful drainage
White Mountains, Calif.-Nev.
Alluvial fan or cone (Montgom-
ery, Marble, and Milner Creeks)
Alluvial slope
Alluvium-filled valley
Bolson basin (Fish Valley)
Contrast between surfaces formed
in different cycles of erosion
Distributary stream (on fans)
Early mature topography (moun-
tain)
Fault-line scarp (western foot of
White Mountains)
Glacial cirque (summit of White
Mountains)
Mountain range
Playa (Fish Valley)
Rugged or youthful mountain
Sand dune
Valley due to dislocation of the
rocks (west of White Moun-
tains)
Yosemite Valley, Calif.
Alluvial fan or cone (below Rocky
Point)
Alluvial slope
Alluvium-filled valley
Canyon or gorge
Cliff (El Capitan and others)
Contrast between surfaces formed
in different cycles of erosion
Distributary stream (on alluvial
slope)
Dome of crystalline rock (Half
Dome and others)

Yosemite Valley, Calif. (Cont.)
Glaciated or trough valley
Hanging valley (Bridalveil Valley
and others)
Lake plain (bottom of Yosemite
Valley)
Roches moutonnées (Liberty Cap
and Mount Broderick)
Rock sculpture controlled by frac-
tures
Rock sculpture controlled by ex-
foliation
Rock slide and talus (foot of cliffs)
Waterfall or rapid

List B

(The asterisk [*] indicates that
the particular feature is well shown
on the map.)

COASTAL FEATURES

Barrier beach
* Aransas Pass, Tex.
* Cape Henry, Va.
* Capitola, Calif.
* Cumberland Island, Ga.
  Oyster Bay, N. Y.
  Point Reyes, Calif.
* Rehoboth, Del.
  Rochester east, N. Y.
Bay bar
  Kilmarnock, Va.
* Montpelier, Idaho-Wyo.-Utah
* Oyster Bay, N. Y.
  Point Reyes, Calif.
  Port Valdez district, Alaska
* Rochester east, N. Y.
  St. Albans, Vt.
Bay bar, abandoned
* Stockton, Utah
Beach, abandoned
* Aransas Pass, Tex.
  Capitola, Calif.
  Cumberland Island, Ga.
  Erie, Pa.
* Kilmarnock, Va.
* Niagara River and vicinity, N. Y.
* Oberlin, Ohio
  Palmyra, N. Y.
  Rochester east, N. Y.
  St. Albans, Vt.
* Stockton, Utah
Delta
  See VALLEYS
Drowned valley
* Cape Henry, Va.
* Kilmarnock, Va.
* La Porte, Tex.
  Oyster Bay, N. Y.
* Point Reyes, Calif.
* Rehoboth, Del.
  Rochester east, N. Y.
* Washington and vicinity, D. C.-
  Md.-Va.

Estuary
* Cape Henry, Va.
* Kilmarnock, Va.
  Point Reyes, Calif.
* Rehoboth, Del.
* Washington and vicinity, D. C.-
  Md.-Va.
Fiord
* Mount Desert, Maine
* Port Valdez district, Alaska
Foreland
* Cape Henry, Va.
Lagoon or coastal lake
* Aransas Pass, Tex.
  Capitola, Calif.
  Erie, Pa.
  Point Reyes, Calif.
  Rehoboth, Del.
  Rochester east, N. Y.
Land-tied island or tombolo
  Kilmarnock, Va.
  Oyster Bay, N. Y.
Offset barrier beach
* Aransas Pass, Tex.
  Cumberland Island, Ga.
  Point Reyes, Calif.
  Rehoboth, Del.
Recurved or hooked spit
  Aransas Pass, Tex.
  Cumberland Island, Ga.
* Erie, Pa.
  Kilmarnock, Va.
  Mount Desert, Maine
  Oyster Bay, N. Y.
  Port Valdez district, Alaska
Recurved or hooked spit, abandoned
* Stockton, Utah
Rock stack
  Honomu, Hawaii
* Point Reyes, Calif.
Spit
  Genoa, N. Y.
  Mount Desert, Maine
* Oyster Bay, N. Y.
  St. Albans, Vt.
* Seattle, Wash.
Thorofare or tidal runway.
  Capitola, Calif.
* Cumberland Island, Ga.
  Rehoboth, Del.
Tidal flat
  Port Valdez district, Alaska
* Seattle, Wash.
* Washington and vicinity, D. C.-
  Md.-Va.
Tidal marsh
  Aransas Pass, Tex.
  Capitola, Calif.
* Cumberland Island, Ga.
  Kilmarnock, Va.
  Rehoboth, Del.
Truncated headland
  Aransas Pass, Tex.
* Point Reyes, Calif.
  Rehoboth, Del.

Wave-cut cliff
  Aransas Pass, **Tex.**
  Capitola, Calif.
  * Erie, Pa.
  * Honomu, Hawaii
  * Houghton, Mich.
  La Porte, Tex.
  * Oberlin, Ohio
  * Oyster Bay, N. Y.
  * Point Reyes, Calif.
  Seattle, Wash.
  * Waukegan, Ill.-Wis.

Wave-cut cliff, abandoned
  * Capitola, Calif.
  * Stockton, Utah
  * Waukegan, Ill.-Wis.

Wave-formed plain
  * Cape Henry, Va.
  Kilmarnock, Va.

Wave-formed terrace
  Capitola, Calif.
  * Erie, Pa.
  * Kilmarnock, Va.
  Point Reyes, Calif.
  * St. Albans, Vt.
  * Stockton, Utah
  Waukegan, Ill.-Wis.

Winged headland
  * Aransas Pass, Tex.
  * Oyster Bay, N. Y.

MOUNTAINS

Alluvial fan or cone
  See VALLEYS
Alluvial slope
  See VALLEYS
Alluvial slope, possibly including
  planed rock slope
  See VALLEYS
Block mountain
  Olancha, Calif.
  Point Reyes, Calif.
  * Van Horn, Tex.
Dissected alluvial slope
  See VALLEYS
Dome of crystalline rock
  * Atlanta, Ga.
  * Yosemite Valley, Calif.
Landslide
  See VALLEYS
Matterhorn peak
  See FEATURES DUE TO GLACIATION
  OF MOUNTAINS
Monadnock
  See RESULTS OF EROSION IN VARIOUS
  STAGES OF THE CYCLE
Mountain modified by alpine glaci-
  ation
  * Gilbert Peak, Utah-Wyo.
  * Glacier National Park, Mont.
  * Manitou, Colo.
  * Mount Rainier National Park,
    Wash.
  Olancha, Calif.
  * Stryker, Mont.

Mountain modified by continental
  glaciation
  * Greylock, Mass.-Vt.
  * Kaaterskill, N. Y.
  * Lake Placid, N. Y.
  * Monadnock, N. H.
  * Mount Desert, Maine
Mountain not glaciated
  * Ballarat, Calif.-Nev.
  * Mount Mitchell, N. C.
  * Natural Bridge, Va.
  * Olancha, Calif.
  * Redlands, Calif.
  * Stockton, Utah
  * Van Horn, Tex.
Mountain peak, isolated
  Greylock, Mass.-Vt.
  * Manitou, Colo.
  * Monadnock, N. H.
  * Mount Hood, Oreg.-Wash.
  * Mount Rainier National Park,
    Wash.
  * Mount Riley, N. Mex.
Mountain range
  * Glacier National Park, Mont.
  * White Mountains, Calif.
Rock slide and talus
  See VALLEYS
Rugged or youthful mountain
  * Ballarat, Calif.-Nev.
  * Glacier National Park, Mont.
  * Redlands, Calif.
  * Stockton, Utah
  White Mountains, Calif.-Nev.
Subdued or old mountains
  * Mount Mitchell, N. C.
Volcanic cone
  See VOLCANIC FEATURES
Wind gap or pass
  Antietam, Md.-Va.-W. Va.
  * Glacier National Park, Mont.
  * Kaaterskill, N. Y.
  Lake Placid, N. Y.
  Loveland, Colo.
  * Mount Mitchell, N. C.
  Mount Rainier National Park,
    Wash.

RIDGES AND HILLS

Cuesta
  * Chisos Mountains, Tex.
  * Grass Creek Basin, Wyo.
  * Van Horn, Tex.
Hogback
  * Loveland, Colo.
Ridges due to hard rocks
  * Antietam, Md.-W. Va.-Va.
  * Chisos Mountains, Tex.
  * De Queen, Ark.-Okla.
  * Everett, Pa.
  Fort Payne, Ala.-Ga.
  Grass Creek Basin, Wyo.
  * Hot Springs and vicinity, Ark.
  * Loveland, Colo.
  Natural Bridge, Va.
  Pawpaw, Md.-W. Va.-Pa.

Ridges due to erosion of an anticline
  * Everett, Pa.
  * Grass Creek Basin, Wyo.
  * Hot Springs and vicinity, Ark.
  * Loveland, Colo.
Ridges due to erosion of a syncline
  * Everett, Pa.
  * Hot Springs and vicinity, Ark.
  * Loveland, Colo.
  * Lower Matanuska Valley, Alaska
  * Natural Bridge, Va.
  Pawpaw, Md.-W. Va.-Pa.
Sand dune
  Aransas Pass, Tex.
  Ballarat, Calif.-Nev.
  * Cape Henry, Va.
  Capitola, Calif.
  Cumberland Island, Ga.
  Erie, Pa.
  Houghton, Mich.
  * Ogallala, Nebr.
  Point Reyes, Calif.
  Rehoboth, Del.
  White Mountains, Calif.
Zigzag ridges
  Everett, Pa.
  Hot Springs and vicinity, Ark.

PLATEAUS AND MESAS

Dissected plateau
  Bright Angel, Ariz.
  * Castlegate, Utah
  * East Cincinnati, Ohio-Ky.
  * Fayetteville, W. Va.
  * Hollow Springs, Tenn.
  * Joplin district, Mo.-Kans.
  * Kimmswick, Mo.-Ill.
  * Mesa Verde National Park, Colo.
  * Milton, W. Va.
  Monticello, Ky.
  Mount Hood, Oreg.-Wash.
  * Pittsburgh, Pa.
  Standingstone, Tenn.
Dissected plateau modified by gla-
  ciation
  * Genoa, N. Y.
  * Monadnock, N. H.
  * Naples, N. Y.
Mesa
  Bright Angel, Ariz.
  * Buck Hill, Tex.
  Crater Lake National Park, Oreg
  Mount Rainier National Park,
    Wash.
Plateau
  Bright Angel, Ariz.
  Fayetteville, W. Va.
  * Fort Payne, Ala.-Ga.
  Greylock, Mass.-Vt.
  * Hollow Springs, Tenn.
  * Malaga, Wash.
  * Olancha, Calif.
  * Standingstone, Tenn.

Terminal moraine (Cont.)
  Lower Matanuska Valley, Alaska
  Manitou, Colo.
  Meriden, Conn.
  * Naples, N. Y.
  Oyster Bay, N. Y.
  Peever, S. Dak.-Minn.
  Rochester east, N. Y.
  * St. Croix Dalles, Wis.-Minn.
  Waukegan, Ill.-Wis.
Valley train
  * Cross Plains, Wis.

FEATURES DUE TO GLACIA-
TION OF MOUNTAINS

Comb ridge or cleaver
  * Gilbert Peak, Utah-Wyo.
  Glacier National Park, Mont.
  * Mount Rainier National Park,
    Wash.
  * Stryker, Mont.
Glacial cirque
  * Gilbert Peak, Utah-Wyo.
  * Glacier National Park, Mont.
  Lower Matanuska Valley, Alaska
  * Manitou, Colo.
  Mount Hood, Oreg.-Wash.
  * Mount Rainier National Park,
    Wash.
  Olancha, Calif.
  * Stryker, Mont.
  White Mountains, Calif.-Nev.
Glacial col
  * Gilbert Peak, Utah-Wyo.
  Mount Rainier National Park,
    Wash.
  * Stryker, Mont.

Glaciated or trough valley
  See VALLEYS
Matterhorn peak
  * Gilbert Peak, Utah-Wyo.
  Glacier National Park, Mont.
  * Mount Rainier National Park,
    Wash.
  Stryker, Mont.
Medial and lateral moraines
  * Mount Rainier National Park,
    Wash.
  * Port Valdez district, Alaska
Mountains modified by alpine glacia-
  tion
  See MOUNTAINS
Nunatak
  * Mount Rainier National Park,
    Wash.
  * Port Valdez district, Alaska
Roches moutonnées
  * Yosemite Valley, Calif.

VOLCANIC FEATURES

Caldera
  * Crater Lake National Park, Oreg.
Dissected volcanic cone
  * Marysville Buttes and vicinity,
    Calif.
Truncated volcanic cone
  * Crater Lake National Park, Oreg.
Volcanic cone
  * Crater Lake National Park, Oreg.
  * Honomu, Hawaii
  * Mount Hood, Oreg.-Wash.
  * Mount Rainier National Park,
    Wash.

Volcanic cone (Cont.)
  * Mount Riley, Ariz.
Wedge segments of volcanic cone
  outlined by erosion
  * Marysville Buttes and vicinity,
    Calif.
  * Mount Rainier National Park,
    Wash.

SOLUTION FEATURES

Natural bridge
  * Natural Bridge, Va.
Solution basin and sinkhole
  Gilbert Peak, Utah-Wyo.
  Hollow Springs, Tenn.
  * Interlachen, Fla.
  Kimmswick, Mo.-Ill.
  * Monticello, Ky.
  Montpelier, Idaho-Wyo.-Utah
  Natural Bridge, Va.
  Pawpaw, Md.-W. Va.-Pa.
  * Peeples, S. C.-Ga.
  Rehoboth, Del.
  * Standingstone, Tenn

MISCELLANEOUS

Continental or subcontinental divide
  * Glacier National Park, Mont.
  * Mount Mitchell, N. C.
  Peever, S. Dak.-Minn.
Fall line
  * Washington and vicinity, D. C.-
    Md.-Va.
Mud spring (mud volcano), extinct
  * La Porte, Tex.

List of Maps

....

Index of Geographical Terms

....

NOTE: Reference is to the page where best definition occurs.

Index

Scale 1: 71,500